# VECTOR ANALYSIS

A SIMON AND SCHUSTER TECH OUTLINE

RAJ MEHRA, EDITOR

# VECTOR ANALYSIS

**HWEI P. HSU, Ph.D.**
Associate Professor
Department of Electrical Engineering
Wayne State University

SIMON and SCHUSTER
TECH OUTLINES

SIMON AND SCHUSTER, NEW YORK

Published by
Simon and Schuster
Reference, Technical and Review Book Division
1 West 39th Street
New York, N.Y. 10018

Printed in the United States of America

# PREFACE

In recent years, the knowledge of vector analysis has become an essential and integral requirement for engineers, mathematicians, physicists, and other scientists. It not only provides a concise and precise means of mathematically analyzing physical and geometrical phenomenon, but also aids in the development of the intuitive understanding of physical and geometrical ideas.

This book can be used as a textbook for a formal course in vector analysis and as a supplement to all standard textbooks because of the unique combination of rigor and informality in the treatment of the subject matter. The hundreds of applications to elementary geometry, mechanics, electromagnetic theory, and fluid mechanics makes it invaluable as a companion text for courses in the numerous fields which employ vector methods.

New concepts, definitions, and the important fundamental theorems (or results) are tinted in grey throughout the text. The graded sets of completely solved problems constitute the integral part of the text, illustrating and amplifying the fundamental concepts and developing the techniques of vector analysis. The supplementary problems are designed not only for exercise but also to strengthen the skill and insight necessary for the practical use of vector techniques.

This book is designed for the student who has the knowledge of an eight-semester hour course in elementary calculus. However, the second half of the book assumes a basic familiarity with advanced calculus and applied mathematics.

The first half of the text develops the algebra and calculus of vectors. In chapter one, vectors are defined and vector algebra is treated without the introduction of a coordinate system. An analytical approach to vector algebra is in chapter two. Differential and integral calculus of vectors is discussed in chapters three and four. Chapter five introduces curvilinear coordinates.

The next four chapters discuss the practical applications of vectors to elementary geometry, mechanics, fluid mechanics, and electromagnetic theory.

The final chapter is on differential forms, and it introduces the definition of exterior differential forms and the concept of exterior calculus. It provides a link between vector analysis and exterior calculus. The author believes that the differential forms and related concepts, which evolved from modern mathematics, are new and powerful analytical tools for the scientist and engineer.

Finally, the author wishes to thank Professor Forest E. Brammer for his encouragement; Professor Robert Barnard for his pertinent and valuable advice; Miss Kathie Aggas for her careful and cheerful typing of the entire manuscript; and the editorial staff of Simon and Schuster Tech Outlines, especially Mr. Raj Mehra and Mrs. Rhea Nichols, for their careful review of the manuscript and their constructive suggestions.

Hwei P. Hsu

Southfield, Michigan

# TABLE OF CONTENTS

# 1 CHAPTER

# ALGEBRA OF VECTORS

## 1.1 Scalars and Vectors

A *scalar* is a physical quantity that is characterized by *magnitude*, such as mass, time, or temperature. It is specified by an ordinary number.

A *vector* is a physical quantity that is characterized by both *magnitude* and *direction*, such as displacement, force, momentum, or velocity. In script a vector is denoted by a letter with an arrow over it, for example, $\vec{A}$. In this text a vector is represented by boldface type, such as **A**.

Graphically, a vector **A** is represented by a *directed line segment* $\overrightarrow{PQ}$ as illustrated in Fig. 1.1. The vector **A** has a *direction* from $P$ to $Q$. The point $P$ is called the *initial point*, and $Q$, the *terminal point* of **A**. The length $|\overrightarrow{PQ}|$ of the line segment represents the *magnitude* of **A** and is denoted by either $A$ or $|\mathbf{A}|$.

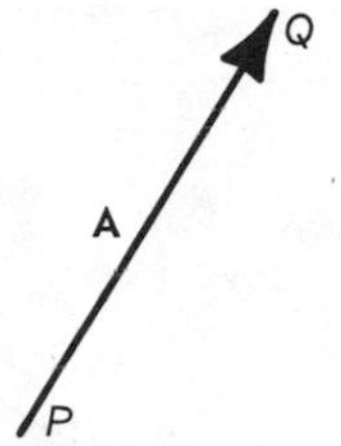


Fig. 1.1 Geometrical representation of a vector.

When the initial point of a vector is fixed, it is called a *fixed* or *localized vector*; whereas, if the initial point is not fixed, it is called a *free* or *nonlocalized vector*. In this text it is assumed that all vectors are free vectors unless otherwise stated.

If the points $P$ and $Q$ in Fig. 1.1 are coincident, then the vector is called a *zero vector*, denoted by **0**. It has zero magnitude and *arbitrary* direction.

Two free vectors **A** and **B** are *equal*,

$$\mathbf{A} = \mathbf{B}, \tag{1.1}$$

when they have the same magnitude and direction, as shown in Fig. 1.2.

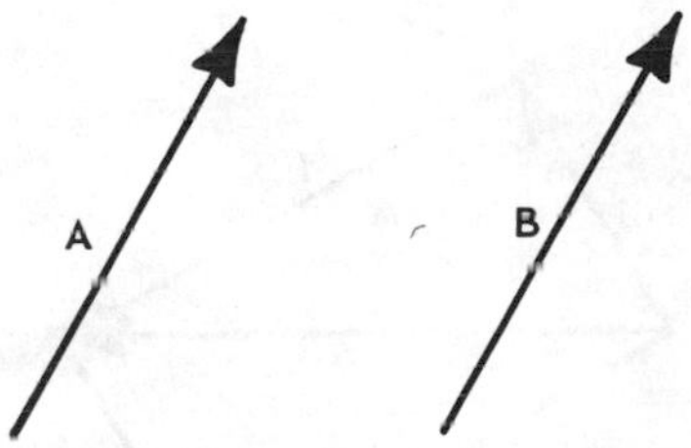


Fig. 1.2 Equal vectors.

This does not imply that two equal vectors coincide in space. Nor does the equality of vectors (1.1) apply to fixed vectors because only one vector has a given magnitude, direction, and initial point.

As a direct consequence of (1.1),

$$\mathbf{A} = \mathbf{B} \text{ implies } \mathbf{B} = \mathbf{A}, \tag{1.2}$$

$$\mathbf{A} = \mathbf{B} \text{ and } \mathbf{B} = \mathbf{C} \text{ implies } \mathbf{A} = \mathbf{C}. \tag{1.3}$$

## 1.2 Multiplication of a Vector by a Scalar

Let **A** be any vector and $m$, any scalar. Then the vector $m\mathbf{A}$, as shown in Fig. 1.3, is defined as follows:

(1) The magnitude of $m\mathbf{A}$ is $|m|\,|\mathbf{A}|$: $|m\mathbf{A}| = |m|\,|\mathbf{A}|$.
(2) If $m > 0$ and $\mathbf{A} \neq \mathbf{0}$, then the direction of $m\mathbf{A}$ is that of **A**.
(3) If $m < 0$ and $\mathbf{A} \neq \mathbf{0}$, then the direction of $m\mathbf{A}$ is opposite to that of **A**.
(4) If $m = 0$ or $\mathbf{A} = \mathbf{0}$, $m\mathbf{A}$ is said to be **0**: $0\mathbf{A} = m\mathbf{0} = \mathbf{0}$.

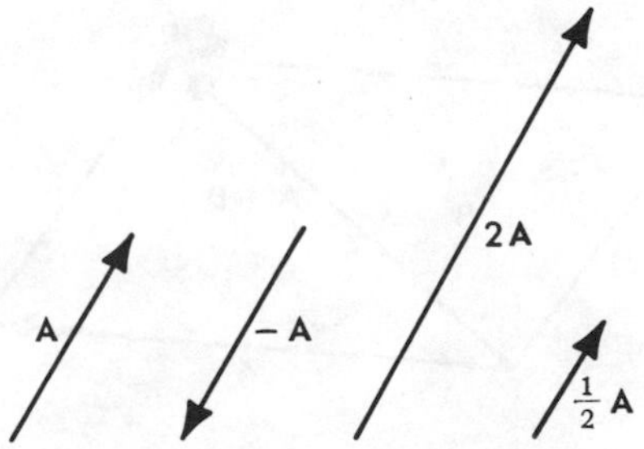


Fig. 1.3 Multiplication of a vector by scalars.

Thus, two nonzero vectors **A** and **B** are *parallel* (designated $\mathbf{A} \| \mathbf{B}$), if and only

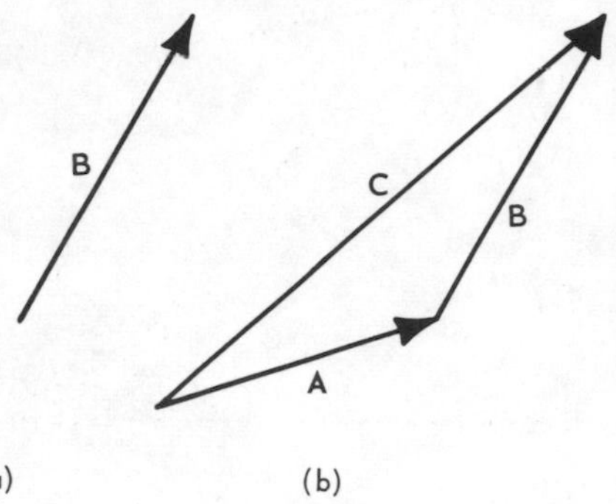


Fig. 1.4 Addition of vectors.

if there exists a scalar $m$ such that

$$\mathbf{B} = m\mathbf{A}. \tag{1.4}$$

Since $\mathbf{0}$ has an arbitrary direction, it is defined as parallel to any vector $\mathbf{A}$ and $\mathbf{A}$ as parallel to $\mathbf{0}$. With this convention, the extended condition for parallelism is

$\mathbf{A} \,||\, \mathbf{B}$ if and only if $\mathbf{B} = m\mathbf{A}$ or $\mathbf{A} = n\mathbf{B}$ for some scalars $m$, $n$.

If $m = -1$, we obtain the *negative* of vector $\mathbf{A}$, denoted by $-\mathbf{A} = (-1)\,\mathbf{A}$, i.e., a vector whose magnitude is that of $\mathbf{A}$, but whose direction is opposite to that of $\mathbf{A}$.

If $\mathbf{A} \neq \mathbf{0}$ and $m = \dfrac{1}{|\mathbf{A}|} = \dfrac{1}{A}$, then we obtain a *unit vector*

$$\mathbf{e}_A = \frac{1}{|\mathbf{A}|}\,\mathbf{A}, \tag{1.5}$$

whose magnitude is $|\mathbf{e}_A| = 1$ and whose direction is the same as that of $\mathbf{A}$. The vector $\mathbf{A}$ is represented by the product of its length and the unit vector $\mathbf{e}_A$:

$$\mathbf{A} = A\,\mathbf{e}_A. \tag{1.6}$$

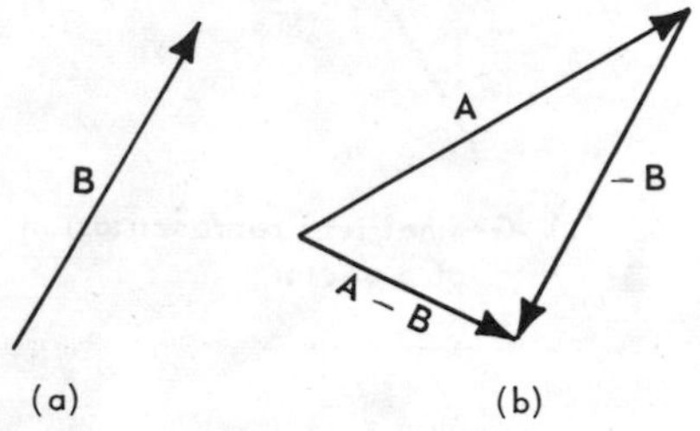


Fig. 1.5 Subtraction of vectors.

## 1.3 Addition and Subtraction of Vectors

Given two vectors $\mathbf{A}$ and $\mathbf{B}$, the *sum* or *resultant*

$$\mathbf{C} = \mathbf{A} + \mathbf{B} \tag{1.7}$$

is a unique vector determined as follows: If the initial point of $\mathbf{B}$ is placed at the terminal point of $\mathbf{A}$, then the resultant $\mathbf{C}$ is the vector whose initial point is at the initial point of $\mathbf{A}$ and whose terminal point is at the terminal point of $\mathbf{B}$. (See Fig. 1.4.)

As shown in Fig. 1.5, the *difference* $(\mathbf{A} - \mathbf{B})$ of two vectors $\mathbf{A}$ and $\mathbf{B}$ is the sum of $\mathbf{A}$ and $(-\mathbf{B})$; i.e.,

$$\mathbf{C} = \mathbf{A} - \mathbf{B} = \mathbf{A} + (-\mathbf{B}). \tag{1.8}$$

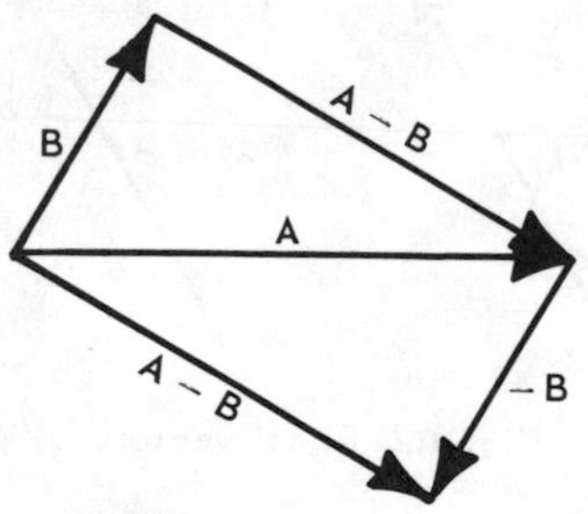


Fig. 1.6 Subtraction of vectors.

If vectors $\mathbf{A}$ and $\mathbf{B}$ have a common initial point, then $\mathbf{A} - \mathbf{B}$ is the vector that goes from the terminal point of $\mathbf{B}$ to the terminal point of $\mathbf{A}$. This is illustrated in Fig. 1.6.

Vector addition has the following properties:

$$\mathbf{A} + \mathbf{B} = \mathbf{B} + \mathbf{A} \qquad \text{[Commutative law]} \tag{1.9}$$

$$\mathbf{A} + (\mathbf{B} + \mathbf{C}) = (\mathbf{A} + \mathbf{B}) + \mathbf{C} \qquad \text{[Associative law]} \tag{1.10}$$

$$m(\mathbf{A} + \mathbf{B}) = m\mathbf{A} + m\mathbf{B} \qquad \text{[Distributive law]} \tag{1.11}$$

$$(m + n)\,\mathbf{A} = m\mathbf{A} + n\mathbf{A} \qquad \text{[Scalar Distributive law]} \tag{1.12}$$

$$\mathbf{A} + \mathbf{0} = \mathbf{A} \qquad \text{[Identity]} \tag{1.13}$$

$$\mathbf{A} + (-\mathbf{A}) = \mathbf{0} \quad \text{or} \quad \mathbf{A} - \mathbf{A} = \mathbf{0} \qquad \text{[Inverse]} \tag{1.14}$$

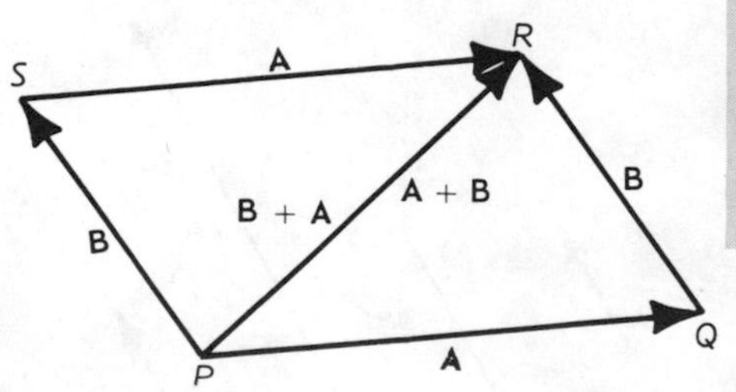


Fig. 1.7 Commutative law of vector addition.

**PROBLEM 1.1** Verify (1.9).

**Solution:** Let $\mathbf{A}$ and $\mathbf{B}$ be two vectors as shown in Fig. 1.7. Then

$$\mathbf{A} + \mathbf{B} = \overrightarrow{PQ} + \overrightarrow{QR} = \overrightarrow{PR},$$

$$\mathbf{B} + \mathbf{A} = \overrightarrow{PS} + \overrightarrow{SR} = \overrightarrow{PR}.$$

Hence, $\mathbf{A} + \mathbf{B} = \mathbf{B} + \mathbf{A}$.

**PROBLEM 1.2** Verify (1.10).

**Solution:** Construct a polygon PQRS, as in Fig. 1.8, having the vectors **A**, **B**, and **C** as consecutive sides. Then,

$$\mathbf{A} + (\mathbf{B} + \mathbf{C}) = \mathbf{A} + \overrightarrow{QS} = \overrightarrow{PQ} + \overrightarrow{QS} = \overrightarrow{PS},$$

$$(\mathbf{A} + \mathbf{B}) + \mathbf{C} = \overrightarrow{PR} + \mathbf{C} = \overrightarrow{PR} + \overrightarrow{RS} = \overrightarrow{PS}.$$

Hence,

$$\mathbf{A} + (\mathbf{B} + \mathbf{C}) = (\mathbf{A} + \mathbf{B}) + \mathbf{C}.$$

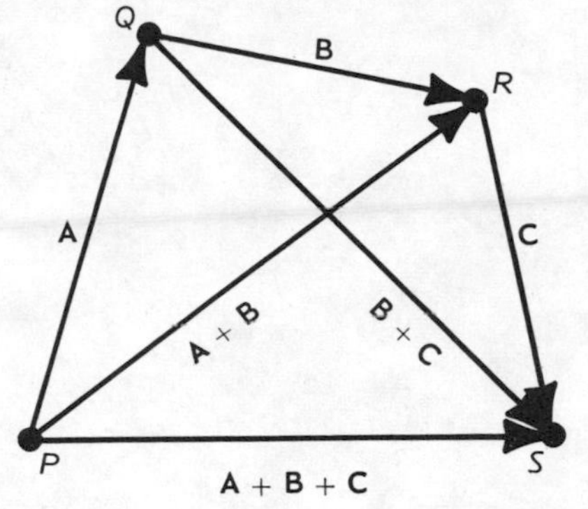

Fig. 1.8 Associative law of vector addition.

**PROBLEM 1.3** Let $O$, $Q$, and $P$ be three distinct points in space and $R$, the midpoint of $PQ$. If $\overrightarrow{OP} = \mathbf{A}$, $\overrightarrow{OQ} = \mathbf{B}$, and $\overrightarrow{OR} = \mathbf{C}$, show that

$$\mathbf{C} = \frac{1}{2}(\mathbf{A} + \mathbf{B}). \tag{1.15}$$

**Solution:** In Fig. 1.9, by the law of vector addition,

$$\mathbf{C} = \mathbf{B} + \overrightarrow{QR}.$$

Now, as in Fig. 1.6,

$$\overrightarrow{QP} = \mathbf{A} - \mathbf{B}.$$

Since $\overrightarrow{QR} = \frac{1}{2}\overrightarrow{QP} = \frac{1}{2}(\mathbf{A} - \mathbf{B})$,

$$\mathbf{C} = \mathbf{B} + \overrightarrow{QR} = \mathbf{B} + \frac{1}{2}(\mathbf{A} - \mathbf{B}) = \frac{1}{2}(\mathbf{A} + \mathbf{B}).$$

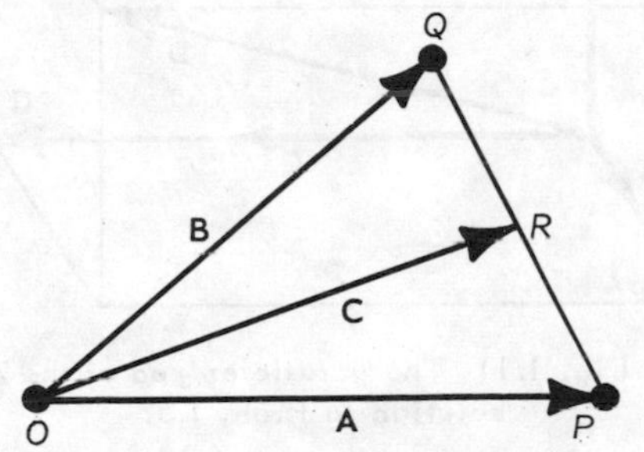

Fig. 1.9 Use of the law of vector addition.

**PROBLEM 1.4** If **A** and **B** are any two nonzero, nonparallel vectors and **C**, any vector in the plane of **A** and **B**, then show that **C** can be expressed as a linear combination of **A** and **B**; i.e.,

$$\mathbf{C} = m\mathbf{A} + n\mathbf{B}, \tag{1.16}$$

where $m$ and $n$ are two uniquely determined scalars.

**Solution:** Since **A** and **B** are not parallel, there exists a parallelogram with **C** as its diagonal and with edges parallel to **A** and **B**. (See Fig. 1.10.) Then,

$$\mathbf{C} = \overrightarrow{PQ} + \overrightarrow{QR}.$$

Now $\overrightarrow{PQ} \,||\, \mathbf{A}$ and $\overrightarrow{QR} \,||\, \mathbf{B}$ which imply that there exist scalars $m$ and $n$ such that

$$\overrightarrow{PQ} = m\mathbf{A}, \quad \overrightarrow{QR} = n\mathbf{B}.$$

Hence,

$$\mathbf{C} = m\mathbf{A} + n\mathbf{B}.$$

To show that $m$ and $n$ are uniquely determined, assume that there exist $m'$ and $n'$ such that

$$\mathbf{C} = m'\mathbf{A} + n'\mathbf{B}. \tag{1.17}$$

Then by subtraction,

$$(m - m')\,\mathbf{A} + (n - n')\,\mathbf{B} = \mathbf{0}, \tag{1.18}$$

or

$$(m - m')\mathbf{A} = (n' - n)\,\mathbf{B}. \tag{1.19}$$

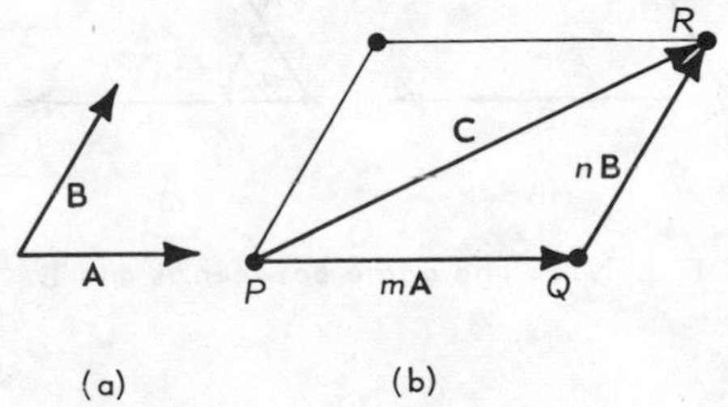

Fig. 1.10 Solution to Prob. 1.4.

But **A** and **B** are nonparallel, hence, nonzero vectors. By (1.4), it is clearly required that $m - m' = 0$ and $n' - n = 0$. If not, one could divide by

$m - m'$ or $n - n'$ to obtain $\mathbf{B} = x\mathbf{A}$ or $\mathbf{A} = y\mathbf{B}$, which would imply that **A** and **B** are parallel. Hence, $m = m'$ and $n = n'$.

**PROBLEM 1.5** If **A**, **B**, and **C** are any three nonzero, nonparallel, noncoplanar vectors and **D**, any other vector in space, then show that **D** can be expressed as a linear combination of **A**, **B**, and **C**; i.e.,

$$\mathbf{D} = m\mathbf{A} + n\mathbf{B} + l\mathbf{C}, \tag{1.20}$$

where $m$, $n$, and $l$ are three uniquely determined scalars.

**Solution:** Since **A**, **B**, and **C** are nonzero, nonparallel, and noncoplanar, there exists a parallelepiped with **D** as its diagonal and with edges parallel to **A**, **B**, and **C**. (See Fig. 1.11.) Hence, there exist scalars $m$, $n$, and $l$ such that

$$\mathbf{D} = m\mathbf{A} + n\mathbf{B} + l\mathbf{C}.$$

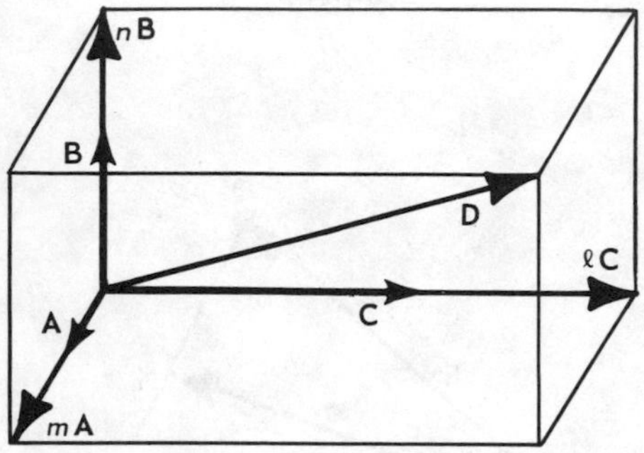


Fig. 1.11 The parallelepiped of the solution to Prob. 1.5.

To show that $m$, $n$, and $l$ are unique, assume that **D** can be expressed as

$$\mathbf{D} = m'\mathbf{A} + n'\mathbf{B} + l'\mathbf{C}. \tag{1.21}$$

Then by subtraction,

$$(m - m')\mathbf{A} + (n - n')\mathbf{B} + (l - l')\mathbf{C} = \mathbf{0}, \tag{1.22}$$

or

$$(m - m')\mathbf{A} = (n' - n)\mathbf{B} + (l' - l)\mathbf{C}. \tag{1.23}$$

The left-hand side of (1.23) is a vector parallel to **A**, and the right-hand side, a vector parallel to the plane of **B** and **C**. Because **A**, **B**, and **C** are nonzero, nonparallel, and noncoplanar, $(m - m')\mathbf{A} = \mathbf{0}$, and, hence, $m = m'$. Similarly, $n = n'$ and $l = l'$.

In general, $n$ given vectors $\mathbf{A}_1, \mathbf{A}_2, \ldots, \mathbf{A}_n$ are *linearly dependent* if at least one of them can be expressed as a linear combination of the other $(n - 1)$ vectors. If none of the vectors can be so represented, they are *linearly independent*. Hence, $n$ vectors $\mathbf{A}_1, \mathbf{A}_2, \ldots, \mathbf{A}_n$ are linearly dependent if and only if there exist scalars $m_i (i = 1, \ldots, n)$, not all zero, such that

$$m_1\mathbf{A}_1 + m_2\mathbf{A}_2 + \cdots + m_n\mathbf{A}_n = \mathbf{0}. \tag{1.24}$$

## 1.4 Scalar or Dot Product

The *scalar* or *dot product* (sometimes called the *inner product*) of two vectors **A** and **B** is a scalar $\mathbf{A} \cdot \mathbf{B}$ (read **A** dot **B**) given by

$$\mathbf{A} \cdot \mathbf{B} = |\mathbf{A}|\,|\mathbf{B}| \cos \theta = AB \cos \theta, \tag{1.25}$$

where $\theta$ is the angle between **A** and **B** and $0 \le \theta \le \pi$. (See Fig. 1.12.)

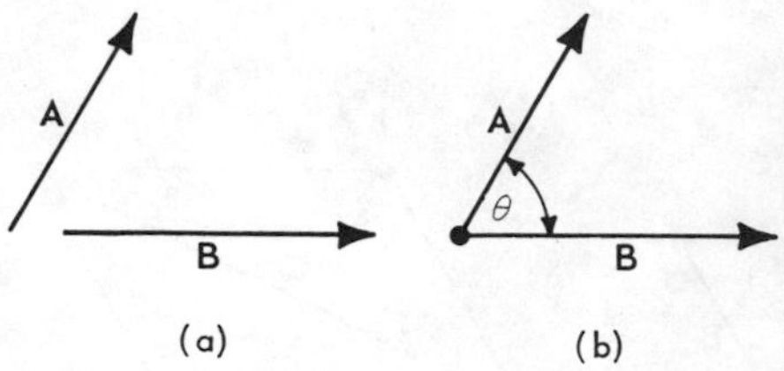


Fig. 1.12 The angle between **A** and **B**.

From (1.25), the *angle* $\theta$ between **A** and **B** can be expressed as

$$\cos \theta = \frac{\mathbf{A} \cdot \mathbf{B}}{AB}, \tag{1.26}$$

or

$$\theta = \cos^{-1}\left(\frac{\mathbf{A} \cdot \mathbf{B}}{AB}\right), \tag{1.27}$$

provided $\mathbf{A} \neq \mathbf{0}$ and $\mathbf{B} \neq \mathbf{0}$.

The *projection* of a vector **A** onto **B**, denoted by $\text{proj}_{\mathbf{B}}\mathbf{A}$, is a vector

$$\text{proj}_{\mathbf{B}}\mathbf{A} = (A\cos\theta)\mathbf{e}_B, \tag{1.28}$$

where $\theta$ is the angle between **A** and **B**, and $\mathbf{e}_B = \frac{1}{B}\mathbf{B}$ is a unit vector along **B**. (See Fig. 1.13.)

The *component* of a vector **A** along a nonzero vector **B**, denoted by $\text{comp}_{\mathbf{B}}\mathbf{A}$, is a scalar

$$\text{comp}_{\mathbf{B}}\mathbf{A} = A\cos\theta = \mathbf{A}\cdot\mathbf{e}_B, \tag{1.29}$$

where $\theta$ is the angle between **A** and **B**. (See Fig. 1.13.)

Using components, the scalar product (1.25) can be expressed as

$$\mathbf{A}\cdot\mathbf{B} = A\,\text{comp}_{\mathbf{A}}\mathbf{B} = B\,\text{comp}_{\mathbf{B}}\mathbf{A}. \tag{1.30}$$

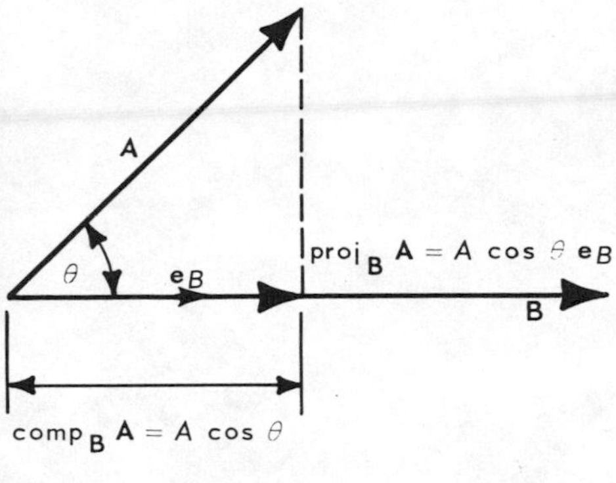


Fig. 1.13 Component and projection of a vector.

The scalar product has the following properties:

$$\mathbf{A}\cdot\mathbf{B} = \mathbf{B}\cdot\mathbf{A} \quad \text{[Commutative law]} \tag{1.31}$$

$$\mathbf{A}\cdot(\mathbf{B}+\mathbf{C}) = \mathbf{A}\cdot\mathbf{B} + \mathbf{A}\cdot\mathbf{C} \quad \text{[Distributive law]} \tag{1.32}$$

$$(m\mathbf{A})\cdot\mathbf{B} = \mathbf{A}\cdot(m\mathbf{B}) = m(\mathbf{A}\cdot\mathbf{B}) \tag{1.33}$$

$$\mathbf{A}\cdot\mathbf{A} = |\mathbf{A}|^2 = A^2, \tag{1.34}$$

where $m$ is an arbitrary scalar.

**PROBLEM 1.6** Verify the commutative law of the scalar product (1.31).

**Solution:** From the definition of the scalar product,

$$\mathbf{A}\cdot\mathbf{B} = AB\cos\theta = BA\cos\theta = \mathbf{B}\cdot\mathbf{A}.$$

**PROBLEM 1.7** Verify the distributive law of the scalar product (1.32).

**Solution:** From Fig. 1.14,

$$PR = PQ + QR,$$

or

$$\text{comp}_{\mathbf{A}}(\mathbf{B}+\mathbf{C}) = \text{comp}_{\mathbf{A}}\mathbf{B} + \text{comp}_{\mathbf{B}}\mathbf{C}. \tag{1.35}$$

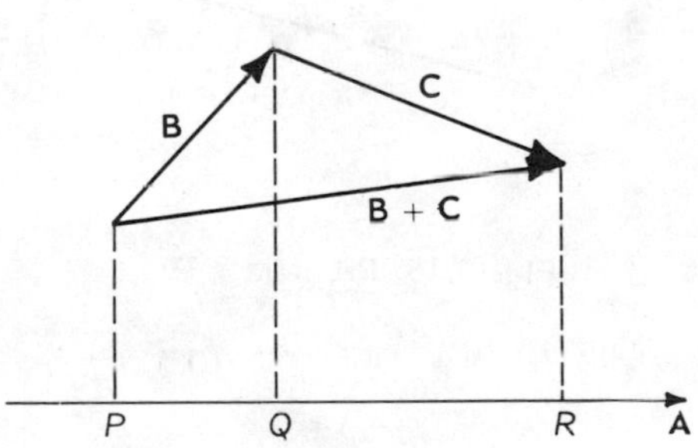


Fig. 1.14 Verification of the distributive law of the scalar product.

If $\mathbf{e}_A$ is a unit vector in the direction of **A**, then from the definition of components (1.29), (1.35) can be rewritten as

$$(\mathbf{B}+\mathbf{C})\cdot\mathbf{e}_A = \mathbf{B}\cdot\mathbf{e}_A + \mathbf{C}\cdot\mathbf{e}_A. \tag{1.36}$$

Multiplying both sides of (1.36) by $A$ and using (1.33),

$$(\mathbf{B}+\mathbf{C})\cdot A\mathbf{e}_A = \mathbf{B}\cdot A\mathbf{e}_A + \mathbf{C}\cdot A\mathbf{e}_A,$$

or, because $\mathbf{A} = A\mathbf{e}_A$,

$$(\mathbf{B}+\mathbf{C})\cdot\mathbf{A} = \mathbf{B}\cdot\mathbf{A} + \mathbf{C}\cdot\mathbf{A}. \tag{1.37}$$

Then using the commutative law of the scalar product (1.31),

$$\mathbf{A}\cdot(\mathbf{B}+\mathbf{C}) = \mathbf{A}\cdot\mathbf{B} + \mathbf{A}\cdot\mathbf{C}.$$

**PROBLEM 1.8** Verify (1.34).

**Solution:** If $\mathbf{A} = \mathbf{B}$, then $\cos\theta = \cos 0 = 1$. Then from the definition of the scalar product (1.25),

$$\mathbf{A}\cdot\mathbf{A} = |\mathbf{A}|^2 = A^2.$$

Two vectors **A** and **B** are *perpendicular* or *orthogonal* to each other (denoted by $\mathbf{A} \perp \mathbf{B}$) if the angle $\theta$ between them is 90°. Since the vector **0** has arbitrary direction, it is considered perpendicular to any vector **A**, and **A**, as perpendicular to **0**.

**PROBLEM 1.9** Show that **A** and **B** are perpendicular to each other if and only if $\mathbf{A} \cdot \mathbf{B} = 0$.

**Solution:** If $\mathbf{A} \cdot \mathbf{B} = AB \cos\theta = 0$, then we can conclude that either $\cos\theta = 0$, i.e., $\theta = \pi/2$ or $A = |\mathbf{A}| = 0$ or $B = |\mathbf{B}| = 0$.

If $\mathbf{A} \neq \mathbf{0}$, and $\mathbf{B} \neq \mathbf{0}$, then $\mathbf{A} \cdot \mathbf{B} = 0$ means that $\mathbf{A} \perp \mathbf{B}$.

Since **0** has an arbitrary direction, it is defined to be perpendicular to any vector **A**.

**PROBLEM 1.10** If $\mathbf{B} \neq \mathbf{0}$ and $\mathbf{A} = \mathbf{A}_1 + \mathbf{A}_2$ so that $\mathbf{A}_1 \| \mathbf{B}$ and $\mathbf{A}_2 \perp \mathbf{B}$, then show that

$$\mathbf{A}_1 = \frac{\mathbf{A} \cdot \mathbf{B}}{B^2} \mathbf{B}, \tag{1.38}$$

$$\mathbf{A}_2 = \mathbf{A} - \frac{\mathbf{A} \cdot \mathbf{B}}{B^2} \mathbf{B}. \tag{1.39}$$

(See Fig. 1.15.)

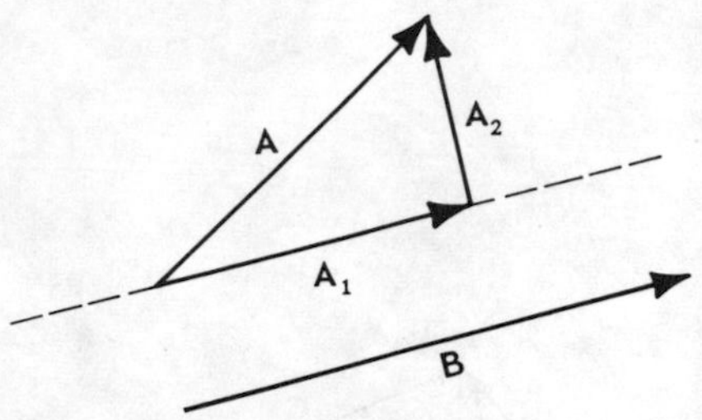


Fig. 1.15 Problem 1.10.

**Solution:** Since $\mathbf{A}_2 \perp \mathbf{B}$, $\mathbf{A}_2 \cdot \mathbf{B} = 0$. Hence,

$$\mathbf{A} \cdot \mathbf{B} = \mathbf{A}_1 \cdot \mathbf{B} + \mathbf{A}_2 \cdot \mathbf{B} = \mathbf{A}_1 \cdot \mathbf{B}. \tag{1.40}$$

Since $\mathbf{A}_1 \| \mathbf{B}$, from the condition for parallelism (1.4), we have for some scalar $m$,

$$\mathbf{A}_1 = m\mathbf{B}. \tag{1.41}$$

Dotting both sides of this equation by **B**,

$$\mathbf{A}_1 \cdot \mathbf{B} = m\mathbf{B} \cdot \mathbf{B} = mB^2.$$

Hence, from (1.40),

$$m = \frac{\mathbf{A}_1 \cdot \mathbf{B}}{B^2} = \frac{\mathbf{A} \cdot \mathbf{B}}{B^2}. \tag{1.42}$$

Thus, from (1.41),

$$\mathbf{A}_1 = \frac{\mathbf{A} \cdot \mathbf{B}}{B^2} \mathbf{B}.$$

Since $\mathbf{A} = \mathbf{A}_1 + \mathbf{A}_2$,

$$\mathbf{A}_2 = \mathbf{A} - \mathbf{A}_1 = \mathbf{A} - \frac{\mathbf{A} \cdot \mathbf{B}}{B^2} \mathbf{B}.$$

Dotting both sides of this equation by **B**,

$$\mathbf{A}_2 \cdot \mathbf{B} = \mathbf{A} \cdot \mathbf{B} - \frac{\mathbf{A} \cdot \mathbf{B}}{B^2} \mathbf{B} \cdot \mathbf{B} = \mathbf{A} \cdot \mathbf{B} - \frac{\mathbf{A} \cdot \mathbf{B}}{B^2} B^2 = \mathbf{A} \cdot \mathbf{B} - \mathbf{A} \cdot \mathbf{B} = 0,$$

which implies $\mathbf{A}_2 \perp \mathbf{B}$. Thus, we see that (1.38) and (1.39) conversely imply that $\mathbf{A}_1 \| \mathbf{B}$ and $\mathbf{A}_2 \perp \mathbf{B}$.

**PROBLEM 1.11.** If $\mathbf{A} \cdot \mathbf{B} = \mathbf{A} \cdot \mathbf{C}$, determine if $\mathbf{B} = \mathbf{C}$.

**Solution:** Since $\mathbf{A} \cdot \mathbf{B} = \mathbf{A} \cdot \mathbf{C}$ can be written as

$$\mathbf{A} \cdot (\mathbf{B} - \mathbf{C}) = 0, \tag{1.43}$$

it can be said only that either **A** is perpendicular to **B** − **C**, or **A** = **0**, or **B** − **C** = **0**; i.e., **B** = **C**. Hence if **A** · **B** = **A** · **C**, it does not necessarily follow that **B** = **C**.

The *law of cosines* states that if three sides of a triangle are of lengths |**A**|, |**B**|, and |**C**|, and if the angle opposite the side of length |**C**| is $\theta$, then

$$C^2 = A^2 + B^2 - 2AB\cos\theta. \tag{1.44}$$

**PROBLEM 1.12** Verify (1.44).

**Solution:** From Fig. 1.16,

$$\mathbf{C} = \mathbf{B} - \mathbf{A}.$$

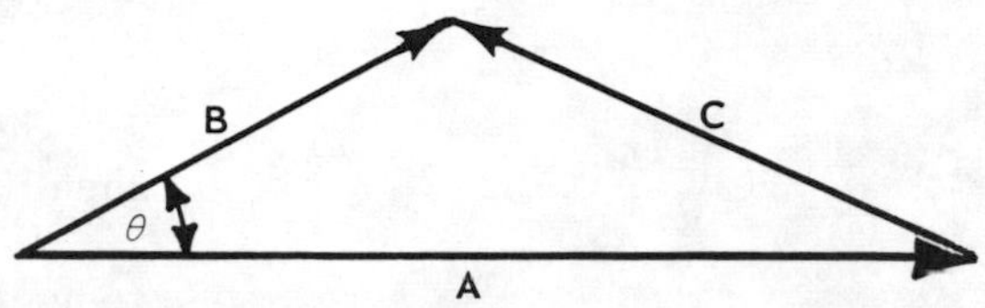


Fig. 1.16 Verification of the law of cosines for a triangle.

Since

$$\begin{aligned}\mathbf{C}\cdot\mathbf{C} &= (\mathbf{B}-\mathbf{A})\cdot(\mathbf{B}-\mathbf{A})\\ &= \mathbf{B}\cdot\mathbf{B} - \mathbf{A}\cdot\mathbf{B} - \mathbf{B}\cdot\mathbf{A} + \mathbf{A}\cdot\mathbf{A}\\ &= \mathbf{A}\cdot\mathbf{A} + \mathbf{B}\cdot\mathbf{B} - 2\mathbf{A}\cdot\mathbf{B},\end{aligned}$$

we have on applying the definitions of the dot product,

$$C^2 = A^2 + B^2 - 2AB\cos\theta.$$

The *Cauchy-Schwarz Inequality* states that if **A** and **B** are two arbitrary vectors, then

$$|\mathbf{A}\cdot\mathbf{B}| \le |\mathbf{A}|\,|\mathbf{B}|. \tag{1.45}$$

**PROBLEM 1.13** Verify (1.45).

**Solution:** Let $m$ be any scalar. Then,

$$\begin{aligned}|m\mathbf{A}+\mathbf{B}|^2 &= (m\mathbf{A}+\mathbf{B})\cdot(m\mathbf{A}+\mathbf{B})\\ &= m^2(\mathbf{A}\cdot\mathbf{A}) + 2m(\mathbf{A}\cdot\mathbf{B}) + (\mathbf{B}\cdot\mathbf{B})\\ &= m^2A^2 + 2m(\mathbf{A}\cdot\mathbf{B}) + B^2.\end{aligned} \tag{1.46}$$

The right-hand side of (1.46) is a quadratic in $m$ except when $|\mathbf{A}| = A = 0$. If $|\mathbf{A}| = A \neq 0$, then adding $(\mathbf{A}\cdot\mathbf{B})^2/A^2$ to (1.46) and also subtracting the same quantity yields

$$\begin{aligned}|m\mathbf{A}+\mathbf{B}|^2 &= m^2A^2 + 2m(\mathbf{A}\cdot\mathbf{B}) + \frac{(\mathbf{A}\cdot\mathbf{B})^2}{A^2} + B^2 - \frac{(\mathbf{A}\cdot\mathbf{B})^2}{A^2}\\ &= \left[mA + \frac{(\mathbf{A}\cdot\mathbf{B})}{A}\right]^2 + \frac{1}{A^2}[A^2B^2 - (\mathbf{A}\cdot\mathbf{B})^2].\end{aligned} \tag{1.47}$$

The left-hand side of (1.47) is nonnegative for any scalar $m$. Substituting $m = -(\mathbf{A}\cdot\mathbf{B})/A^2$,

$$\frac{1}{A^2}[A^2B^2 - (\mathbf{A}\cdot\mathbf{B})^2] \ge 0. \tag{1.48}$$

Since $A^2 = |\mathbf{A}|^2 > 0$,

$$(\mathbf{A}\cdot\mathbf{B})^2 \le A^2B^2 = |\mathbf{A}|^2\,|\mathbf{B}|^2,$$

or

$$|\mathbf{A}\cdot\mathbf{B}| \le |\mathbf{A}|\,|\mathbf{B}|. \tag{1.49}$$

If $|\mathbf{A}| = A = 0$, then $\mathbf{A} = \mathbf{0}$; hence, $\mathbf{A}\cdot\mathbf{B} = 0$. Thus (1.45) is also true, and the equality holds in this case.

**Alternate Solution:** From (1.25),

$$|\mathbf{A}\cdot\mathbf{B}| = |AB\cos\theta| = AB\,|\cos\theta|. \tag{1.50}$$

Since $|\cos\theta| \le 1$,

$$|\mathbf{A}\cdot\mathbf{B}| = AB\,|\cos\theta| \le AB = |\mathbf{A}|\,|\mathbf{B}|.$$

The equal sign holds for the case of $\cos\theta = \pm 1$, i.e., $\theta = 0$ or $180°$, or $\mathbf{A} \parallel \mathbf{B}$.

The *triangle inequality* states that if **A** and **B** are two arbitrary vectors, then

$$|\mathbf{A}+\mathbf{B}| \le |\mathbf{A}| + |\mathbf{B}|. \tag{1.51}$$

**PROBLEM 1.14** Verify (1.51).

**Solution:** From the left-hand side of (1.51),

$$\begin{aligned} |\mathbf{A}+\mathbf{B}|^2 &= (\mathbf{A}+\mathbf{B})\cdot(\mathbf{A}+\mathbf{B}) \\ &= (\mathbf{A}\cdot\mathbf{A}) + 2(\mathbf{A}\cdot\mathbf{B}) + (\mathbf{B}\cdot\mathbf{B}) \\ &= |\mathbf{A}|^2 + 2(\mathbf{A}\cdot\mathbf{B}) + |\mathbf{B}|^2. \end{aligned} \tag{1.52}$$

From the Cauchy-Schwarz inequality (1.45),

$$(\mathbf{A}\cdot\mathbf{B}) \le |\mathbf{A}|\,|\mathbf{B}|.$$

Hence,

$$|\mathbf{A}+\mathbf{B}|^2 \le |\mathbf{A}|^2 + 2|\mathbf{A}|\,|\mathbf{B}| + |\mathbf{B}|^2 = (|\mathbf{A}| + |\mathbf{B}|)^2 \tag{1.53}$$

or

$$|\mathbf{A}+\mathbf{B}| \le |\mathbf{A}| + |\mathbf{B}|.$$

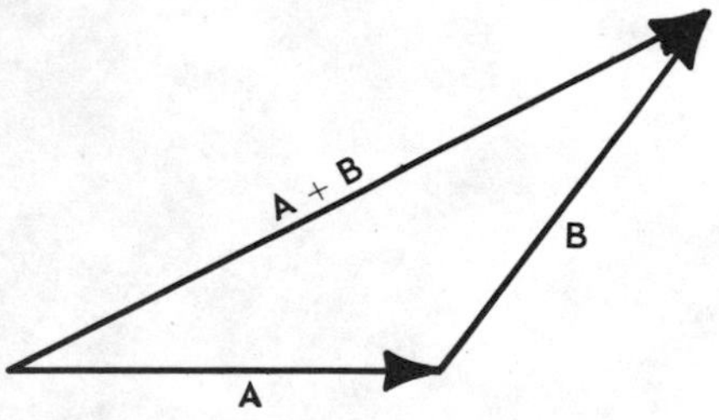


Fig. 1.17 Verification of the triangle inequality.

The triangle inequality (1.51) proves that the sum of the lengths of two sides of a triangle is greater than the length of the third side. (See Fig. 1.17.)

## 1.5 Vector or Cross Product

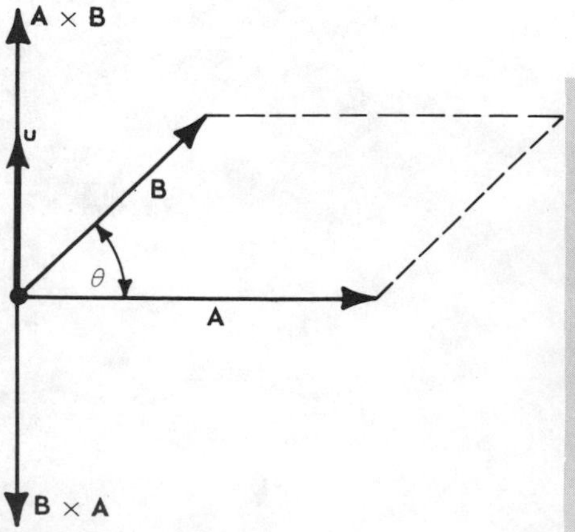


Fig. 1.18 The vector product of two vectors.

The *vector* or *cross product* (sometimes called the *outer product*) of two vectors **A** and **B** is a vector $\mathbf{A}\times\mathbf{B}$ (read **A** cross **B**) given by

$$\mathbf{A}\times\mathbf{B} = |\mathbf{A}|\,|\mathbf{B}|\sin\theta\,\mathbf{u} = (AB\sin\theta)\mathbf{u}, \tag{1.54}$$

where $\theta$ is the angle between **A** and **B**, $0 \le \theta \le \pi$, and **u** is a unit vector such that $\mathbf{u}\perp\mathbf{A}$, $\mathbf{u}\perp\mathbf{B}$. The direction of **u** is that of the advance of a right-hand screw as **A** rotates toward **B** through the angle $\theta$. (See Fig. 1.18.)

The vector product has the following properties:

$$\mathbf{A}\times\mathbf{B} = -\mathbf{B}\times\mathbf{A} \qquad \text{[Anticommutative or Skew-Symmetry law]} \tag{1.55}$$

$$\mathbf{A}\times(\mathbf{B}+\mathbf{C}) = \mathbf{A}\times\mathbf{B} + \mathbf{A}\times\mathbf{C} \qquad \text{[Distributive law]} \tag{1.56}$$

$$(m\mathbf{A})\times\mathbf{B} = \mathbf{A}\times(m\mathbf{B}) = m\mathbf{A}\times\mathbf{B} \tag{1.57}$$

$$\mathbf{A}\times\mathbf{A} = \mathbf{0} \tag{1.58}$$

**PROBLEM 1.15** Verify (1.55).

**Solution:** Let $\theta$ be the angle between **A** and **B** and $0 \le \theta \le \pi$. Then,

$$|\mathbf{B} \times \mathbf{A}| = |\mathbf{B}||\mathbf{A}| \sin\theta = BA \sin\theta = AB \sin\theta = |\mathbf{A} \times \mathbf{B}|; \qquad (1.59)$$

but the direction of $\mathbf{B} \times \mathbf{A}$ is opposite to that of $\mathbf{A} \times \mathbf{B}$. Hence, we have $\mathbf{B} \times \mathbf{A} = -\mathbf{A} \times \mathbf{B}$. (See Fig. 1.18.)

**PROBLEM 1.16** Show that the area $S$ of a parallelogram with vectors **A** and **B** forming adjacent sides is

$$S = |\mathbf{A} \times \mathbf{B}| = |\mathbf{B} \times \mathbf{A}|. \qquad (1.60)$$

**Solution:** Figure 1.19 shows the parallelogram. If $h$ is the perpendicular distance from the terminal point of **B** to the edge of **A**, then $S = Ah$. But $h = B \sin\theta$. Hence, $S = AB \sin\theta = |\mathbf{A} \times \mathbf{B}| = |\mathbf{B} \times \mathbf{A}|$.

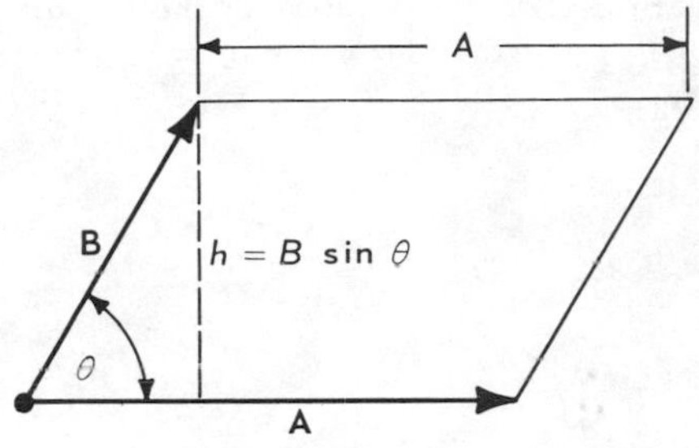

Fig. 1.19 The parallelogram of Prob. 1.16.

From the result of Prob. 1.16, the area of a triangle, with vectors **A** and **B** as sides, is $1/2\,|\mathbf{A} \times \mathbf{B}|$.

**PROBLEM 1.17** Verify (1.58).

**Solution:** From the anticommutative law (1.55), $\mathbf{A} \times \mathbf{A} = -\mathbf{A} \times \mathbf{A}$, when $\mathbf{A} = \mathbf{B}$. Thus, $\mathbf{A} \times \mathbf{A} = \mathbf{0}$. This is consistent with (1.54), since $\theta = 0$ implies $\sin\theta = 0$, and, hence, $|\mathbf{A} \times \mathbf{A}| = A^2 \sin 0^\circ = 0$. We shall often use (1.54) for parallel vectors, even though **u** is not properly defined. Thus,

$$\mathbf{A} \times \mathbf{A} = (A^2 \sin 0)\mathbf{u} = \mathbf{0}$$

for any choice of **u** in (1.54).

**PROBLEM 1.18** Show that **A** is parallel to **B** if and only if $\mathbf{A} \times \mathbf{B} = \mathbf{0}$.

**Solution:** If $\mathbf{A} \parallel \mathbf{B}$, then from (1.4), there exists a scalar $m$ such that $\mathbf{B} = m\mathbf{A}$. Thus using (1.57-8), $\mathbf{A} \times \mathbf{B} = \mathbf{A} \times (m\mathbf{A}) = m\mathbf{A} \times \mathbf{A} = m\mathbf{0} = \mathbf{0}$.

If **A** is not parallel to **B**, then $\mathbf{A} \neq \mathbf{0}$, $\mathbf{B} \neq \mathbf{0}$, and $0 < \theta < \pi$. Thus, $|\mathbf{A}| \neq 0$, $|\mathbf{B}| \neq 0$, and $\sin\theta \neq 0$. Hence, from (1.54),

$$\mathbf{A} \times \mathbf{B} = |\mathbf{A}||\mathbf{B}| \sin\theta\, \mathbf{u} \neq \mathbf{0}.$$

Thus, $\mathbf{A} \parallel \mathbf{B}$ if and only if $\mathbf{A} \times \mathbf{B} = \mathbf{0}$.

*Lagrange's identity* states that if **A** and **B** are arbitrary vectors, then

$$|\mathbf{A} \times \mathbf{B}|^2 = |\mathbf{A}|^2 |\mathbf{B}|^2 - (\mathbf{A} \cdot \mathbf{B})^2. \qquad (1.61)$$

**PROBLEM 1.19** Verify (1.61).

**Solution:** From (1.54),

$$\begin{aligned} |\mathbf{A} \times \mathbf{B}|^2 &= |\mathbf{A}|^2 |\mathbf{B}|^2 \sin^2\theta \\ &= |\mathbf{A}|^2 |\mathbf{B}|^2 (1 - \cos^2\theta) \\ &= |\mathbf{A}|^2 |\mathbf{B}|^2 - |\mathbf{A}|^2 |\mathbf{B}|^2 \cos^2\theta. \end{aligned}$$

Hence, using (1.25), $|\mathbf{A} \times \mathbf{B}|^2 = |\mathbf{A}|^2 |\mathbf{B}|^2 - (\mathbf{A} \cdot \mathbf{B})^2$.

The *law of sines* states that if $\alpha$, $\beta$, and $\gamma$ are the angles opposite the three sides of a triangle of lengths $|\mathbf{A}|$, $|\mathbf{B}|$, and $|\mathbf{C}|$, then

$$\frac{A}{\sin\alpha} = \frac{B}{\sin\beta} = \frac{C}{\sin\gamma}.$$

**PROBLEM 1.20** Using vectors, derive the law of sines for a triangle from (1.54).

**Solution:** From Fig. 1.20,

$$\mathbf{C} = \mathbf{B} - \mathbf{A}. \tag{1.62}$$

Then $\mathbf{C} \times \mathbf{C} = \mathbf{C} \times (\mathbf{B} - \mathbf{A})$, and $\mathbf{0} = \mathbf{C} \times \mathbf{B} - \mathbf{C} \times \mathbf{A}$ or

$$\mathbf{C} \times \mathbf{A} = \mathbf{C} \times \mathbf{B}. \tag{1.63}$$

Thus, $CA \sin(180° - \beta) = CB \sin \alpha$. Since $\sin(180° - \beta) = \sin \beta$, we have $CA \sin \beta = CB \sin \alpha$, or

$$\frac{A}{\sin \alpha} = \frac{B}{\sin \beta}. \tag{1.64}$$

Similarly,

$$\frac{A}{\sin \alpha} = \frac{C}{\sin \gamma}. \tag{1.65}$$

Then (1.64) and (1.65) give the law of sines:

$$\frac{A}{\sin \alpha} = \frac{B}{\sin \beta} = \frac{C}{\sin \gamma}. \tag{1.66}$$

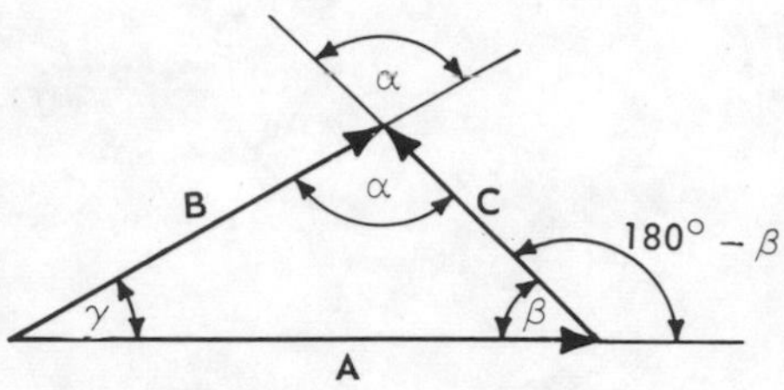

Fig. 1.20 Verification of the law of sines for a triangle.

## 1.6 Scalar Triple Product

The *scalar triple product* of three vectors **A**, **B**, and **C** is a scalar $\mathbf{A} \cdot (\mathbf{B} \times \mathbf{C})$, or simply,

$$\mathbf{A} \cdot \mathbf{B} \times \mathbf{C}. \tag{1.67}$$

**PROBLEM 1.21** Give a geometrical interpretation of $\mathbf{A} \cdot \mathbf{B} \times \mathbf{C}$.

**Solution:** Figure 1.21 shows a parallelepiped whose sides are **A**, **B**, and **C**. From (1.60), the area $S$ of which the vectors **B** and **C** are adjacent edges is

$$S = |\mathbf{B} \times \mathbf{C}|. \tag{1.68}$$

If $h$ is the altitude, then

$$h = |\mathbf{A}|\, |\cos \theta|, \tag{1.69}$$

where $\theta$ is the angle between **A** and $\mathbf{B} \times \mathbf{C}$. Thus the volume of the parallelepiped is

$$V = hS = |\mathbf{A}|\, |\mathbf{B} \times \mathbf{C}|\, |\cos \theta| = |\mathbf{A} \cdot \mathbf{B} \times \mathbf{C}|. \tag{1.70}$$

It is seen from (1.70) that when $0 < \theta < \pi/2$ as in Fig. 1.21(a), $\mathbf{A} \cdot \mathbf{B} \times \mathbf{C} > 0$, and when $\pi/2 < \theta < \pi$ as in Fig. 1.21(b), $\mathbf{A} \cdot \mathbf{B} \times \mathbf{C} < 0$. Hence **A**, **B**, and **C** form a *positive triple* if and only if $\mathbf{A} \cdot \mathbf{B} \times \mathbf{C} > 0$. If $\mathbf{A} \cdot \mathbf{B} \times \mathbf{C} = 0$, then **A**, **B**, and **C** are coplanar.

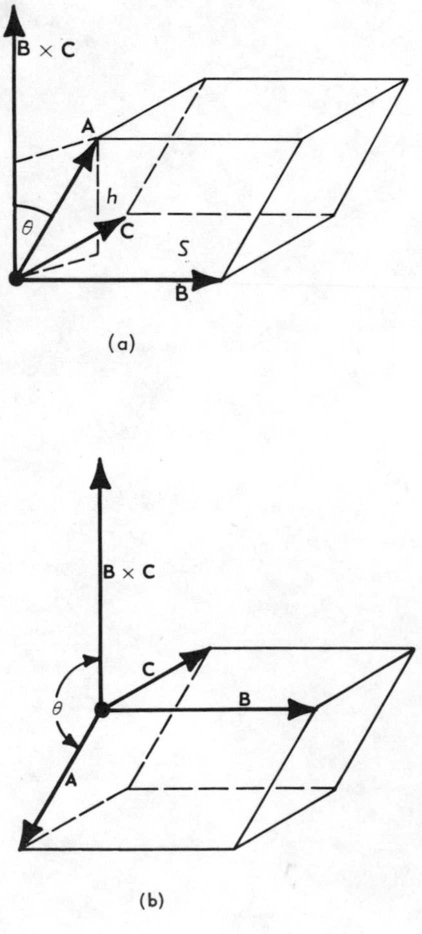

Fig. 1.21 Volume of a parallelepiped: (a) $0 < \theta < \frac{1}{2}\pi$, (b) $\frac{1}{2}\pi < \theta < \pi$.

**PROBLEM 1.22** If vectors **A**, **B**, and **C** are coplanar, show that $\mathbf{A} \cdot \mathbf{B} \times \mathbf{C} = 0$.

**Solution:** If **A**, **B**, and **C** are coplanar, the altitude of the parallelepiped formed by them is zero. Hence, from (1.70), we have $\mathbf{A} \cdot \mathbf{B} \times \mathbf{C} = 0$.

**PROBLEM 1.23** Show that if any two vectors in a scalar triple product are equal, then that product is zero; i.e.,

$$\mathbf{A}\cdot\mathbf{A}\times\mathbf{C}=0,\quad \mathbf{A}\cdot\mathbf{B}\times\mathbf{B}=0,\quad \mathbf{C}\cdot\mathbf{B}\times\mathbf{C}=0. \tag{1.71}$$

**Solution:** From the definition of a vector product (1.54), $\mathbf{A}\times\mathbf{C}$ is perpendicular to **A**. Hence their dot product is zero; i.e., $\mathbf{A}\cdot\mathbf{A}\times\mathbf{C}=0$. Since $\mathbf{B}\times\mathbf{B}=\mathbf{0}$,

$$\mathbf{A}\cdot\mathbf{B}\times\mathbf{B}=\mathbf{A}\cdot\mathbf{0}=0.$$

Similarly, since $\mathbf{B}\times\mathbf{C}$ is perpendicular to **C**, the scalar product

$$\mathbf{C}\cdot(\mathbf{B}\times\mathbf{C})=0.$$

**Alternate Solution:** If any two of the vectors **A**, **B**, **C** are equal, then **A**, **B**, and **C** are coplanar. Hence, from Prob. 1.22, $\mathbf{A}\cdot\mathbf{B}\times\mathbf{C}=0$.

**PROBLEM 1.24** Show that, for vectors **A**, **B**, and **C**,

$$\mathbf{A}\cdot\mathbf{B}\times\mathbf{C}=\mathbf{A}\times\mathbf{B}\cdot\mathbf{C}. \tag{1.72}$$

**Solution:** First consider the geometric meaning of $\mathbf{A}\cdot\mathbf{B}\times\mathbf{C}$. Excluding a sign change, it is the volume of a parallelepiped whose sides are **A**, **B**, and **C**. This volume is equal to $\pm\,\mathbf{C}\cdot\mathbf{A}\times\mathbf{B}$. Thus,

$$\mathbf{A}\cdot\mathbf{B}\times\mathbf{C}=\pm\,\mathbf{C}\cdot\mathbf{A}\times\mathbf{B}. \tag{1.73}$$

But by the commutative law of the scalar product,

$$\mathbf{C}\cdot\mathbf{A}\times\mathbf{B}=\mathbf{A}\times\mathbf{B}\cdot\mathbf{C}. \tag{1.74}$$

Therefore,

$$\mathbf{A}\cdot\mathbf{B}\times\mathbf{C}=\pm\,\mathbf{A}\times\mathbf{B}\cdot\mathbf{C}. \tag{1.75}$$

To determine the sign, note that if **A**, **B**, and **C** form a positive system, so do **C**, **A**, and **B**. Similarly, if **A**, **B**, and **C** form a negative system, so do **C**, **A**, and **B**. Thus, $\mathbf{A}\cdot\mathbf{B}\times\mathbf{C}$ and $\mathbf{C}\cdot\mathbf{A}\times\mathbf{B}$ always have the same sign, i.e.,

$$\mathbf{A}\cdot\mathbf{B}\times\mathbf{C}=\mathbf{A}\times\mathbf{B}\cdot\mathbf{C}.$$

Problem 1.24 shows that in a scalar triple product, the dot and cross can be interchanged without changing its value. Thus, for simplicity,

$$\mathbf{A}\cdot\mathbf{B}\times\mathbf{C}=[\mathbf{ABC}]. \tag{1.76}$$

**PROBLEM 1.25** Show that

$$[\mathbf{ABC}]=[\mathbf{BCA}]=[\mathbf{CAB}]=-[\mathbf{ACB}]=-[\mathbf{BAC}]=-[\mathbf{CBA}]. \tag{1.77}$$

**Solution:** Using the commutative law of the scalar product and the result of Prob. 1.24,

$$\begin{aligned}[\mathbf{ABC}]=\mathbf{A}\cdot\mathbf{B}\times\mathbf{C}&=\mathbf{B}\times\mathbf{C}\cdot\mathbf{A}\\&=\mathbf{B}\cdot\mathbf{C}\times\mathbf{A}\\&=[\mathbf{BCA}],\end{aligned}$$

$$\begin{aligned}[\mathbf{ABC}]=\mathbf{A}\cdot\mathbf{B}\times\mathbf{C}&=\mathbf{A}\cdot[-(\mathbf{C}\times\mathbf{B})]\\&=-\mathbf{A}\cdot\mathbf{C}\times\mathbf{B}\\&=-[\mathbf{ACB}].\end{aligned}$$

The other equations are proved similarly.

It is seen from (1.77) that any cyclic permutation of the vectors **A**, **B**, and **C** in the triple scalar product will give the same result, while an acyclic permutation will give the negative result.

**PROBLEM 1.26** Using the scalar triple product, prove that

$$\mathbf{A} \times (\mathbf{B} + \mathbf{C}) = \mathbf{A} \times \mathbf{B} + \mathbf{A} \times \mathbf{C}. \qquad [1.56]$$

**Solution:** Let

$$\mathbf{U} = \mathbf{A} \times (\mathbf{B} + \mathbf{C}) - \mathbf{A} \times \mathbf{B} - \mathbf{A} \times \mathbf{C}. \qquad (1.78)$$

The dot product of $\mathbf{U}$ with an arbitrary vector $\mathbf{V}$ yields

$$\mathbf{V} \cdot \mathbf{U} = \mathbf{V} \cdot [\mathbf{A} \times (\mathbf{B} + \mathbf{C})] - \mathbf{V} \cdot \mathbf{A} \times \mathbf{B} - \mathbf{V} \cdot \mathbf{A} \times \mathbf{C}. \qquad (1.79)$$

From the distributive law of the scalar product (1.32) and (1.72), by interchanging the dot and cross,

$$\begin{aligned} \mathbf{V} \cdot \mathbf{U} &= \mathbf{V} \times \mathbf{A} \cdot (\mathbf{B} + \mathbf{C}) - \mathbf{V} \times \mathbf{A} \cdot \mathbf{B} - \mathbf{V} \times \mathbf{A} \cdot \mathbf{C} \qquad (1.80) \\ &= \mathbf{V} \times \mathbf{A} \cdot \mathbf{B} + \mathbf{V} \times \mathbf{A} \cdot \mathbf{C} - \mathbf{V} \times \mathbf{A} \cdot \mathbf{B} - \mathbf{V} \times \mathbf{A} \cdot \mathbf{C} \\ &= 0. \qquad (1.81) \end{aligned}$$

Thus, (1.81) implies that $\mathbf{V} \perp \mathbf{U}$. Since $\mathbf{V}$ is arbitrary, we choose $\mathbf{V} = \mathbf{U}$. Thus, $\mathbf{U} \cdot \mathbf{U} = 0$, and, hence, $\mathbf{U} = \mathbf{0}$.

## 1.7 Vector Triple Product

The *vector triple product* of three vectors $\mathbf{A}$, $\mathbf{B}$, and $\mathbf{C}$ is the vector

$$\mathbf{A} \times (\mathbf{B} \times \mathbf{C}). \qquad (1.82)$$

**PROBLEM 1.27** Show that

$$\mathbf{A} \times (\mathbf{B} \times \mathbf{C}) = (\mathbf{A} \cdot \mathbf{C})\mathbf{B} - (\mathbf{A} \cdot \mathbf{B})\mathbf{C}. \qquad (1.83)$$

**Solution:** First note that (1.83) is true if $\mathbf{B}$ and $\mathbf{C}$ are parallel. It then follows that either $\mathbf{B} = m\mathbf{C}$ or $\mathbf{C} = n\mathbf{B}$ for some scalars $m$ and $n$. Hence, both sides of (1.83) are $\mathbf{0}$. Equation (1.83) is also true if $\mathbf{A} = \mathbf{A}'$ is perpendicular to $\mathbf{B}$ and to $\mathbf{C}$. It then follows that $\mathbf{A}'$ is parallel to $\mathbf{B} \times \mathbf{C}$. Hence, both sides of (1.83) are $\mathbf{0}$:

$$\mathbf{A}' \times (\mathbf{B} \times \mathbf{C}) = (\mathbf{A}' \cdot \mathbf{C})\mathbf{B} - (\mathbf{A}' \cdot \mathbf{B})\mathbf{C} \qquad (1.84)$$

if $\mathbf{A}' \cdot \mathbf{C} = 0$, $\mathbf{A}' \cdot \mathbf{B} = 0$.

To prove that (1.83) is true if $\mathbf{A} = \mathbf{C}$, let

$$\mathbf{V} = \mathbf{C} \times (\mathbf{B} \times \mathbf{C}) - [(\mathbf{C} \cdot \mathbf{C})\mathbf{B} - (\mathbf{C} \cdot \mathbf{B})\mathbf{C}]. \qquad (1.85)$$

Note that $\mathbf{C} \times (\mathbf{B} \times \mathbf{C})$ is perpendicular to $\mathbf{B} \times \mathbf{C}$ and hence is in the plane of $\mathbf{B}$ and $\mathbf{C}$. Thus $\mathbf{V}$ is also in the plane of $\mathbf{B}$ and $\mathbf{C}$; i.e.,

$$\mathbf{V} = x\mathbf{B} + y\mathbf{C} \qquad (1.86)$$

for some scalars $x$ and $y$. Using (1.85),

$$\begin{aligned} \mathbf{B} \cdot \mathbf{V} &= \mathbf{B} \cdot \mathbf{C} \times (\mathbf{B} \times \mathbf{C}) - [(\mathbf{C} \cdot \mathbf{C})(\mathbf{B} \cdot \mathbf{B}) - (\mathbf{C} \cdot \mathbf{B})(\mathbf{C} \cdot \mathbf{B})] \\ &= (\mathbf{B} \times \mathbf{C}) \cdot (\mathbf{B} \times \mathbf{C}) - [\,|\mathbf{C}|^2 |\mathbf{B}|^2 - (\mathbf{C} \cdot \mathbf{B})^2]. \end{aligned}$$

Therefore,

$$\mathbf{B} \cdot \mathbf{V} = 0 \qquad (1.87)$$

by (1.61). Also, from (1.85),

$$\mathbf{C} \cdot \mathbf{V} = \mathbf{C} \cdot \mathbf{C} \times (\mathbf{B} \times \mathbf{C}) - [(\mathbf{C} \cdot \mathbf{C})(\mathbf{C} \cdot \mathbf{B}) - (\mathbf{C} \cdot \mathbf{B})(\mathbf{C} \cdot \mathbf{C})],$$

or

$$\mathbf{C} \cdot \mathbf{V} = 0. \tag{1.88}$$

However, (1.86–8) imply that $\mathbf{V} = \mathbf{0}$. Multiply (1.87) by $x$, (1.88) by $y$, and add to obtain

$$(x\mathbf{B} + y\mathbf{C}) \cdot \mathbf{V} = 0. \tag{1.89}$$

Using (1.86), we obtain $\mathbf{V} \cdot \mathbf{V} = 0$ or $\mathbf{V} = \mathbf{0}$. Therefore, using (1.85),

$$\mathbf{C} \times (\mathbf{B} \times \mathbf{C}) = (\mathbf{C} \cdot \mathbf{C})\mathbf{B} - (\mathbf{B} \cdot \mathbf{C})\mathbf{C}. \tag{1.90}$$

Now we can prove from (1.90) by skew symmetry that (1.83) is also true if $\mathbf{B} = \mathbf{C}$; i.e.,

$$\mathbf{B} \times (\mathbf{B} \times \mathbf{C}) = -\mathbf{B} \times (\mathbf{C} \times \mathbf{B}). \tag{1.91}$$

Interchanging $\mathbf{B}$ and $\mathbf{C}$ in (1.90) yields

$$\begin{aligned} \mathbf{B} \times (\mathbf{B} \times \mathbf{C}) &= -[(\mathbf{B} \cdot \mathbf{B})\mathbf{C} - (\mathbf{C} \cdot \mathbf{B})\mathbf{B}] \\ &= (\mathbf{B} \cdot \mathbf{C})\mathbf{B} - (\mathbf{B} \cdot \mathbf{B})\mathbf{C}, \end{aligned} \tag{1.92}$$

which verifies (1.83) for the case when $\mathbf{B} = \mathbf{C}$.

Now multiply (1.90) by $u$, (1.92) by $v$, and add using $\mathbf{A}_1 = u\mathbf{C} + v\mathbf{B}$:

$$u\mathbf{C} \times (\mathbf{B} \times \mathbf{C}) = (u\mathbf{C} \cdot \mathbf{C})\mathbf{B} - (u\mathbf{C} \cdot \mathbf{B})\mathbf{C}, \tag{1.93}$$

$$v\mathbf{B} \times (\mathbf{B} \times \mathbf{C}) = (v\mathbf{B} \cdot \mathbf{C})\mathbf{B} - (v\mathbf{B} \cdot \mathbf{B})\mathbf{C}, \tag{1.94}$$

$$\mathbf{A}_1 \times (\mathbf{B} \times \mathbf{C}) = (\mathbf{A}_1 \cdot \mathbf{C})\mathbf{B} - (\mathbf{A}_1 \cdot \mathbf{B})\mathbf{C}. \tag{1.95}$$

This proves that (1.83) is true if $\mathbf{A} = \mathbf{A}_1$ is in the plane of $\mathbf{B}$ and $\mathbf{C}$. But any vector $\mathbf{A}$ can be written as

$$\mathbf{A} = \mathbf{A}_1 + \mathbf{A}', \tag{1.96}$$

where $\mathbf{A}_1$ is in the plane of $\mathbf{B}$ and $\mathbf{C}$, and $\mathbf{A}'$ is perpendicular to that plane. Thus, adding (1.84) and (1.95),

$$(\mathbf{A}_1 + \mathbf{A}') \times (\mathbf{B} \times \mathbf{C}) = [(\mathbf{A}_1 + \mathbf{A}') \cdot \mathbf{C}]\mathbf{B} - [(\mathbf{A}_1 + \mathbf{A}') \cdot \mathbf{B}]\mathbf{C}, \tag{1.97}$$

which is the required result, since $\mathbf{A} = \mathbf{A}_1 + \mathbf{A}'$ by (1.96).

**PROBLEM 1.28** Show that

$$(\mathbf{A} \times \mathbf{B}) \times \mathbf{C} = (\mathbf{A} \cdot \mathbf{C})\mathbf{B} - (\mathbf{B} \cdot \mathbf{C})\mathbf{A}. \tag{1.98}$$

**Solution:** From the anticommutative law of a vector product (1.55),

$$(\mathbf{A} \times \mathbf{B}) \times \mathbf{C} = -\mathbf{C} \times (\mathbf{A} \times \mathbf{B}). \tag{1.99}$$

Replacing $\mathbf{A}$, $\mathbf{B}$, and $\mathbf{C}$ in (1.83) by $\mathbf{C}$, $\mathbf{A}$, and $\mathbf{B}$, respectively,

$$\mathbf{C} \times (\mathbf{A} \times \mathbf{B}) = (\mathbf{C} \cdot \mathbf{B})\mathbf{A} - (\mathbf{C} \cdot \mathbf{A})\mathbf{B}. \tag{1.100}$$

Hence,

$$(\mathbf{A} \times \mathbf{B}) \times \mathbf{C} = -[(\mathbf{C} \cdot \mathbf{B})\mathbf{A} - (\mathbf{C} \cdot \mathbf{A})\mathbf{B}] = (\mathbf{A} \cdot \mathbf{C})\mathbf{B} - (\mathbf{B} \cdot \mathbf{C})\mathbf{A}.$$

It is clear from (1.83) and (1.98) that

$$\mathbf{A} \times (\mathbf{B} \times \mathbf{C}) \neq (\mathbf{A} \times \mathbf{B}) \times \mathbf{C}.$$

The identities

$$\mathbf{A} \times (\mathbf{B} \times \mathbf{C}) = (\mathbf{A} \cdot \mathbf{C})\mathbf{B} - (\mathbf{A} \cdot \mathbf{B})\mathbf{C}, \qquad [1.83]$$

$$(\mathbf{A}\times\mathbf{B})\times\mathbf{C} = (\mathbf{A}\cdot\mathbf{C})\mathbf{B} - (\mathbf{B}\cdot\mathbf{C})\mathbf{A} \qquad [1.98]$$

are easily remembered if the following so-called *middle-term* rule is noted:

The vector product is equal to the middle vector whose coefficient is the scalar product of the remaining vectors minus the other vector in the parentheses whose coefficient is the scalar product of the remaining vectors.

**PROBLEM 1.29** Show that

$$(\mathbf{A}\times\mathbf{B})\times(\mathbf{C}\times\mathbf{D}) = [\mathbf{ABD}]\mathbf{C} - [\mathbf{ABC}]\mathbf{D}, \qquad (1.101)$$

$$(\mathbf{A}\times\mathbf{B})\times(\mathbf{C}\times\mathbf{D}) = [\mathbf{CDA}]\mathbf{B} - [\mathbf{CDB}]\mathbf{A}. \qquad (1.102)$$

**Solution:** Let $\mathbf{A}\times\mathbf{B} = \mathbf{E}$; then from (1.83),

$$\begin{aligned}(\mathbf{A}\times\mathbf{B})\times(\mathbf{C}\times\mathbf{D}) &= \mathbf{E}\times(\mathbf{C}\times\mathbf{D})\\ &= (\mathbf{E}\cdot\mathbf{D})\mathbf{C} - (\mathbf{E}\cdot\mathbf{C})\mathbf{D}\\ &= (\mathbf{A}\times\mathbf{B}\cdot\mathbf{D})\mathbf{C} - (\mathbf{A}\times\mathbf{B}\cdot\mathbf{C})\mathbf{D}\\ &= [\mathbf{ABD}]\mathbf{C} - [\mathbf{ABC}]\mathbf{D}.\end{aligned}$$

Similarly, if we let $\mathbf{C}\times\mathbf{D} = \mathbf{F}$, then from (1.98),

$$\begin{aligned}(\mathbf{A}\times\mathbf{B})\times(\mathbf{C}\times\mathbf{D}) &= (\mathbf{A}\times\mathbf{B})\times\mathbf{F}\\ &= (\mathbf{F}\cdot\mathbf{A})\mathbf{B} - (\mathbf{F}\cdot\mathbf{B})\mathbf{A}\\ &= (\mathbf{C}\times\mathbf{D}\cdot\mathbf{A})\mathbf{B} - (\mathbf{C}\times\mathbf{D}\cdot\mathbf{B})\mathbf{A}\\ &= (\mathbf{C}\cdot\mathbf{D}\times\mathbf{A})\mathbf{B} - (\mathbf{C}\cdot\mathbf{D}\times\mathbf{B})\mathbf{A}\\ &= [\mathbf{CDA}]\mathbf{B} - [\mathbf{CDB}]\mathbf{A}.\end{aligned}$$

**PROBLEM 1.30** Show that any vector $\mathbf{D}$ in three dimensions can be expressed as a linear combination of any three given noncoplanar vectors $\mathbf{A}$, $\mathbf{B}$, and $\mathbf{C}$.

**Solution:** Equating (1.101) and (1.102),

$$[\mathbf{ABD}]\mathbf{C} - [\mathbf{ABC}]\mathbf{D} = [\mathbf{CDA}]\mathbf{B} - [\mathbf{CDB}]\mathbf{A}. \qquad (1.103)$$

Hence, if $[\mathbf{ABC}] \neq 0$, i.e., if $\mathbf{A}$, $\mathbf{B}$, and $\mathbf{C}$ are noncoplanar, then, by using (1.77),

$$\begin{aligned}\mathbf{D} &= \frac{1}{[\mathbf{ABC}]}\left([\mathbf{CDB}]\mathbf{A} - [\mathbf{CDA}]\mathbf{B} + [\mathbf{ABD}]\mathbf{C}\right)\\ &= \frac{1}{[\mathbf{ABC}]}\left([\mathbf{DBC}]\mathbf{A} + [\mathbf{DCA}]\mathbf{B} + [\mathbf{DAB}]\mathbf{C}\right). \qquad (1.104)\end{aligned}$$

Thus, (1.104) shows that a vector $\mathbf{D}$ can be expressed as a linear combination of any three given noncoplanar vectors $\mathbf{A}$, $\mathbf{B}$, and $\mathbf{C}$, and gives a formula for this expression.

From the result of this problem, we can conclude that four vectors in three-dimensional space are always linearly dependent.

The *extended Lagrange identity* states that for the four vectors $\mathbf{A}$, $\mathbf{B}$, $\mathbf{C}$, and $\mathbf{D}$,

$$(\mathbf{A}\times\mathbf{B})\cdot(\mathbf{C}\times\mathbf{D}) = (\mathbf{A}\cdot\mathbf{C})(\mathbf{B}\cdot\mathbf{D}) - (\mathbf{B}\cdot\mathbf{C})(\mathbf{A}\cdot\mathbf{D}). \qquad (1.105)$$

**PROBLEM 1.31** Verify (1.105).

**Solution:** Considering the left-hand side as a scalar triple product and using (1.83),

$$(\mathbf{A}\times\mathbf{B})\cdot(\mathbf{C}\times\mathbf{D}) = \mathbf{A}\cdot[\mathbf{B}\times(\mathbf{C}\times\mathbf{D})] = \mathbf{A}\cdot[(\mathbf{B}\cdot\mathbf{D})\mathbf{C} - (\mathbf{B}\cdot\mathbf{C})\mathbf{D}]$$
$$= (\mathbf{A}\cdot\mathbf{C})(\mathbf{B}\cdot\mathbf{D}) - (\mathbf{B}\cdot\mathbf{C})(\mathbf{A}\cdot\mathbf{D}).$$

By setting $\mathbf{C} = \mathbf{A}$ and $\mathbf{D} = \mathbf{B}$ in (1.105),

$$(\mathbf{A}\times\mathbf{B})\cdot(\mathbf{A}\times\mathbf{B}) = (\mathbf{A}\cdot\mathbf{A})(\mathbf{B}\cdot\mathbf{B}) - (\mathbf{A}\cdot\mathbf{B})(\mathbf{A}\cdot\mathbf{B});$$

i.e., the Lagrange identity

$$|\mathbf{A}\times\mathbf{B}|^2 = |\mathbf{A}|^2|\mathbf{B}|^2 - (\mathbf{A}\cdot\mathbf{B})^2. \qquad [1.61]$$

The *Jacobi identity* states that, for arbitrary vectors **A**, **B**, and **C**,

$$\mathbf{A}\times(\mathbf{B}\times\mathbf{C}) + \mathbf{B}\times(\mathbf{C}\times\mathbf{A}) + \mathbf{C}\times(\mathbf{A}\times\mathbf{B}) = \mathbf{0}. \qquad (1.106)$$

**PROBLEM 1.32** Verify (1.106).

**Solution:** Using (1.83),

$$\mathbf{A}\times(\mathbf{B}\times\mathbf{C}) = (\mathbf{A}\cdot\mathbf{C})\mathbf{B} - (\mathbf{A}\cdot\mathbf{B})\mathbf{C},$$
$$\mathbf{B}\times(\mathbf{C}\times\mathbf{A}) = (\mathbf{B}\cdot\mathbf{A})\mathbf{C} - (\mathbf{B}\cdot\mathbf{C})\mathbf{A},$$
$$\mathbf{C}\times(\mathbf{A}\times\mathbf{B}) = (\mathbf{C}\cdot\mathbf{B})\mathbf{A} - (\mathbf{C}\cdot\mathbf{A})\mathbf{B}.$$

Adding the above identities, (1.106) follows.

**PROBLEM 1.33** Show that

$$(\mathbf{A}\times\mathbf{B})\cdot(\mathbf{B}\times\mathbf{C})\times(\mathbf{C}\times\mathbf{A}) = [\mathbf{ABC}]^2. \qquad (1.107)$$

**Solution:** From (1.101),

$$(\mathbf{B}\times\mathbf{C})\times(\mathbf{C}\times\mathbf{A}) = [\mathbf{BCA}]\mathbf{C} - [\mathbf{BCC}]\mathbf{A}$$
$$= [\mathbf{ABC}]\mathbf{C}. \qquad (1.108)$$

Hence,

$$(\mathbf{A}\times\mathbf{B})\cdot(\mathbf{B}\times\mathbf{C})\times(\mathbf{C}\times\mathbf{A}) = (\mathbf{A}\times\mathbf{B})\cdot[\mathbf{ABC}]\mathbf{C}$$
$$= [\mathbf{ABC}]\,(\mathbf{A}\times\mathbf{B})\cdot\mathbf{C}$$
$$= [\mathbf{ABC}]\,[\mathbf{ABC}]$$
$$= [\mathbf{ABC}]^2.$$

## 1.8 Reciprocal Sets of Vectors

Let $\mathbf{a}_1$ $\mathbf{a}_2$, $\mathbf{a}_3$ and $\mathbf{b}_1$, $\mathbf{b}_2$, $\mathbf{b}_3$ be sets of vectors that satisfy

$$\mathbf{a}_m\cdot\mathbf{b}_n = \delta_{mn}, \qquad (1.109)$$

where $\delta_{mn}$ is the *Kronecker delta* and is defined as

$$\delta_{mn} = \begin{cases} 1, & \text{if } m = n \\ 0, & \text{if } m \neq n, \text{ where } m \text{ and } n \text{ are integers.} \end{cases} \qquad (1.110)$$

Then these vectors are said to be *reciprocal sets* of vectors.

**PROBLEM 1.34** If $\mathbf{a}_1$, $\mathbf{a}_2$, $\mathbf{a}_3$ and $\mathbf{b}_1$, $\mathbf{b}_2$, $\mathbf{b}_3$ are reciprocal sets of vectors, then show that $[\mathbf{a}_1\,\mathbf{a}_2\,\mathbf{a}_3] \neq 0$ and $[\mathbf{b}_1\,\mathbf{b}_2\,\mathbf{b}_3] \neq 0$.

**Solution:** Proof is by contradiction. If $[\mathbf{a}_1\, \mathbf{a}_2\, \mathbf{a}_3] = 0$, then from the result of Prob. 1.22, the vectors $\mathbf{a}_1$, $\mathbf{a}_2$, and $\mathbf{a}_3$ are coplanar and are, thus, linearly dependent. Hence, one of the vectors is a linear combination of the others, e.g.,

$$\mathbf{a}_3 = k_1\mathbf{a}_1 + k_2\mathbf{a}_2. \tag{1.111}$$

Dotting both sides of (1.111) with $\mathbf{b}_3$ and using the definition of reciprocal sets of vectors (1.109),

$$1 = \mathbf{a}_3 \cdot \mathbf{b}_3 = k_1\, \mathbf{a}_1 \cdot \mathbf{b}_3 + k_2\, \mathbf{a}_2 \cdot \mathbf{b}_3 = 0,$$

which is a contradiction. Hence, we conclude that

$$[\mathbf{a}_1\, \mathbf{a}_2\, \mathbf{a}_3] \neq 0. \tag{1.112}$$

Similarly, we can show that

$$[\mathbf{b}_1\, \mathbf{b}_2\, \mathbf{b}_3] \neq 0. \tag{1.113}$$

**PROBLEM 1.35** If $\mathbf{a}_1$, $\mathbf{a}_2$, $\mathbf{a}_3$ and $\mathbf{b}_1$, $\mathbf{b}_2$, $\mathbf{b}_3$ are reciprocal sets of vectors, then show that

$$\mathbf{b}_1 = \frac{\mathbf{a}_2 \times \mathbf{a}_3}{[\mathbf{a}_1\, \mathbf{a}_2\, \mathbf{a}_3]}, \quad \mathbf{b}_2 = \frac{\mathbf{a}_3 \times \mathbf{a}_1}{[\mathbf{a}_1\, \mathbf{a}_2\, \mathbf{a}_3]}, \quad \mathbf{b}_3 = \frac{\mathbf{a}_1 \times \mathbf{a}_2}{[\mathbf{a}_1\, \mathbf{a}_2\, \mathbf{a}_3]}, \tag{1.114}$$

$$\mathbf{a}_1 = \frac{\mathbf{b}_2 \times \mathbf{b}_3}{[\mathbf{b}_1\, \mathbf{b}_2\, \mathbf{b}_3]}, \quad \mathbf{a}_2 = \frac{\mathbf{b}_3 \times \mathbf{b}_1}{[\mathbf{b}_1\, \mathbf{b}_2\, \mathbf{b}_3]}, \quad \mathbf{a}_3 = \frac{\mathbf{b}_1 \times \mathbf{b}_2}{[\mathbf{b}_1\, \mathbf{b}_2\, \mathbf{b}_3]}. \tag{1.115}$$

**Solution:** From (1.109),

$$\mathbf{b}_1 \cdot \mathbf{a}_2 = \mathbf{b}_1 \cdot \mathbf{a}_3 = 0, \tag{1.116}$$

$$\mathbf{b}_1 \cdot \mathbf{a}_1 = 1, \tag{1.117}$$

where $\mathbf{b}_1$ is orthogonal to both $\mathbf{a}_2$ and $\mathbf{a}_3$. Hence, we can write

$$\mathbf{b}_1 = \lambda(\mathbf{a}_2 \times \mathbf{a}_3). \tag{1.118}$$

Then from (1.117),

$$\mathbf{a}_1 \cdot \mathbf{b}_1 = \lambda \mathbf{a}_1 \cdot (\mathbf{a}_2 \times \mathbf{a}_3) = \lambda[\mathbf{a}_1\, \mathbf{a}_2\, \mathbf{a}_3] = 1. \tag{1.119}$$

Thus,

$$\lambda = \frac{1}{[\mathbf{a}_1\, \mathbf{a}_2\, \mathbf{a}_3]}, \tag{1.120}$$

$$\mathbf{b}_1 = \frac{\mathbf{a}_2 \times \mathbf{a}_3}{[\mathbf{a}_1\, \mathbf{a}_2\, \mathbf{a}_3]}.$$

Similarly,

$$\mathbf{b}_2 = \frac{\mathbf{a}_3 \times \mathbf{a}_1}{[\mathbf{a}_1\, \mathbf{a}_2\, \mathbf{a}_3]}, \quad \mathbf{b}_3 = \frac{\mathbf{a}_1 \times \mathbf{a}_2}{[\mathbf{a}_1\, \mathbf{a}_2\, \mathbf{a}_3]}.$$

From the relative symmetry in $\mathbf{a}_1$, $\mathbf{a}_2$, $\mathbf{a}_3$, and $\mathbf{b}_1$, $\mathbf{b}_2$, $\mathbf{b}_3$, (1.115) can be obtained directly from (1.114) by interchanging $\mathbf{a}_1$, $\mathbf{a}_2$, $\mathbf{a}_3$ and $\mathbf{b}_1$, $\mathbf{b}_2$, $\mathbf{b}_3$, respectively.

**PROBLEM 1.36** If $\mathbf{a}_1$, $\mathbf{a}_2$, and $\mathbf{a}_3$ are nonzero, noncoplanar vectors, then show that any vector $\mathbf{d}$ can be represented as

$$\mathbf{d} = (\mathbf{d} \cdot \mathbf{b}_1)\mathbf{a}_1 + (\mathbf{d} \cdot \mathbf{b}_2)\mathbf{a}_2 + (\mathbf{d} \cdot \mathbf{b}_3)\mathbf{a}_3, \tag{1.121}$$

where $\mathbf{a}_1$, $\mathbf{a}_2$, $\mathbf{a}_3$ and $\mathbf{b}_1$, $\mathbf{b}_2$, $\mathbf{b}_3$ are reciprocal sets of vectors.

**Solution:** From (1.104),

$$\mathbf{D} = \frac{1}{[\mathbf{ABC}]}\{[\mathbf{DBC}]\mathbf{A} + [\mathbf{DCA}]\mathbf{B} + [\mathbf{DAB}]\mathbf{C}\}.$$

Let $\mathbf{A} = \mathbf{a}_1$, $\mathbf{B} = \mathbf{a}_2$, $\mathbf{C} = \mathbf{a}_3$, and $\mathbf{D} = \mathbf{d}$; then from (1.114),

$$\begin{aligned}
\mathbf{d} &= \frac{1}{[\mathbf{a}_1\ \mathbf{a}_2\ \mathbf{a}_3]}\{[\mathbf{d}\mathbf{a}_2\ \mathbf{a}_3]\mathbf{a}_1 + [\mathbf{d}\mathbf{a}_3\ \mathbf{a}_1]\mathbf{a}_2 + [\mathbf{d}\mathbf{a}_1\ \mathbf{a}_2]\mathbf{a}_3\} \\
&= \frac{1}{[\mathbf{a}_1\ \mathbf{a}_2\ \mathbf{a}_3]}\{\mathbf{d}\cdot(\mathbf{a}_2\times\mathbf{a}_3)\mathbf{a}_1 + \mathbf{d}\cdot(\mathbf{a}_3\times\mathbf{a}_1)\mathbf{a}_2 + \mathbf{d}\cdot(\mathbf{a}_1\times\mathbf{a}_2)\mathbf{a}_3\} \\
&= \mathbf{d}\cdot\frac{\mathbf{a}_2\times\mathbf{a}_3}{[\mathbf{a}_1\ \mathbf{a}_2\ \mathbf{a}_3]}\mathbf{a}_1 + \mathbf{d}\cdot\frac{(\mathbf{a}_3\times\mathbf{a}_1)}{[\mathbf{a}_1\ \mathbf{a}_2\ \mathbf{a}_3]}\mathbf{a}_2 + \mathbf{d}\cdot\frac{(\mathbf{a}_1\times\mathbf{a}_2)}{[\mathbf{a}_1\ \mathbf{a}_2\ \mathbf{a}_3]}\mathbf{a}_3 \\
&= (\mathbf{d}\cdot\mathbf{b}_1)\mathbf{a}_1 + (\mathbf{d}\cdot\mathbf{b}_2)\mathbf{a}_2 + (\mathbf{d}\cdot\mathbf{b}_3)\mathbf{a}_3.
\end{aligned}$$

If every vector in three dimensions can be expressed as a linear combination of nonzero vectors $\mathbf{a}_1$, $\mathbf{a}_2$, and $\mathbf{a}_3$, as shown in (1.121), then we say that the three vectors $\mathbf{a}_1$, $\mathbf{a}_2$, and $\mathbf{a}_3$ *span* the space. In addition, if these three vectors are independent, then they constitute a *basis*.

**PROBLEM 1.37** Show that for two reciprocal sets of vectors $\mathbf{a}_1$, $\mathbf{a}_2$, $\mathbf{a}_3$ and $\mathbf{b}_1$, $\mathbf{b}_2$, $\mathbf{b}_3$,

$$[\mathbf{a}_1\ \mathbf{a}_2\ \mathbf{a}_3] = \frac{1}{[\mathbf{b}_1\ \mathbf{b}_2\ \mathbf{b}_3]}. \tag{1.122}$$

**Solution:** If $\mathbf{a}_1$, $\mathbf{a}_2$, $\mathbf{a}_3$ and $\mathbf{b}_1$, $\mathbf{b}_2$, $\mathbf{b}_3$ are reciprocal sets of vectors, then from (1.107) and (1.115),

$$\begin{aligned}
[\mathbf{a}_1\ \mathbf{a}_2\ \mathbf{a}_3] = \mathbf{a}_1\cdot\mathbf{a}_2\times\mathbf{a}_3 &= \frac{1}{[\mathbf{b}_1\ \mathbf{b}_2\ \mathbf{b}_3]^3}(\mathbf{b}_2\times\mathbf{b}_3)\cdot[(\mathbf{b}_3\times\mathbf{b}_1)\times(\mathbf{b}_1\times\mathbf{b}_2)] \\
&= \frac{1}{[\mathbf{b}_1\ \mathbf{b}_2\ \mathbf{b}_3]^3}[\mathbf{b}_1\ \mathbf{b}_2\ \mathbf{b}_3]^2 \\
&= \frac{1}{[\mathbf{b}_1\ \mathbf{b}_2\ \mathbf{b}_3]}.
\end{aligned}$$

## 1.9 Supplementary Problems

**PROBLEM 1.38** Show that if there exist scalars $m$ and $n$, not both zero, such that $m\mathbf{A} + n\mathbf{B} = \mathbf{0}$, then $\mathbf{A}$ and $\mathbf{B}$ are parallel.

**PROBLEM 1.39** If $\mathbf{A}$ and $\mathbf{B}$ are nonparallel vectors such that $\mathbf{C} = (m + n - 1)\mathbf{A} + (m + n)\mathbf{B}$, $\mathbf{D} = (m - n)\mathbf{A} + (2m - n + 1)\mathbf{B}$, find $m$ and $n$ such that $\mathbf{C} = 3\mathbf{D}$.
*Answer:* $m = -2/3$, $n = -1/12$.

**PROBLEM 1.40** Prove that $(\mathbf{A} + \mathbf{B})\cdot(\mathbf{C} + \mathbf{D}) = \mathbf{A}\cdot\mathbf{C} + \mathbf{A}\cdot\mathbf{D} + \mathbf{B}\cdot\mathbf{C} + \mathbf{B}\cdot\mathbf{D}$.

**PROBLEM 1.41** Given two vectors $\mathbf{A}$ and $\mathbf{B}$, show that $|\mathbf{A} + \mathbf{B}|^2 = |\mathbf{A}|^2 + |\mathbf{B}|^2$ if and only if $\mathbf{A}$ and $\mathbf{B}$ are orthogonal, which is the *Pythagorean Theorem*.

**PROBLEM 1.42** Show that $\mathbf{A}\cdot\mathbf{B} = \frac{1}{4}(|\mathbf{A} + \mathbf{B}|^2 - |\mathbf{A} - \mathbf{B}|^2)$.

**PROBLEM 1.43** Prove that $(\mathbf{A} + \mathbf{B})\cdot(\mathbf{A} - \mathbf{B}) = A^2 - B^2$, and give a geometrical interpretation.

**PROBLEM 1.44** If $\mathbf{a}$ and $\mathbf{b}$ are unit vectors and $\theta$ is the angle between them, show that

$$\frac{1}{2}\,|\mathbf{a}-\mathbf{b}| = \left|\sin\frac{1}{2}\,\theta\right|.$$

[*Hint:* $|\mathbf{a}-\mathbf{b}|^2 = (\mathbf{a}-\mathbf{b})\cdot(\mathbf{a}-\mathbf{b})$.]

**PROBLEM 1.45** Prove that $(\mathbf{A}-\mathbf{B})\times(\mathbf{A}+\mathbf{B}) = 2\mathbf{A}\times\mathbf{B}$, and give a geometrical interpretation.

**PROBLEM 1.46** Let $ABC$ be any triangle, $O$, any point, $\mathbf{a} = \overrightarrow{OA}$, $\mathbf{b} = \overrightarrow{OB}$, $\mathbf{c} = \overrightarrow{OC}$. Show that the area of $ABC$ is equal to $\frac{1}{2}\,|\mathbf{a}\times\mathbf{b}+\mathbf{b}\times\mathbf{c}+\mathbf{c}\times\mathbf{a}|$.

**PROBLEM 1.47** Prove that

$$(\mathbf{a}-\mathbf{d})\times(\mathbf{b}-\mathbf{c}) + (\mathbf{b}-\mathbf{d})\times(\mathbf{c}-\mathbf{a}) + (\mathbf{c}-\mathbf{d})\times(\mathbf{a}-\mathbf{b}) = 2(\mathbf{a}\times\mathbf{b}+\mathbf{b}\times\mathbf{c}+\mathbf{c}\times\mathbf{a}),$$

and give a geometrical interpretation.

**PROBLEM 1.48** Prove that if $\mathbf{A}$, $\mathbf{B}$, and $\mathbf{C}$ are nonparallel vectors and $\mathbf{A}\times\mathbf{B} = \mathbf{B}\times\mathbf{C} = \mathbf{C}\times\mathbf{A}$, then $\mathbf{A}+\mathbf{B}+\mathbf{C} = \mathbf{0}$. Give a geometrical interpretation.

**PROBLEM 1.49** If $\mathbf{A}\times\mathbf{B} = \mathbf{A}\times\mathbf{C}$, can we conclude that $\mathbf{B} = \mathbf{C}$?

**PROBLEM 1.50** Show that $(\mathbf{A}+\mathbf{B})\cdot(\mathbf{B}+\mathbf{C})\times(\mathbf{C}+\mathbf{A}) = 2[\mathbf{ABC}]$.

**PROBLEM 1.51** Show that $(\mathbf{A}\times\mathbf{B})\cdot(\mathbf{C}\times\mathbf{D}) + (\mathbf{B}\times\mathbf{C})\cdot(\mathbf{A}\times\mathbf{D}) + (\mathbf{C}\times\mathbf{A})\cdot(\mathbf{B}\times\mathbf{D}) = 0$.

**PROBLEM 1.52** If $\mathbf{A}$, $\mathbf{B}$, $\mathbf{C}$, and $\mathbf{D}$ are coplanar, show that $(\mathbf{A}\times\mathbf{B})\times(\mathbf{C}\times\mathbf{D}) = \mathbf{0}$. Is the converse true?

**PROBLEM 1.53** Prove that a necessary and sufficient condition that $\mathbf{A}\times(\mathbf{B}\times\mathbf{C}) = (\mathbf{A}\times\mathbf{B})\times\mathbf{C}$ is $(\mathbf{A}\times\mathbf{C})\times\mathbf{B} = \mathbf{0}$.

**PROBLEM 1.54** Prove that if $\mathbf{A}$, $\mathbf{B}$, and $\mathbf{C}$ are noncoplanar and $\mathbf{A}\times(\mathbf{B}\times\mathbf{C}) = (\mathbf{A}\times\mathbf{B})\times\mathbf{C} = \mathbf{0}$, then $\mathbf{A}$, $\mathbf{B}$, and $\mathbf{C}$ are mutually perpendicular.

**PROBLEM 1.55** If $\mathbf{A} = A_1\mathbf{i} + A_2\mathbf{j} + A_3\mathbf{k}$, $\mathbf{B} = B_1\mathbf{i} + B_2\mathbf{j} + B_3\mathbf{k}$, and $\mathbf{C} = C_1\mathbf{i} + C_2\mathbf{j} + C_3\mathbf{k}$, show that

$$[\mathbf{A}\;\mathbf{B}\;\mathbf{C}] = \begin{vmatrix} A_1 & A_2 & A_3 \\ B_1 & B_2 & B_3 \\ C_1 & C_2 & C_3 \end{vmatrix}\,[\mathbf{i}\;\mathbf{j}\;\mathbf{k}].$$

**PROBLEM 1.56** Prove that $\mathbf{A}$, $\mathbf{B}$, and $\mathbf{C}$ are linearly dependent if and only if $[\mathbf{ABC}] = 0$. Interpret linear dependence and independence geometrically.

**PROBLEM 1.57** Prove by using vectors that the perpendicular bisectors of the sides of a triangle are concurrent. (See Chap. 6 for more applications.)

**PROBLEM 1.58** If $\mathbf{a}_1$, $\mathbf{a}_2$, $\mathbf{a}_3$ and $\mathbf{b}_1$, $\mathbf{b}_2$, $\mathbf{b}_3$ are reciprocal sets of vectors, show that $\mathbf{a}_2\times\mathbf{a}_3$, $\mathbf{a}_3\times\mathbf{a}_1$, $\mathbf{a}_1\times\mathbf{a}_2$ and $\mathbf{b}_2\times\mathbf{b}_3$, $\mathbf{b}_3\times\mathbf{b}_1$, $\mathbf{b}_1\times\mathbf{b}_2$ are also reciprocal sets.

**PROBLEM 1.59** If $\mathbf{a}_1$, $\mathbf{a}_2$, $\mathbf{a}_3$ and $\mathbf{b}_1$, $\mathbf{b}_2$, $\mathbf{b}_3$ are reciprocal sets of vectors, show that $\mathbf{a}_1\times\mathbf{b}_1 + \mathbf{a}_2\times\mathbf{b}_2 + \mathbf{a}_3\times\mathbf{b}_3 = \mathbf{0}$.

# VECTORS IN THE RECTANGULAR COORDINATE SYSTEM

CHAPTER 2

In this chapter, we shall deal with an algebraic theory of vectors. This analytical approach will both facilitate the development of the algebraic properties of vectors and reprove many of the previous results.

In Chap. 1, a vector was represented as a directed line segment. Now if we place the initial point of vector **A** at the origin of a rectangular coordinate system, then vector **A** can be specified by the rectangular coordinates $(x_1, y_1, z_1)$ of the terminal point, as shown in Fig. 2.1. Thus there is a one-to-one correspondence between the *set of triples of numbers* (coordinates of points in space) and the *set of vectors* whose initial points are at the origin. Consequently, a *vector* in three dimensions is often defined as an *ordered triple of real numbers*; i.e.,

$$\mathbf{A} = [A_1, A_2, A_3], \tag{2.1}$$

where $A_1$, $A_2$, and $A_3$ are called the *components of* **A**, relative to the given coordinate system, and are real numbers.

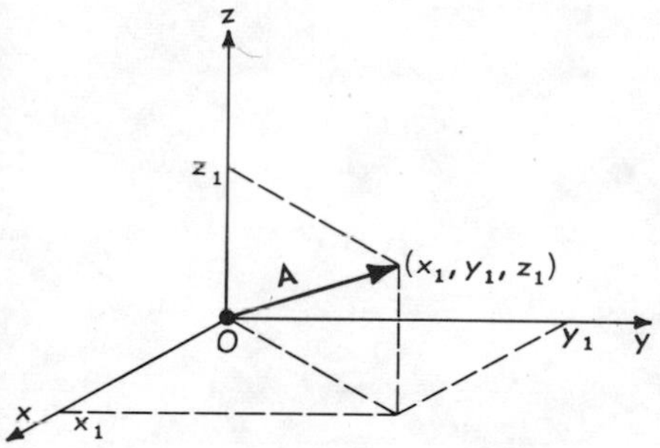


Fig. 2.1 Vector **A** in a rectangular coordinate system.

We should note that there are infinitely many possible coordinate systems, so that the same vector will have different components in different systems. In the following, however, we shall consider only the rectangular coordinate system.

The *zero vector* **0** is a vector whose components are all zero; i.e.,

$$\mathbf{0} = [0, 0, 0]. \tag{2.2}$$

## 2.1 Vector Algebra

Two vectors are *equal* if, and only if, their corresponding components are equal. Analytically, if $\mathbf{A} = [A_1, A_2, A_3]$ and $\mathbf{B} = [B_1, B_2, B_3]$,

$$\mathbf{A} = \mathbf{B} \Leftrightarrow A_1 = B_1,\ A_2 = B_2,\ A_3 = B_3. \tag{2.3}$$

The *product* of a vector **A** and a scalar $m$ is obtained by multiplication of the components of **A** by $m$; i.e.,

$$m\mathbf{A} = m[A_1, A_2, A_3] = [mA_1, mA_2, mA_3]. \tag{2.4}$$

By setting $m = -1$, the *negative* of **A** is

$$-\mathbf{A} = (-1)\mathbf{A} = [-A_1, -A_2, -A_3], \tag{2.5}$$

and by setting $m = 0$, the *zero vector* is

$$\mathbf{0} = 0\mathbf{A} = [0, 0, 0]. \tag{2.6}$$

The *sum* or *resultant* of two vectors **A** and **B** is a vector **C** obtained by addition of the corresponding components of **A** and **B**; i.e.,

$$\mathbf{C} = \mathbf{A} + \mathbf{B},$$

where

$$\mathbf{C} = [C_1, C_2, C_3] = [A_1 + B_1, A_2 + B_2, A_3 + B_3]. \tag{2.7}$$

The *difference* **A** − **B** of two vectors **A** and **B** is a vector **C** obtained by addition of **A** and −**B**; i.e.,

$$\mathbf{C} = \mathbf{A} - \mathbf{B} = \mathbf{A} + (-1)\mathbf{B},$$

where

$$\mathbf{C} = [C_1, C_2, C_3] = [A_1 - B_1, A_2 - B_2, A_3 - B_3]. \tag{2.8}$$

From the above definitions (2.3)-(2.8), because vectors and their components have the same properties,

$$\mathbf{A} + \mathbf{B} = \mathbf{B} + \mathbf{A} \qquad \text{[Commutative law]} \tag{2.9}$$

$$\mathbf{A} + (\mathbf{B} + \mathbf{C}) = (\mathbf{A} + \mathbf{B}) + \mathbf{C} \qquad \text{[Associative law]} \tag{2.10}$$

$$m(\mathbf{A} + \mathbf{B}) = m\mathbf{A} + m\mathbf{B} \qquad \text{[Distributive law]} \tag{2.11}$$

$$(m + n)\mathbf{A} = m\mathbf{A} + n\mathbf{A} \tag{2.12}$$

$$\mathbf{A} + \mathbf{0} = \mathbf{A} \qquad \text{[Identity]} \tag{2.13}$$

$$\mathbf{A} + (-\mathbf{A}) = \mathbf{0} \text{ or } \mathbf{A} - \mathbf{A} = \mathbf{0}. \qquad \text{[Inverse]} \tag{2.14}$$

**PROBLEM 2.1** Verify the properties (2.9), (2.12), and (2.14).

**Solution:** From (2.7),

$$\begin{aligned}\mathbf{A} + \mathbf{B} &= [A_1 + B_1, A_2 + B_2, A_3 + B_3]\\ &= [B_1 + A_1, B_2 + A_2, B_3 + A_3]\\ &= \mathbf{B} + \mathbf{A}, \end{aligned} \qquad [2.9]$$

$$\begin{aligned}(m + n)\mathbf{A} &= [(m + n)A_1, (m + n)A_2, (m + n)A_3]\\ &= [mA_1 + nA_1, mA_2 + nA_2, mA_3 + nA_3]\\ &= m\mathbf{A} + n\mathbf{A}, \end{aligned} \qquad [2.12]$$

$$\begin{aligned}\mathbf{A} - \mathbf{A} &= [A_1 - A_1, A_2 - A_2, A_3 - A_3]\\ &= \mathbf{0} = [0, 0, 0]. \end{aligned} \qquad [2.14]$$

The *magnitude* or *length* of the vector $\mathbf{A} = [A_1, A_2, A_3]$ in Fig. 2.1 is denoted by $|\mathbf{A}|$ or $A$, and

$$|\mathbf{A}| = A = (A_1^2 + A_2^2 + A_3^2)^{\frac{1}{2}}. \tag{2.15}$$

Then the *unit vector* $\mathbf{e}_A$ along **A** is

$$\begin{aligned}\mathbf{e}_A &= \frac{1}{|\mathbf{A}|}\mathbf{A} = \frac{1}{A}[A_1, A_2, A_3]\\ &= \left[\frac{A_1}{A}, \frac{A_2}{A}, \frac{A_3}{A}\right]. \end{aligned} \tag{2.16}$$

**PROBLEM 2.2** Show that for a vector **A** and a scalar $m$,

$$|m\mathbf{A}| = |m|\,|\mathbf{A}|. \tag{2.17}$$

**Solution:** Since $m\mathbf{A} = [mA_1, mA_2, mA_3]$, then from (2.15),

$$|m\mathbf{A}| = [(mA_1)^2 + (mA_2)^2 + (mA_3)^2]^{\frac{1}{2}}$$
$$= |m|\,(A_1^2 + A_2^2 + A_3^2)^{\frac{1}{2}}$$
$$= |m|\,|\mathbf{A}|.$$

**PROBLEM 2.3** If $\mathbf{A} \neq \mathbf{0}$ and $\mathbf{B} \neq \mathbf{0}$, determine the condition under which the vector $\mathbf{A} = [A_1, A_2, A_3]$ will be parallel to the vector $\mathbf{B} = [B_1, B_2, B_3]$.

**Solution:** If the vectors $\mathbf{A}$ and $\mathbf{B}$ are parallel, then for some scalar $m$,

$$\mathbf{B} = m\mathbf{A}, \tag{2.18}$$

and $B_1 = mA_1$, $B_2 = mA_2$, $B_3 = mA_3$. Hence,

$$\frac{B_1}{A_1} = \frac{B_2}{A_2} = \frac{B_3}{A_3},$$

or

$$A_1 : A_2 : A_3 = B_1 : B_2 : B_3.$$

Conversely, this system of equations implies (2.18); therefore the vectors are parallel.

## 2.2 Base Vectors

The three unit vectors

$$\mathbf{i} = [1, 0, 0], \qquad \mathbf{j} = [0, 1, 0], \qquad \mathbf{k} = [0, 0, 1] \tag{2.19}$$

are the *base vectors* of the rectangular coordinate system. Geometrically, they are unit vectors in the positive direction along the $x$-, $y$-, and $z$-axes, respectively, as shown in Fig. 2.2.

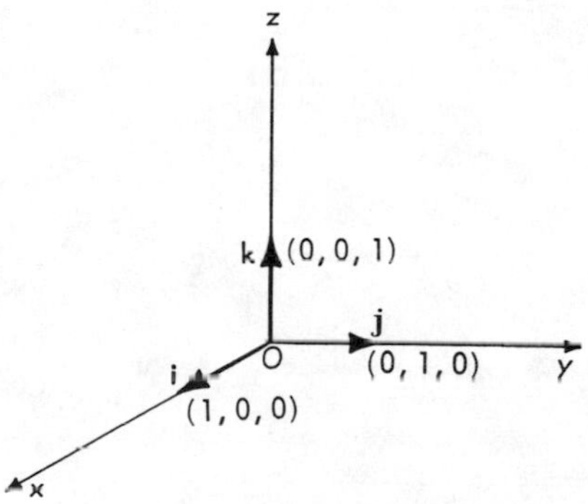


Fig. 2.2 Base vectors in a rectangular coordinate system.

**PROBLEM 2.4** Show that any vector in three dimensions can be expressed as a linear combination of the base vectors $\mathbf{i}$, $\mathbf{j}$, and $\mathbf{k}$.

**Solution:** Given vector $\mathbf{A} = [A_1, A_2, A_3]$,

$$[A_1, A_2, A_3] = [A_1 + 0 + 0,\ 0 + A_2 + 0,\ 0 + 0 + A_3]$$
$$= [A_1, 0, 0] + [0, A_2, 0] + [0, 0, A_3]$$
$$= A_1[1, 0, 0] + A_2[0, 1, 0] + A_3[0, 0, 1], \tag{2.20}$$

or

$$\mathbf{A} = A_1\mathbf{i} + A_2\mathbf{j} + A_3\mathbf{k}. \tag{2.21}$$

From (2.20) or (2.21) (and because the coefficients of $\mathbf{i}$, $\mathbf{j}$, and $\mathbf{k}$ are precisely the components of $\mathbf{A}$), we conclude that every vector in three dimensions can be expressed as a linear combination of the base vectors.

A *position vector* $\mathbf{r}$ is determined by a point in space with the coordinates $(x, y, z)$; i.e.,

$$\mathbf{r} = [x, y, z]$$
$$= x\mathbf{i} + y\mathbf{j} + z\mathbf{k}. \tag{2.22}$$

**PROBLEM 2.5** Show that a vector **R** with its initial and terminal points at $(x_1, y_1, z_1)$ and $(x_2, y_2, z_2)$, respectively, is

$$\begin{aligned}\mathbf{R} &= \mathbf{r}_2 - \mathbf{r}_1 \\ &= [x_2 - x_1,\ y_2 - y_1,\ z_2 - z_1] \\ &= (x_2 - x_1)\mathbf{i} + (y_2 - y_1)\mathbf{j} + (z_2 - z_1)\mathbf{k}. \end{aligned} \tag{2.23}$$

**Solution:** Points $(x_1, y_1, z_1)$ and $(x_2, y_2, z_2)$ determine the position vectors

$$\mathbf{r}_1 = x_1\mathbf{i} + y_1\mathbf{j} + z_1\mathbf{k},$$
$$\mathbf{r}_2 = x_2\mathbf{i} + y_2\mathbf{j} + z_2\mathbf{k}.$$

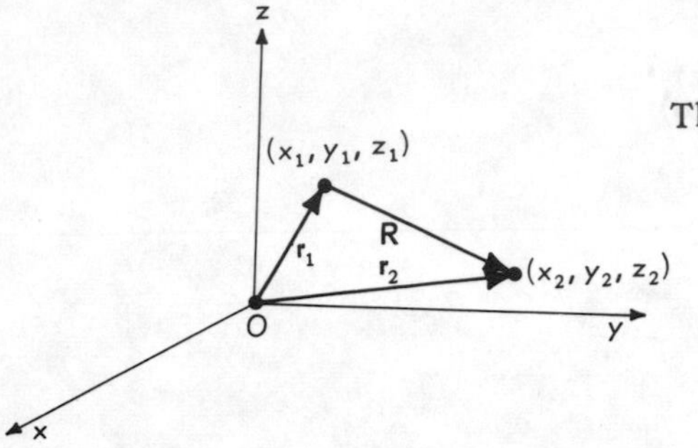


Fig. 2.3 Solution to Prob. 2.5.

Then from Fig. 2.3,

$$\begin{aligned}\mathbf{R} &= \mathbf{r}_2 - \mathbf{r}_1 \\ &= (x_2 - x_1)\mathbf{i} + (y_2 - y_1)\mathbf{j} + (z_2 - z_1)\mathbf{k}.\end{aligned}$$

## 2.3 Analytical Expressions for Multiplication of Vectors

The *scalar* (or *dot* or *inner*) *product* of vectors **A** and **B** is a scalar

$$\mathbf{A}\cdot\mathbf{B} = A_1B_1 + A_2B_2 + A_3B_3. \tag{2.24}$$

The *vector* (or *cross* or *outer*) product of vectors **A** and **B** is a vector

$$\mathbf{A}\times\mathbf{B} = [A_2B_3 - A_3B_2,\ A_3B_1 - A_1B_3,\ A_1B_2 - A_2B_1], \tag{2.25}$$

or

$$\mathbf{A}\times\mathbf{B} = (A_2B_3 - A_3B_2)\mathbf{i} + (A_3B_1 - A_1B_3)\mathbf{j} + (A_1B_2 - A_2B_1)\mathbf{k}. \tag{2.26}$$

In determinant form, (2.26) can be written as

$$\mathbf{A}\times\mathbf{B} = \begin{vmatrix} \mathbf{i} & \mathbf{j} & \mathbf{k} \\ A_1 & A_2 & A_3 \\ B_1 & B_2 & B_3 \end{vmatrix}. \tag{2.27}$$

**PROBLEM 2.6** Show that

$$\mathbf{A}\cdot\mathbf{B} = \mathbf{B}\cdot\mathbf{A} \quad \text{[Commutative law]}, \tag{2.28}$$
$$\mathbf{A}\times\mathbf{B} = -\mathbf{B}\times\mathbf{A} \quad \text{[Anticommutative law]}. \tag{2.29}$$

**Solution:** By definition (2.24),

$$\begin{aligned}\mathbf{A}\cdot\mathbf{B} &= A_1B_1 + A_2B_2 + A_3B_3 \\ &= B_1A_1 + B_2A_2 + B_3A_3 \\ &= \mathbf{B}\cdot\mathbf{A}.\end{aligned}$$

From (2.27),

$$\mathbf{A}\times\mathbf{B} = \begin{vmatrix} \mathbf{i} & \mathbf{j} & \mathbf{k} \\ A_1 & A_2 & A_3 \\ B_1 & B_2 & B_3 \end{vmatrix} = -\begin{vmatrix} \mathbf{i} & \mathbf{j} & \mathbf{k} \\ B_1 & B_2 & B_3 \\ A_1 & A_2 & A_3 \end{vmatrix} = -\mathbf{B}\times\mathbf{A}$$

since the interchange of the second and third rows of the determinant changes its sign.

**PROBLEM 2.7** Show that the vector product of a vector **A** with itself is the zero vector; i.e.,

$$\mathbf{A} \times \mathbf{A} = \mathbf{0}. \tag{2.30}$$

**Solution:** Using (2.25) and setting **A** = **B**,

$$\mathbf{A} \times \mathbf{A} = [A_2A_3 - A_3A_2,\ A_3A_1 - A_1A_3,\ A_1A_2 - A_2A_1] = [0, 0, 0] = \mathbf{0}.$$

**PROBLEM 2.8** Prove the distributive laws for the scalar and vector products; i.e.,

$$\mathbf{A} \cdot (\mathbf{B} + \mathbf{C}) = \mathbf{A} \cdot \mathbf{B} + \mathbf{A} \cdot \mathbf{C}, \tag{2.31}$$

$$\mathbf{A} \times (\mathbf{B} + \mathbf{C}) = \mathbf{A} \times \mathbf{B} + \mathbf{A} \times \mathbf{C}. \tag{2.32}$$

**Solution:** From (2.7), $\mathbf{B} + \mathbf{C} = [B_1 + C_1,\ B_2 + C_2,\ B_3 + C_3]$. Hence, by (2.24),

$$\begin{aligned} \mathbf{A} \cdot (\mathbf{B} + \mathbf{C}) &= A_1(B_1 + C_1) + A_2(B_2 + C_2) + A_3(B_3 + C_3) \\ &= (A_1B_1 + A_2B_2 + A_3B_3) + (A_1C_1 + A_2C_2 + A_3C_3) \\ &= \mathbf{A} \cdot \mathbf{B} + \mathbf{A} \cdot \mathbf{C}. \end{aligned}$$

From (2.27),

$$\begin{aligned} \mathbf{A} \times (\mathbf{B} + \mathbf{C}) &= \begin{vmatrix} \mathbf{i} & \mathbf{j} & \mathbf{k} \\ A_1 & A_2 & A_3 \\ B_1 + C_1 & B_2 + C_2 & B_3 + C_3 \end{vmatrix} \\ &= \begin{vmatrix} \mathbf{i} & \mathbf{j} & \mathbf{k} \\ A_1 & A_2 & A_3 \\ B_1 & B_2 & B_3 \end{vmatrix} + \begin{vmatrix} \mathbf{i} & \mathbf{j} & \mathbf{k} \\ A_1 & A_2 & A_3 \\ C_1 & C_2 & C_3 \end{vmatrix} \\ &= \mathbf{A} \times \mathbf{B} + \mathbf{A} \times \mathbf{C}. \end{aligned}$$

**PROBLEM 2.9** If **i**, **j**, and **k** are the base vectors defined in (2.19), then verify the following vector and scalar products:

$$\mathbf{i} \cdot \mathbf{i} = \mathbf{j} \cdot \mathbf{j} = \mathbf{k} \cdot \mathbf{k} = 1, \tag{2.33a}$$

$$\mathbf{i} \cdot \mathbf{j} = \mathbf{j} \cdot \mathbf{k} = \mathbf{k} \cdot \mathbf{i} = 0, \tag{2.33b}$$

$$\mathbf{j} \cdot \mathbf{i} = \mathbf{k} \cdot \mathbf{j} = \mathbf{i} \cdot \mathbf{k} = 0, \tag{2.33c}$$

$$\mathbf{i} \times \mathbf{i} = \mathbf{j} \times \mathbf{j} = \mathbf{k} \times \mathbf{k} = \mathbf{0}, \tag{2.34a}$$

$$\mathbf{i} \times \mathbf{j} = \mathbf{k}, \qquad \mathbf{j} \times \mathbf{k} = \mathbf{i}, \qquad \mathbf{k} \times \mathbf{i} = \mathbf{j}, \tag{2.34b}$$

$$\mathbf{j} \times \mathbf{i} = -\mathbf{k}, \qquad \mathbf{k} \times \mathbf{j} = -\mathbf{i}, \qquad \mathbf{i} \times \mathbf{k} = -\mathbf{j}. \tag{2.34c}$$

**Solution:** Since $\mathbf{i} = [1, 0, 0]$, $\mathbf{j} = [0, 1, 0]$, and $\mathbf{k} = [0, 0, 1]$, by definition of the dot product (2.24),

$$\begin{aligned} \mathbf{i} \cdot \mathbf{i} &= 1 \cdot 1 + 0 \cdot 0 + 0 \cdot 0 = 1, \\ \mathbf{j} \cdot \mathbf{j} &= 0 \cdot 0 + 1 \cdot 1 + 0 \cdot 0 = 1, \\ \mathbf{k} \cdot \mathbf{k} &= 0 \cdot 0 + 0 \cdot 0 + 1 \cdot 1 = 1, \\ \mathbf{i} \cdot \mathbf{j} &= 1 \cdot 0 + 0 \cdot 1 + 0 \cdot 0 = 0, \\ \mathbf{j} \cdot \mathbf{k} &= 0 \cdot 0 + 1 \cdot 0 + 0 \cdot 1 = 0, \\ \mathbf{k} \cdot \mathbf{i} &= 0 \cdot 1 + 0 \cdot 0 + 1 \cdot 0 = 0. \end{aligned}$$

Equation (2.33c) follows from (2.33b) because the commutative law (2.28) holds for the dot product. Equation (2.34a) follows from (2.30) because the vector product of a vector with itself is the zero vector. (See Prob. 2.7.)

Next, by the definition of the vector product (2.25),

$$\mathbf{i} \times \mathbf{j} = [0 \cdot 0 - 0 \cdot 0,\ 0 \cdot 0 - 1 \cdot 0,\ 1 \cdot 1 - 0 \cdot 0] = [0, 0, 1] = \mathbf{k},$$
$$\mathbf{j} \times \mathbf{k} = [1 \cdot 1 - 0 \cdot 0,\ 0 \cdot 0 - 0 \cdot 1,\ 0 \cdot 0 - 1 \cdot 0] = [1, 0, 0] = \mathbf{i},$$
$$\mathbf{k} \times \mathbf{i} = [0 \cdot 0 - 1 \cdot 0,\ 1 \cdot 1 - 0 \cdot 0,\ 0 \cdot 0 - 0 \cdot 1] = [0, 1, 0] = \mathbf{j}.$$

| $\cdot$ | i | j | k |
|---|---|---|---|
| i | 1 | 0 | 0 |
| j | 0 | 1 | 0 |
| k | 0 | 0 | 1 |

*Table 2.1 Dot Product of the base vectors of Rectangular Coordinates.*

Equation (2.34c) follows from the anticommutative law (2.29). The relations (2.33) can be rewritten as

$$\mathbf{e}_m \cdot \mathbf{e}_n = \delta_{mn}, \tag{2.35}$$

where $\mathbf{e}_1 = \mathbf{i}$, $\mathbf{e}_2 = \mathbf{j}$, $\mathbf{e}_3 = \mathbf{k}$, and $\delta_{mn}$ is the Kronecker delta defined by

$$\delta_{mn} = \begin{cases} 1, & \text{if } m = n \\ 0, & \text{if } m \neq n. \end{cases} \qquad [1.110]$$

The results of (2.33-4) are shown in Tables 2.1-2 for easy reference.

| $\times$ | i | j | k |
|---|---|---|---|
| i | 0 | k | −j |
| j | −k | 0 | i |
| k | j | −i | 0 |

*Table 2.2 Cross Product of the base vectors of Rectangular Coordinates.*

**PROBLEM 2.10** Using the relations (2.33) and (2.34), verify the definitions of the dot and vector products, (2.24) and (2.25).

**Solution:** Let $\mathbf{A} = A_1\mathbf{i} + A_2\mathbf{j} + A_3\mathbf{k}$ and $\mathbf{B} = B_1\mathbf{i} + B_2\mathbf{j} + B_3\mathbf{k}$. Then,

$$\begin{aligned} \mathbf{A} \cdot \mathbf{B} &= (A_1\mathbf{i} + A_2\mathbf{j} + A_3\mathbf{k}) \cdot (B_1\mathbf{i} + B_2\mathbf{j} + B_3\mathbf{k}) \\ &= A_1B_1\mathbf{i} \cdot \mathbf{i} + A_1B_2\mathbf{i} \cdot \mathbf{j} + A_1B_3\mathbf{i} \cdot \mathbf{k} \\ &\quad + A_2B_1\mathbf{j} \cdot \mathbf{i} + A_2B_2\mathbf{j} \cdot \mathbf{j} + A_2B_3\mathbf{j} \cdot \mathbf{k} \\ &\quad + A_3B_1\mathbf{k} \cdot \mathbf{i} + A_3B_2\mathbf{k} \cdot \mathbf{j} + A_3B_3\mathbf{k} \cdot \mathbf{k} \\ &= A_1B_1 + A_2B_2 + A_3B_3. \end{aligned}$$

For the vector product,

$$\begin{aligned} \mathbf{A} \times \mathbf{B} &= (A_1\mathbf{i} + A_2\mathbf{j} + A_3\mathbf{k}) \times (B_1\mathbf{i} + B_2\mathbf{j} + B_3\mathbf{k}) \\ &= A_1B_1\mathbf{i} \times \mathbf{i} + A_1B_2\mathbf{i} \times \mathbf{j} + A_1B_3\mathbf{i} \times \mathbf{k} \\ &\quad + A_2B_1\mathbf{j} \times \mathbf{i} + A_2B_2\mathbf{j} \times \mathbf{j} + A_2B_3\mathbf{j} \times \mathbf{k} \\ &\quad + A_3B_1\mathbf{k} \times \mathbf{i} + A_3B_2\mathbf{k} \times \mathbf{j} + A_3B_3\mathbf{k} \times \mathbf{k} \\ &= A_1B_2\mathbf{k} - A_1B_3\mathbf{j} - A_2B_1\mathbf{k} + A_2B_3\mathbf{i} + A_3B_1\mathbf{j} - A_3B_2\mathbf{i} \\ &= (A_2B_3 - A_3B_2)\mathbf{i} + (A_3B_1 - A_1B_3)\mathbf{j} + (A_1B_2 - A_2B_1)\mathbf{k} \\ &= [(A_2B_3 - A_3B_2),\ (A_3B_1 - A_1B_3),\ (A_1B_2 - A_2B_1)]. \end{aligned}$$

**PROBLEM 2.11** Given two vectors

$$\mathbf{A} = [2, 4, 6] = 2\mathbf{i} + 4\mathbf{j} + 6\mathbf{k}, \qquad \mathbf{B} = [1, -3, 2] = \mathbf{i} - 3\mathbf{j} + 2\mathbf{k},$$

compute the scalar and vector products $\mathbf{A} \cdot \mathbf{B}$ and $\mathbf{A} \times \mathbf{B}$.

**Solution:** The scalar product is $\mathbf{A} \cdot \mathbf{B} = (2)(1) + (4)(-3) + (6)(2) = 2.$

Then from the definition of the vector product (2.27),

$$\begin{aligned} \mathbf{A} \times \mathbf{B} &= \begin{vmatrix} \mathbf{i} & \mathbf{j} & \mathbf{k} \\ 2 & 4 & 6 \\ 1 & -3 & 2 \end{vmatrix} \\ &= [(4)(2) - (6)(-3)]\mathbf{i} - [(2)(2) - (6)(1)]\mathbf{j} + [(2)(-3) - (4)(1)]\mathbf{k} \\ &= 26\mathbf{i} + 2\mathbf{j} - 10\mathbf{k} \\ &= [26, 2, \ 10]. \end{aligned}$$

Let $\theta$ denote the angle between two nonzero vectors $\mathbf{A} = [A_1, A_2, A_3]$ and $\mathbf{B} = [B_1, B_2, B_3]$. Then the angle $\theta$ is given by

$$\cos\theta = \frac{A_1B_1 + A_2B_2 + A_3B_3}{[A_1^2 + A_2^2 + A_3^2]^{\frac{1}{2}}\,[B_1^2 + B_2^2 + B_3^2]^{\frac{1}{2}}}. \tag{2.36}$$

**PROBLEM 2.12** Verify (2.36).

**Solution:** Let $\mathbf{e}_A$ and $\mathbf{e}_B$ be the two unit vectors along **A** and **B**, respectively. Then from the definition of a unit vector (2.16),

$$\mathbf{e}_A = \left[\frac{A_1}{A}, \frac{A_2}{A}, \frac{A_3}{A}\right] = [a_1, a_2, a_3], \tag{2.37}$$

$$\mathbf{e}_B = \left[\frac{B_1}{B}, \frac{B_2}{B}, \frac{B_3}{B}\right] = [b_1, b_2, b_3], \tag{2.38}$$

where

$$A = |\mathbf{A}| = (A_1^2 + A_2^2 + A_3^2)^{\frac{1}{2}}, \qquad B = |\mathbf{B}| = (B_1^2 + B_2^2 + B_3^2)^{\frac{1}{2}}. \tag{2.39}$$

Now represent $\mathbf{e}_A$ and $\mathbf{e}_B$ by the line segments $\overrightarrow{OP}$ and $\overrightarrow{OQ}$, as shown in Fig. 2.4a. Then the magnitude of $\overrightarrow{PQ}$ is given by the positive square root of

$$\begin{aligned} |\overrightarrow{PQ}|^2 &= (a_1 - b_1)^2 + (a_2 - b_2)^2 + (a_3 - b_3)^2 \\ &= a_1^2 + a_2^2 + a_3^2 + b_1^2 + b_2^2 + b_3^2 - 2(a_1b_1 + a_2b_2 + a_3b_3) \\ &= 2 - 2(a_1b_1 + a_2b_2 + a_3b_3) \end{aligned} \tag{2.40}$$

since $\mathbf{e}_A$ and $\mathbf{e}_B$ are unit vectors; i.e., $a_1^2 + a_2^2 + a_3^2 = b_1^2 + b_2^2 + b_3^2 = 1$.

Next, consider a triangle $ORS$ in the $xy$-plane with vertices at (0, 0, 0), (1, 0, 0), and ($\cos\theta$, $\sin\theta$, 0), as shown in Fig. 2.4(b). Then the triangles $ORS$ and $OPQ$ are congruent. Thus,

$$\begin{aligned} |\overrightarrow{PQ}|^2 = |\overrightarrow{RS}|^2 &= (1 - \cos\theta)^2 + (0 - \sin\theta)^2 + (0 - 0)^2 \\ &= 1 - 2\cos\theta + \cos^2\theta + \sin^2\theta \\ &= 2 - 2\cos\theta \end{aligned} \tag{2.41}$$

since $\cos^2\theta + \sin^2\theta = 1$. Equating (2.40) and (2.41),

$$\cos\theta = a_1b_1 + a_2b_2 + a_3b_3 \tag{2.42}$$

$$= \mathbf{e}_A \cdot \mathbf{e}_B \tag{2.43}$$

$$= \frac{\mathbf{A}\cdot\mathbf{B}}{AB} \tag{2.44}$$

$$= \frac{A_1B_1 + A_2B_2 + A_3B_3}{(A_1^2 + A_2^2 + A_3^2)^{\frac{1}{2}}\,(B_1^2 + B_2^2 + B_3^2)^{\frac{1}{2}}}.$$

Note that (2.44) can be obtained simply from the definition of the scalar product (1.25).

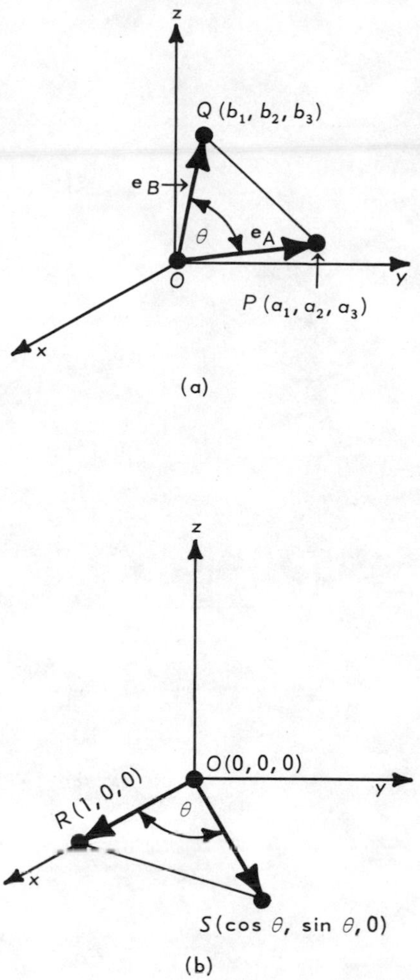


Fig. 2.4 Solution to Prob. 2.12.

**PROBLEM 2.13** Show that

$$(A_1B_1 + A_2B_2 + A_3B_3)^2 \leq (A_1^2 + A_2^2 + A_3^2)(B_1^2 + B_2^2 + B_3^2). \tag{2.45}$$

**Solution:** Let $\mathbf{A} = [A_1, A_2, A_3]$ and $\mathbf{B} = [B_1, B_2, B_3]$. Then from (2.36),

$$(\mathbf{A}\cdot\mathbf{B})^2 = A^2B^2\cos^2\theta \leq A^2B^2 = |\mathbf{A}|^2\,|\mathbf{B}|^2, \tag{2.46}$$

since $\cos^2\theta \le 1$. Hence, from the definition of the dot product (2.24),

$$(A_1B_1 + A_2B_2 + A_3B_3)^2 \le (A_1^2 + A_2^2 + A_3^2)(B_1^2 + B_2^2 + B_3^2).$$

**PROBLEM 2.14** Find the angle $\theta$ between the vectors $\mathbf{A} = [2, 4, 6]$ and $\mathbf{B} = [1, -3, 2]$.

**Solution:** From (2.36),

$$\cos\theta = \frac{(2)(1) + (4)(-3) + (6)(2)}{(4 + 16 + 36)^{\frac{1}{2}}(1 + 9 + 4)^{\frac{1}{2}}} = \frac{2}{\sqrt{56}\sqrt{14}} = \frac{1}{14}.$$

Hence, $\theta = \cos^{-1}(1/14) = 85°54'$.

**PROBLEM 2.15** Show that the vectors $\mathbf{A} = [2, 3, -1]$ and $\mathbf{B} = [1, 0, 2]$ are perpendicular.

**Solution:** From (2.44), we conclude that $\mathbf{A}$ and $\mathbf{B}$ would be perpendicular if $\mathbf{A}\cdot\mathbf{B} = 0$. Now $\mathbf{A}\cdot\mathbf{B} = (2)(1) + (3)(0) + (-1)(2) = 2 + 0 - 2 = 0$; therefore they are perpendicular.

**PROBLEM 2.16** Show that the vector $\mathbf{A}\times\mathbf{B}$ is perpendicular to $\mathbf{A}$ and $\mathbf{B}$.

**Solution:** From the definition of the vector product (2.25),

$$\mathbf{A}\times\mathbf{B} = [A_2B_3 - A_3B_2,\ A_3B_1 - A_1B_3,\ A_1B_2 - A_2B_1].$$

The dot products of $\mathbf{A}\times\mathbf{B}$ with $\mathbf{A}$ and $\mathbf{B}$ are

$$\begin{aligned}\mathbf{A}\cdot(\mathbf{A}\times\mathbf{B}) &= A_1(A_2B_3 - A_3B_2) + A_2(A_3B_1 - A_1B_3) + A_3(A_1B_2 - A_2B_1)\\ &= A_1A_2B_3 - A_1A_3B_2 + A_2A_3B_1 - A_2A_1B_3 + A_3A_1B_2 - A_3A_2B_1\\ &= 0, \qquad (2.47)\\ \mathbf{B}\cdot(\mathbf{A}\times\mathbf{B}) &= B_1(A_2B_3 - A_3B_2) + B_2(A_3B_1 - A_1B_3) + B_3(A_1B_2 - A_2B_1)\\ &= B_1A_2B_3 - B_1A_3B_2 + B_2A_3B_1 - B_2A_1B_3 + B_3A_1B_2 - B_3A_2B_1\\ &= 0. \qquad (2.48)\end{aligned}$$

Hence, $\mathbf{A}\times\mathbf{B}$ is perpendicular to $\mathbf{A}$ and $\mathbf{B}$.

**PROBLEM 2.17** Find a unit vector $\mathbf{u}$ that is perpendicular to both $\mathbf{A} = [2, 1, 1]$ and $\mathbf{B} = [1, -1, 2]$.

**Solution:** From the result of Prob. 2.16, $\mathbf{A}\times\mathbf{B}$ is perpendicular to $\mathbf{A}$ and $\mathbf{B}$. Hence the vector perpendicular to $\mathbf{A}$ and $\mathbf{B}$ is

$$\begin{aligned}\mathbf{A}\times\mathbf{B} &= \begin{vmatrix}\mathbf{i} & \mathbf{j} & \mathbf{k}\\ 2 & 1 & 1\\ 1 & -1 & 2\end{vmatrix}\\ &= 3\mathbf{i} - 3\mathbf{j} - 3\mathbf{k}\\ &= [3, -3, -3],\end{aligned}$$

and the magnitude of $\mathbf{A}\times\mathbf{B}$ is

$$|\mathbf{A}\times\mathbf{B}| = [3^2 + (-3)^2 + (-3)^2]^{\frac{1}{2}} = \sqrt{27} = 3\sqrt{3}.$$

Thus, a unit vector $\mathbf{u}$ that is perpendicular to both $\mathbf{A}$ and $\mathbf{B}$ is

$$\mathbf{u} = \frac{\mathbf{A}\times\mathbf{B}}{|\mathbf{A}\times\mathbf{B}|} = \frac{1}{3\sqrt{3}}[3, -3, -3] = \left[\frac{1}{\sqrt{3}}, -\frac{1}{\sqrt{3}}, -\frac{1}{\sqrt{3}}\right].$$

Note that $-\mathbf{u} = [-1/\sqrt{3}, 1/\sqrt{3}, 1/\sqrt{3}]$ is also a unit vector that is perpendicular to **A** and **B**.

The *direction cosines* of a vector **A** are defined by the three numbers $\cos\alpha$, $\cos\beta$, and $\cos\gamma$, where $\alpha$, $\beta$, and $\gamma$ are the angles between **A** and the positive $x$-, $y$-, and $z$-axes, respectively, of the rectangular coordinate system. (See Fig. 2.5.)

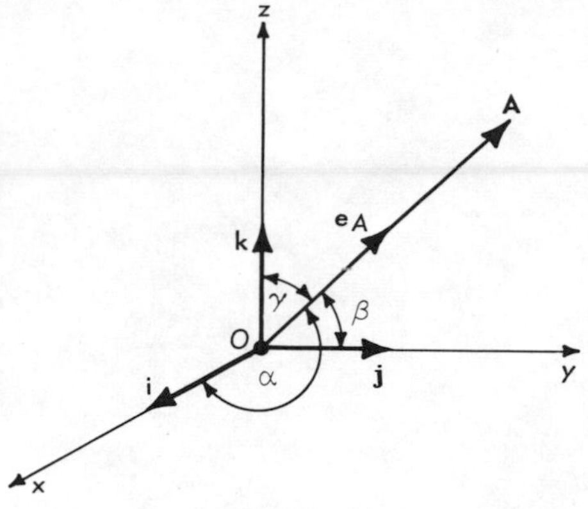


Fig. 2.5 The direction cosines of a vector.

**PROBLEM 2.18** (a) Find the direction cosines of **A** in terms of its components and magnitude. (b) Show that

$$\cos^2\alpha + \cos^2\beta + \cos^2\gamma = 1. \tag{2.49}$$

**Solution:** (a) From (2.43) and the definition of the direction cosines,

$$\cos\alpha = \mathbf{i}\cdot\mathbf{e}_A, \qquad \cos\beta = \mathbf{j}\cdot\mathbf{e}_A, \qquad \cos\gamma = \mathbf{k}\cdot\mathbf{e}_A, \tag{2.50}$$

where **i**, **j**, and **k** are the base vectors defined in (2.19), and $\mathbf{e}_A$ is the unit vector along **A**. Hence, from (2.16), (2.19), and the definition of the scalar product (2.24),

$$\cos\alpha = \frac{A_1}{A}, \qquad \cos\beta = \frac{A_2}{A}, \qquad \cos\gamma = \frac{A_3}{A}. \tag{2.51}$$

(b) From (2.51),

$$\cos^2\alpha + \cos^2\beta + \cos^2\gamma = \frac{A_1^2}{A^2} + \frac{A_2^2}{A^2} + \frac{A_3^2}{A^2} = \frac{A_1^2 + A_2^2 + A_3^2}{A^2} = \frac{A^2}{A^2} = 1.$$

The *scalar triple product* of three vectors **A**, **B**, and **C** is the scalar $\mathbf{A}\cdot\mathbf{B}\times\mathbf{C}$, denoted by $[\mathbf{ABC}]$. In determinant form, it is expressed as

$$[\mathbf{ABC}] = \mathbf{A}\cdot\mathbf{B}\times\mathbf{C} = \begin{vmatrix} A_1 & A_2 & A_3 \\ B_1 & B_2 & B_3 \\ C_1 & C_2 & C_3 \end{vmatrix}. \tag{2.52}$$

**PROBLEM 2.19** Verify (2.52).

**Solution:** From the definition of the vector product (2.27),

$$\begin{aligned}\mathbf{B}\times\mathbf{C} &= \begin{vmatrix} \mathbf{i} & \mathbf{j} & \mathbf{k} \\ B_1 & B_2 & B_3 \\ C_1 & C_2 & C_3 \end{vmatrix} \\ &= (B_2C_3 - B_3C_2)\mathbf{i} + (B_3C_1 - B_1C_3)\mathbf{j} + (B_1C_2 - B_2C_1)\mathbf{k} \\ &= [B_2C_3 - B_1C_2,\ B_3C_1 - B_1C_3,\ B_1C_2 - B_2C_1].\end{aligned}$$

Hence, from the definition of the scalar product (2.24),

$$\begin{aligned}[\mathbf{ABC}] = \mathbf{A}\cdot\mathbf{B}\times\mathbf{C} &= A_1(B_2C_3 - B_3C_2) + A_2(B_3C_1 - B_1C_3) + A_3(B_1C_2 - B_2C_1) \\ &= A_1\begin{vmatrix} B_2 & B_3 \\ C_2 & C_3 \end{vmatrix} - A_2\begin{vmatrix} B_1 & B_3 \\ C_1 & C_3 \end{vmatrix} + A_3\begin{vmatrix} B_1 & B_2 \\ C_1 & C_2 \end{vmatrix} \\ &= \begin{vmatrix} A_1 & A_2 & A_3 \\ B_1 & B_2 & B_3 \\ C_1 & C_2 & C_3 \end{vmatrix}.\end{aligned}$$

**PROBLEM 2.20** Show that

$$[\mathbf{ABC}] = [\mathbf{BCA}] = [\mathbf{CAB}] = -[\mathbf{ACB}] = -[\mathbf{BAC}] = -[\mathbf{CBA}]. \tag{2.53}$$

**Solution:** Because the interchange of two rows of a determinant always changes its sign, it follows from (2.52) that

$$\begin{vmatrix} A_1 & A_2 & A_3 \\ B_1 & B_2 & B_3 \\ C_1 & C_2 & C_3 \end{vmatrix} = -\begin{vmatrix} A_1 & A_2 & A_3 \\ C_1 & C_2 & C_3 \\ B_1 & B_2 & B_3 \end{vmatrix} = \begin{vmatrix} C_1 & C_2 & C_3 \\ A_1 & A_2 & A_3 \\ B_1 & B_2 & B_3 \end{vmatrix}$$

$$= -\begin{vmatrix} C_1 & C_2 & C_3 \\ B_1 & B_2 & B_3 \\ A_1 & A_2 & A_3 \end{vmatrix} = \begin{vmatrix} B_1 & B_2 & B_3 \\ C_1 & C_2 & C_3 \\ A_1 & A_2 & A_3 \end{vmatrix} = -\begin{vmatrix} B_1 & B_2 & B_3 \\ A_1 & A_2 & A_3 \\ C_1 & C_2 & C_3 \end{vmatrix}.$$

In other words, $[\mathbf{ABC}] = -[\mathbf{ACB}] = [\mathbf{CAB}] = -[\mathbf{CBA}] = [\mathbf{BCA}] = -[\mathbf{BAC}]$. (See Prob. 1.25.)

**PROBLEM 2.21** Show that if any two vectors in a scalar triple product are equal, then that product is zero. (See Prob. 1.23.)

**Solution:** This follows from the result of Prob. 2.19 and a property of determinants which states that if any two rows of a determinant are the same, then the value of the determinant is always zero.

**PROBLEM 2.22** Show that

$$\mathbf{A} \cdot \mathbf{B} \times \mathbf{C} = \mathbf{A} \times \mathbf{B} \cdot \mathbf{C}. \tag{2.54}$$

**Solution:** From the result of Prob. 2.20, we have $[\mathbf{ABC}] = [\mathbf{CAB}]$, or

$$\mathbf{A} \cdot \mathbf{B} \times \mathbf{C} = \mathbf{C} \cdot \mathbf{A} \times \mathbf{B}. \tag{2.55}$$

Now, from the commutative law of the scalar product (2.28),

$$\mathbf{C} \cdot \mathbf{A} \times \mathbf{B} = \mathbf{A} \times \mathbf{B} \cdot \mathbf{C}. \tag{2.56}$$

Hence, $\mathbf{A} \cdot \mathbf{B} \times \mathbf{C} = \mathbf{A} \times \mathbf{B} \cdot \mathbf{C}$.

**PROBLEM 2.23** Show that

$$[\mathbf{i\,j\,k}] = [\mathbf{j\,k\,i}] = [\mathbf{k\,i\,j}] = 1, \tag{2.57}$$

$$[\mathbf{i\,k\,j}] = [\mathbf{k\,j\,i}] = [\mathbf{j\,i\,k}] = -1. \tag{2.58}$$

**Solution:** From the definition of the scalar triple product (2.52),

$$[\mathbf{i\,j\,k}] = \begin{vmatrix} 1 & 0 & 0 \\ 0 & 1 & 0 \\ 0 & 0 & 1 \end{vmatrix} = 1.$$

The others follow from the relation (2.53).

**PROBLEM 2.24** Show that the three vectors $\mathbf{A} = [2, 0, 1]$, $\mathbf{B} = [0, 3, 4]$, and $\mathbf{C} = [8, -3, 0]$ are coplanar, and express $\mathbf{C}$ as a linear combination of $\mathbf{A}$ and $\mathbf{B}$.

**Solution:** In Prob. 1.21, it was shown that the absolute value of $[\mathbf{ABC}]$ is the volume of the parallelepiped defined by $\mathbf{A}$, $\mathbf{B}$, and $\mathbf{C}$. Hence, if $\mathbf{A}$, $\mathbf{B}$, and $\mathbf{C}$ are coplanar, the volume is 0, and $[\mathbf{ABC}] = 0$. Conversely, if $[\mathbf{ABC}] = 0$, the vectors are coplanar.

Now from (2.52),

$$[\mathbf{ABC}] = \begin{vmatrix} 2 & 0 & 1 \\ 0 & 3 & 4 \\ 8 & -3 & 0 \end{vmatrix} = 0.$$

Hence, **A**, **B**, and **C** are coplanar. Next, let **C** be expressed as $\mathbf{C} = \lambda_1\mathbf{A} + \lambda_2\mathbf{B}$. Then using the operations of scalars and vectors (2.4) and (2.7),

$$\begin{aligned}[8, -3, 0] &= \lambda_1[2, 0, 1] + \lambda_2[0, 3, 4] \\ &= [2\lambda_1, 0, \lambda_1] + [0, 3\lambda_2, 4\lambda_2] \\ &= [2\lambda_1, 3\lambda_2, \lambda_1 + 4\lambda_2].\end{aligned}$$

Thus according to the definition of equality of vectors (2.3),

$$8 = 2\lambda_1, \quad -3 = 3\lambda_2, \quad 0 = \lambda_1 + 4\lambda_2.$$

Hence, $\lambda_1 = 4$, $\lambda_2 = -1$, and $\mathbf{C} = 4\mathbf{A} - \mathbf{B}$.

**PROBLEM 2.25** Using components, show that

$$\mathbf{A} \times (\mathbf{B} \times \mathbf{C}) = (\mathbf{A} \cdot \mathbf{C})\mathbf{B} - (\mathbf{A} \cdot \mathbf{B})\mathbf{C}. \tag{2.59}$$

**Solution:** Using the definition of the vector product,

$$\begin{aligned}\mathbf{B} \times \mathbf{C} &= \begin{vmatrix} \mathbf{i} & \mathbf{j} & \mathbf{k} \\ B_1 & B_2 & B_3 \\ C_1 & C_2 & C_3 \end{vmatrix} \\ &= (B_2C_3 - B_3C_2)\mathbf{i} + (B_3C_1 - B_1C_3)\mathbf{j} + (B_1C_2 - B_2C_1)\mathbf{k}.\end{aligned}$$

Then,

$$\begin{aligned}\mathbf{A} \times (\mathbf{B} \times \mathbf{C}) &= \begin{vmatrix} \mathbf{i} & \mathbf{j} & \mathbf{k} \\ A_1 & A_2 & A_3 \\ (B_2C_3 - B_3C_2) & (B_3C_1 - B_1C_3) & (B_1C_2 - B_2C_1) \end{vmatrix} \\ &= [A_2(B_1C_2 - B_2C_1) - A_3(B_3C_1 - B_1C_3)]\mathbf{i} + [A_3(B_2C_3 - B_3C_2) \\ &\quad -A_1(B_1C_2 - B_2C_1)]\mathbf{j} + [A_1(B_3C_1 - B_1C_3) \\ &\quad -A_2(B_2C_3 - B_3C_2)]\mathbf{k} \\ &= (A_2B_1C_2 - A_2B_2C_1 - A_3B_3C_1 + A_3B_1C_3)\mathbf{i} \\ &\quad + (A_3B_2C_3 - A_3B_3C_2 - A_1B_1C_2 + A_1B_2C_1)\mathbf{j} \\ &\quad + (A_1B_3C_1 - A_1B_1C_3 - A_2B_2C_3 + A_2B_3C_2)\mathbf{k}.\end{aligned} \tag{2.60}$$

Since

$$\begin{aligned}(\mathbf{A} \cdot \mathbf{C})\mathbf{B} &= (A_1C_1 + A_2C_2 + A_3C_3)(B_1\mathbf{i} + B_2\mathbf{j} + B_3\mathbf{k}) \\ &= (A_1B_1C_1 + A_2B_1C_2 + A_3B_1C_3)\mathbf{i} + (A_1B_2C_1 + A_2B_2C_2 + A_3B_2C_3)\mathbf{j} \\ &\quad + (A_1B_3C_1 + A_2B_3C_2 + A_3B_3C_3)\mathbf{k}, \\ (\mathbf{A} \cdot \mathbf{B})\mathbf{C} &= (A_1B_1 + A_2B_2 + A_3B_3)(C_1\mathbf{i} + C_2\mathbf{j} + C_3\mathbf{k}) \\ &= (A_1B_1C_1 + A_2B_2C_1 + A_3B_3C_1)\mathbf{i} + (A_1B_1C_2 + A_2B_2C_2 + A_3B_3C_2)\mathbf{j} \\ &\quad + (A_1B_1C_3 + A_2B_2C_3 + A_3B_3C_3)\mathbf{k},\end{aligned}$$

we have

$$\begin{aligned}(\mathbf{A} \cdot \mathbf{C})\mathbf{B} - (\mathbf{A} \cdot \mathbf{B})\mathbf{C} &= (A_2B_1C_2 + A_3B_1C_3 - A_2B_2C_1 - A_3B_3C_1)\mathbf{i} + (A_1B_2C_1 + A_3B_2C_3 \\ &\quad - A_1B_1C_2 - A_3B_3C_2)\mathbf{j} + (A_1B_3C_1 + A_2B_3C_2 - A_1B_1C_3 - A_2B_2C_3)\mathbf{k}.\end{aligned} \tag{2.61}$$

Comparing (2.60) and (2.61), $\mathbf{A} \times (\mathbf{B} \times \mathbf{C}) = (\mathbf{A} \cdot \mathbf{C})\mathbf{B} - (\mathbf{A} \cdot \mathbf{B})\mathbf{C}$.

**PROBLEM 2.26** Let $\mathbf{A} = [1, 2, -3]$, $\mathbf{B} = [2, -1, 1]$, and $\mathbf{C} = [-1, 1, -1]$. (a) Calculate $\mathbf{A} \times (\mathbf{B} \times \mathbf{C})$ and verify (2.59). (b) Calculate $(\mathbf{A} \times \mathbf{B}) \times \mathbf{C}$ and verify

$$(\mathbf{A} \times \mathbf{B}) \times \mathbf{C} = (\mathbf{A} \cdot \mathbf{C})\mathbf{B} - (\mathbf{B} \cdot \mathbf{C})\mathbf{A}. \tag{2.62}$$

**Solution:** (a) To calculate $\mathbf{A} \times (\mathbf{B} \times \mathbf{C})$,

$$\mathbf{B} \times \mathbf{C} = \begin{vmatrix} \mathbf{i} & \mathbf{j} & \mathbf{k} \\ 2 & -1 & 1 \\ -1 & 1 & -1 \end{vmatrix} = 0\mathbf{i} + 1\mathbf{j} + 1\mathbf{k} = [0, 1, 1]$$

and, hence,

$$\mathbf{A} \times (\mathbf{B} \times \mathbf{C}) = \begin{vmatrix} \mathbf{i} & \mathbf{j} & \mathbf{k} \\ 1 & 2 & -3 \\ 0 & 1 & 1 \end{vmatrix} = 5\mathbf{i} - 1\mathbf{j} + 1\mathbf{k} = [5, -1, 1].$$

Since $(\mathbf{A} \cdot \mathbf{C})\mathbf{B} = [(1)(-1) + (2)(1) + (-3)(-1)]\,[2, -1, 1] = 4[2, -1, 1] = [8, -4, 4]$, $(\mathbf{A} \cdot \mathbf{B})\mathbf{C} = [(1)(2) + (2)(-1) + (-3)(1)]\,[-1, 1, -1] = -3[-1, 1, -1] = [3, -3, 3]$,

we conclude that

$$\begin{aligned} (\mathbf{A} \cdot \mathbf{C})\mathbf{B} - (\mathbf{A} \cdot \mathbf{B})\mathbf{C} &= [8, -4, 4] - [3, -3, 3] \\ &= [5, -1, 1] \\ &= \mathbf{A} \times (\mathbf{B} \times \mathbf{C}). \end{aligned}$$

(b) To calculate $(\mathbf{A} \times \mathbf{B}) \times \mathbf{C}$,

$$\mathbf{A} \times \mathbf{B} = \begin{vmatrix} \mathbf{i} & \mathbf{j} & \mathbf{k} \\ 1 & 2 & -3 \\ 2 & -1 & 1 \end{vmatrix} = -1\mathbf{i} - 7\mathbf{j} - 5\mathbf{k} = [-1, -7, -5]$$

and, hence,

$$(\mathbf{A} \times \mathbf{B}) \times \mathbf{C} = \begin{vmatrix} \mathbf{i} & \mathbf{j} & \mathbf{k} \\ -1 & -7 & -5 \\ -1 & 1 & -1 \end{vmatrix} = 12\mathbf{i} + 4\mathbf{j} - 8\mathbf{k} = [12, 4, -8].$$

From Part (a), we have $(\mathbf{A} \cdot \mathbf{C})\mathbf{B} = [8, -4, 4]$. Then

$$\begin{aligned} (\mathbf{B} \cdot \mathbf{C})\mathbf{A} &= [(2)(-1) + (-1)(1) + (1)(-1)]\,[1, 2, -3] \\ &= -4[1, 2, -3] \\ &= [-4, -8, 12]. \end{aligned}$$

Consequently,

$$\begin{aligned} (\mathbf{A} \cdot \mathbf{C})\mathbf{B} - (\mathbf{B} \cdot \mathbf{C})\mathbf{A} &= [8, -4, 4] - [-4, -8, 12] \\ &= [12, 4, -8] \\ &= (\mathbf{A} \times \mathbf{B}) \times \mathbf{C}. \end{aligned}$$

Note also that $(\mathbf{A} \times \mathbf{B}) \times \mathbf{C} \neq \mathbf{A} \times (\mathbf{B} \times \mathbf{C})$.

## 2.4 Reciprocal Basis

A set of three nonzero, noncoplanar vectors, $\mathbf{a}_1$, $\mathbf{a}_2$, and $\mathbf{a}_3$, is called a *basis* because any other vector in three dimensions can be expressed as a linear combination of them. The basis is said to be *right-handed* or *left-handed* according to whether the scalar triple product $[\mathbf{a}_1\ \mathbf{a}_2\ \mathbf{a}_3]$ is positive or negative. In Prob. 1.36 we have shown that any vector can be expressed linearly in terms of noncoplanar vectors $\mathbf{a}_1$, $\mathbf{a}_2$, and $\mathbf{a}_3$ by (1.121) with the use of a *reciprocal basis.*

A second basis $\mathbf{b}_1$, $\mathbf{b}_2$, $\mathbf{b}_3$ is said to be a *reciprocal basis* to $\mathbf{a}_1$, $\mathbf{a}_2$, $\mathbf{a}_3$ if

$$\mathbf{a}_m \cdot \mathbf{b}_n = \delta_{mn} = \begin{cases} 1 & \text{if } m = n \\ 0 & \text{if } m \neq n, \end{cases} \tag{1.110}$$

where $\delta_{mn}$ is the Kronecker delta.

**PROBLEM 2.27** Let $\mathbf{a}_1 = [-1, 1, 1]$, $\mathbf{a}_2 = [1, -1, 1]$, and $\mathbf{a}_3 = [1, 1, -1]$. (a) Show that $\mathbf{a}_1$, $\mathbf{a}_2$, and $\mathbf{a}_3$ constitute a basis. (b) Obtain a reciprocal basis to $\mathbf{a}_1$, $\mathbf{a}_2$, $\mathbf{a}_3$.

**Solution:** (a) Since

$$[\mathbf{a}_1\ \mathbf{a}_2\ \mathbf{a}_3] = \begin{vmatrix} -1 & 1 & 1 \\ 1 & -1 & 1 \\ 1 & 1 & -1 \end{vmatrix} = 4 \neq 0,$$

the vectors $\mathbf{a}_1$, $\mathbf{a}_2$, and $\mathbf{a}_3$ are noncoplanar and, hence, can constitute a basis.

(b) From (1.114), the reciprocal basis $\mathbf{b}_1$, $\mathbf{b}_2$, $\mathbf{b}_3$ is

$$\mathbf{b}_1 = \frac{\mathbf{a}_2 \times \mathbf{a}_3}{[\mathbf{a}_1\ \mathbf{a}_2\ \mathbf{a}_3]} = \frac{1}{4}\begin{vmatrix} \mathbf{i} & \mathbf{j} & \mathbf{k} \\ 1 & -1 & 1 \\ 1 & 1 & -1 \end{vmatrix}$$

$$= \frac{1}{4}(0\mathbf{i} + 2\mathbf{j} + 2\mathbf{k})$$

$$= \frac{1}{4}[0, 2, 2]$$

$$= \left[0, \frac{1}{2}, \frac{1}{2}\right],$$

$$\mathbf{b}_2 = \frac{\mathbf{a}_3 \times \mathbf{a}_1}{[\mathbf{a}_1\ \mathbf{a}_2\ \mathbf{a}_3]} = \frac{1}{4}\begin{vmatrix} \mathbf{i} & \mathbf{j} & \mathbf{k} \\ 1 & 1 & -1 \\ -1 & 1 & 1 \end{vmatrix}$$

$$= \frac{1}{4}(2\mathbf{i} + 0\mathbf{j} + 2\mathbf{k})$$

$$= \frac{1}{4}[2, 0, 2]$$

$$= \left[\frac{1}{2}, 0, \frac{1}{2}\right],$$

$$\mathbf{b}_3 = \frac{\mathbf{a}_1 \times \mathbf{a}_2}{[\mathbf{a}_1\ \mathbf{a}_2\ \mathbf{a}_3]} = \frac{1}{4}\begin{vmatrix} \mathbf{i} & \mathbf{j} & \mathbf{k} \\ -1 & 1 & 1 \\ 1 & -1 & 1 \end{vmatrix}$$

$$= \frac{1}{4}(2\mathbf{i} + 2\mathbf{j} + 0\mathbf{k})$$

$$= \frac{1}{4}[2, 2, 0]$$

$$= \left[\frac{1}{2}, \frac{1}{2}, 0\right].$$

**PROBLEM 2.28** Express $\mathbf{A} = [1, 2, 3]$ as a linear combination of the set of vectors $\mathbf{a}_1$, $\mathbf{a}_2$, and $\mathbf{a}_3$ given in Prob. 2.27.

**Solution:** From Prob. 1.36,

$$\mathbf{A} = (\mathbf{A} \cdot \mathbf{b}_1)\mathbf{a}_1 + (\mathbf{A} \cdot \mathbf{b}_2)\mathbf{a}_2 + (\mathbf{A} \cdot \mathbf{b}_3)\mathbf{a}_3, \tag{2.63}$$

where $\mathbf{b}_1$, $\mathbf{b}_2$, and $\mathbf{b}_3$ form the reciprocal basis to $\mathbf{a}_1$, $\mathbf{a}_2$, $\mathbf{a}_3$. Hence, using the result of Prob. 2.27(b),

$$\mathbf{A} \cdot \mathbf{b}_1 = (1)(0) + (2)\left(\frac{1}{2}\right) + (3)\left(\frac{1}{2}\right) = \frac{5}{2},$$

$$\mathbf{A} \cdot \mathbf{b}_2 = (1)\left(\frac{1}{2}\right) + (2)(0) + (3)\left(\frac{1}{2}\right) = 2,$$

$$\mathbf{A} \cdot \mathbf{b}_3 = (1)\left(\frac{1}{2}\right) + (2)\left(\frac{1}{2}\right) + (3)(0) = \frac{3}{2}.$$

Thus, $\mathbf{A} = \frac{5}{2}\,\mathbf{a}_1 + 2\mathbf{a}_2 + \frac{3}{2}\,\mathbf{a}_3$.

To check the solution:

$$\begin{aligned}\frac{5}{2}\mathbf{a}_1 + 2\mathbf{a}_2 + \frac{3}{2}\mathbf{a}_3 &= \frac{5}{2}[-1, 1, 1] + 2[1, -1, 1] + \frac{3}{2}[1, 1, -1] \\ &= \left[-\frac{5}{2}, \frac{5}{2}, \frac{5}{2}\right] + [2, -2, 2] + \left[\frac{3}{2}, \frac{3}{2}, -\frac{3}{2}\right] \\ &= \left[-\frac{5}{2} + 2 + \frac{3}{2}, \frac{5}{2} - 2 + \frac{3}{2}, \frac{5}{2} + 2 - \frac{3}{2}\right] \\ &= [1, 2, 3] \\ &= \mathbf{A}.\end{aligned}$$

**PROBLEM 2.29** Show that $\mathbf{i}$, $\mathbf{j}$, and $\mathbf{k}$ form a self-reciprocal basis.

**Solution:** By the definition of the scalar triple product,

$$[\mathbf{i}\ \mathbf{j}\ \mathbf{k}] = \begin{vmatrix} 1 & 0 & 0 \\ 0 & 1 & 0 \\ 0 & 0 & 1 \end{vmatrix} = 1,$$

and from (2.34b), $\mathbf{i} \times \mathbf{j} = \mathbf{k}$, $\mathbf{j} \times \mathbf{k} = \mathbf{i}$, $\mathbf{k} \times \mathbf{i} = \mathbf{j}$.

If $\mathbf{i}'$, $\mathbf{j}'$, and $\mathbf{k}'$ form the reciprocal basis to $\mathbf{i}$, $\mathbf{j}$, and $\mathbf{k}$, then by using (1.114),

$$\mathbf{i}' = \frac{\mathbf{j} \times \mathbf{k}}{[\mathbf{i}\ \mathbf{j}\ \mathbf{k}]} = \mathbf{i}, \quad \mathbf{j}' = \frac{\mathbf{k} \times \mathbf{i}}{[\mathbf{i}\ \mathbf{j}\ \mathbf{k}]} = \mathbf{j}, \quad \mathbf{k}' = \frac{\mathbf{i} \times \mathbf{j}}{[\mathbf{i}\ \mathbf{j}\ \mathbf{k}]} = \mathbf{k}. \tag{2.64}$$

Hence, we see that $\mathbf{i}$, $\mathbf{j}$, and $\mathbf{k}$ form a self-reciprocal basis.

From this result and (2.63), we can express any vector $\mathbf{A}$ as

$$\mathbf{A} = (\mathbf{A} \cdot \mathbf{i})\mathbf{i} + (\mathbf{A} \cdot \mathbf{j})\mathbf{j} + (\mathbf{A} \cdot \mathbf{k})\mathbf{k}. \tag{2.65}$$

## 2.5 Orthonormal Basis

A set of three nonzero vectors, $\mathbf{u}_1$, $\mathbf{u}_2$, $\mathbf{u}_3$, is called an *orthogonal basis* if and only if they are mutually orthogonal; i.e.,

$$\mathbf{u}_m \cdot \mathbf{u}_n = 0 \quad \text{for all } m \neq n. \tag{2.66}$$

It is called an *orthonormal basis* if and only if

$$\mathbf{u}_m \cdot \mathbf{u}_n = \delta_{mn} = \begin{cases} 1 & \text{if } m = n \\ 0 & \text{if } m \neq n. \end{cases} \tag{2.67}$$

In other words, the orthonormal basis is an orthogonal basis; in addition, each vector of the basis $\mathbf{u}_1$, $\mathbf{u}_2$, and $\mathbf{u}_3$ is a unit vector. Hence, $\mathbf{u}_1$, $\mathbf{u}_2$, and $\mathbf{u}_3$ are sometimes called *orthonormal vectors*. We also note that the base vectors $\mathbf{i} = [1, 0, 0]$, $\mathbf{j} = [0, 1, 0]$, and $\mathbf{k} = [0, 0, 1]$ form an orthonormal basis.

**PROBLEM 2.30** Let $\mathbf{u}_1$, $\mathbf{u}_2$, and $\mathbf{u}_3$ form an orthonormal basis. Then show that this set of vectors is linearly independent.

**Solution:** To prove that an orthonormal set is linearly independent, it is sufficient, from (1.24), to show that if

$$\lambda_1 \mathbf{u}_1 + \lambda_2 \mathbf{u}_2 + \lambda_3 \mathbf{u}_3 = \mathbf{0}, \tag{2.68}$$

then $\lambda_1 = \lambda_2 = \lambda_3 = 0$. Taking the dot product of both sides of (2.68) with $\mathbf{u}_1$,

$$(\lambda_1 \mathbf{u}_1 + \lambda_2 \mathbf{u}_2 + \lambda_3 \mathbf{u}_3) \cdot \mathbf{u}_1 = \lambda_1 \mathbf{u}_1 \cdot \mathbf{u}_1 + \lambda_2 \mathbf{u}_2 \cdot \mathbf{u}_1 + \lambda_3 \mathbf{u}_3 \cdot \mathbf{u}_1 = \mathbf{0} \cdot \mathbf{u}_1,$$

and, consequently, $\lambda_1 \mathbf{u}_1 \cdot \mathbf{u}_1 + \lambda_2 \mathbf{u}_2 \cdot \mathbf{u}_1 + \lambda_3 \mathbf{u}_3 \cdot \mathbf{u}_1 = 0$.

From the definition of an orthonormal basis (2.67),

$$\mathbf{u}_1 \cdot \mathbf{u}_1 = 1, \quad \mathbf{u}_2 \cdot \mathbf{u}_1 = \mathbf{u}_3 \cdot \mathbf{u}_1 = 0. \tag{2.69}$$

Hence, we obtain $\lambda_1 = 0$.

Similarly, we dot (2.68) with $\mathbf{u}_2$ and $\mathbf{u}_3$, respectively, to obtain $\lambda_2 = \lambda_3 = 0$. Hence, the orthonormal set $\mathbf{u}_1$, $\mathbf{u}_2$, $\mathbf{u}_3$ is linearly independent.

**PROBLEM 2.31** Let $\mathbf{u}_1$, $\mathbf{u}_2$, and $\mathbf{u}_3$ form an orthonormal basis. Then show that given any vector $\mathbf{A}$,

$$\mathbf{A} = (\mathbf{A} \cdot \mathbf{u}_1)\mathbf{u}_1 + (\mathbf{A} \cdot \mathbf{u}_2)\mathbf{u}_2 + (\mathbf{A} \cdot \mathbf{u}_3)\mathbf{u}_3. \tag{2.70}$$

**Solution:** Since $\mathbf{u}_1$, $\mathbf{u}_2$, and $\mathbf{u}_3$ form an orthonormal basis, any vector $\mathbf{A}$ can be expressed as a linear combination of them; i.e.,

$$\mathbf{A} = \lambda_1 \mathbf{u}_1 + \lambda_2 \mathbf{u}_2 + \lambda_3 \mathbf{u}_3. \tag{2.71}$$

Taking the dot product of both sides of (2.71) with $\mathbf{u}_1$ and using (2.69),

$$\mathbf{A} \cdot \mathbf{u}_1 = (\lambda_1 \mathbf{u}_1 + \lambda_2 \mathbf{u}_2 + \lambda_3 \mathbf{u}_3) \cdot \mathbf{u}_1 = \lambda_1 \mathbf{u}_1 \cdot \mathbf{u}_1 + \lambda_2 \mathbf{u}_2 \cdot \mathbf{u}_1 + \lambda_3 \mathbf{u}_3 \cdot \mathbf{u}_1 = \lambda_1.$$

Similarly, we find that $\mathbf{A} \cdot \mathbf{u}_2 = \lambda_2$ and $\mathbf{A} \cdot \mathbf{u}_3 = \lambda_3$. Hence (2.70) follows.

Note that an orthonormal basis, by (2.67), is self-reciprocal. Hence, (2.70) is also a consequence of (1.121).

**PROBLEM 2.32** Show that for a given set of linearly independent vectors $\mathbf{a}_1$, $\mathbf{a}_2$, $\mathbf{a}_3$, an orthonormal basis $\mathbf{u}_1$, $\mathbf{u}_2$, $\mathbf{u}_3$ can be constructed such that $\mathbf{u}_1$ is a scalar multiple of $\mathbf{a}_1$, $\mathbf{u}_2$ is a linear combination of $\mathbf{a}_1$ and $\mathbf{a}_2$, and $\mathbf{u}_3$ is a linear combination of $\mathbf{a}_1$, $\mathbf{a}_2$, and $\mathbf{a}_3$.

**Solution:** Since $\mathbf{a}_1$, $\mathbf{a}_2$, and $\mathbf{a}_3$ are linearly independent, none of them can be the zero vector. Now, since $\mathbf{u}_1$ is a unit vector,

$$\mathbf{u}_1 = m\mathbf{a}_1 = \frac{1}{|\mathbf{a}_1|}\,\mathbf{a}_1. \tag{2.72}$$

Then since $\mathbf{u}_2$ is to be a linear combination of $\mathbf{a}_1$ and $\mathbf{a}_2$, it is also a linear combination of $\mathbf{u}_1$ and $\mathbf{a}_2$ and is orthogonal to $\mathbf{u}_1$. We therefore consider a vector $\mathbf{v}_2$ such that

$$\mathbf{v}_2 = \mathbf{a}_2 + m_1\mathbf{u}_1, \tag{2.73}$$

where $m_1$ is so determined that $\mathbf{v}_2$ is orthogonal to $\mathbf{u}_1$. Setting $\mathbf{v}_2 \cdot \mathbf{u}_1 = 0$,

$$0 = (\mathbf{a}_2 \cdot \mathbf{u}_1) + m_1(\mathbf{u}_1 \cdot \mathbf{u}_1) = (\mathbf{a}_2 \cdot \mathbf{u}_1) + m_1$$

since $\mathbf{u}_1 \cdot \mathbf{u}_1 = 1$. Hence, $m_1 = -(\mathbf{a}_2 \cdot \mathbf{u}_1)$, and

$$\mathbf{v}_2 = \mathbf{a}_2 - (\mathbf{a}_2 \cdot \mathbf{u}_1)\mathbf{u}_1. \tag{2.74}$$

The vector $\mathbf{v}_2$ is now orthogonal to $\mathbf{u}_1$, but it is not a unit vector in general. Thus, $\mathbf{u}_2$ can be found by setting

$$\mathbf{u}_2 = \frac{1}{|\mathbf{v}_2|}\mathbf{v}_2. \tag{2.75}$$

Note that $\mathbf{v}_2 \neq \mathbf{0}$ in (2.74); if $\mathbf{v}_2 = 0$, $\mathbf{a}_2$ would be a multiple of $\mathbf{u}_1$ and hence, of $\mathbf{a}_1$.

To determine $\mathbf{u}_3$, we proceed in a similar manner. We consider a vector $\mathbf{v}_3$ such that

$$\mathbf{v}_3 = \mathbf{a}_3 + m_1\mathbf{u}_1 + m_2\mathbf{u}_2, \tag{2.76}$$

where $m_1$ and $m_2$ are so determined that $\mathbf{v}_3$ is orthogonal to $\mathbf{u}_1$ and $\mathbf{u}_2$. Setting $\mathbf{v}_3 \cdot \mathbf{u}_1 = 0$, $\mathbf{v}_3 \cdot \mathbf{u}_2 = 0$, respectively, we obtain $\mathbf{a}_3 \cdot \mathbf{u}_1 + m_1 = 0$ and $\mathbf{a}_3 \cdot \mathbf{u}_2 + m_2 = 0$ since $\mathbf{u}_1 \cdot \mathbf{u}_1 = \mathbf{u}_2 \cdot \mathbf{u}_2 = 1$ and $\mathbf{u}_1 \cdot \mathbf{u}_2 = \mathbf{u}_2 \cdot \mathbf{u}_1 = 0$. Hence, $m_1 = -(\mathbf{a}_3 \cdot \mathbf{u}_1)$ and $m_2 = -(\mathbf{a}_3 \cdot \mathbf{u}_2)$, and

$$\mathbf{v}_3 = \mathbf{a}_3 - (\mathbf{a}_3 \cdot \mathbf{u}_1)\mathbf{u}_1 - (\mathbf{a}_3 \cdot \mathbf{u}_2)\mathbf{u}_2. \tag{2.77}$$

Note, as before, that $\mathbf{v}_3 \neq \mathbf{0}$ in (2.77); if $\mathbf{v}_3 = 0$, $\mathbf{a}_3$ would be a linear combination of $\mathbf{u}_1$ and $\mathbf{u}_2$ and, hence, of $\mathbf{a}_1$ and $\mathbf{a}_2$. The unit vector $\mathbf{u}_3$ is then given by

$$\mathbf{u}_3 = \frac{1}{|\mathbf{v}_3|}\mathbf{v}_3. \tag{2.78}$$

The process performed in this problem is known as the *Gram-Schmidt orthogonalization process.*

**PROBLEM 2.33** If $\mathbf{a}_1 = [-1, 1, 1]$, $\mathbf{a}_2 = [1, -1, 1]$, and $\mathbf{a}_3 = [1, 1, -1]$, then (a) construct an orthonormal basis $\mathbf{u}_1$, $\mathbf{u}_2$, $\mathbf{u}_3$, and (b) express $\mathbf{A} = [1, 2, 3]$ in terms of $\mathbf{u}_1$, $\mathbf{u}_2$, and $\mathbf{u}_3$.

**Solution:** (a) Using the same process as in Prob. 2.32, we start from (2.72); i.e.,

$$\mathbf{u}_1 = \frac{1}{|\mathbf{a}_1|}\mathbf{a}_1 = \frac{1}{\sqrt{3}}[-1, 1, 1] = \left[-\frac{1}{\sqrt{3}}, \frac{1}{\sqrt{3}}, \frac{1}{\sqrt{3}}\right].$$

From (2.74),

$$\begin{aligned}\mathbf{v}_2 &= \mathbf{a}_2 - (\mathbf{a}_2 \cdot \mathbf{u}_1)\mathbf{u}_1 \\ &= [1, -1, 1] - \left(-\frac{1}{\sqrt{3}}\right)\left[-\frac{1}{\sqrt{3}}, \frac{1}{\sqrt{3}}, \frac{1}{\sqrt{3}}\right] \\ &= [1, -1, 1] - \left[\frac{1}{3}, -\frac{1}{3}, -\frac{1}{3}\right] \\ &= \left[\frac{2}{3}, -\frac{2}{3}, \frac{4}{3}\right],\end{aligned}$$

and its magnitude is

$$|\mathbf{v}_2| = \frac{1}{3}\sqrt{4 + 4 + 16} = \frac{2}{3}\sqrt{6}.$$

Hence,

$$\mathbf{u}_2 = \frac{1}{|\mathbf{v}_2|}\mathbf{v}_2 = \frac{3}{2\sqrt{6}}\left[\frac{2}{3}, -\frac{2}{3}, \frac{4}{3}\right] = \left[\frac{1}{\sqrt{6}}, -\frac{1}{\sqrt{6}}, \frac{2}{\sqrt{6}}\right].$$

Next, from (2.77),

$$\begin{aligned}\mathbf{v}_3 &= \mathbf{a}_3 - (\mathbf{a}_3 \cdot \mathbf{u}_1)\mathbf{u}_1 - (\mathbf{a}_3 \cdot \mathbf{u}_2)\mathbf{u}_2 \\ &= [1, 1, -1] - \left(-\frac{1}{\sqrt{3}}\right)\left[-\frac{1}{\sqrt{3}}, \frac{1}{\sqrt{3}}, \frac{1}{\sqrt{3}}\right] - \left(-\frac{2}{\sqrt{6}}\right)\left[\frac{1}{\sqrt{6}}, -\frac{1}{\sqrt{6}}, \frac{2}{\sqrt{6}}\right] \\ &= [1, 1, -1] - \left[\frac{1}{3}, -\frac{1}{3}, -\frac{1}{3}\right] - \left[-\frac{2}{6}, \frac{2}{6}, -\frac{4}{6}\right] \\ &= [1, 1, 0],\end{aligned}$$

and its magnitude is

$$|\mathbf{v}_3| = \sqrt{1+1+0} = \sqrt{2}.$$

Hence,

$$\mathbf{u}_3 = \frac{1}{|\mathbf{v}_3|}\mathbf{v}_3 = \frac{1}{\sqrt{2}}[1, 1, 0] = \left[\frac{1}{\sqrt{2}}, \frac{1}{\sqrt{2}}, 0\right].$$

Thus we obtain the orthonormal basis

$$\mathbf{u}_1 = \left[-\frac{1}{\sqrt{3}}, \frac{1}{\sqrt{3}}, \frac{1}{\sqrt{3}}\right], \quad \mathbf{u}_2 = \left[\frac{1}{\sqrt{6}}, -\frac{1}{\sqrt{6}}, \frac{2}{\sqrt{6}}\right], \quad \mathbf{u}_3 = \left[\frac{1}{\sqrt{2}}, \frac{1}{\sqrt{2}}, 0\right].$$

(b) From (2.70),

$$\mathbf{A} = (\mathbf{A} \cdot \mathbf{u}_1)\mathbf{u}_1 + (\mathbf{A} \cdot \mathbf{u}_2)\mathbf{u}_2 + (\mathbf{A} \cdot \mathbf{u}_3)\mathbf{u}_3.$$

Now for $\mathbf{A} = [1, 2, 3]$ and the constructed orthonormal basis obtained in Part (a),

$$\mathbf{A} \cdot \mathbf{u}_1 = \frac{4}{\sqrt{3}}, \quad \mathbf{A} \cdot \mathbf{u}_2 = \frac{5}{\sqrt{6}}, \quad \mathbf{A} \cdot \mathbf{u}_3 = \frac{3}{\sqrt{2}}.$$

Thus,

$$\mathbf{A} = [1, 2, 3] = \frac{4}{\sqrt{3}}\mathbf{u}_1 + \frac{5}{\sqrt{6}}\mathbf{u}_2 + \frac{3}{\sqrt{2}}\mathbf{u}_3.$$

To check our solution:

$$\begin{aligned}\frac{4}{\sqrt{3}}\mathbf{u}_1 + \frac{5}{\sqrt{6}}\mathbf{u}_2 + \frac{3}{\sqrt{2}}\mathbf{u}_3 &= \frac{4}{\sqrt{3}}\left[-\frac{1}{\sqrt{3}}, \frac{1}{\sqrt{3}}, \frac{1}{\sqrt{3}}\right] + \frac{5}{\sqrt{6}}\left[\frac{1}{\sqrt{6}}, -\frac{1}{\sqrt{6}}, \frac{2}{\sqrt{6}}\right] \\ &\quad + \frac{3}{\sqrt{2}}\left[\frac{1}{\sqrt{2}}, \frac{1}{\sqrt{2}}, 0\right] \\ &= \left[-\frac{4}{3}, \frac{4}{3}, \frac{4}{3}\right] + \left[\frac{5}{6}, -\frac{5}{6}, \frac{10}{6}\right] + \left[\frac{3}{2}, \frac{3}{2}, 0\right] \\ &= \left[-\frac{4}{3} + \frac{5}{6} + \frac{3}{2}, \frac{4}{3} - \frac{5}{6} + \frac{3}{2}, \frac{4}{3} + \frac{10}{6} + 0\right] \\ &= [1, 2, 3] \\ &= \mathbf{A}.\end{aligned}$$

The *Gram-Schmidt orthogonalization process* (Prob. 2.32) can also be used to determine the linear dependency of a given set of vectors.

**PROBLEM 2.34** Determine whether vectors [1, 2, −1], [2, 7, 1], and [1, 8, 5] are dependent, and if so, express one of them as a linear combination of the others.

**Solution:** Let $\mathbf{a}_1 = [1, 2, -1]$, $\mathbf{a}_2 = [2, 7, 1]$, and $\mathbf{a}_3 = [1, 8, 5]$; then define

$$\mathbf{v}_1 = \mathbf{a}_1 = [1, 2, -1], \tag{2.79}$$

$$\mathbf{v}_2 = \mathbf{a}_2 + m_1\mathbf{v}_1,$$

where $m_1$ is so determined that $\mathbf{v}_2$ is orthogonal to $\mathbf{v}_1$. Let $\mathbf{v}_2 \cdot \mathbf{v}_1 = 0$; then,

$$0 = (\mathbf{a}_2 \cdot \mathbf{v}_1) + m_1(\mathbf{v}_1 \cdot \mathbf{v}_1).$$

Hence,

$$m_1 = -\frac{(\mathbf{a}_2 \cdot \mathbf{v}_1)}{(\mathbf{v}_1 \cdot \mathbf{v}_1)},$$

$$\mathbf{v}_2 = \mathbf{a}_2 - \frac{(\mathbf{a}_2 \cdot \mathbf{v}_1)}{(\mathbf{v}_1 \cdot \mathbf{v}_1)}\mathbf{v}_1. \tag{2.80}$$

Since

$$\mathbf{a}_2 \cdot \mathbf{v}_1 = \mathbf{a}_2 \cdot \mathbf{a}_1 = (2)(1) + (7)(2) + (1)(-1) = 15,$$

$$\mathbf{v}_1 \cdot \mathbf{v}_1 = \mathbf{a}_1 \cdot \mathbf{a}_1 = 1^2 + 2^2 + (-1)^2 = 6,$$

the vector $\mathbf{v}_2$ is

$$\mathbf{v}_2 = \mathbf{a}_2 - \frac{15}{6}\mathbf{v}_1 = \mathbf{a}_2 - \frac{5}{2}\mathbf{v}_1 = [2, 7, 1] - \frac{5}{2}[1, 2, -1] = \left[-\frac{1}{2}, 2, \frac{7}{2}\right] \tag{2.81}$$

$$= \frac{1}{2}[-1, 4, 7].$$

Next, let $\mathbf{v}_3 = \mathbf{a}_3 + n_1\mathbf{v}_1 + n_2\mathbf{v}_2$, where $n_1$ and $n_2$ are so determined that $\mathbf{v}_3$ is orthogonal to $\mathbf{v}_1$ and $\mathbf{v}_2$. Setting $\mathbf{v}_3 \cdot \mathbf{v}_1 = 0$ and $\mathbf{v}_3 \cdot \mathbf{v}_2 = 0$,

$$0 = (\mathbf{a}_3 \cdot \mathbf{v}_1) + n_1(\mathbf{v}_1 \cdot \mathbf{v}_1) + n_2(\mathbf{v}_2 \cdot \mathbf{v}_1), \qquad 0 = (\mathbf{a}_3 \cdot \mathbf{v}_2) + n_1(\mathbf{v}_1 \cdot \mathbf{v}_2) + n_2(\mathbf{v}_2 \cdot \mathbf{v}_2).$$

Since $(\mathbf{v}_1 \cdot \mathbf{v}_2) = (\mathbf{v}_2 \cdot \mathbf{v}_1) = 0$,

$$n_1 = -\frac{(\mathbf{a}_3 \cdot \mathbf{v}_1)}{(\mathbf{v}_1 \cdot \mathbf{v}_1)}, \quad n_2 = -\frac{(\mathbf{a}_3 \cdot \mathbf{v}_2)}{(\mathbf{v}_2 \cdot \mathbf{v}_2)}.$$

Hence,

$$\mathbf{v}_3 = \mathbf{a}_3 - \frac{(\mathbf{a}_3 \cdot \mathbf{v}_1)}{(\mathbf{v}_1 \cdot \mathbf{v}_1)}\mathbf{v}_1 - \frac{(\mathbf{a}_3 \cdot \mathbf{v}_2)}{(\mathbf{v}_2 \cdot \mathbf{v}_2)}\mathbf{v}_2. \tag{2.82}$$

Because

$$\mathbf{a}_3 \cdot \mathbf{v}_1 = \mathbf{a}_3 \cdot \mathbf{a}_1 = (1)(1) + (8)(2) + (5)(-1) = 12,$$

$$\mathbf{a}_3 \cdot \mathbf{v}_2 = (1)\left(-\frac{1}{2}\right) + (8)(2) + (5)\left(\frac{7}{2}\right) = 33,$$

$$\mathbf{v}_2 \cdot \mathbf{v}_2 = \left(-\frac{1}{2}\right)^2 + (2)^2 + \left(\frac{7}{2}\right)^2 = \frac{33}{2},$$

the vector $\mathbf{v}_3$ is

$$\mathbf{v}_3 = \mathbf{a}_3 - \frac{12}{6}\mathbf{v}_1 - 2\mathbf{v}_2 = \mathbf{a}_3 - 2\mathbf{v}_1 - 2\mathbf{v}_2; \tag{2.83}$$

that is,

$$\begin{aligned} \mathbf{v}_3 &= [1, 8, 5] - 2[1, 2, -1] - 2\left[-\frac{1}{2}, 2, \frac{7}{2}\right] \\ &= [0, 0, 0] \\ &= \mathbf{0}. \end{aligned} \tag{2.84}$$

Thus, the vectors $\mathbf{a}_1$, $\mathbf{a}_2$, and $\mathbf{a}_3$ are dependent. By (2.79), (2.81), and (2.84),

$$\mathbf{a}_3 = 2\mathbf{v}_1 + 2\mathbf{v}_2 = 2\mathbf{a}_1 + 2\left(\mathbf{a}_2 - \frac{5}{2}\mathbf{a}_1\right) = -3\mathbf{a}_1 + 2\mathbf{a}_2,$$

which is the desired expression.

**PROBLEM 2.35** Construct the reciprocal basis of $\mathbf{u}_1$, $\mathbf{u}_2$, $\mathbf{u}_3$ obtained in Prob. 2.33.

**Solution:** Let $\mathbf{u}_1'$, $\mathbf{u}_2'$, and $\mathbf{u}_3'$ form the reciprocal basis of $\mathbf{u}_1$, $\mathbf{u}_2$, $\mathbf{u}_3$. Then using (1.114),

$$\mathbf{u}_1' = \frac{\mathbf{u}_2 \times \mathbf{u}_3}{[\mathbf{u}_1\ \mathbf{u}_2\ \mathbf{u}_3]}, \quad \mathbf{u}_2' = \frac{\mathbf{u}_3 \times \mathbf{u}_1}{[\mathbf{u}_1\ \mathbf{u}_2\ \mathbf{u}_3]}, \quad \mathbf{u}_3' = \frac{\mathbf{u}_1 \times \mathbf{u}_2}{[\mathbf{u}_1\ \mathbf{u}_2\ \mathbf{u}_3]}.$$

From Prob. 2.33(a),

$$\mathbf{u}_1 = \left[-\frac{1}{\sqrt{3}}, \frac{1}{\sqrt{3}}, \frac{1}{\sqrt{3}}\right], \quad \mathbf{u}_2 = \left[\frac{1}{\sqrt{6}}, -\frac{1}{\sqrt{6}}, \frac{2}{\sqrt{6}}\right], \quad \mathbf{u}_3 = \left[\frac{1}{\sqrt{2}}, \frac{1}{\sqrt{2}}, 0\right].$$

Because

$$\begin{aligned} [\mathbf{u}_1\ \mathbf{u}_2\ \mathbf{u}_3] &= \begin{vmatrix} -\frac{1}{\sqrt{3}} & \frac{1}{\sqrt{3}} & \frac{1}{\sqrt{3}} \\ \frac{1}{\sqrt{6}} & -\frac{1}{\sqrt{6}} & \frac{2}{\sqrt{6}} \\ \frac{1}{\sqrt{2}} & \frac{1}{\sqrt{2}} & 0 \end{vmatrix} \\ &= \frac{1}{\sqrt{6}} \cdot \frac{1}{\sqrt{2}} \cdot \frac{1}{\sqrt{3}} + \frac{1}{\sqrt{3}} \cdot \frac{2}{\sqrt{6}} \cdot \frac{1}{\sqrt{2}} - \left(\frac{1}{\sqrt{3}}\right)\left(-\frac{1}{\sqrt{6}}\right)\left(\frac{1}{\sqrt{2}}\right) \\ &\quad - \left(-\frac{1}{\sqrt{3}}\right)\left(\frac{1}{\sqrt{2}}\right)\left(\frac{2}{\sqrt{6}}\right) \\ &= 6 \cdot \frac{1}{\sqrt{36}} \\ &= 6 \cdot \frac{1}{6} \\ &= 1, \end{aligned}$$

$$\begin{aligned} \mathbf{u}_2 \times \mathbf{u}_3 &= \begin{vmatrix} \mathbf{i} & \mathbf{j} & \mathbf{k} \\ \frac{1}{\sqrt{6}} & -\frac{1}{\sqrt{6}} & \frac{2}{\sqrt{6}} \\ \frac{1}{\sqrt{2}} & \frac{1}{\sqrt{2}} & 0 \end{vmatrix} \\ &= -\left(\frac{2}{\sqrt{6}}\right)\left(\frac{1}{\sqrt{2}}\right)\mathbf{i} + \left(\frac{2}{\sqrt{6}}\right)\left(\frac{1}{\sqrt{2}}\right)\mathbf{j} + \left[\left(\frac{1}{\sqrt{6}}\right)\left(\frac{1}{\sqrt{2}}\right) - \left(-\frac{1}{\sqrt{6}}\right)\left(\frac{1}{\sqrt{2}}\right)\right]\mathbf{k} \\ &= -\frac{1}{\sqrt{3}}\mathbf{i} + \frac{1}{\sqrt{3}}\mathbf{j} + \frac{1}{\sqrt{3}}\mathbf{k} \\ &= \left[-\frac{1}{\sqrt{3}}, \frac{1}{\sqrt{3}}, \frac{1}{\sqrt{3}}\right], \end{aligned}$$

$$\mathbf{u}_3 \times \mathbf{u}_1 = \begin{vmatrix} \mathbf{i} & \mathbf{j} & \mathbf{k} \\ \frac{1}{\sqrt{2}} & \frac{1}{\sqrt{2}} & 0 \\ -\frac{1}{\sqrt{3}} & \frac{1}{\sqrt{3}} & \frac{1}{\sqrt{3}} \end{vmatrix}$$

$$= \frac{1}{\sqrt{6}}\,\mathbf{i} - \frac{1}{\sqrt{6}}\,\mathbf{j} + \frac{2}{\sqrt{6}}\,\mathbf{k}$$

$$= \left[\frac{1}{\sqrt{6}}, -\frac{1}{\sqrt{6}}, \frac{2}{\sqrt{6}}\right],$$

$$\mathbf{u}_1 \times \mathbf{u}_2 = \begin{vmatrix} \mathbf{i} & \mathbf{j} & \mathbf{k} \\ -\frac{1}{\sqrt{3}} & \frac{1}{\sqrt{3}} & \frac{1}{\sqrt{3}} \\ \frac{1}{\sqrt{6}} & -\frac{1}{\sqrt{6}} & \frac{2}{\sqrt{6}} \end{vmatrix}$$

$$= \frac{3}{\sqrt{18}}\,\mathbf{i} - \frac{3}{\sqrt{18}}\,\mathbf{j} + 0\mathbf{k}$$

$$= \frac{1}{\sqrt{2}}\,\mathbf{i} - \frac{1}{\sqrt{2}}\,\mathbf{j} + 0\mathbf{k}$$

$$= \left[\frac{1}{\sqrt{2}}, -\frac{1}{\sqrt{2}}, 0\right],$$

the reciprocal basis is

$$\mathbf{u}_1' = \frac{\mathbf{u}_2 \times \mathbf{u}_3}{[\mathbf{u}_1\ \mathbf{u}_2\ \mathbf{u}_3]} = \left[-\frac{1}{\sqrt{3}}, \frac{1}{\sqrt{3}}, \frac{1}{\sqrt{3}}\right] = \mathbf{u}_1,$$

$$\mathbf{u}_2' = \frac{\mathbf{u}_3 \times \mathbf{u}_1}{[\mathbf{u}_1\ \mathbf{u}_2\ \mathbf{u}_3]} = \left[\frac{1}{\sqrt{6}}, -\frac{1}{\sqrt{6}}, \frac{2}{\sqrt{6}}\right] = \mathbf{u}_2,$$

$$\mathbf{u}_3' = \frac{\mathbf{u}_1 \times \mathbf{u}_2}{[\mathbf{u}_1\ \mathbf{u}_2\ \mathbf{u}_3]} = \left[\frac{1}{\sqrt{2}}, -\frac{1}{\sqrt{2}}, 0\right] = \mathbf{u}_3.$$

This example illustrates the fact that an orthonormal basis is automatically self-reciprocal.

## 2.6 Supplementary Problems

**PROBLEM 2.36** Let $\mathbf{A} = [2, -3, 6]$ and $\mathbf{B} = [1, 8, -4]$. Find (a) $|\mathbf{A}|$ and $|\mathbf{B}|$, (b) $|\mathbf{A} - \mathbf{B}|$, (c) $\mathbf{A} \cdot \mathbf{B}$, (d) direction cosine of $\mathbf{A}$, (e) angle between $\mathbf{A}$ and $\mathbf{B}$, and (f) $\mathbf{A} \times \mathbf{B}$.

*Answer:* (a) 7, 9, (b) $\sqrt{222}$, (c) $-46$, (d) $2/7, -3/7, 6/7$, (e) $136°54'$, (f) $[-36, 14, 19]$.

**PROBLEM 2.37** Let $\mathbf{A} = [1, 2, 1]$, $\mathbf{B} = [2, 0, -1]$, and $\mathbf{C} = [0, -1, 2]$. Evaluate (a) $[\mathbf{ABC}]$, (b) $\mathbf{A} \times (\mathbf{B} \times \mathbf{C})$, (c) $(\mathbf{A} \times \mathbf{B}) \times \mathbf{C}$, (d) $(\mathbf{A} \times \mathbf{B}) \times (\mathbf{B} \times \mathbf{C})$, and (e) $(\mathbf{B} \cdot \mathbf{C})(\mathbf{A} \times \mathbf{B})$.

*Answer:* (a) $-11$, (b) $[0, 1, -2]$, (c) $[2, 4, 2]$, (d) $[-22, 0, 11]$, (e) $[4, -6, 8]$.

**PROBLEM 2.38** Find a unit vector parallel to the sum of the vectors $\mathbf{A} = [2, 4, -5]$ and $\mathbf{B} = [1, 2, 3]$.

*Answer:* $\left[\frac{3}{7}, \frac{6}{7}, -\frac{2}{7}\right]$ or $\left[-\frac{3}{7}, -\frac{6}{7}, \frac{2}{7}\right]$.

**PROBLEM 2.39** Find the value of $m$ such that $\mathbf{A} = [m, -2, 1]$ and $\mathbf{B} = [2m, m, -4]$ are perpendicular.
*Answer:* 2 or −1.

**PROBLEM 2.40** Find a unit vector that makes an angle of 45° with the vector $\mathbf{A} = [2, 2, -1]$ and an angle of 60° with $\mathbf{B} = [0, 1, -1]$.
*Answer:* $\left[\frac{1}{\sqrt{2}}, 0, -\frac{1}{\sqrt{2}}\right]$ or $\left[\frac{1}{3\sqrt{2}}, \frac{4}{3\sqrt{2}}, \frac{1}{3\sqrt{2}}\right]$.

**PROBLEM 2.41** Find a unit vector parallel to the $xy$-plane and perpendicular to the vector $[4, -3, -1]$.
*Answer:* $\left[\frac{3}{5}, \frac{4}{5}, 0\right]$ or $\left[-\frac{3}{5}, -\frac{4}{5}, 0\right]$.

**PROBLEM 2.42** Find the area of the triangle with vertices (3, 5, 2), (1, −1, 6), and (−2, 1, 4) by evaluating the magnitude of a vector product.
*Answer:* $3\sqrt{21}$.

**PROBLEM 2.43** If $\mathbf{A} = [1, 2, 1]$, $\mathbf{B} = [2, 0, -1]$, and $\mathbf{C} = [0, -1, 2]$, verify $\mathbf{A} \times (\mathbf{B} \times \mathbf{C}) = (\mathbf{A} \cdot \mathbf{C})\mathbf{B} - (\mathbf{A} \cdot \mathbf{B})\mathbf{C}$, and $(\mathbf{A} \times \mathbf{B}) \times \mathbf{C} = (\mathbf{A} \cdot \mathbf{C})\mathbf{B} - (\mathbf{B} \cdot \mathbf{C})\mathbf{A}$.

**PROBLEM 2.44** Find a unit vector perpendicular to both of the vectors $[2, 1, -1]$ and $[3, 4, -1]$.
*Answer:* $\left[\frac{3}{\sqrt{35}}, -\frac{1}{\sqrt{35}}, \frac{5}{\sqrt{35}}\right]$ or $\left[-\frac{3}{\sqrt{35}}, \frac{1}{\sqrt{35}}, -\frac{5}{\sqrt{35}}\right]$.

**PROBLEM 2.45** Find the value of $m$ that makes the vectors $\mathbf{A} = [1, 1, -1]$, $\mathbf{B} = [2, -1, 1]$, and $\mathbf{C} = [m, -1, m]$ coplanar.
*Answer:* 1.

**PROBLEM 2.46** Determine whether the following vectors are linearly dependent or independent: (a) $[1, 1, 0]$, $[0, 1, 1]$, $[1, 0, 1]$, and (b) $[1, -6, 2]$, $[0, 2, 7]$, $[-2, 12, -4]$.
*Answer:* (a) independent, (b) dependent.

**PROBLEM 2.47** If $\mathbf{a}_1 = [1, 1, 0]$, $\mathbf{a}_2 = [0, 1, 0]$, and $\mathbf{a}_3 = [1, 1, 1]$, find their reciprocal set of vectors.
*Answer:* $\mathbf{b}_1 = [1, 0, -1]$, $\mathbf{b}_2 = [-1, 1, 0]$, and $\mathbf{b}_3 = [0, 0, 1]$.

**PROBLEM 2.48** For Prob. 2.47, verify that $[\mathbf{a}_1\ \mathbf{a}_2\ \mathbf{a}_3] = \frac{1}{[\mathbf{b}_1\ \mathbf{b}_2\ \mathbf{b}_3]}$.

**PROBLEM 2.49** Express $\mathbf{d} = [5, 3, -1]$ as a linear combination of the set of vectors $\mathbf{a}_1$, $\mathbf{a}_2$, and $\mathbf{a}_3$ of Prob. 2.47.
*Answer:* $6\mathbf{a}_1 - 2\mathbf{a}_2 - \mathbf{a}_3$.

**PROBLEM 2.50** Express $\mathbf{d} = [5, 3, -1]$ as a linear combination of the set of vectors $\mathbf{b}_1$, $\mathbf{b}_2$, and $\mathbf{b}_3$ obtained in Prob. 2.47.
*Answer:* $8\mathbf{b}_1 + 3\mathbf{b}_2 + 7\mathbf{b}_3$.

**PROBLEM 2.51** Construct an orthonormal set from $\mathbf{A} = [1, 3, 0]$ and $\mathbf{B} = [-1, 1, 0]$.

*Answer:* $\mathbf{u}_1 = \left[\frac{1}{\sqrt{10}}, \frac{3}{\sqrt{10}}, 0\right]$, $\mathbf{u}_2 = \left[\frac{3}{\sqrt{10}}, \frac{1}{\sqrt{10}}, 0\right]$, $\mathbf{u}_3 = [0, 0, 1]$.

**PROBLEM 2.52** Express the vector [2, 2, 2] as a linear combination of the orthonormal set obtained in Prob. 2.51.

*Answer:* $\frac{4\sqrt{10}}{5}\mathbf{u}_1 + \frac{2\sqrt{10}}{5}\mathbf{u}_2 + 2\mathbf{u}_3$.

**PROBLEM 2.53** Give a geometrical interpretation to the Gram-Schmidt orthogonalization process in Prob. 2.32.

**PROBLEM 2.54** Let $\mathbf{u}_1$, $\mathbf{u}_2$, and $\mathbf{u}_3$ form an orthonormal basis. If $\mathbf{A} = a_1\mathbf{u}_1 + a_2\mathbf{u}_2 + a_3\mathbf{u}_3$ and $\mathbf{B} = b_1\mathbf{u}_1 + b_2\mathbf{u}_2 + b_3\mathbf{u}_3$, then show that $\mathbf{A}\cdot\mathbf{B} = a_1b_1 + a_2b_2 + a_3b_3$.

**PROBLEM 2.55** Let $\mathbf{u}_1$, $\mathbf{u}_2$, and $\mathbf{u}_3$ form an orthonormal basis that constitutes a right-hand orthonormal system. If $\mathbf{A} = a_1\mathbf{u}_1 + a_2\mathbf{u}_2 + a_3\mathbf{u}_3$ and $\mathbf{B} = b_1\mathbf{u}_1 + b_2\mathbf{u}_2 + b_3\mathbf{u}_3$, then show that $\mathbf{A}\times\mathbf{B} = (a_2b_3 - a_3b_2)\mathbf{u}_1 + (a_3b_1 - a_1b_3)\mathbf{u}_2 + (a_1b_2 - a_2b_1)\mathbf{u}_3$.

**PROBLEM 2.56** Using components verify the following identities:

(a) $(\mathbf{A}\cdot\mathbf{B})^2 + (\mathbf{A}\times\mathbf{B})^2 = (AB)^2$;
(b) $(\mathbf{A}\times\mathbf{B})\cdot(\mathbf{C}\times\mathbf{D}) = (\mathbf{A}\cdot\mathbf{C})(\mathbf{B}\cdot\mathbf{D}) - (\mathbf{A}\cdot\mathbf{D})(\mathbf{B}\cdot\mathbf{C})$;
(c) $(\mathbf{A}\times\mathbf{B})\times(\mathbf{C}\times\mathbf{D}) = [\mathbf{ABD}]\mathbf{C} - [\mathbf{ABC}]\mathbf{D}$;
(d) $\mathbf{A}\times(\mathbf{B}\times\mathbf{C}) + \mathbf{B}\times(\mathbf{C}\times\mathbf{A}) + \mathbf{C}\times(\mathbf{A}\times\mathbf{B}) = \mathbf{0}$.

**PROBLEM 2.57** Prove the identity

$$(a^2 + b^2 + c^2)(a'^2 + b'^2 + c'^2) = (aa' + bb' + cc')^2 + (ab' - a'b)^2 + (bc' - b'c)^2 + (ca' - c'a)^2.$$

[*Hint:* Let $\mathbf{A} = [a, b, c]$, $\mathbf{B} = [a', b', c']$, and use the result of Prob. 2.56.]

**PROBLEM 2.58** Let $\mathbf{u}_1$ and $\mathbf{u}_2$ be unit vectors in the $xy$-plane making angles $\alpha$ and $\beta$, respectively, with the positive $x$-axis. Prove that

(a) $\mathbf{u}_1 = \cos\alpha\,\mathbf{i} + \sin\alpha\,\mathbf{j}$, $\mathbf{u}_2 = \cos\beta\,\mathbf{i} + \sin\beta\,\mathbf{j}$;
(b) $\cos(\alpha - \beta) = \cos\alpha\cos\beta + \sin\alpha\sin\beta$;
(c) $\sin(\alpha - \beta) = \sin\alpha\cos\beta - \cos\alpha\sin\beta$.

[*Hint:* Consider $\mathbf{u}_1\cdot\mathbf{u}_2$ and $\mathbf{u}_1\times\mathbf{u}_2$.]

**PROBLEM 2.59** Let $\mathbf{u}_1$ and $\mathbf{u}_2$ be unit vectors in the $xy$-plane making angles $\alpha$ and $-\beta$, respectively, with the positive $x$-axis. Prove that

(a) $\mathbf{u}_1 = \cos\alpha\,\mathbf{i} + \sin\alpha\,\mathbf{j}$, $\mathbf{u}_2 = \cos\beta\,\mathbf{i} - \sin\beta\,\mathbf{j}$;
(b) $\cos(\alpha + \beta) = \cos\alpha\cos\beta - \sin\alpha\sin\beta$;
(c) $\sin(\alpha + \beta) = \sin\alpha\cos\beta + \cos\alpha\sin\beta$.

**PROBLEM 2.60** If the definition of the length of a vector $\mathbf{A} = [\mathbf{A}_1, \mathbf{A}_2, \mathbf{A}_3]$ is

$$|\mathbf{A}| = \max(|\mathbf{A}_1|, |\mathbf{A}_2|, |\mathbf{A}_3|),$$

then prove that

(a) $|\mathbf{A}| > 0$; (b) $|\mathbf{A}| = 0$ if and only if $\mathbf{A} = \mathbf{0}$;
(c) $|\mathbf{A} + \mathbf{B}| \le |\mathbf{A}| + |\mathbf{B}|$; (d) $|\mathbf{A}\cdot\mathbf{B}| \le |\mathbf{A}|\,|\mathbf{B}|$.

# 3 CHAPTER

# VECTOR DIFFERENTIAL CALCULUS

If $t$ is a scalar variable, then a *scalar function* $f$ assigns to each $t$ in some interval a unique scalar $f(t)$ called the *value* of $f$ at $t$. In general, the variable represents either time or a set of coordinates.

A *vector function* $\mathbf{f}$ of a single scalar variable $t$ assigns to each $t$ in some interval a unique vector $\mathbf{f}(t)$ called the *value* of $\mathbf{f}$ at $t$.

In a rectangular coordinate system that is independent of a scalar variable $t$,

$$\begin{aligned} \mathbf{f}(t) &= [f_1(t),\ f_2(t),\ f_3(t)] \\ &= f_1(t)\,\mathbf{i} + f_2(t)\,\mathbf{j} + f_3(t)\mathbf{k}, \end{aligned} \tag{3.1}$$

where $f_1(t)$, $f_2(t)$, and $f_3(t)$ are scalar functions of $t$ and are called the components of $\mathbf{f}(t)$.

## 3.1 Limits and Continuity of Vectors

Let a vector function $\mathbf{f}(t)$ be defined for all values of $t$ in some neighborhood about a point $t_0$, except possibly for the value of $t_0$. Then $\mathbf{a}$ is the *limit vector* of $\mathbf{f}(t)$ as $t$ approaches $t_0$ and is written as

$$\lim_{t \to t_0} \mathbf{f}(t) = \mathbf{a} \tag{3.2}$$

if and only if, for an arbitrary $\varepsilon > 0$, there exists a number $\delta > 0$ such that

$$|\mathbf{f}(t) - \mathbf{a}| < \varepsilon \quad \text{whenever } 0 < |t - t_0| < \delta.$$

This definition becomes the definition for the limit of a scalar function if $\mathbf{f}(t)$ is replaced by a scalar function and $\mathbf{a}$, by a scalar.

A vector function $\mathbf{f}(t)$ is said to be *continuous* at $t = t_0$ if it is defined in some neighborhood of $t_0$ and

$$\lim_{t \to t_0} \mathbf{f}(t) = \mathbf{f}(t_0). \tag{3.3}$$

Thus using (3.2), $\mathbf{f}(t)$ is continuous at $t = t_0$ if and only if, for $\varepsilon > 0$, there is a $\delta > 0$ such that

$$|\mathbf{f}(t) - \mathbf{f}(t_0)| < \varepsilon \quad \text{whenever } |t - t_0| < \delta.$$

**PROBLEM 3.1** If $\mathbf{f} = f_1(t)\mathbf{i} + f_2(t)\mathbf{j} + f_3(t)\mathbf{k}$ and $\mathbf{a} = a_1\mathbf{i} + a_2\mathbf{j} + a_3\mathbf{k}$, then show that

$$\lim_{t \to t_0} \mathbf{f}(t) = \mathbf{a} \tag{3.4}$$

if and only if

$$\lim_{t \to t_0} f_i(t) = a_i, \quad i = 1, 2, 3. \tag{3.5}$$

**Solution:** If $\lim_{t \to t_0} \mathbf{f}(t) = \mathbf{a}$, then, for an arbitrary $\varepsilon > 0$, there exists $\delta > 0$ such that $|\mathbf{f}(t) - \mathbf{a}| < \varepsilon$ whenever $0 < |t - t_0| < \delta$. Thus,

$$\mathbf{f}(t) - \mathbf{a} = [f_1(t) - a_1]\mathbf{i} + [f_2(t) - a_2]\mathbf{j} + [f_3(t) - a_3]\mathbf{k},$$

and for $0 < |t - t_0| < \delta$,

$$|f_i(t) - a_i| \leq |\mathbf{f}(t) - \mathbf{a}| < \varepsilon,$$

where $i = 1, 2, 3$. Hence,

$$\lim_{t \to t_0} f_i(t) = a_i.$$

Conversely, if $\lim_{t \to t_0} f_i(t) = a_i$, $(i = 1, 2, 3)$ for every $\varepsilon > 0$, then there exists $\delta > 0$ such that $|f_i(t) - a_i| < \varepsilon/3$ whenever $0 < |t - t_0| < \delta$. Then using the triangle inequality for absolute values,

$$\begin{aligned} |\mathbf{f}(t) - \mathbf{a}| &= |[f_1(t) - a_1]\mathbf{i} + [f_2(t) - a_2]\mathbf{j} + [f_3(t) - a_3]\mathbf{k}| \\ &\leq |f_1(t) - a_1| + |f_2(t) - a_2| + |f_3(t) - a_3| \\ &< \varepsilon. \end{aligned}$$

Hence, $\lim_{t \to t_0} \mathbf{f}(t) = \mathbf{a}$.

**PROBLEM 3.2** Show that the limit of the sum of two vector functions is the sum of their limits; that is, if $\lim_{t \to t_0} \mathbf{f}(t) = \mathbf{a}$ and $\lim_{t \to t_0} \mathbf{g}(t) = b$, then

$$\lim_{t \to t_0} [\mathbf{f}(t) + \mathbf{g}(t)] = \mathbf{a} + \mathbf{b}. \tag{3.6}$$

**Solution:** If $\lim_{t \to t_0} \mathbf{f}(t) = \mathbf{a}$ and $\lim_{t \to t_0} \mathbf{g}(t) = \mathbf{b}$, then for every $\varepsilon > 0$, there exists $\delta > 0$ such that for $0 < |t - t_0| < \delta$,

$$|\mathbf{f}(t) - \mathbf{a}| < \tfrac{1}{2}\varepsilon \quad \text{and} \quad |\mathbf{g}(t) - \mathbf{b}| < \tfrac{1}{2}\varepsilon.$$

Then, using the triangle inequality for absolute values,

$$\begin{aligned} |[\mathbf{f}(t) + \mathbf{g}(t)] - (\mathbf{a} + \mathbf{b})| &= |[\mathbf{f}(t) - \mathbf{a}] + [\mathbf{g}(t) - \mathbf{b}]| \\ &\leq |\mathbf{f}(t) - \mathbf{a}| + |\mathbf{g}(t) - \mathbf{b}| \\ &< \varepsilon. \end{aligned}$$

Hence, $\lim_{t \to t_0} [\mathbf{f}(t) + \mathbf{g}(t)] = \mathbf{a} + \mathbf{b}$.

**PROBLEM 3.3** If $\lim_{t \to t_0} \mathbf{f}(t) = \mathbf{a}$, and $\lim_{t \to t_0} \phi(t) = c$, then show that

$$\lim_{t \to t_0} \phi(t)\mathbf{f}(t) = c\mathbf{a}. \tag{3.7}$$

**Solution:** If $\lim_{t \to t_0} \mathbf{f}(t) = \mathbf{a}$ and $\lim_{t \to t_0} \phi(t) = c$, then for $0 < \varepsilon' < 1$ ($\varepsilon'$ to be found later), there exists $\delta > 0$ such that for $|t - t_0| < \delta$, $|\mathbf{f}(t) - \mathbf{a}| < \varepsilon'$ and $|\phi(t) - c| < \varepsilon'$. Then,

$$|\phi(t)| = |c + [\phi(t) - c]| < |c| + \varepsilon' < |c| + 1.$$

Writing

$$\begin{aligned}\phi(t)\,\mathbf{f}(t) - c\mathbf{a} &= \phi(t)\,\mathbf{f}(t) - \phi(t)\,\mathbf{a} + \phi(t)\,\mathbf{a} - c\mathbf{a}\\ &= \phi(t)\,[\mathbf{f}(t) - \mathbf{a}] + [\phi(t) - c]\,\mathbf{a},\end{aligned}$$

we have

$$\begin{aligned}|\phi(t)\,\mathbf{f}(t) - c\mathbf{a}| &= |\phi(t)\,[\mathbf{f}(t) - \mathbf{a}] + [\phi(t) - c]\,\mathbf{a}|\\ &\le |\phi(t)|\;|\mathbf{f}(t) - \mathbf{a}| + |\phi(t) - c|\;|\mathbf{a}|\\ &< (|c| + 1)\,\varepsilon' + \varepsilon'\,|\mathbf{a}|\\ &= \varepsilon'(|c| + 1 + |\mathbf{a}|).\end{aligned}$$

Thus, if we choose $\varepsilon' < \varepsilon/(|c| + 1 + |\mathbf{a}|)$ and also $\varepsilon' < 1$,

$$|\phi(t)\,\mathbf{f}(t) - c\mathbf{a}| < \varepsilon.$$

Hence,

$$\lim_{t\to t_0} \phi(t)\,\mathbf{f}(t) = c\mathbf{a}. \qquad [3.7]$$

If $\mathbf{f}(t) = \mathbf{a}$ and $\lim_{t\to t_0} \phi(t) = c$, then (3.7) reduces to

$$\lim_{t\to t_0} \phi(t)\,\mathbf{a} = c\mathbf{a}. \qquad (3.8)$$

**PROBLEM 3.4** Show that a vector function $\mathbf{f}(t) = f_1(t)\,\mathbf{i} + f_2(t)\,\mathbf{j} + f_3(t)\,\mathbf{k}$ is continuous at $t_0$ if $f_i(t)$ $(i = 1, 2, 3)$ is continuous at $t_0$.

**Solution:** Since $\mathbf{f}(t)$ is continuous at $t = t_0$, we have $\lim_{t\to t_0} \mathbf{f}(t) = \mathbf{f}(t_0)$. Again $\mathbf{f}(t) = f_1(t)\mathbf{i} + f_2(t)\mathbf{j} + f_3(t)\mathbf{k}$; therefore $\mathbf{f}(t_0) = f_1(t_0)\mathbf{i} + f_2(t_0)\mathbf{j} + f_3(t_0)\mathbf{k}$. Using (3.6),

$$\begin{aligned}\lim_{t\to t_0} \mathbf{f}(t) &= \lim_{t\to t_0} [f_1(t)\,\mathbf{i} + f_2(t)\,\mathbf{j} + f_3(t)\,\mathbf{k}]\\ &= \lim_{t\to t_0} f_1(t)\,\mathbf{i} + \lim_{t\to t_0} f_2(t)\,\mathbf{j} + \lim_{t\to t_0} f_3(t)\,\mathbf{k}.\end{aligned}$$

Since $\mathbf{i}$, $\mathbf{j}$, and $\mathbf{k}$ are constants, from (3.8),

$$\lim_{t\to t_0} \mathbf{f}(t) = \mathbf{i}\lim_{t\to t_0} f_1(t) + \mathbf{j}\lim_{t\to t_0} f_2(t) + \mathbf{k}\lim_{t\to t_0} f_3(t).$$

Now $f_i(t)$ is continuous at $t = t_0$. Therefore,

$$\mathbf{i}\lim_{t\to t_0} f_1(t) + \mathbf{j}\lim_{t\to t_0} f_2(t) + \mathbf{k}\lim_{t\to t_0} f_3(t) = f_1(t_0)\,\mathbf{i} + f_2(t_0)\,\mathbf{j} + f_3(t_0)\,\mathbf{k}.$$

Then from the definition of equality of vectors,

$$\lim_{t\to t_0} f_i(t) = f_i(t_0), \quad \text{where } i = 1, 2, 3.$$

## 3.2 Differentiation of Vectors

The *derivative* $\mathbf{f}'(t)$ of a vector function $\mathbf{f}(t)$ is defined by

$$\mathbf{f}'(t) = \frac{d\mathbf{f}(t)}{dt} = \lim_{\Delta t\to 0} \frac{\mathbf{f}(t + \Delta t) - \mathbf{f}(t)}{\Delta t}. \qquad (3.9)$$

The vector $\mathbf{f}(t)$ is also said to be *differentiable*, and the derivative $\mathbf{f}'(t)$ is also a vector function. Thus, if $\mathbf{f}(t) = f_1(t)\,\mathbf{i} + f_2(t)\,\mathbf{j} + f_3(t)\,\mathbf{k}$, then $\mathbf{f}'(t)$ exists if and only if the derivatives

$$f_i'(t) = \lim_{\Delta t \to 0} \frac{f_i(t + \Delta t) - f_i(t)}{\Delta t} \tag{3.10}$$

of $f_i(t)$ $(i = 1, 2, 3)$ exist, and

$$\mathbf{f}'(t) = f_1'(t)\,\mathbf{i} + f_2'(t)\,\mathbf{j} + f_3'(t)\,\mathbf{k}. \tag{3.11}$$

Higher derivatives of a vector function are defined in a manner similar to that for a scalar function of a single variable. Thus,

$$\mathbf{f}''(t) = \frac{d^2\mathbf{f}(t)}{dt^2} = \frac{d}{dt}\left[\frac{d\mathbf{f}(t)}{dt}\right], \tag{3.12}$$

and so forth.

From elementary calculus, we know that a *differentiable function is necessarily continuous but the converse is not true.* The same can be said about a vector function in view of (3.11). In this book, unless stated otherwise, we only consider those functions that are differentiable to any order needed in a particular discussion.

The rules for differentiation of vector functions are similar to those for scalar functions with one exception. To differentiate the vector product of vector functions, the order of factors must be preserved, because the vector product is not a commutative operation.

If $\mathbf{A}(t)$, $\mathbf{B}(t)$, and $\mathbf{C}(t)$ are differentiable vector functions and $\phi(t)$ is a differentiable scalar function, then

(1) $$\frac{d}{dt}[\mathbf{A}(t) + \mathbf{B}(t)] = \mathbf{A}'(t) + \mathbf{B}'(t), \tag{3.13}$$

(2) $$\frac{d}{dt}[\phi(t)\,\mathbf{A}(t)] = \phi(t)\,\mathbf{A}'(t) + \phi'(t)\,\mathbf{A}(t), \tag{3.14}$$

(3) $$\frac{d}{dt}[\mathbf{A}(t)\cdot\mathbf{B}(t)] = \mathbf{A}(t)\cdot\mathbf{B}'(t) + \mathbf{A}'(t)\cdot\mathbf{B}(t), \tag{3.15}$$

(4) $$\frac{d}{dt}[\mathbf{A}(t)\times\mathbf{B}(t)] = \mathbf{A}(t)\times\mathbf{B}'(t) + \mathbf{A}'(t)\times\mathbf{B}(t), \tag{3.16}$$

(5) $$\frac{d}{dt}[\mathbf{A}(t)\cdot\mathbf{B}(t)\times\mathbf{C}(t)] = \mathbf{A}'(t)\cdot\mathbf{B}(t)\times\mathbf{C}(t) + \mathbf{A}(t)\cdot\mathbf{B}'(t)\times\mathbf{C}(t) + \mathbf{A}(t)\cdot\mathbf{B}(t)\times\mathbf{C}'(t), \tag{3.17}$$

(6) $$\frac{d}{dt}\{\mathbf{A}(t)\times[\mathbf{B}(t)\times\mathbf{C}(t)]\} = \mathbf{A}'(t)\times[\mathbf{B}(t)\times\mathbf{C}(t)] + \mathbf{A}(t)\times[\mathbf{B}'(t)\times\mathbf{C}(t)] + \mathbf{A}(t)\times[\mathbf{B}(t)\times\mathbf{C}'(t)]. \tag{3.18}$$

(7) *Chain rule*: If $t = g(s)$ is differentiable, then

$$\frac{d\mathbf{A}(t)}{ds} = \frac{d\mathbf{A}[g(s)]}{ds} = \frac{dA(t)}{dt}\frac{dg(s)}{ds}. \tag{3.19}$$

**PROBLEM 3.5** Prove (3.14).

**Solution:** If $\mathbf{f}(t) = \phi(t)\,\mathbf{A}(t)$, then we have $\mathbf{f}(t+\Delta t) = \phi(t+\Delta t)\,\mathbf{A}(t+\Delta t)$, and

$$\begin{aligned}\mathbf{f}(t+\Delta t) - \mathbf{f}(t) &= \phi(t+\Delta t)\,\mathbf{A}(t+\Delta t) - \phi(t)\,\mathbf{A}(t)\\ &= \phi(t+\Delta t)\,[\mathbf{A}(t+\Delta t) - \mathbf{A}(t)] + [\phi(t+\Delta t) - \phi(t)]\,\mathbf{A}(t).\end{aligned}$$

Divide both sides by $\Delta t$ and let $\Delta t$ approach zero to obtain

$$\frac{d}{dt}[\phi(t)\,\mathbf{A}(t)] = \mathbf{f}'(t)$$

$$= \lim_{\Delta t\to 0} \frac{\mathbf{f}(t+\Delta t) - \mathbf{f}(t)}{\Delta t}$$

$$= \lim_{\Delta t\to 0} \phi(t+\Delta t)\left[\frac{\mathbf{A}(t+\Delta t) - \mathbf{A}(t)}{\Delta t}\right] + \lim_{\Delta t\to 0}\left[\frac{\phi(t+\Delta t) - \phi(t)}{\Delta t}\right]\mathbf{A}(t)$$

$$= \phi(t)\,\mathbf{A}'(t) + \phi'(t)\,\mathbf{A}(t).$$

**Special cases:** If $\phi(t) = k$ is a constant scalar, then

$$\frac{d}{dt}[k\,\mathbf{A}(t)] = k\,\mathbf{A}'(t). \tag{3.20}$$

If $\mathbf{A}(t) = \mathbf{a}$ is a constant vector, then

$$\frac{d}{dt}[\phi(t)\,\mathbf{a}] = \phi'(t)\,\mathbf{a}. \tag{3.21}$$

**PROBLEM 3.6** Prove (3.15).

**Solution:** If $\psi(t) = \mathbf{A}(t)\cdot\mathbf{B}(t)$, then

$$\begin{aligned}\psi(t+\Delta t) - \psi(t) &= \mathbf{A}(t+\Delta t)\cdot\mathbf{B}(t+\Delta t) - \mathbf{A}(t)\cdot\mathbf{B}(t)\\ &= \mathbf{A}(t+\Delta t)\cdot[\mathbf{B}(t+\Delta t) - \mathbf{B}(t)] + [\mathbf{A}(t+\Delta t) - \mathbf{A}(t)]\cdot\mathbf{B}(t).\end{aligned}$$

Divide both sides by $\Delta t$ and let $\Delta t$ approach zero to obtain

$$\psi'(t) = \frac{d}{dt}[\mathbf{A}(t)\cdot\mathbf{B}(t)] = \mathbf{A}(t)\cdot\mathbf{B}'(t) + \mathbf{A}'(t)\cdot\mathbf{B}(t).$$

**Alternate Solution:** Let $\mathbf{A}(t) = [A_1(t), A_2(t), A_3(t)]$ and $\mathbf{B}(t) = [B_1(t), B_2(t), B_3(t)]$. Then, from the definition of the dot product (2.24),

$$\begin{aligned}\frac{d}{dt}[\mathbf{A}(t)\cdot\mathbf{B}(t)] &= \frac{d}{dt}[A_1(t)\,B_1(t) + A_2(t)\,B_2(t) + A_3(t)\,B_3(t)]\\ &= A_1(t)\,B_1'(t) + A_1'(t)\,B_1(t) + A_2(t)\,B_2'(t) + A_2'(t)\,B_2(t)\\ &\quad + A_3(t)\,B_3'(t) + A_3'(t)\,B_3(t)\\ &= [A_1(t)\,B_1'(t) + A_2(t)\,B_2'(t) + A_3(t)\,B_3'(t)] + [A_1'(t)\,B_1(t)\\ &\quad + A_2'(t)\,B_2(t) + A_3'(t)\,B_3(t)]\\ &= \mathbf{A}(t)\cdot\mathbf{B}'(t) + \mathbf{A}'(t)\cdot\mathbf{B}(t).\end{aligned}$$

**PROBLEM 3.7** Show that the derivative of a vector of constant magnitude is orthogonal to it. (This includes the possibility that the derivative is the zero vector.)

**Solution:** If $\mathbf{B}(t) = \mathbf{A}(t)$ in (3.15), then

$$\frac{d}{dt}[\mathbf{A}(t)\cdot\mathbf{A}(t)] = 2\mathbf{A}(t)\cdot\mathbf{A}'(t). \tag{3.22}$$

But,

$$\mathbf{A}(t)\cdot\mathbf{A}(t) = |\mathbf{A}(t)|^2 = \text{constant}. \tag{3.23}$$

Thus, the derivative is

$$\frac{d}{dt}[\mathbf{A}(t)\cdot\mathbf{A}(t)] = 0. \tag{3.24}$$

Hence, from (3.22),

$$2\mathbf{A}(t)\cdot\mathbf{A}'(t) = 0. \tag{3.25}$$

Therefore,

$$\mathbf{A}(t)\cdot\mathbf{A}'(t) = 0; \tag{3.26}$$

that is, a vector is orthogonal to its derivative.

**PROBLEM 3.8** Prove (3.16).

**Solution:** If $\mathbf{f}(t) = \mathbf{A}(t) \times \mathbf{B}(t)$, then

$$\mathbf{f}(t+\Delta t) - \mathbf{f}(t) = \mathbf{A}(t+\Delta t)\times\mathbf{B}(t+\Delta t) - \mathbf{A}(t)\times\mathbf{B}(t).$$

Adding and subtracting $\mathbf{A}(t+\Delta t)\times\mathbf{B}(t)$ and simplifying yields

$$\mathbf{f}(t+\Delta t) - \mathbf{f}(t) = \mathbf{A}(t+\Delta t)\times[\mathbf{B}(t+\Delta t) - \mathbf{B}(t)] + [\mathbf{A}(t+\Delta t) - \mathbf{A}(t)]\times\mathbf{B}(t).$$

Dividing both sides by $\Delta t$ and taking the limit as $\Delta t \longrightarrow 0$,

$$\mathbf{f}'(t) = \frac{d}{dt}[\mathbf{A}(t)\times\mathbf{B}(t)] = \mathbf{A}(t)\times\mathbf{B}'(t) + \mathbf{A}'(t)\times\mathbf{B}(t).$$

It is stressed again that the order of factors must be preserved.

**PROBLEM 3.9** Show that

$$\frac{d}{dt}[\mathbf{A}(t)\times\mathbf{A}'(t)] = \mathbf{A}(t)\times\mathbf{A}''(t). \tag{3.27}$$

**Solution:** If $\mathbf{B}(t) = \mathbf{A}'(t)$ in (3.16), then

$$\frac{d}{dt}[\mathbf{A}(t)\times\mathbf{A}'(t)] = \mathbf{A}(t)\times\mathbf{A}''(t) + \mathbf{A}'(t)\times\mathbf{A}'(t).$$

From (2.30),

$$\mathbf{A}'(t)\times\mathbf{A}'(t) = \mathbf{0},$$

and (3.27) follows.

**PROBLEM 3.10** If $\mathbf{f}(t) = e^{2t}\,\mathbf{a} + e^{3t}\,\mathbf{b}$, where $\mathbf{a}$ and $\mathbf{b}$ are constant vectors, show that

$$\mathbf{f}''(t) - 5\mathbf{f}'(t) + 6\mathbf{f}(t) = \mathbf{0}.$$

**Solution:** Since $\mathbf{f}(t) = e^{2t}\,\mathbf{a} + e^{3t}\,\mathbf{b}$, then from (3.13) and (3.21),

$$\mathbf{f}'(t) = 2e^{2t}\,\mathbf{a} + 3e^{3t}\,\mathbf{b},$$

$$\mathbf{f}''(t) = 4e^{2t}\,\mathbf{a} + 9e^{3t}\,\mathbf{b}.$$

Therefore,

$$\begin{aligned}\mathbf{f}''(t) - 5\mathbf{f}'(t) + 6\mathbf{f}(t) &= 4e^{2t}\,\mathbf{a} + 9e^{3t}\,\mathbf{b} - 10e^{2t}\,\mathbf{a} - 15e^{3t}\,\mathbf{b} + 6e^{2t}\,\mathbf{a} + 6e^{3t}\,\mathbf{b}\\ &= (4-10+6)\,e^{2t}\,\mathbf{a} + (9-15+6)\,e^{3t}\,\mathbf{b}\\ &= \mathbf{0}.\end{aligned}$$

## 3.3 Partial Derivatives of Vector Functions of More than One Variable

A *vector function* **f** of two variables $u$ and $v$ assigns to each point $(u, v)$ in some region a unique vector $\mathbf{f}(u, v)$ called the value of **f** at $(u, v)$. Similarly, $\mathbf{f}(u, v, w)$ is a *vector function* of three variables $u$, $v$, and $w$.

In a rectangular coordinate system that is independent of three scalar variables $u$, $v$, and $w$,

$$\begin{aligned}\mathbf{f}(u, v, w) &= [f_1(u, v, w),\ f_2(u, v, w),\ f_3(u, v, w)] \\ &= f_1(u, v, w)\mathbf{i} + f_2(u, v, w)\mathbf{j} + f_3(u, v, w)\mathbf{k},\end{aligned} \tag{3.28}$$

where $f_1$, $f_2$, and $f_3$ are the scalar functions of $u$, $v$, and $w$ and are called the *components* of $\mathbf{f}(u, v, w)$.

The *partial derivative* $\mathbf{f}_u$ of **f** with respect to $u$ is defined by

$$\mathbf{f}_u = \frac{\partial \mathbf{f}}{\partial u} = \lim_{\Delta u \to 0} \frac{\mathbf{f}(u + \Delta u, v, w) - \mathbf{f}(u, v, w)}{\Delta u}, \tag{3.29}$$

provided that this limit exists. Similarly, we define the partial derivatives of **f** with respect to $v$ and $w$ by

$$\mathbf{f}_v = \frac{\partial \mathbf{f}}{\partial v} = \lim_{\Delta v \to 0} \frac{\mathbf{f}(u, v + \Delta v, w) - \mathbf{f}(u, v, w)}{\Delta v}, \tag{3.30}$$

$$\mathbf{f}_w = \frac{\partial \mathbf{f}}{\partial w} = \lim_{\Delta w \to 0} \frac{\mathbf{f}(u, v, w + \Delta w) - \mathbf{f}(u, v, w)}{\Delta w}, \tag{3.31}$$

provided that these limits exist.

The partial derivatives of higher order can also be defined in this way. For example,

$$\mathbf{f}_{uu} = \frac{\partial^2 \mathbf{f}}{\partial u^2} = \frac{\partial}{\partial u}\left(\frac{\partial \mathbf{f}}{\partial u}\right),$$

$$\mathbf{f}_{uv} = \frac{\partial^2 \mathbf{f}}{\partial v \partial u} = \frac{\partial}{\partial v}\left(\frac{\partial \mathbf{f}}{\partial u}\right),$$

$$\mathbf{f}_{vu} = \frac{\partial^2 \mathbf{f}}{\partial u \partial v} = \frac{\partial}{\partial u}\left(\frac{\partial \mathbf{f}}{\partial v}\right).$$

As seen in Sec. 3.2, if **A** and **B** are differentiable vector functions of $u$, $v$, and $w$, and $\phi$ is a differentiable scalar function of $u$, $v$, and $w$, then

(1) $$\frac{\partial}{\partial u}(\mathbf{A} + \mathbf{B}) = \mathbf{A}_u + \mathbf{B}_u, \tag{3.32}$$

(2) $$\frac{\partial}{\partial u}(\phi \mathbf{A}) = \phi \mathbf{A}_u + \phi_u \mathbf{A}, \tag{3.33}$$

(3) $$\frac{\partial}{\partial u}(\mathbf{A} \cdot \mathbf{B}) = \mathbf{A} \cdot \mathbf{B}_u + \mathbf{A}_u \cdot \mathbf{B}, \tag{3.34}$$

(4) $$\frac{\partial}{\partial u}(\mathbf{A} \times \mathbf{B}) = \mathbf{A} \times \mathbf{B}_u + \mathbf{A}_u \times \mathbf{B}. \tag{3.35}$$

It should be noted that the order of the factors that appear in (3.35) must be maintained.

**PROBLEM 3.11** If $\mathbf{f}(u, v, w) = f_1(u, v, w)\mathbf{i} + f_2(u, v, w)\mathbf{j} + f_3(u, v, w)\mathbf{k}$, then show that

$$\mathbf{f}_u = \frac{\partial \mathbf{f}}{\partial u} = \frac{\partial f_1}{\partial u}\mathbf{i} + \frac{\partial f_2}{\partial u}\mathbf{j} + \frac{\partial f_3}{\partial u}\mathbf{k}. \tag{3.36}$$

**Solution:** From the definition of a partial derivative (3.29),

$$\mathbf{f}_u = \lim_{\Delta u \to 0} \frac{\mathbf{f}(u + \Delta u,\ v, w) - \mathbf{f}(u, v, w)}{\Delta u}$$

$$= \lim_{\Delta u \to 0} \left[ \frac{f_1(u + \Delta u,\ v, w) - f_1(u, v, w)}{\Delta u}\mathbf{i} + \frac{f_2(u + \Delta u,\ v, w) - f_2(u, v, w)}{\Delta u}\mathbf{j} + \frac{f_3(u + \Delta u,\ v, w) - f_3(u, v, w)}{\Delta u}\mathbf{k} \right]$$

$$= \frac{\partial f_1}{\partial u}\mathbf{i} + \frac{\partial f_2}{\partial u}\mathbf{j} + \frac{\partial f_3}{\partial u}\mathbf{k}.$$

**PROBLEM 3.12** If $\mathbf{f}(u, v) = e^{uv}\,\mathbf{i} + (u - v)\,\mathbf{j} + u(\sin v)\,\mathbf{k}$, calculate (a) $\mathbf{f}_u$, (b) $\mathbf{f}_v$, (c) $\mathbf{f}_{uu}$, and (d) $\mathbf{f}_u \times \mathbf{f}_v$.

**Solution:** From (3.36),

(a) $$\mathbf{f}_u = \frac{\partial}{\partial u}(e^{uv})\,\mathbf{i} + \frac{\partial}{\partial u}(u - v)\,\mathbf{j} + \frac{\partial}{\partial u}(u \sin v)\,\mathbf{k}$$
$$= ve^{uv}\,\mathbf{i} + \mathbf{j} + (\sin v)\,\mathbf{k};$$

(b) $$\mathbf{f}_v = \frac{\partial}{\partial v}(e^{uv})\,\mathbf{i} + \frac{\partial}{\partial v}(u - v)\,\mathbf{j} + \frac{\partial}{\partial v}(u \sin v)\,\mathbf{k}$$
$$= ue^{uv}\,\mathbf{i} - \mathbf{j} + u(\cos v)\,\mathbf{k}:$$

(c) $$\mathbf{f}_{uu} = \frac{\partial}{\partial u}\mathbf{f}_u = \frac{\partial}{\partial u}(ve^{uv})\,\mathbf{i} + \frac{\partial}{\partial u}(1)\,\mathbf{j} + \frac{\partial}{\partial u}(\sin v)\,\mathbf{k}$$
$$= v^2 e^{uv}\,\mathbf{i};$$

(d) according to (2.27) and from the results of parts (a) and (b),

$$\mathbf{f}_u \times \mathbf{f}_v = \begin{vmatrix} \mathbf{i} & \mathbf{j} & \mathbf{k} \\ ve^{uv} & 1 & \sin v \\ ue^{uv} & -1 & u \cos v \end{vmatrix}$$

$$= (u \cos v + \sin v)\,\mathbf{i} + u(\sin v - v \cos v)\,e^{uv}\,\mathbf{j} - (v + u)\,e^{uv}\,\mathbf{k}.$$

## 3.4 Space Curves

Let $\mathbf{f}(t)$ be a vector function of a scalar variable $t$; i.e.,

$$\mathbf{f}(t) = f_1(t)\,\mathbf{i} + f_2(t)\,\mathbf{j} + f_3(t)\,\mathbf{k}, \tag{3.37}$$

where $f_1(t)$, $f_2(t)$, and $f_3(t)$ are scalar functions of $t$. Then for each value of $t$, there is a *position vector*

$$\mathbf{r} = x\,\mathbf{i} + y\,\mathbf{j} + z\,\mathbf{k}, \tag{3.38}$$

whose initial point is at the origin of a given coordinate system and whose terminal point specifies a point $P$ in space. As $t$ varies, $P$ is said to move in a *curved* path. Thus from the definition of the equality of vectors,

$$x = f_1(t), \quad y = f_2(t), \quad z = f_3(t). \tag{3.39}$$

Equations (3.39) are called the *parametric equations* of the curve C in space, which is a function of $\mathbf{f}(t)$ with $t$ as *parameter*.

As shown in Fig. 3.1, let $P$ be a fixed point on a curve C for which $\mathbf{f} = \mathbf{f}(t)$, and $Q$, the point that corresponds to $\mathbf{f}(t + \Delta t)$. Then,

$$\lim_{\Delta t \to 0} \frac{\mathbf{f}(t + \Delta t) - \mathbf{f}(t)}{\Delta t} = \lim_{\Delta t \to 0} \frac{\overrightarrow{PQ}}{\Delta t} = \mathbf{f}'(t) \tag{3.40}$$

is a vector that is *tangent* to the space curve C at $P$; this vector is called the *tangent vector* to C at $P$.

A point $t_i$ on a space curve C is called a *singular point* of C if $|\mathbf{f}'(t_i)| = 0$; otherwise, it is called a *nonsingular point*.

The *direction* of the space curve C at a nonsingular point $P$ is that of the tangent vector to C at $P$.

A *smooth vector function* is a vector function that has a continuous derivative and no singular points.

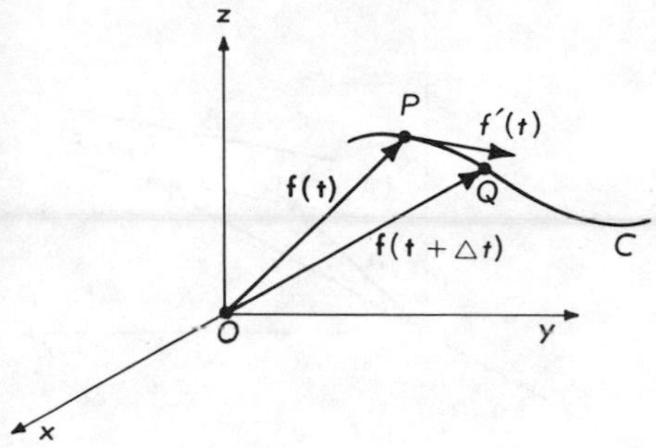


Fig. 3.1 A tangent to a space curve.

**PROBLEM 3.13** Sketch the curve C represented by the vector function

$$\mathbf{f}(t) = (a \cos t)\mathbf{i} + (a \sin t)\mathbf{j}, \quad 0 \leq t \leq 2\pi, \tag{3.41}$$

in space, and find its direction at the point (0, $a$, 0).

**Solution:** The parametric equations of the curve C represented by $\mathbf{f}(t)$ are

$$x = a \cos t, \quad y = a \sin t, \quad z = 0. \tag{3.42}$$

From (3.42),

$$x^2 + y^2 = a^2 (\cos^2 t + \sin^2 t) = a^2.$$

At $t = 0$,

$$x = a, \quad y = 0, \quad z = 0,$$

and at $t - 2\pi$,

$$x = a, \quad y = 0, \quad z = 0.$$

The curve C is a circle on the $xy$-plane centered at the origin with radius $a$, and it begins and terminates at the point $(a, 0, 0)$ as $t$ changes from 0 to $2\pi$. (See Fig. 3.2.)

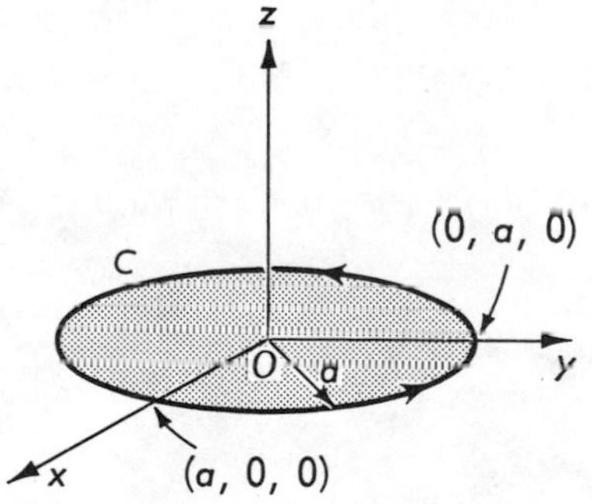


Fig. 3.2 Solution to Prob. 3.13.

The point $(0, a, 0)$ corresponds to that at $t = \pi/2$. Now from (3.41),

$$\mathbf{f}'(t) = -a \sin t\ \mathbf{i} + a \cos t\ \mathbf{j}.$$

Thus,

$$\mathbf{f}'\left(\frac{\pi}{2}\right) = -a \sin\left(\frac{\pi}{2}\right)\mathbf{i} + a \cos\left(\frac{\pi}{2}\right)\mathbf{j}$$

$$= -a\ \mathbf{i}.$$

Hence, the direction of the curve at $(0, a, 0)$, is in the negative direction of the $x$-axis.

**PROBLEM 3.14** (a) Find the vector function $\mathbf{f}(t)$ that represents the line $L$ that passes through a point $(A_1, A_2, A_3)$ and is parallel to a given nonzero vector $\mathbf{B} = [B_1, B_2, B_3]$. (b) Find the parametric equations for the line $L$.

**Solution:** (a) Represent the points $(A_1, A_2, A_3)$ and $(x, y, z)$ by the position vectors $\mathbf{A} = [A_1, A_2, A_3]$ and $\mathbf{r} = [x, y, z]$, respectively.

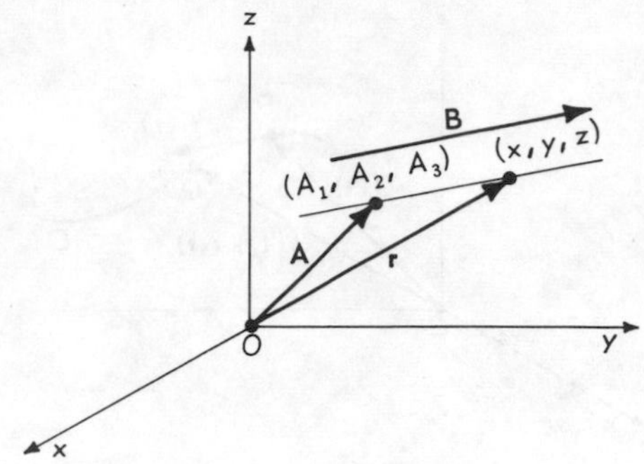


Fig. 3.3 Solution to Prob. 3.14.

From Fig. 3.3 it is apparent that the point $(x, y, z)$ will lie on the desired line if and only if $\mathbf{r} - \mathbf{A}$ is parallel to $\mathbf{B}$. Now, from (1.4), two vectors are parallel if and only if they are scalar multiples of each other; thus,

$$\mathbf{r} - \mathbf{A} = t\,\mathbf{B}, \tag{3.43}$$

where $t$ is some scalar. Rewriting (3.43),

$$\mathbf{r} = \mathbf{A} + t\,\mathbf{B}. \tag{3.44}$$

Hence, letting $\mathbf{r} = \mathbf{f}(t)$, we obtain the desired vector function

$$\mathbf{f}(t) = \mathbf{A} + t\,\mathbf{B}. \tag{3.45}$$

(b) Writing (3.44) in terms of the components of the vectors,

$$x = A_1 + tB_1, \quad y = A_2 + tB_2, \quad z = A_3 + tB_3, \tag{3.46}$$

which are the parametric equations for the line $L$ that passes through $(A_1, A_2, A_3)$ and is parallel to $\mathbf{B} = [B_1, B_2, B_3]$.

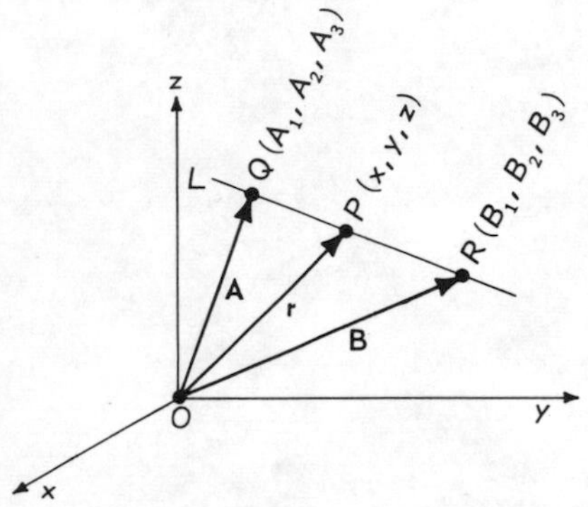


Fig. 3.4 Solution to Prob. 3.15.

**PROBLEM 3.15** (a) Find the vector function $\mathbf{f}(t)$ that represents the straight line $L$ that passes through the points $(A_1, A_2, A_3)$ and $(B_1, B_2, B_3)$. (b) Find the parametric equations for the line $L$.

**Solution:** (a) Represent the two points $(A_1, A_2, A_3)$ and $(B_1, B_2, B_3)$ by the position vectors $\mathbf{A} = [A_1, A_2, A_3]$ and $\mathbf{B} = [B_1, B_2, B_3]$, respectively. Let a point $(x, y, z)$ on $L$ be represented by the position vector $\mathbf{r} = [x, y, z]$. Then from Fig. 3.4, we see that there must be a scalar $t$ such that

$$\overrightarrow{QP} = t\,\overrightarrow{QR}.$$

Now $\overrightarrow{QP} = \mathbf{r} - \mathbf{A}$ and $\overrightarrow{QR} = \mathbf{B} - \mathbf{A}$; thus,

$$\mathbf{r} - \mathbf{A} = t\,(\mathbf{B} - \mathbf{A}), \tag{3.47}$$

or, on simplification,

$$\mathbf{r} = \mathbf{A} + t\,(\mathbf{B} - \mathbf{A}) = (1 - t)\,\mathbf{A} + t\,\mathbf{B}. \tag{3.48}$$

Hence, letting $\mathbf{r} = \mathbf{f}(t)$, we obtain the desired vector function

$$\mathbf{f}(t) = (1 - t)\,\mathbf{A} + t\,\mathbf{B}. \tag{3.49}$$

(b) Writing (3.48) in terms of the vector components, we obtain the parametric equations for the line; i.e.,

$$x = (1 - t)\,A_1 + tB_1, \quad y = (1 - t)\,A_2 + tB_2, \quad z = (1 - t)\,A_3 + tB_3. \tag{3.50}$$

Eliminating the parametric $t$ from (3.50),

$$\frac{x - A_1}{B_1 - A_1} = \frac{y - A_2}{B_2 - A_2} = \frac{z - A_3}{B_3 - A_3}, \tag{3.51}$$

which is the *nonparametric equation* of the line.

**PROBLEM 3.16** If a space curve C is represented by a smooth vector function $\mathbf{f}(t)$ for $a \leq t \leq b$, then show that its length $l$ is given by the integral

$$l = \int_a^b |\,\mathbf{f}'(t)\,|\, dt = \int_a^b [\mathbf{f}'(t) \cdot \mathbf{f}'(t)]^{1/2}\, dt. \tag{3.52}$$

**Solution:** If $\mathbf{f}(t) = f_1(t)\,\mathbf{i} + f_2(t)\,\mathbf{j} + f_3(t)\,\mathbf{k}$, then C can be described by the parametric equations $x = f_1(t)$, $y = f_2(t)$, $z = f_3(t)$ for $a < t < b$.

The *element of arc* $ds$ on $C$ is then defined from elementary calculus by

$$ds^2 = dx^2 + dy^2 + dz^2. \tag{3.53}$$

From (3.53) and the parametric equations,

$$\begin{aligned}\frac{ds}{dt} &= \left[\left(\frac{df_1}{dt}\right)^2 + \left(\frac{df_2}{dt}\right)^2 + \left(\frac{df_3}{dt}\right)^2\right]^{1/2} \\ &= \{[f_1'(t)]^2 + [f_2'(t)]^2 + [f_3'(t)]^2\}^{1/2} \\ &= [\mathbf{f}'(t)\cdot\mathbf{f}'(t)]^{1/2} \\ &= |\,\mathbf{f}'(t)\,|.\end{aligned} \tag{3.54}$$

Hence, the element of arc $ds$ is

$$ds = |\,\mathbf{f}'(t)\,|\; dt. \tag{3.55}$$

Thus, the total length $l$ is the integral of $ds$ over $C$; i.e.,

$$l = \int_C ds = \int_a^b |\,\mathbf{f}'(t)\,|\,dt = \int_a^b [\mathbf{f}'(t)\cdot\mathbf{f}'(t)]^{1/2}\,dt.$$

**PROBLEM 3.17** Find the length of the curve represented by the vector function

$$\mathbf{f}(t) = (a\cos t)\,\mathbf{i} + (a\sin t)\,\mathbf{j}, \quad 0 \le t \le 2\pi. \qquad [3.41]$$

**Solution:** The derivative of $\mathbf{f}(t)$ is

$$\mathbf{f}'(t) = -a\sin t\,\mathbf{i} + a\cos t\,\mathbf{j}, \quad 0 \le t \le 2\pi, \tag{3.56}$$

and its magnitude is

$$|\,\mathbf{f}'(t)\,| = (a^2\sin^2 t + a^2\cos^2 t)^{1/2} = a. \tag{3.57}$$

Thus, from (3.52), the length of the curve is

$$l = \int_0^{2\pi} |\,\mathbf{f}'(t)\,|\,dt = \int_0^{2\pi} a\,dt = 2\pi a. \tag{3.58}$$

The *arc length* $s(t)$ of a curve is a function of the scalar variable $t$ from some fixed point $a$ to $t$. It is the length $l$ of $C$ with the fixed upper limit $b$ in (3.52) replaced by $t$; i.e.,

$$s(t) = \int_a^t |\,\mathbf{f}'(t)\,|\,dt. \tag{3.59}$$

**PROBLEM 3.18** Show that the arc length $s$ may serve as a parameter in the representations of curves with no singular points.

**Solution:** Differentiating the arc length, (3.59), of a curve, we obtain for $a \le t \le b$,

$$\frac{ds}{dt} = |\,\mathbf{f}'(t)\,| > 0. \tag{3.60}$$

Thus, $s$ is an increasing and continuous function in $a \le t \le b$. This implies that $s$ has a unique inverse $t = q(s)$ for $0 \le s \le l$. Hence, a smooth vector function

$$\mathbf{g}(s) = \mathbf{f}[q(s)] \tag{3.61}$$

with parameter $s$ can represent the same curve $C$ that is represented by $\mathbf{f}(t)$.

By setting the position vector $\mathbf{r} = [x, y, z]$ as

$$\mathbf{r} = \mathbf{g}(s) = g_1(s)\,\mathbf{i} + g_2(s)\,\mathbf{j} + g_3(s)\,\mathbf{k}, \tag{3.62}$$

we obtain the parametric equations of $C$ with parameter $s$; i.e.,

$$x = g_1(s), \quad y = g_2(s), \quad z = g_3(s). \tag{3.63}$$

Instead of the vector functions $\mathbf{f}(t)$ or $\mathbf{g}(s)$ to represent the space curve $C$, we often use $\mathbf{r}(t)$ or $\mathbf{r}(s)$. Thus,

$$\mathbf{f}(t) = \mathbf{r}(t) = x(t)\mathbf{i} + y(t)\mathbf{j} + z(t)\mathbf{k}, \qquad a \leq t \leq b, \tag{3.64}$$

$$\mathbf{g}(s) = \mathbf{r}(s) = x(s)\mathbf{i} + y(s)\mathbf{j} + z(s)\mathbf{k}, \quad 0 \leq s \leq l. \tag{3.65}$$

Although the same functional forms, $\mathbf{r}(t)$ and $\mathbf{r}(s)$, are used, it should be noted that $\mathbf{r}(s)$ is not obtained from $\mathbf{r}(t)$ by simply changing the parameter $t$ to $s$. Rather $\mathbf{r}(s)$ is obtained from $\mathbf{r}(t)$ by changing the parameter $t$ to $q(s)$. Problem 3.19 illustrates this point.

**PROBLEM 3.19** A curve $C$ is denoted by the vector function

$$f(t) = a \cos t\, \mathbf{i} + a \sin t\, \mathbf{j}, \quad 0 \leq t \leq 2\pi.$$

Represent $C$ by a vector function with the arc length $s$ as the parameter. (Cf., Prob. 3.17.)

**Solution:** From the definition of arc length (3.59), and using (3.57),

$$s = \int_0^t |\mathbf{f}'(t)|\, dt = \int_0^t a\, dt = at. \tag{3.66}$$

Hence, $t = s/a$, and the desired vector function is

$$\mathbf{g}(s) = \mathbf{f}\left(\frac{s}{a}\right) = \left[a \cos\left(\frac{s}{a}\right)\right]\mathbf{i} + \left[a \sin\left(\frac{s}{a}\right)\right]\mathbf{j}, \quad 0 \leq s \leq 2\pi a. \tag{3.67}$$

**PROBLEM 3.20** When a curve $C$ is represented by a vector function $\mathbf{g}(s)$ with arc length $s$ as the parameter, show that

$$\frac{d\mathbf{g}(s)}{ds} = \mathbf{g}'(s) = \mathbf{T}, \tag{3.68}$$

where $\mathbf{T}$ is the unit tangent vector to $C$ at any point.

**Solution:** From (3.40), the tangent vector to the curve $C$ represented by the smooth vector function $\mathbf{f}(t)$ at any point is the vector $\mathbf{f}'(t)$. Hence, for $|\mathbf{f}'(t)| \neq 0$, the unit tangent vector $\mathbf{T}$ to $C$ at any point is expressed by

$$\mathbf{T} = \frac{\mathbf{f}'(t)}{|\mathbf{f}'(t)|}. \tag{3.69}$$

Now since $\mathbf{g}(s) = \mathbf{f}[q(s)]$ and $t = q(s)$, we have on differentiating and using the chain rule,

$$\frac{d\mathbf{g}(s)}{ds} = \mathbf{g}'(s) = \mathbf{f}'(t)\frac{dt}{ds} = \frac{\mathbf{f}'(t)}{\frac{ds}{dt}} = \frac{\mathbf{f}'(t)}{|\mathbf{f}'(t)|}. \tag{3.70}$$

Hence, from (3.69–70),

$$\mathbf{g}'(s) = \frac{\mathbf{f}'(t)}{|\mathbf{f}'(t)|} = \mathbf{T}.$$

**PROBLEM 3.21** Find the unit tangent vector to the curve $C$ represented by the vector function

$$\mathbf{f}(t) = (a \cos t)\mathbf{i} + (a \sin t)\mathbf{j}, \quad 0 \le t \le 2\pi,$$

at $t = \pi/2$. (Cf., Prob. 3.13.)

**Solution:** From (3.67), the curve $C$ is also represented by

$$\mathbf{g}(s) = \left[a \cos\left(\frac{s}{a}\right)\right]\mathbf{i} + \left[a \sin\left(\frac{s}{a}\right)\right]\mathbf{j}, \quad 0 \le s \le 2\pi a. \qquad [3.67]$$

From (3.68), the unit tangent vector $\mathbf{T}$ to $C$ at any point is

$$\mathbf{T} = \mathbf{g}'(s) = -\left[\sin\left(\frac{s}{a}\right)\right]\mathbf{i} + \left[\cos\left(\frac{s}{a}\right)\right]\mathbf{j}, \quad 0 \le s \le 2\pi a. \qquad (3.71)$$

Now, from (3.66), we have at $t = \pi/2$, $s = at|_{t=\pi/2} = \frac{1}{2}a\pi$. Hence, at point $t = \pi/2$ or $s = a\pi/2$, the unit tangent vector is

$$\mathbf{T} = -\left[\sin\left(\frac{\pi}{2}\right)\right]\mathbf{i} + \left[\cos\left(\frac{\pi}{2}\right)\right]\mathbf{j} = -\mathbf{i}, \qquad (3.72)$$

since $\sin(\pi/2) = 1$ and $\cos(\pi/2) = 0$.

Alternatively, the same result can be obtained from (3.69) by using (3.56) and (3.57). Thus, for $0 \le t \le 2\pi$,

$$\mathbf{T} = \frac{\mathbf{f}'(t)}{|\mathbf{f}'(t)|} = \frac{1}{a}[-(a \sin t)\mathbf{i} + (a \cos t)\mathbf{j}]$$

$$= -(\sin t)\mathbf{i} + (\cos t)\mathbf{j}. \qquad (3.73)$$

Hence, at $t = \pi/2$,

$$\mathbf{T} = -\left[\sin\left(\frac{\pi}{2}\right)\right]\mathbf{i} + \left[\cos\left(\frac{\pi}{2}\right)\right]\mathbf{j} = -\mathbf{i}.$$

**PROBLEM 3.22** Show that the vector defined by $d\mathbf{T}/ds$ is normal or perpendicular to the unit tangent vector $\mathbf{T}$ at any point on the curve $C$.

**Solution:** Since $\mathbf{T}$ is the unit tangent vector, the dot product yields

$$\mathbf{T} \cdot \mathbf{T} = 1. \qquad (3.74)$$

Differentiating both sides with respect to $s$,

$$\frac{d\mathbf{T}}{ds} \cdot \mathbf{T} = 0, \qquad (3.75)$$

which implies that $d\mathbf{T}/ds$ is normal to $\mathbf{T}$. (See Prob. 3.7.)

## 3.5 Surfaces

In Sec. 3.4, vector equations of the type

$$\mathbf{r}(t) = x(t)\mathbf{i} + y(t)\mathbf{j} + z(t)\mathbf{k} \qquad (3.76)$$

in the single parameter $t$ describe space curves. The parametric representation of the space curves is

$$x = x(t), \quad y = y(t), \quad z = z(t). \qquad (3.77)$$

*Surfaces*, in general, are described by the parametric equations of the type

$$x = x(u, v), \quad y = y(u, v), \quad z = z(u, v), \qquad (3.78)$$

where $u$ and $v$ are parameters. If $v$ is fixed, i.e., $v = c$, a constant, then (3.78) becomes a one-parameter expression, which describes a space curve along which

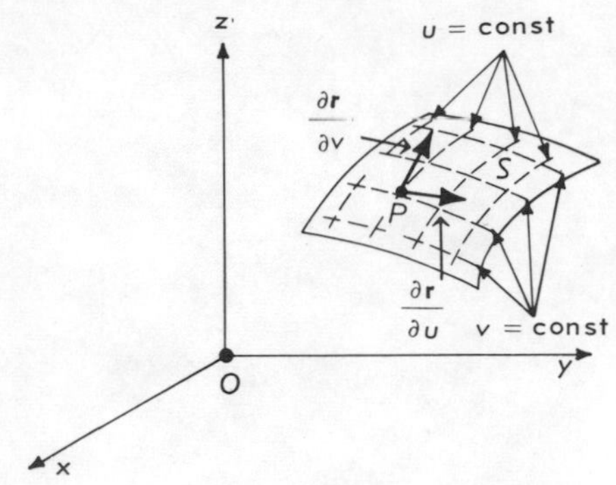


Fig. 3.5 A surface in space.

$u$ varies. This is the curve designated by $v = c$. Thus for each $v$, there exists a space curve. Similarly, $v$ varies along the curve $u = k$, a constant. The locus of all the curves $v = c$ and $u = k$ forms a *surface* $S$. The parameters $u$ and $v$ are called the *curvilinear coordinates* of the point $s$ on the surface, and the $u$-curves and $v$-curves are called *parametric curves*. See Fig. 3.5.

If the terminal point of the position vector $\mathbf{r}$ generates the surface $S$, then (3.78) can be rewritten as

$$\mathbf{r}(u, v) = x(u, v)\mathbf{i} + y(u, v)\mathbf{j} + z(u, v)\mathbf{k}. \tag{3.79}$$

**PROBLEM 3.23** Show that the unit vector $\mathbf{n}$, defined by

$$\mathbf{n} = \frac{\mathbf{r}_u \times \mathbf{r}_v}{|\mathbf{r}_u \times \mathbf{r}_v|}, \tag{3.80}$$

where $\mathbf{r}_u = \dfrac{\partial \mathbf{r}}{\partial u}$, $\mathbf{r}_v = \dfrac{\partial \mathbf{r}}{\partial v}$, is normal to the surface $S$ represented by $\mathbf{r}(u, v)$ if $\mathbf{r}_u \times \mathbf{r}_v \neq \mathbf{0}$.

**Solution:** According to (3.40), at any point $P$,

$$\mathbf{r}_u = \frac{\partial \mathbf{r}}{\partial u} = \frac{\partial x}{\partial u}\mathbf{i} + \frac{\partial y}{\partial u}\mathbf{j} + \frac{\partial z}{\partial u}\mathbf{k} \tag{3.81}$$

is a tangent vector to a constant curve $v$ at $P$. Similarly,

$$\mathbf{r}_v = \frac{\partial \mathbf{r}}{\partial v} = \frac{\partial x}{\partial v}\mathbf{i} + \frac{\partial y}{\partial v}\mathbf{j} + \frac{\partial z}{\partial v}\mathbf{k} \tag{3.82}$$

is a tangent vector to a constant curve $u$ at $P$. Hence, it follows that at any point $P$, the vector $\mathbf{r}_u \times \mathbf{r}_v$ is normal to the surface $S$ at $P$. Since $|\mathbf{r}_u \times \mathbf{r}_v|$ is the magnitude of this vector,

$$\mathbf{n} = \frac{\mathbf{r}_u \times \mathbf{r}_v}{|\mathbf{r}_u \times \mathbf{r}_v|}$$

is a unit normal vector to $S$ at $P$.

A point $(u, v)$ on a surface $S$ is called a *singular point* if $\mathbf{r}_u \times \mathbf{r}_v = \mathbf{0}$; otherwise, it is called a *nonsingular point*. If $\mathbf{r}_u$ and $\mathbf{r}_v$ are continuous, then the tangent planes exist only at the nonsingular points. Geometrically, the condition for $\mathbf{r}_u \times \mathbf{r}_v \neq \mathbf{0}$ is that the curves $u = k$ and $v = c$, where $k$ and $c$ are constant, are nonsingular and are *not* tangent to each other at their point of intersection.

**PROBLEM 3.24** Find a unit normal vector $\mathbf{n}$ for a surface $S$ represented by

$$x = x, \quad y = y, \quad z = z(x, y), \tag{3.83}$$

where $x$ and $y$ are parameters.

**Solution:** From (3.83), the surface $S$ can be represented by

$$\mathbf{r}(x, y) = x\mathbf{i} + y\mathbf{j} + z(x, y)\mathbf{k}. \tag{3.84}$$

Hence, the partial derivatives are

$$\mathbf{r}_x = \frac{\partial \mathbf{r}}{\partial x} = \frac{\partial x}{\partial x}\mathbf{i} + \frac{\partial y}{\partial x}\mathbf{j} + \frac{\partial z}{\partial x}\mathbf{k} = \mathbf{i} + \frac{\partial z}{\partial x}\mathbf{k}, \tag{3.85}$$

$$\mathbf{r}_y = \frac{\partial \mathbf{r}}{\partial y} = \frac{\partial x}{\partial y}\mathbf{i} + \frac{\partial y}{\partial y}\mathbf{j} + \frac{\partial z}{\partial y}\mathbf{k} = \mathbf{j} + \frac{\partial z}{\partial y}\mathbf{k}. \tag{3.86}$$

Now, the vector product of $\mathbf{r}_x$ and $\mathbf{r}_y$ is

$$\mathbf{r}_x \times \mathbf{r}_y = \begin{vmatrix} \mathbf{i} & \mathbf{j} & \mathbf{k} \\ 1 & 0 & \dfrac{\partial z}{\partial x} \\ 0 & 1 & \dfrac{\partial z}{\partial y} \end{vmatrix} = -\frac{\partial z}{\partial x}\mathbf{i} - \frac{\partial z}{\partial y}\mathbf{j} + \mathbf{k}. \tag{3.87}$$

Thus, the magnitude is

$$|\mathbf{r}_x \times \mathbf{r}_y| = \left[\left(\frac{\partial z}{\partial x}\right)^2 + \left(\frac{\partial z}{\partial y}\right)^2 + 1\right]^{1/2}. \tag{3.88}$$

Hence, from (3.80), the unit normal vector is

$$\mathbf{n} = \frac{\mathbf{r}_x \times \mathbf{r}_y}{|\mathbf{r}_x \times \mathbf{r}_y|} = \frac{-\dfrac{\partial z}{\partial x}\mathbf{i} - \dfrac{\partial z}{\partial y}\mathbf{j} + \mathbf{k}}{\left[\left(\dfrac{\partial z}{\partial x}\right)^2 + \left(\dfrac{\partial z}{\partial y}\right)^2 + 1\right]^{1/2}}. \tag{3.89}$$

**PROBLEM 3.25** Find a unit normal vector $\mathbf{n}$ for a surface $S$ that is represented by

$$\phi(x, y, z) = 0. \tag{3.90}$$

**Solution:** If we regard (3.90) as implicitly defining $z$ as a function of $x$ and $y$, we can assume that $\phi_z \neq 0$. Then from elementary calculus, (3.85), and (3.86), the partial derivatives are

$$\mathbf{r}_x = \mathbf{i} + \frac{\partial z}{\partial x}\mathbf{k} = \mathbf{i} - \frac{\dfrac{\partial \phi}{\partial x}}{\dfrac{\partial \phi}{\partial z}}\mathbf{k} = \mathbf{i} - \frac{\phi_x}{\phi_z}\mathbf{k}, \tag{3.91}$$

$$\mathbf{r}_y = \mathbf{j} + \frac{\partial z}{\partial y}\mathbf{k} = \mathbf{j} - \frac{\dfrac{\partial \phi}{\partial y}}{\dfrac{\partial \phi}{\partial z}}\mathbf{k} = \mathbf{j} - \frac{\phi_y}{\phi_z}\mathbf{k}. \tag{3.92}$$

Hence, the vector product is

$$\begin{aligned} \mathbf{r}_x \times \mathbf{r}_y &= \begin{vmatrix} \mathbf{i} & \mathbf{j} & \mathbf{k} \\ 1 & 0 & -\dfrac{\phi_x}{\phi_z} \\ 0 & 1 & -\dfrac{\phi_y}{\phi_z} \end{vmatrix} \\ &= \frac{\phi_x}{\phi_z}\mathbf{i} + \frac{\phi_y}{\phi_z}\mathbf{j} + \mathbf{k} \\ &= \frac{1}{\phi_z}(\phi_x\mathbf{i} + \phi_y\mathbf{j} + \phi_z\mathbf{k}), \end{aligned} \tag{3.93}$$

so that the unit normal vector is

$$\mathbf{n} = \frac{\mathbf{r}_x \times \mathbf{r}_y}{|\mathbf{r}_x \times \mathbf{r}_y|} = \frac{\phi_x\mathbf{i} + \phi_y\mathbf{j} + \phi_z\mathbf{k}}{[(\phi_x)^2 + (\phi_y)^2 + (\phi_z)^2]^{1/2}} = \frac{\dfrac{\partial \phi}{\partial x}\mathbf{i} + \dfrac{\partial \phi}{\partial y}\mathbf{j} + \dfrac{\partial \phi}{\partial z}\mathbf{k}}{\left[\left(\dfrac{\partial \phi}{\partial x}\right)^2 + \left(\dfrac{\partial \phi}{\partial y}\right)^2 + \left(\dfrac{\partial \phi}{\partial z}\right)^2\right]^{1/2}}. \tag{3.94}$$

If $\phi_x \neq 0$ or $\phi_y \neq 0$, a similar computation would yield the same result.

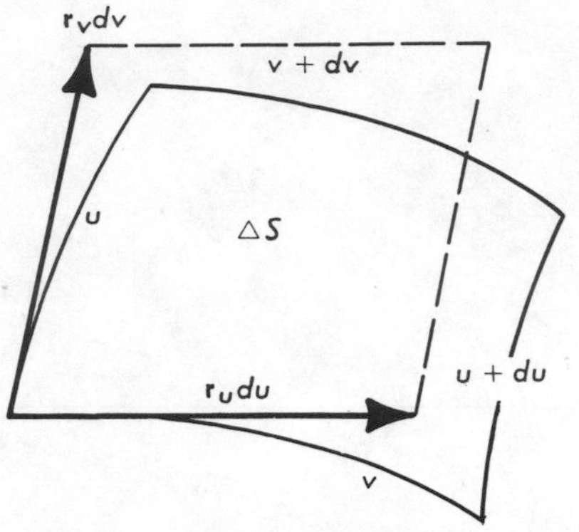


Fig. 3.6 A differential element of surface area.

The *differential element of surface area* is a vector given by

$$d\mathbf{S} = \frac{\partial \mathbf{r}}{\partial u}\, du \times \frac{\partial \mathbf{r}}{\partial v}\, dv = \mathbf{r}_u \times \mathbf{r}_v\, dudv. \tag{3.95}$$

From the definition of a unit normal vector (3.80), we see that $d\mathbf{S}$ is a vector normal to the surface represented by $\mathbf{r}(u, v)$ at any point $P$; its magnitude,

$$dS = |d\mathbf{S}| = |\mathbf{r}_u \times \mathbf{r}_v|\, dudv, \tag{3.96}$$

is approximately equal to the surface area S that is bounded by four curves on S. (See Fig. 3.6.)

From (3.80) and (3.96), (3.95) can be rewritten as

$$d\mathbf{S} = \mathbf{n}\, dS. \tag{3.97}$$

The *surface area* of S can then be obtained by integrating (3.97) over S; i.e.,

$$S = \iint dS = \iint \mathbf{n} \cdot d\mathbf{S}, \tag{3.98}$$

where $\mathbf{n}$ is a unit normal vector of S at any point $P$.

**PROBLEM 3.26** Find the surface area for a surface $S$ that is represented by

$$x = a \sin\theta \cos\phi, \quad y = a \sin\theta \sin\phi, \quad z = a\cos\theta, \tag{3.99}$$

where $0 < \theta < \pi$ and $0 < \phi < 2\pi$.

**Solution:** Here the two parameters $\theta$ and $\phi$ are used instead of $u$ and $v$. Hence,

$$\begin{aligned}\mathbf{r}_\theta &= \frac{\partial \mathbf{r}}{\partial \theta} = \frac{\partial x}{\partial \theta}\mathbf{i} + \frac{\partial y}{\partial \theta}\mathbf{j} + \frac{\partial z}{\partial \theta}\mathbf{k}\\ &= a\cos\theta\cos\phi\,\mathbf{i} + a\cos\theta\sin\phi\,\mathbf{j} - a\sin\theta\,\mathbf{k},\\ \mathbf{r}_\phi &= \frac{\partial \mathbf{r}}{\partial \phi} = \frac{\partial x}{\partial \phi}\mathbf{i} + \frac{\partial y}{\partial \phi}\mathbf{j} + \frac{\partial z}{\partial \phi}\mathbf{k}\\ &= -a\sin\theta\sin\phi\,\mathbf{i} + a\sin\theta\cos\phi\,\mathbf{j}.\end{aligned}$$

Thus, the vector product is

$$\begin{aligned}\mathbf{r}_\theta \times \mathbf{r}_\phi &= \begin{vmatrix} \mathbf{i} & \mathbf{j} & \mathbf{k} \\ a\cos\theta\cos\phi & a\cos\theta\sin\phi & -a\sin\theta \\ -a\sin\theta\sin\phi & a\sin\theta\cos\phi & 0 \end{vmatrix}\\ &= a^2\sin^2\theta\cos\phi\,\mathbf{i} + a^2\sin^2\theta\sin\phi\,\mathbf{j} + a^2\sin\theta\cos\theta\,\mathbf{k},\end{aligned}$$

and its magnitude is

$$\begin{aligned}|\mathbf{r}_\theta \times \mathbf{r}_\phi| &= a^2\sin\theta[\sin^2\theta\cos^2\phi + \sin^2\theta\sin^2\phi + \cos^2\theta]^{1/2}\\ &= a^2\sin\theta[\sin^2\theta\,(\cos^2\phi + \sin^2\phi) + \cos^2\theta]^{1/2}\\ &= a^2\sin\theta.\end{aligned}$$

Hence, from (3.96), the magnitude of the differential element of the surface area is

$$dS = a^2 \sin\theta\, d\theta d\phi. \tag{3.100}$$

Thus, on integrating, the surface area is

$$S = \iint dS = \int_0^{2\pi} \int_0^{\pi} a^2 \sin\theta \, d\theta d\phi = 2\pi a^2 \int_0^{\pi} \sin\theta \, d\theta$$

$$= 2\pi a^2 (-\cos\theta)\Big|_0^{\pi}$$

$$= 2\pi a^2 \{-[(-1) - 1]\}$$

$$= 4\pi a^2.$$

It is noted that (3.99) are the parametric equations for a sphere

$$x^2 + y^2 + z^2 = a^2. \tag{3.101}$$

From Fig. 3.7, (3.100) can be obtained by observation. Thus, if we hold $\phi$ fixed and vary $\theta$ by $d\theta$, we obtain an arc of length $a\,d\theta$. Holding $\theta$ fixed and varying $\phi$ by $d\phi$, we obtain an arc of a circle of radius $a \sin\theta$ with the length, $a \sin\theta \, d\phi$. Hence the element of differential area $dS$ can be expressed as

$$dS = a\,d\theta \cdot a \sin\theta \, d\phi = a^2 \sin\theta \, d\theta d\phi.$$

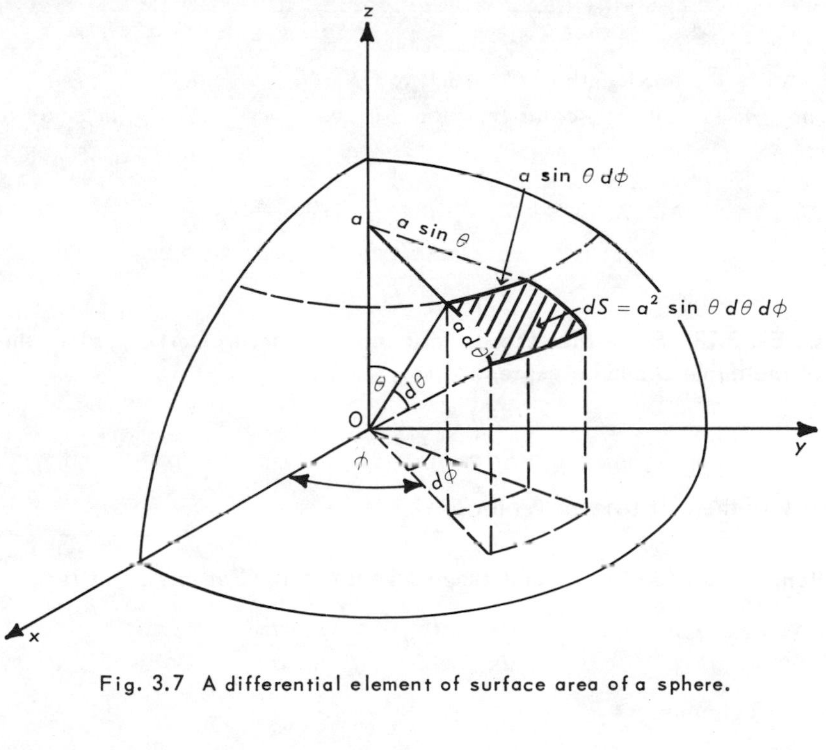


Fig. 3.7 A differential element of surface area of a sphere.

**PROBLEM 3.27** Express the differential element of surface area $dS$ for a surface $S$ that is represented by

$$z = z(x, y). \tag{3.102}$$

**Solution:** From (3.88),

$$|\mathbf{r}_x \times \mathbf{r}_y| = \left[1 + \left(\frac{\partial z}{\partial x}\right)^2 + \left(\frac{\partial z}{\partial y}\right)^2\right]^{1/2}.$$

Hence, using (3.96),

$$dS = |\mathbf{r}_x \times \mathbf{r}_y| \, dxdy = \left[1 + \left(\frac{\partial z}{\partial x}\right)^2 + \left(\frac{\partial z}{\partial y}\right)^2\right]^{1/2} dxdy. \tag{3.103}$$

## 3.6 Directional Derivative and Gradient

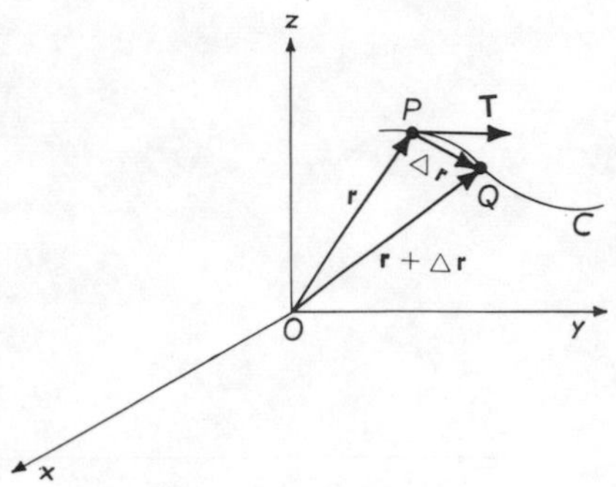


Fig. 3.8 The directional derivative.

*A scalar field* $\phi(x, y, z)$ is the totality of scalars $\phi(x, y, z)$ assigned to each point $(x, y, z)$ of a region $R$ in space.

A *vector field* $\mathbf{f}(x, y, z)$ is the totality of vectors $\mathbf{f}(x, y, z)$ assigned to each point $(x, y, z)$ of a region $R$ in space.

Let $P(x, y, z)$ be a nonsingular point on a curve $C$ in space and $Q(x + \Delta x, y + \Delta y, z + \Delta z)$, any other point on $C$. (See Fig. 3.8.) Then the position vectors $\mathbf{r}$ and $\mathbf{r} + \Delta\mathbf{r}$ of $P$ and $Q$ are

$$\mathbf{r} = x\mathbf{i} + y\mathbf{j} + z\mathbf{k},$$

$$\mathbf{r} + \Delta\mathbf{r} = (x + \Delta x)\mathbf{i} + (y + \Delta y)\mathbf{j} + (z + \Delta z)\mathbf{k}.$$

Let $\phi(x, y, z)$ be a continuous and differentiable scalar function in a region $R$ that contains the arc of $C$ from $P$ to $Q$. Then, the *directional derivative* of $\phi(x, y, z)$ at $P$ in the direction of the unit tangent vector $\mathbf{T}$ to $C$ at $P$ is defined as

$$\frac{\partial\phi}{\partial s} = \lim_{\Delta s \to 0} \frac{\phi(x + \Delta x, y + \Delta y, z + \Delta z) - \phi(x, y, z)}{\Delta s}, \tag{3.104}$$

where $\Delta s$ is the arc length of $C$ from $P$ to $Q$.

The *gradient* of the scalar function $\phi(x, y, z)$, written as *grad* $\phi$, is a vector defined by

$$\text{grad}\ \phi \equiv \frac{\partial\phi}{\partial x}\mathbf{i} + \frac{\partial\phi}{\partial y}\mathbf{j} + \frac{\partial\phi}{\partial z}\mathbf{k}. \tag{3.105}$$

**PROBLEM 3.28** Show that the directional derivative of $\phi(x, y, z)$ in the direction of the curve $C$ can be expressed as

$$\frac{\partial\phi}{\partial s} = \text{grad}\ \phi \cdot \mathbf{T}, \tag{3.106}$$

where $\mathbf{T}$ is the unit tangent vector to $C$.

**Solution:** From (3.68), the unit tangent vector $\mathbf{T}$ to $C$ at any point is

$$\mathbf{T} = \frac{d\mathbf{r}}{ds} = \frac{dx}{ds}\mathbf{i} + \frac{dy}{ds}\mathbf{j} + \frac{dz}{ds}\mathbf{k}. \tag{3.107}$$

Now from calculus,

$$\frac{\partial\phi}{\partial s} = \frac{\partial\phi}{\partial x}\frac{dx}{ds} + \frac{\partial\phi}{\partial y}\frac{dy}{ds} + \frac{\partial\phi}{\partial z}\frac{dz}{ds}, \tag{3.108}$$

which is the form of a scalar product of grad $\phi$ and $\mathbf{T}$. Hence,

$$\frac{\partial\phi}{\partial s} = \text{grad}\ \phi \cdot \mathbf{T}.$$

By introducing the *differential operator* $\nabla$ (read *nabla* or *del*),

$$\nabla \equiv \frac{\partial}{\partial x}\mathbf{i} + \frac{\partial}{\partial y}\mathbf{j} + \frac{\partial}{\partial z}\mathbf{k}, \tag{3.109}$$

the gradient of $\phi$ is written as

$$\text{grad } \phi = \nabla\phi = \left(\frac{\partial}{\partial x}\mathbf{i} + \frac{\partial}{\partial y}\mathbf{j} + \frac{\partial}{\partial z}\mathbf{k}\right)\phi = \frac{\partial\phi}{\partial x}\mathbf{i} + \frac{\partial\phi}{\partial y}\mathbf{j} + \frac{\partial\phi}{\partial z}\mathbf{k}. \tag{3.110}$$

From (3.110), the properties of the gradient are

$$\nabla(c\phi) = c\,\nabla\phi, \tag{3.111}$$

$$\nabla(\phi + \psi) = \nabla\phi + \nabla\psi, \tag{3.112}$$

$$\nabla(\phi\psi) = \phi\nabla\psi + \psi\nabla\phi, \tag{3.113}$$

where $\phi$ and $\psi$ are differentiable scalar functions in some region in space, and c is a constant.

**PROBLEM 3.29** Verify (3.113).

**Solution:** From the definition of the gradient (3.110),

$$\begin{aligned}\nabla(\phi\psi) &= \frac{\partial}{\partial x}(\phi\psi)\mathbf{i} + \frac{\partial}{\partial y}(\phi\psi)\mathbf{j} + \frac{\partial}{\partial z}(\phi\psi)\mathbf{k}\\ &= \left(\phi\frac{\partial\psi}{\partial x} + \psi\frac{\partial\phi}{\partial x}\right)\mathbf{i} + \left(\phi\frac{\partial\psi}{\partial y} + \psi\frac{\partial\phi}{\partial y}\right)\mathbf{j} + \left(\phi\frac{\partial\psi}{\partial z} + \psi\frac{\partial\phi}{\partial z}\right)\mathbf{k}\\ &= \phi\left(\frac{\partial\psi}{\partial x}\mathbf{i} + \frac{\partial\psi}{\partial y}\mathbf{j} + \frac{\partial\psi}{\partial z}\mathbf{k}\right) + \psi\left(\frac{\partial\phi}{\partial x}\mathbf{i} + \frac{\partial\phi}{\partial y}\mathbf{j} + \frac{\partial\phi}{\partial z}\mathbf{k}\right)\\ &= \phi\nabla\psi + \psi\nabla\phi.\end{aligned}$$

**PROBLEM 3.30** Show that the magnitude and direction of the gradient $\nabla\phi$ is independent of the coordinate system. That is, show that the magnitude of the gradient $|\nabla\phi|$ is equal to the maximum value of the directional derivative of $\phi(x, y, z)$, and its direction is that of the maximum rate of increase of the function $\phi$.

**Solution:** From the definitions of the directional derivative (3.106) and the scalar product (1.25), the directional derivative of $\phi$ at a point $(x, y, z)$ is

$$\frac{\partial\phi}{\partial s} = \nabla\phi\cdot\mathbf{T} = |\nabla\phi|\,|\mathbf{T}|\cos\theta = |\nabla\phi|\cos\theta, \tag{3.114}$$

where $\theta$ is the angle between $\nabla\phi$ and the unit tangent vector $\mathbf{T}$ to the curve $C$. Since $-1 \leq \cos\theta \leq 1$, $\partial\phi/\partial s$ is maximum when $\theta = 0$, i.e., when the direction of $\mathbf{T}$ is the direction of $\nabla\phi$, and

$$\left.\frac{\partial\phi}{\partial s}\right|_{max} = |\nabla\phi|. \tag{3.115}$$

Thus the magnitude of the gradient is $\partial\phi/\partial s|_{max}$, and its direction is in the direction of the maximum rate of increase of the function $\phi$.

**PROBLEM 3.31** If $\phi(x, y, z)$ is a scalar function and $\nabla\phi \neq \mathbf{0}$ at a point $P$ in space, then show that $\nabla\phi$ is perpendicular to the surface S defined by

$$\phi(x, y, z) = c, \tag{3.116}$$

where c is a constant.

**Solution:** Using (3.94) of Prob. 3.25, a unit normal vector $\mathbf{n}$ for the surface $S$ defined by (3.116) is

$$\mathbf{n} = \frac{\dfrac{\partial\phi}{\partial x}\mathbf{i} + \dfrac{\partial\phi}{\partial y}\mathbf{j} + \dfrac{\partial\phi}{\partial z}\mathbf{k}}{\left[\left(\dfrac{\partial\phi}{\partial x}\right)^2 + \left(\dfrac{\partial\phi}{\partial y}\right)^2 + \left(\dfrac{\partial\phi}{\partial z}\right)^2\right]^{1/2}} = \frac{\nabla\phi}{|\nabla\phi|}. \tag{3.117}$$

Hence, we conclude that $\nabla\phi$ is perpendicular to $S$.

**Alternate Solution:** If we assume that a space curve $C$ that lies on a surface $S$ is represented by

$$\mathbf{r}(t) = x(t)\,\mathbf{i} + y(t)\,\mathbf{j} + z(t)\,\mathbf{k},$$

then from (3.116), we have, for constant c,

$$\phi[x(t),\ y(t),\ z(t)] = c.$$

By differentiating this with respect to $t$,

$$\frac{\partial\phi}{\partial x}x'(t) + \frac{\partial\phi}{\partial y}y'(t) + \frac{\partial\phi}{\partial z}z'(t) = \nabla\phi\cdot\mathbf{r}'(t) = 0, \tag{3.118}$$

where from (3.40), the vector tangent to $C$ at $P$ is

$$\mathbf{r}'(t) = x'(t)\,\mathbf{i} + y'(t)\,\mathbf{j} + z'(t)\,\mathbf{k}.$$

Now (3.118) implies that $\nabla\phi \perp \mathbf{r}'(t)$, i.e., $\nabla\phi$ is perpendicular to $C$ at $P$.

This reasoning can be applied to any smooth curve on the surface $S$ that passes through $P$. Hence, $\nabla\phi$ is perpendicular to every such curve at $P$, which can be the case only if $\nabla\phi$ is perpendicular to the surface $S$.

**PROBLEM 3.32** Find (a) the directional derivative of $\phi(x,y,z) = x^2 + y^2 + z^2$ in the direction from $P(1,1,0)$ to $Q(2,1,1)$ and (b) its maximum value and direction at $(1,1,0)$.

**Solution:** (a) Let the position vectors $\mathbf{r}_1 = [1,1,0]$ and $\mathbf{r}_2 = [2,1,1]$ represent the points $P(1,1,0)$ and $Q(2,1,1)$, and let $\mathbf{T}$ be the unit vector in the direction from $P$ to $Q$. Then from the definition of a unit vector and (2.23),

$$\mathbf{T} = \frac{\mathbf{r}_2 - \mathbf{r}_1}{|\mathbf{r}_2 - \mathbf{r}_1|} = \frac{(2-1)\,\mathbf{i} + (1-1)\,\mathbf{j} + (1-0)\,\mathbf{k}}{[(2-1)^2 + (1-1)^2 + (1-0)^2]^{1/2}} = \frac{\mathbf{i}+\mathbf{k}}{\sqrt{2}}$$

$$= \frac{1}{\sqrt{2}}\mathbf{i} + \frac{1}{\sqrt{2}}\mathbf{k}$$

$$= \left[\frac{1}{\sqrt{2}},\ 0,\ \frac{1}{\sqrt{2}}\right].$$

Now from (3.110) with given $\phi(x,y,z)$,

$$\nabla\phi = 2x\,\mathbf{i} + 2y\,\mathbf{j} + 2z\,\mathbf{k}.$$

Thus at $(1,1,0)$, the gradient is

$$\nabla\phi = 2\,\mathbf{i} + 2\,\mathbf{j} + 0\,\mathbf{k} = [2,2,0],$$

and its magnitude is

$$|\nabla\phi| = (2^2 + 2^2 + 0)^{1/2} = 2\sqrt{2}.$$

Hence, by (3.106) the directional derivative of $\phi$ at $(1,1,0)$ is

$$\frac{\partial\phi}{\partial s} = \nabla\phi\cdot\mathbf{T} = (2)\left(\frac{1}{\sqrt{2}}\right) + (2)(0) + (0)\left(\frac{1}{\sqrt{2}}\right) = \sqrt{2}.$$

This means that the value of $\phi$ increases by $\sqrt{2}$ per unit distance as it proceeds from $P(1, 1, 0)$ to $Q(2, 1, 1)$.

(b) The maximum value of $\partial\phi/\partial s$ at $(1, 1, 0)$ is $|\nabla\phi| = 2\sqrt{2}$, and its direction is that of $\nabla\phi = [2, 2, 0]$.

**PROBLEM 3.33** Find a unit normal vector $\mathbf{n}$ to the surface given by $z = x^2 + y^2$ at the point $(1, 0, 1)$.

**Solution:** Since $z = x^2 + y^2$, the surface is defined by

$$\phi(x, y, z) \equiv x^2 + y^2 - z = 0.$$

Now the gradient is $\nabla\phi = 2x\mathbf{i} + 2y\mathbf{j} - \mathbf{k}$.

Thus at $(1, 0, 1)$, $\nabla\phi = 2\mathbf{i} - \mathbf{k}$. Hence, from (3.117), the unit vector is

$$\mathbf{n} = \frac{\nabla\phi}{|\nabla\phi|} = \frac{2\mathbf{i} - \mathbf{k}}{[2^2 + 0 + (-1)^2]^{1/2}} = \frac{2\mathbf{i} - \mathbf{k}}{\sqrt{5}} = \left[\frac{2}{\sqrt{5}}, 0, -\frac{1}{\sqrt{5}}\right].$$

**PROBLEM 3.34** For an arbitrary constant vector $\mathbf{a}$, show that

$$\nabla(\mathbf{a}\cdot\mathbf{r}) = \mathbf{a}, \tag{3.119}$$

where $\mathbf{r}$ is the position vector.

**Solution:** Let $\mathbf{a} = [a_1, a_2, a_3]$, and since $\mathbf{r} = [x, y, z]$,

$$\mathbf{a}\cdot\mathbf{r} = a_1x + a_2y + a_3z.$$

Thus,

$$\begin{aligned}\nabla(\mathbf{a}\cdot\mathbf{r}) &= \frac{\partial}{\partial x}(a_1x + a_2y + a_3z)\mathbf{i} + \frac{\partial}{\partial y}(a_1x + a_2y + a_3z)\mathbf{j} + \frac{\partial}{\partial z}(a_1x + a_2y + a_3z)\mathbf{k}\\ &= a_1\mathbf{i} + a_2\mathbf{j} + a_3\mathbf{k}\\ &= \mathbf{a}.\end{aligned}$$

**PROBLEM 3.35** If $\phi = \phi(x, y, z)$, show that

$$\nabla\phi\cdot d\mathbf{r} = d\phi. \tag{3.120}$$

**Solution:** If $\mathbf{r} = x\mathbf{i} + y\mathbf{j} + z\mathbf{k}$, then its differential is

$$d\mathbf{r} = dx\,\mathbf{i} + dy\,\mathbf{j} + dz\,\mathbf{k}.$$

From (3.110), $\nabla\phi = \dfrac{\partial\phi}{\partial x}\mathbf{i} + \dfrac{\partial\phi}{\partial y}\mathbf{j} + \dfrac{\partial\phi}{\partial z}\mathbf{k}$. Hence, on taking the scalar product,

$$\nabla\phi\cdot d\mathbf{r} = \frac{\partial\phi}{\partial x}dx + \frac{\partial\phi}{\partial y}dy + \frac{\partial\phi}{\partial z}dz = d\phi.$$

Identity (3.120) can be written as

$$(d\mathbf{r}\cdot\nabla)\phi = d\phi. \tag{3.121}$$

**PROBLEM 3.36** If $\phi = \phi(x, y, z, t)$, show that

$$d\phi = d\mathbf{r}\cdot\nabla\phi + \frac{\partial\phi}{\partial t}dt. \tag{3.122}$$

**Solution:** If $\phi = \phi(x, y, z, t)$, from calculus, its differential is

$$d\phi = \frac{\partial \phi}{\partial x}\, dx + \frac{\partial \phi}{\partial y}\, dy + \frac{\partial \phi}{\partial z}\, dz + \frac{\partial \phi}{\partial t}\, dt.$$

From the results of Prob. 3.35,

$$d\phi = (\nabla \phi)\cdot d\mathbf{r} + \frac{\partial \phi}{\partial t}\, dt$$

$$= d\mathbf{r}\cdot \nabla \phi + \frac{\partial \phi}{\partial t}\, dt.$$

**PROBLEM 3.37** Find $\nabla \phi$ if $\phi = r = |\mathbf{r}| = (x^2 + y^2 + z^2)^{1/2}$.

**Solution:** The surface defined by $\phi = r = (x^2 + y^2 + z^2)^{1/2}$ = const is a sphere with the center at the origin (0, 0, 0). Hence, according to the result of Prob. 3.31, $\nabla r$ is normal to the sphere, and therefore, it is parallel to the position vector $\mathbf{r} = [x, y, z]$. Thus, we can write $\nabla r = k\mathbf{r}$. Now from (3.120),

$$dr = \nabla r \cdot d\mathbf{r} = k\,\mathbf{r}\cdot d\mathbf{r} = kr\, dr.$$

Thus,

$$k = \frac{1}{r},$$

and hence,

$$\nabla r = \frac{1}{r}\,\mathbf{r} = \mathbf{e}_r, \tag{3.123}$$

where $\mathbf{e}_r$ is the unit vector in the direction of the position vector $\mathbf{r}$.

**Alternate Solution:** From (3.110), the gradient is

$$\nabla r = \nabla (x^2 + y^2 + z^2)^{1/2}$$

$$= \frac{\partial}{\partial x}(x^2 + y^2 + z^2)^{1/2}\,\mathbf{i} + \frac{\partial}{\partial y}(x^2 + y^2 + z^2)^{1/2}\,\mathbf{j} + \frac{\partial}{\partial z}(x^2 + y^2 + z^2)^{1/2}\,\mathbf{k}$$

$$= \frac{1}{2}\,\frac{2x}{(x^2 + y^2 + z^2)^{1/2}}\,\mathbf{i} + \frac{1}{2}\,\frac{2y}{(x^2 + y^2 + z^2)^{1/2}}\,\mathbf{j} + \frac{1}{2}\,\frac{2z}{(x^2 + y^2 + z^2)^{1/2}}\,\mathbf{k}$$

$$= \frac{x}{r}\,\mathbf{i} + \frac{y}{r}\,\mathbf{j} + \frac{z}{r}\,\mathbf{k}$$

$$= \frac{1}{r}\,\mathbf{r}$$

$$= \mathbf{e}_r.$$

**PROBLEM 3.38** If $\phi = \phi(u)$, where $u = u(x, y, z)$, then show that

$$\nabla \phi = \nabla \phi(u) = \phi'(u)\nabla u. \tag{3.124}$$

**Solution:** From (3.110), the gradient is

$$\nabla \phi = \nabla \phi(u) = \frac{\partial \phi}{\partial x}\,\mathbf{i} + \frac{\partial \phi}{\partial y}\,\mathbf{j} + \frac{\partial \phi}{\partial z}\,\mathbf{k}$$

$$= \phi'(u)\,\frac{\partial u}{\partial x}\,\mathbf{i} + \phi'(u)\,\frac{\partial u}{\partial y}\,\mathbf{j} + \phi'(u)\,\frac{\partial u}{\partial z}\,\mathbf{k}$$

$$= \phi'(u)\left(\frac{\partial u}{\partial x}\,\mathbf{i} + \frac{\partial u}{\partial y}\,\mathbf{j} + \frac{\partial u}{\partial z}\,\mathbf{k}\right)$$

$$= \phi'(u)\nabla u.$$

**PROBLEM 3.39** If $r = |\mathbf{r}| = (x^2 + y^2 + z^2)^{1/2}$, find $\nabla r^n$ and $\nabla(1/r)$, where $n$ is any real number.

**Solution:** Let $\phi = \phi(r) = r^n$. Then from (3.124) and the result (3.123) of Prob. 3.37,

$$\begin{aligned}\nabla(r^n) = \frac{d}{dr}(r^n)\nabla r &= nr^{n-1}\nabla r \\ &= nr^{n-1}\mathbf{e}_r \\ &= nr^{n-2}\mathbf{r}.\end{aligned} \tag{3.125}$$

Setting $n = -1$ in (3.125),

$$\nabla\left(\frac{1}{r}\right) = -\frac{1}{r^3}\mathbf{r} = -\frac{1}{r^2}\mathbf{e}_r. \tag{3.126}$$

## 3.7 The Operator $\nabla$

The vector differential operator

$$\nabla = \frac{\partial}{\partial x}\mathbf{i} + \frac{\partial}{\partial y}\mathbf{j} + \frac{\partial}{\partial z}\mathbf{k} \qquad [3.109]$$

is *not* a vector, but an operator. It may be considered as a *symbolic* vector. Thus if $\phi$ is a scalar field, then $\phi\nabla$ is still an operator, whereas $\nabla\phi$ yields the important vector function called the *gradient*. Similarly, if $\mathbf{f}$ is a differentiable vector function, then $\mathbf{f}\cdot\nabla$ and $\mathbf{f}\times\nabla$ are still operators, whereas $\nabla\cdot\mathbf{f}$ and $\nabla\times\mathbf{f}$ yield important scalar and vector functions, respectively. (See Secs. 3.8–9.)

Hence, multiplying $\nabla$ on the left yields operators, while multiplying it on the right yields important scalar and vector functions. In other words, $\nabla$ only operates on what follows it.

## 3.8 Divergence of a Vector Function

If a vector function $\mathbf{f} = [f_1, f_2, f_3]$, where $f_1$, $f_2$, and $f_3$ are scalar functions, then its scalar or dot product with the symbolic vector $\nabla$ is

$$\begin{aligned}\nabla\cdot\mathbf{f} &= \left(\frac{\partial}{\partial x}\mathbf{i} + \frac{\partial}{\partial y}\mathbf{j} + \frac{\partial}{\partial z}\mathbf{k}\right)\cdot(f_1\mathbf{i} + f_2\mathbf{j} + f_3\mathbf{k}) \\ &= \frac{\partial f_1}{\partial x} + \frac{\partial f_2}{\partial y} + \frac{\partial f_3}{\partial z}.\end{aligned}$$

Hence, a vector function $\mathbf{f}$ is transformed into a scalar function when operated on by $\nabla$ from the left. This scalar function is called the *divergence* of the vector function $\mathbf{f}$ and is written as div $\mathbf{f}$. Thus,

$$\operatorname{div}\mathbf{f} = \nabla\cdot\mathbf{f} = \frac{\partial f_1}{\partial x} + \frac{\partial f_2}{\partial y} + \frac{\partial f_3}{\partial z}. \tag{3.127}$$

Although the definition (3.127) does not give any physical or geometrical meaning to the concept of divergence, it gives its easy computational form. Other definitions of divergence, as well as its physical interpretation, are given in Chap. 4.

**PROBLEM 3.40** If $\mathbf{f}$ and $\mathbf{g}$ are two vector functions, show that

$$\nabla\cdot(\mathbf{f}+\mathbf{g}) = \nabla\cdot\mathbf{f} + \nabla\cdot\mathbf{g}. \tag{3.128}$$

**Solution:** Let $\mathbf{f} = [f_1, f_2, f_3]$ and $\mathbf{g} = [g_1, g_2, g_3]$. Then,

$$\mathbf{f} + \mathbf{g} = (f_1 + g_1)\mathbf{i} + (f_2 + g_2)\mathbf{j} + (f_3 + g_3)\mathbf{k}.$$

Now by (3.127),

$$\begin{aligned}\nabla \cdot (\mathbf{f} + \mathbf{g}) &= \frac{\partial}{\partial x}(f_1 + g_1) + \frac{\partial}{\partial y}(f_2 + g_2) + \frac{\partial}{\partial z}(f_3 + g_3)\\ &= \left(\frac{\partial f_1}{\partial x} + \frac{\partial f_2}{\partial y} + \frac{\partial f_3}{\partial z}\right) + \left(\frac{\partial g_1}{\partial x} + \frac{\partial g_2}{\partial y} + \frac{\partial g_3}{\partial z}\right)\\ &= \nabla \cdot \mathbf{f} + \nabla \cdot \mathbf{g}.\end{aligned}$$

**PROBLEM 3.41** If $\mathbf{r}$ is the position vector, find the divergence $\nabla \cdot \mathbf{r}$.

**Solution:** If $\mathbf{r} = x\mathbf{i} + y\mathbf{j} + z\mathbf{k}$, then from (3.127),

$$\nabla \cdot \mathbf{r} = \frac{\partial x}{\partial x} + \frac{\partial y}{\partial y} + \frac{\partial z}{\partial z} = 3. \tag{3.129}$$

**PROBLEM 3.42** Find the divergence of $\mathbf{f} = xyz\,\mathbf{i} + x^2y^2z\,\mathbf{j} + yz^3\mathbf{k}$.

**Solution:** From (3.127), the divergence is

$$\begin{aligned}\text{div}\,\mathbf{f} = \nabla \cdot \mathbf{f} &= \frac{\partial f_1}{\partial x} + \frac{\partial f_2}{\partial y} + \frac{\partial f_3}{\partial z}\\ &= \frac{\partial}{\partial x}(xyz) + \frac{\partial}{\partial y}(x^2y^2z) + \frac{\partial}{\partial z}(yz^3)\\ &= yz + 2x^2yz + 3yz^2.\end{aligned} \tag{3.130}$$

If $\phi$ is a scalar function, then the *divergence of the gradient* of $\phi$ is

$$\text{div}\,(\text{grad}\,\phi) = \frac{\partial^2\phi}{\partial x^2} + \frac{\partial^2\phi}{\partial y^2} + \frac{\partial^2\phi}{\partial z^2}. \tag{3.131}$$

**PROBLEM 3.43** Verify (3.131).

**Solution:** The gradient is

$$\nabla\phi = \frac{\partial\phi}{\partial x}\mathbf{i} + \frac{\partial\phi}{\partial y}\mathbf{j} + \frac{\partial\phi}{\partial z}\mathbf{k}.$$

Hence,

$$\begin{aligned}\text{div}\,(\text{grad}\,\phi) = \nabla \cdot (\nabla\phi) &= \frac{\partial}{\partial x}\left(\frac{\partial\phi}{\partial x}\right) + \frac{\partial}{\partial y}\left(\frac{\partial\phi}{\partial y}\right) + \frac{\partial}{\partial z}\left(\frac{\partial\phi}{\partial z}\right)\\ &= \frac{\partial^2\phi}{\partial x^2} + \frac{\partial^2\phi}{\partial y^2} + \frac{\partial^2\phi}{\partial z^2}.\end{aligned}$$

The divergence of the gradient $\nabla \cdot \nabla$ is written as $\nabla^2$. Then $\nabla \cdot (\nabla\phi)$ is written as $\nabla \cdot \nabla\phi = \nabla^2\phi$. The operator $\nabla^2$ is called the Laplacian; i.e.,

$$\text{Laplacian} = \nabla^2 = \frac{\partial^2}{\partial x^2} + \frac{\partial^2}{\partial y^2} + \frac{\partial^2}{\partial z^2}, \tag{3.132}$$

$$\nabla^2\phi = \left(\frac{\partial^2}{\partial x^2} + \frac{\partial^2}{\partial y^2} + \frac{\partial^2}{\partial z^2}\right)\phi = \frac{\partial^2\phi}{\partial x^2} + \frac{\partial^2\phi}{\partial y^2} + \frac{\partial^2\phi}{\partial z^2}. \qquad [3.131]$$

A scalar function $\phi$ is said to be *harmonic* if it is continuous, has continuous second partial derivatives, and satisfies *Laplace's equation*

$$\nabla^2 \phi = 0. \tag{3.133}$$

**PROBLEM 3.44** Show that the function $1/r$, where $r = |\mathbf{r}| = (x^2 + y^2 + z^2)^{1/2}$, is a harmonic function, provided $r \neq 0$.

**Solution:** Clearly $1/r$ is continuous because $x^2$, $y^2$, $z^2$, and $r$ are continuous. Then from (3.131), the Laplacian is

$$\nabla^2\left(\frac{1}{r}\right) = \left(\frac{\partial^2}{\partial x^2} + \frac{\partial^2}{\partial y^2} + \frac{\partial^2}{\partial z^2}\right)(x^2 + y^2 + z^2)^{-1/2}.$$

Now the first and second partial derivatives of $1/r$ with respect to $x$ are

$$\frac{\partial}{\partial x}(x^2 + y^2 + z^2)^{-1/2} = -x(x^2 + y^2 + z^2)^{-3/2},$$

$$\begin{aligned}\frac{\partial^2}{\partial x^2}(x^2 + y^2 + z^2)^{-1/2} &= \frac{\partial}{\partial x}[-x(x^2 + y^2 + z^2)^{-3/2}]\\ &= 3x^2(x^2 + y^2 + z^2)^{-5/2} - (x^2 + y^2 + z^2)^{-3/2}\\ &= 3x^2 r^{-5} - r^{-3}.\end{aligned} \tag{3.134}$$

Similarly, the second partial derivatives of $1/r$ with respect to $y$ and $z$ are

$$\frac{\partial^2}{\partial y^2}(x^2 + y^2 + z^2)^{-1/2} = 3y^2 r^{-5} - r^{-3}, \tag{3.135}$$

$$\frac{\partial^2}{\partial z^2}(x^2 + y^2 + z^2)^{-1/2} = 3z^2 r^{-5} - r^{-3}. \tag{3.136}$$

Since $x$, $y$, $z$, and $r$ are continuous, the second partial derivatives are also continuous if $r \neq 0$.

Adding (3.134–6),

$$\nabla^2\left(\frac{1}{r}\right) = 3r^{-5}(x^2 + y^2 + z^2) - 3r^{-3} = 3r^{-5}r^2 - 3r^{-3} = 3r^{-3} - 3r^{-3} = 0, \tag{3.137}$$

provided $r \neq 0$. Thus Laplace's equation is satisfied, and the function $1/r$ is harmonic.

## 3.9 Curl of a Vector Function

If a vector function $\mathbf{f} = [f_1, f_2, f_3]$, where $f_1$, $f_2$, and $f_3$ are scalar functions with continuous first derivatives, then its vector or cross product with the symbolic vector $\nabla$ is

$$\begin{aligned}\nabla \times \mathbf{f} &= \left(\frac{\partial}{\partial x}\mathbf{i} + \frac{\partial}{\partial y}\mathbf{j} + \frac{\partial}{\partial z}\mathbf{k}\right) \times (f_1\mathbf{i} + f_2\mathbf{j} + f_3\mathbf{k})\\ &= \begin{vmatrix} \mathbf{i} & \mathbf{j} & \mathbf{k} \\ \frac{\partial}{\partial x} & \frac{\partial}{\partial y} & \frac{\partial}{\partial z} \\ f_1 & f_2 & f_3 \end{vmatrix}\\ &= \left(\frac{\partial f_3}{\partial y} - \frac{\partial f_2}{\partial z}\right)\mathbf{i} + \left(\frac{\partial f_1}{\partial z} - \frac{\partial f_3}{\partial x}\right)\mathbf{j} + \left(\frac{\partial f_2}{\partial x} - \frac{\partial f_1}{\partial y}\right)\mathbf{k}.\end{aligned} \tag{3.138}$$

We call this vector function the *curl* (curl **f**) or *rotation* (rot **f**) of the vector function **f**; i.e.,

$$\text{curl or rot } \mathbf{f} = \nabla \times \mathbf{f}. \tag{3.139}$$

It should be noted that $\nabla \times \mathbf{f}$ is not necessarily perpendicular to **f**, although we treat $\nabla$ as a symbolic vector. The physical meaning of the curl of **f** is discussed in Chap. 4.

**PROBLEM 3.45** If **f** and **g** are two vector functions, show that

$$\nabla \times (\mathbf{f} + \mathbf{g}) = \nabla \times \mathbf{f} + \nabla \times \mathbf{g}. \tag{3.140}$$

**Solution:** Let $\mathbf{f} = [f_1, f_2, f_3]$ and $\mathbf{g} = [g_1, g_2, g_3]$. Then,

$$\mathbf{f} + \mathbf{g} = (f_1 + g_1)\,\mathbf{i} + (f_2 + g_2)\,\mathbf{j} + (f_3 + g_3)\,\mathbf{k}.$$

Hence,

$$\begin{aligned}\nabla \times (\mathbf{f} + \mathbf{g}) &= \left[\frac{\partial (f_3 + g_3)}{\partial y} - \frac{\partial (f_2 + g_2)}{\partial z}, \ldots\right] \\ &= \left(\frac{\partial f_3}{\partial y} - \frac{\partial f_2}{\partial z}, \ldots\right) + \left(\frac{\partial g_3}{\partial y} - \frac{\partial g_2}{\partial z}, \ldots\right) \\ &= \nabla \times \mathbf{f} + \nabla \times \mathbf{g}.\end{aligned}$$

**PROBLEM 3.46** If **r** is the position vector, find $\nabla \times \mathbf{r}$.

**Solution:** Since $\mathbf{r} = x\,\mathbf{i} + y\,\mathbf{j} + z\,\mathbf{k}$, from (3.138), the curl is

$$\nabla \times \mathbf{r} = \begin{vmatrix} \mathbf{i} & \mathbf{j} & \mathbf{k} \\ \dfrac{\partial}{\partial x} & \dfrac{\partial}{\partial y} & \dfrac{\partial}{\partial z} \\ x & y & z \end{vmatrix} = \mathbf{0}. \tag{3.141}$$

**PROBLEM 3.47** Find the curl of $\mathbf{f} = xyz\,\mathbf{i} + x^2y^2z\,\mathbf{j} + yz^3\,\mathbf{k}$.

**Solution:** From (3.138), the curl is

$$\begin{aligned}\nabla \times \mathbf{f} &= \begin{vmatrix} \mathbf{i} & \mathbf{j} & \mathbf{k} \\ \dfrac{\partial}{\partial x} & \dfrac{\partial}{\partial y} & \dfrac{\partial}{\partial z} \\ xyz & x^2y^2z & yz^3 \end{vmatrix} \\ &= \left[\frac{\partial}{\partial y}(yz^3) - \frac{\partial}{\partial z}(x^2y^2z)\right]\mathbf{i} + \left[\frac{\partial}{\partial z}(xyz) - \frac{\partial}{\partial x}(yz^3)\right]\mathbf{j} \\ &\quad + \left[\frac{\partial}{\partial x}(x^2y^2z) - \frac{\partial}{\partial y}(xyz)\right]\mathbf{k} \\ &= (z^3 - x^2y^2)\,\mathbf{i} + (xy)\,\mathbf{j} + (2\,xy^2z - xz)\,\mathbf{k}.\end{aligned}$$

If $\phi$ is a scalar function with continuous second derivatives, then the *curl of the gradient* of $\phi$ is the zero vector; i.e.,

$$\nabla \times (\nabla \phi) = \mathbf{0}. \tag{3.142}$$

**PROBLEM 3.48** Verify (3.142)

**Solution:** The gradient of $\phi$ is

$$\nabla\phi = \frac{\partial\phi}{\partial x}\mathbf{i} + \frac{\partial\phi}{\partial y}\mathbf{j} + \frac{\partial\phi}{\partial z}\mathbf{k}.$$

Hence, assuming that $\phi$ has continuous second partial derivatives,

$$\nabla\times(\nabla\phi) = \begin{vmatrix} \mathbf{i} & \mathbf{j} & \mathbf{k} \\ \frac{\partial}{\partial x} & \frac{\partial}{\partial y} & \frac{\partial}{\partial z} \\ \frac{\partial\phi}{\partial x} & \frac{\partial\phi}{\partial y} & \frac{\partial\phi}{\partial z} \end{vmatrix}$$

$$= \left(\frac{\partial^2\phi}{\partial y\,\partial z} - \frac{\partial^2\phi}{\partial z\,\partial y}\right)\mathbf{i} + \left(\frac{\partial^2\phi}{\partial z\,\partial x} - \frac{\partial^2\phi}{\partial x\,\partial z}\right)\mathbf{j} + \left(\frac{\partial^2\phi}{\partial x\,\partial y} - \frac{\partial^2\phi}{\partial y\,\partial x}\right)\mathbf{k}$$

$$= \mathbf{0}$$

since the second derivatives are continuous, and hence,

$$\frac{\partial^2\phi}{\partial y\,\partial z} = \frac{\partial^2\phi}{\partial z\,\partial y}, \quad \frac{\partial^2\phi}{\partial z\,\partial x} = \frac{\partial^2\phi}{\partial x\,\partial z}, \quad \frac{\partial^2\phi}{\partial x\,\partial y} = \frac{\partial^2\phi}{\partial y\,\partial x}.$$

If the vector function $\mathbf{f} = [f_1, f_2, f_3]$, where the scalar components $f_1$, $f_2$, and $f_3$ have continuous second derivatives, then the *divergence of the curl* of $\mathbf{f}$ *is zero*; that is,

$$\nabla\cdot(\nabla\times\mathbf{f}) = 0. \tag{3.143}$$

**PROBLEM 3.49** Verify (3.143).

**Solution:** If $\mathbf{f} = f_1\mathbf{i} + f_2\mathbf{j} + f_3\mathbf{k}$, then from (3.138), its curl is

$$\nabla\times\mathbf{f} = \left(\frac{\partial f_3}{\partial y} - \frac{\partial f_2}{\partial z}\right)\mathbf{i} + \left(\frac{\partial f_1}{\partial z} - \frac{\partial f_3}{\partial x}\right)\mathbf{j} + \left(\frac{\partial f_2}{\partial x} - \frac{\partial f_1}{\partial y}\right)\mathbf{k}.$$

Hence, assuming that $\mathbf{f}$ has continuous second partial derivatives, from (3.127), the divergence of the curl is

$$\nabla\cdot(\nabla\times\mathbf{f}) = \frac{\partial}{\partial x}\left(\frac{\partial f_3}{\partial y} - \frac{\partial f_2}{\partial z}\right) + \frac{\partial}{\partial y}\left(\frac{\partial f_1}{\partial z} - \frac{\partial f_3}{\partial x}\right) + \frac{\partial}{\partial z}\left(\frac{\partial f_2}{\partial x} - \frac{\partial f_1}{\partial y}\right)$$

$$= \frac{\partial^2 f_3}{\partial x\,\partial y} - \frac{\partial^2 f_2}{\partial x\,\partial z} + \frac{\partial^2 f_1}{\partial y\,\partial z} - \frac{\partial^2 f_3}{\partial y\,\partial x} + \frac{\partial^2 f_2}{\partial z\,\partial x} - \frac{\partial^2 f_1}{\partial z\,\partial y}$$

$$= 0$$

since the second derivatives are continuous, and, hence,

$$\frac{\partial^2 f_3}{\partial x\,\partial y} = \frac{\partial^2 f_3}{\partial y\,\partial x}, \quad \frac{\partial^2 f_2}{\partial x\,\partial z} = \frac{\partial^2 f_2}{\partial z\,\partial x}, \quad \frac{\partial^2 f_1}{\partial y\,\partial z} = \frac{\partial^2 f_1}{\partial z\,\partial y}.$$

**PROBLEM 3.50** Show that if $\mathbf{B} = \nabla\times\mathbf{A}$, then $\mathbf{A}$ is not uniquely determined by $\mathbf{B}$.

**Solution:** If $\psi$ is any arbitrary scalar function, let

$$\mathbf{A}' = \mathbf{A} + \nabla\psi. \tag{3.144}$$

Then from (3.140), the curl of $\mathbf{A}'$ is

$$\begin{aligned} \nabla\times\mathbf{A}' &= \nabla\times(\mathbf{A} + \nabla\psi) \\ &= \nabla\times\mathbf{A} + \nabla\times(\nabla\psi) \\ &= \nabla\times\mathbf{A} \end{aligned} \tag{3.145}$$

since $\nabla \times (\nabla \psi) = \mathbf{0}$ from (3.142). Thus $\mathbf{B}$ can be expressed as $\mathbf{B} = \nabla \times \mathbf{A}'$, which indicates that $\mathbf{A}$ is not uniquely determined from $\mathbf{B}$, because $\psi$ is arbitrary.

## 3.10 Operations with $\nabla$ and Some Vector Identities

Using the operator $\nabla$, we have defined gradient, divergence, and curl to obtain vector and scalar quantities. In this section, we shall consider the various combinations of the operator $\nabla$ and the vector and scalar functions.

It should be stressed that the order in which the symbols appear in expressions using $\nabla$ is very important, because the operator $\nabla$ only operates on what follows. Thus, for example,

$$(\mathbf{f} \cdot \nabla)\mathbf{g} \neq \mathbf{g}(\mathbf{f} \cdot \nabla).$$

The left side of this expression is a vector field, while the right side is an operator. (See Prob. 3.51.)

**PROBLEM 3.51** Determine the meaning that can be assigned to $(\mathbf{f} \cdot \nabla)\phi$ and $(\mathbf{f} \cdot \nabla)\mathbf{g}$. (See Prob. 3.35.)

**Solution:** Since $\nabla$ is a differential operator with respect to the space coordinates, it only operates on what follows. Thus we interpret $(\mathbf{f} \cdot \nabla)\phi$ as the dot product of the vector $\mathbf{f}$ and the gradient $\nabla\phi$; i.e.,

$$(\mathbf{f} \cdot \nabla)\phi = \mathbf{f} \cdot (\nabla\phi). \tag{3.146}$$

Similar results can be obtained by interpreting $\nabla$ as a symbolic vector; i.e.,

$$\nabla = \frac{\partial}{\partial x}\mathbf{i} + \frac{\partial}{\partial y}\mathbf{j} + \frac{\partial}{\partial z}\mathbf{k}.$$

Then taking its left scalar product with $\mathbf{f}$,

$$\mathbf{f} \cdot \nabla = f_1 \frac{\partial}{\partial x} + f_2 \frac{\partial}{\partial y} + f_3 \frac{\partial}{\partial z}. \tag{3.147}$$

Thus,

$$\begin{aligned}(\mathbf{f} \cdot \nabla)\phi &= \left(f_1 \frac{\partial}{\partial x} + f_2 \frac{\partial}{\partial y} + f_3 \frac{\partial}{\partial z}\right)\phi \\ &= f_1 \frac{\partial \phi}{\partial x} + f_2 \frac{\partial \phi}{\partial y} + f_3 \frac{\partial \phi}{\partial z} \\ &= \mathbf{f} \cdot (\nabla\phi).\end{aligned}$$

Since $\nabla \mathbf{g}$ is not defined, we use the differential operator (3.147) that operates on $\mathbf{g}$ to obtain

$$\begin{aligned}(\mathbf{f} \cdot \nabla)\mathbf{g} &= \left(f_1 \frac{\partial}{\partial x} + f_2 \frac{\partial}{\partial y} + f_3 \frac{\partial}{\partial z}\right)\mathbf{g} \\ &= f_1 \frac{\partial \mathbf{g}}{\partial x} + f_2 \frac{\partial \mathbf{g}}{\partial y} + f_3 \frac{\partial \mathbf{g}}{\partial z}.\end{aligned} \tag{3.148}$$

**PROBLEM 3.52** Find $(\mathbf{f} \cdot \nabla)\phi$ and $(\mathbf{f} \cdot \nabla)\mathbf{g}$ at (1, 1, 1) if $\mathbf{f} = -y\mathbf{i} + x\mathbf{j} + z\mathbf{k}$, $\mathbf{g} = 3xyz^2\mathbf{i} + 2xy^3\mathbf{j} - x^2yz\mathbf{k}$, and $\phi = xyz$.

**Solution:** Since

$$\nabla\phi = \frac{\partial}{\partial x}(xyz)\,\mathbf{i} + \frac{\partial}{\partial y}(xyz)\,\mathbf{j} + \frac{\partial}{\partial z}(xyz)\,\mathbf{k} = yz\,\mathbf{i} + xz\,\mathbf{j} + xy\,\mathbf{k},$$

we have

$$(\mathbf{f}\cdot\nabla)\phi = \mathbf{f}\cdot\nabla\phi = (-y)(yz) + (x)(xz) + (z)(xy)$$
$$= -y^2z + x^2z + xyz.$$

Then at (1, 1, 1), $(\mathbf{f}\cdot\nabla)\phi = -1 + 1 + 1 = 1$.

Multiplying $\mathbf{f}\cdot\nabla$ by g on the right yields

$$(\mathbf{f}\cdot\nabla)\,\mathbf{g} = (-y)\frac{\partial}{\partial x}(3xyz^2\mathbf{i} + 2xy^3\mathbf{j} - x^2yz\mathbf{k})$$
$$+ (x)\frac{\partial}{\partial y}(3xyz^2\mathbf{i} + 2xy^3\mathbf{j} - x^2yz\mathbf{k})$$
$$+ (z)\frac{\partial}{\partial z}(3xyz^2\mathbf{i} + 2xy^3\mathbf{j} - x^2yz\mathbf{k})$$
$$= (-y)(3yz^2\mathbf{i} + 2y^3\mathbf{j} - 2xyz\mathbf{k}) + (x)(3xz^2\mathbf{i} + 6xy^2\mathbf{j} - x^2z\mathbf{k})$$
$$+ (z)(6xyz\,\mathbf{i} - x^2y\mathbf{k})$$
$$= (-3y^2z^2 + 3x^2z^2 + 6xyz^2)\mathbf{i} + (-2y^4 + 6x^2y^2)\mathbf{j}$$
$$+ (2xy^2z - x^3z - x^2yz)\mathbf{k}.$$

Then at (1, 1, 1),

$$(\mathbf{f}\cdot\nabla)\,\mathbf{g} = (-3 + 3 + 6)\,\mathbf{i} + (-2 + 6)\,\mathbf{j} + (2 - 1 - 1)\,\mathbf{k} = 4\mathbf{j} = [0, 4, 0].$$

**PROBLEM 3.53** If $\mathbf{r}$ is the position vector, show that

$$(\mathbf{f}\cdot\nabla)\,\mathbf{r} = \mathbf{f}. \tag{3.149}$$

**Solution:** If $\mathbf{r} = x\,\mathbf{i} + y\,\mathbf{j} + z\,\mathbf{k}$, then

$$(\mathbf{f}\cdot\nabla)\,\mathbf{r} = f_1\frac{\partial\mathbf{r}}{\partial x} + f_2\frac{\partial\mathbf{r}}{\partial y} + f_3\frac{\partial\mathbf{r}}{\partial z}$$
$$= f_1\,\mathbf{i} + f_2\,\mathbf{j} + f_3\,\mathbf{k}$$
$$= \mathbf{f}.$$

**PROBLEM 3.54** Show that

$$(d\mathbf{r}\cdot\nabla)\,\mathbf{f} = d\mathbf{f}. \tag{3.150}$$

**Solution:** From (3.147),

$$d\mathbf{r}\cdot\nabla = dx\frac{\partial}{\partial x} + dy\frac{\partial}{\partial y} + dz\frac{\partial}{\partial z}.$$

Hence,

$$(d\mathbf{r}\cdot\nabla)\,\mathbf{f} = dx\frac{\partial\mathbf{f}}{\partial x} + dy\frac{\partial\mathbf{f}}{\partial y} + dz\frac{\partial\mathbf{f}}{\partial z}$$
$$= \frac{\partial\mathbf{f}}{\partial x}dx + \frac{\partial\mathbf{f}}{\partial y}dy + \frac{\partial\mathbf{f}}{\partial z}dz$$
$$= d\mathbf{f}.$$

**PROBLEM 3.55** If $\mathbf{f} = \mathbf{f}(x, y, z, t)$, then show that

$$d\mathbf{f} = (d\mathbf{r}\cdot\nabla)\mathbf{f} + \frac{\partial \mathbf{f}}{\partial t}\,dt. \tag{3.151}$$

**Solution:** Since $\mathbf{f} = \mathbf{f}(x, y, z, t)$, we have from the definition of differentials,

$$\begin{aligned} d\mathbf{f} &= \frac{\partial \mathbf{f}}{\partial x}\,dx + \frac{\partial \mathbf{f}}{\partial y}\,dy + \frac{\partial \mathbf{f}}{\partial z}\,dz + \frac{\partial \mathbf{f}}{\partial t}\,dt \\ &= dx\,\frac{\partial \mathbf{f}}{\partial x} + dy\,\frac{\partial \mathbf{f}}{\partial y} + dz\,\frac{\partial \mathbf{f}}{\partial z} + \frac{\partial \mathbf{f}}{\partial t}\,dt \\ &= (d\mathbf{r}\cdot\nabla)\mathbf{f} + \frac{\partial \mathbf{f}}{\partial t}\,dt. \end{aligned}$$

**PROBLEM 3.56** Determine the meaning that can be given to $(\mathbf{f}\times\nabla)\phi$ and $(\mathbf{f}\times\nabla)\mathbf{g}$.

**Solution:** Since the operator $\nabla$ only operates on what follows, we interpret $(\mathbf{f}\times\nabla)\phi$ as the vector product of $\mathbf{f}$ and the gradient $\nabla\phi$; i.e.,

$$(\mathbf{f}\times\nabla)\phi = \mathbf{f}\times(\nabla\phi). \tag{3.152}$$

Similar results can be obtained by interpreting $\nabla$ as a symbolic vector; i.e.,

$$\nabla = \frac{\partial}{\partial x}\mathbf{i} + \frac{\partial}{\partial y}\mathbf{j} + \frac{\partial}{\partial z}\mathbf{k}.$$

Since $\mathbf{f}\times\nabla$ is an operator,

$$\begin{aligned} \mathbf{f}\times\nabla &= \begin{vmatrix} \mathbf{i} & \mathbf{j} & \mathbf{k} \\ f_1 & f_2 & f_3 \\ \frac{\partial}{\partial x} & \frac{\partial}{\partial y} & \frac{\partial}{\partial z} \end{vmatrix} \\ &= \left(f_2\frac{\partial}{\partial z} - f_3\frac{\partial}{\partial y}\right)\mathbf{i} + \left(f_3\frac{\partial}{\partial x} - f_1\frac{\partial}{\partial z}\right)\mathbf{j} + \left(f_1\frac{\partial}{\partial y} - f_2\frac{\partial}{\partial x}\right)\mathbf{k}. \end{aligned} \tag{3.153}$$

Thus,

$$\begin{aligned} (\mathbf{f}\times\nabla)\phi &= \left[\left(f_2\frac{\partial}{\partial z} - f_3\frac{\partial}{\partial y}\right)\mathbf{i} + \left(f_3\frac{\partial}{\partial x} - f_1\frac{\partial}{\partial z}\right)\mathbf{j} + \left(f_1\frac{\partial}{\partial y} - f_2\frac{\partial}{\partial x}\right)\mathbf{k}\right]\phi \\ &= \left(f_2\frac{\partial\phi}{\partial z} - f_3\frac{\partial\phi}{\partial y}\right)\mathbf{i} + \left(f_3\frac{\partial\phi}{\partial x} - f_1\frac{\partial\phi}{\partial z}\right)\mathbf{j} + \left(f_1\frac{\partial\phi}{\partial y} - f_2\frac{\partial\phi}{\partial x}\right)\mathbf{k} \\ &= \mathbf{f}\times(\nabla\phi). \end{aligned}$$

No definition is assigned to $(\mathbf{f}\times\nabla)\mathbf{g}$, since it is a kind of a differential operator with vector quantities.

Even though no meaning is assigned to quantities such as $\nabla\mathbf{g}$ and $(\mathbf{f}\times\nabla)\mathbf{g}$, they are generalizations of vectors and are called *dyadics*. Formally, a dyadic is a generalization of a vector.

**PROBLEM 3.57** If $\mathbf{f}$ and $\mathbf{g}$ are two vector functions, show that

$$(\mathbf{f}\times\nabla)\cdot\mathbf{g} = \mathbf{f}\cdot(\nabla\times\mathbf{g}). \tag{3.154}$$

**Solution:** From (3.153),

$$(\mathbf{f}\times\nabla)\cdot\mathbf{g} = \left(f_2\frac{\partial}{\partial z} - f_3\frac{\partial}{\partial y}\right)(\mathbf{i}\cdot\mathbf{g}) + \left(f_3\frac{\partial}{\partial x} - f_1\frac{\partial}{\partial z}\right)(\mathbf{j}\cdot\mathbf{g}) + \left(f_1\frac{\partial}{\partial y} - f_2\frac{\partial}{\partial x}\right)(\mathbf{k}\cdot\mathbf{g})$$

$$= \left(f_2\frac{\partial g_1}{\partial z} - f_3\frac{\partial g_1}{\partial y}\right) + \left(f_3\frac{\partial g_2}{\partial x} - f_1\frac{\partial g_2}{\partial z}\right) + \left(f_1\frac{\partial g_3}{\partial y} - f_2\frac{\partial g_3}{\partial x}\right)$$

$$= f_1\left(\frac{\partial g_3}{\partial y} - \frac{\partial g_2}{\partial z}\right) + f_2\left(\frac{\partial g_1}{\partial z} - \frac{\partial g_3}{\partial x}\right) + f_3\left(\frac{\partial g_2}{\partial x} - \frac{\partial g_1}{\partial y}\right)$$

$$= \mathbf{f}\cdot(\nabla\times\mathbf{g})$$

since $\mathbf{i}\cdot\mathbf{g} = g_1$, $\mathbf{j}\cdot\mathbf{g} = g_2$, and $\mathbf{k}\cdot\mathbf{g} = g_3$.

Now we shall consider a group of well-known vector identities that involve the operator $\nabla$. Although these identities can all be verified by direct expansion using the components of the vector function, we shall establish these identities heuristically by treating $\nabla$ as a symbolic vector as well as a differential operator. Then the expressions are manipulated according to the appropriate formulas from vector algebra. In the final result $\nabla$ is given its operational meaning.

**PROBLEM 3.58** Prove that

$$\nabla\cdot(\phi\mathbf{f}) = \phi\nabla\cdot\mathbf{f} + \mathbf{f}\cdot\nabla\phi. \tag{3.155}$$

**Solution:** Since $\nabla$ is a differential operator, the rule for the differentiation of a product can be expressed as

$$\nabla\cdot(\phi\mathbf{f}) = \nabla_\phi\cdot(\phi\mathbf{f}) + \nabla_\mathbf{f}\cdot(\phi\mathbf{f}).$$

The dot product $\nabla_\phi\cdot(\phi\mathbf{f})$ means that $\mathbf{f}$ is fixed and $\nabla$ operates on $\phi$. Similarly, $\nabla_\mathbf{f}\cdot(\phi\mathbf{f})$ means that $\phi$ is fixed and $\nabla$ operates on $\mathbf{f}$. Since $\nabla\cdot\phi$ is not defined,

$$\nabla_\phi\cdot(\phi\mathbf{f}) = \mathbf{f}\cdot\nabla\phi,$$

$$\nabla_\mathbf{f}\cdot(\phi\mathbf{f}) = \phi\nabla\cdot\mathbf{f}.$$

Adding the above two equations,

$$\nabla\cdot(\phi\mathbf{f}) = \mathbf{f}\cdot\nabla\phi + \phi\cdot\nabla\mathbf{f}.$$

**Alternate Solution:** By using components,

$$\nabla\cdot(\phi\mathbf{f}) = \frac{\partial}{\partial x}(\phi f_1) + \frac{\partial}{\partial y}(\phi f_2) + \frac{\partial}{\partial z}(\phi f_3)$$

$$= \phi\frac{\partial f_1}{\partial x} + f_1\frac{\partial\phi}{\partial x} + \phi\frac{\partial f_2}{\partial y} + f_2\frac{\partial\phi}{\partial y} + \phi\frac{\partial f_3}{\partial z} + f_3\frac{\partial\phi}{\partial z}$$

$$= \phi\left(\frac{\partial f_1}{\partial x} + \frac{\partial f_2}{\partial y} + \frac{\partial f_3}{\partial z}\right) + \left(f_1\frac{\partial\phi}{\partial x} + f_2\frac{\partial\phi}{\partial y} + f_3\frac{\partial\phi}{\partial z}\right)$$

$$= \phi\nabla\cdot\mathbf{f} + \mathbf{f}\cdot\nabla\phi.$$

**PROBLEM 3.59** Prove that

$$\nabla\times(\phi\mathbf{f}) = \phi\nabla\times\mathbf{f} + (\nabla\phi)\times\mathbf{f} = \phi\nabla\times\mathbf{f} - \mathbf{f}\times\nabla\phi. \tag{3.156}$$

**Solution:** Since $\nabla\times(\phi\mathbf{f}) = \nabla_\phi\times(\phi\mathbf{f}) + \nabla_\mathbf{f}\times(\phi\mathbf{f})$ and $\nabla\times\phi$ is not defined,

$$\nabla_\phi \times (\phi \mathbf{f}) = (\nabla\phi) \times \mathbf{f} = -\mathbf{f} \times \nabla\phi,$$
$$\nabla_\mathbf{f} \times (\phi \mathbf{f}) = \phi\nabla \times \mathbf{f}.$$

Hence, adding these two equations,

$$\nabla \times (\phi \mathbf{f}) = (\nabla\phi) \times \mathbf{f} + \phi\nabla \times \mathbf{f} = \phi\nabla \times \mathbf{f} - \mathbf{f} \times \nabla\phi.$$

**PROBLEM 3.60** Prove that

$$\nabla \cdot (\mathbf{f} \times \mathbf{g}) = \mathbf{g} \cdot (\nabla \times \mathbf{f}) - \mathbf{f} \cdot (\nabla \times \mathbf{g}). \tag{3.157}$$

**Solution:** We can write

$$\nabla \cdot (\mathbf{f} \times \mathbf{g}) = \nabla_\mathbf{f} \cdot (\mathbf{f} \times \mathbf{g}) + \nabla_\mathbf{g} \cdot (\mathbf{f} \times \mathbf{g}),$$

where the subscripts have the same significance as before; that is, $\nabla_\mathbf{f} \cdot (\mathbf{f} \times \mathbf{g})$ means that $\mathbf{g}$ is fixed and $\nabla$ operates on $\mathbf{f}$. From (1.77),

$$\nabla_\mathbf{f} \cdot (\mathbf{f} \times \mathbf{g}) = \mathbf{g} \cdot \nabla \times \mathbf{f},$$
$$\nabla_\mathbf{g} \cdot (\mathbf{f} \times \mathbf{g}) = -\mathbf{f} \cdot \nabla \times \mathbf{g}.$$

Thus,

$$\nabla \cdot (\mathbf{f} \times \mathbf{g}) = \mathbf{g} \cdot \nabla \times \mathbf{f} - \mathbf{f} \cdot \nabla \times \mathbf{g}.$$

**PROBLEM 3.61** Verify

$$\nabla \times (\mathbf{f} \times \mathbf{g}) = \mathbf{f}(\nabla \cdot \mathbf{g}) - \mathbf{g}(\nabla \cdot \mathbf{f}) + (\mathbf{g} \cdot \nabla)\mathbf{f} - (\mathbf{f} \cdot \nabla)\mathbf{g}. \tag{3.158}$$

**Solution:** Since $\nabla \times (\mathbf{f} \times \mathbf{g}) = \nabla_\mathbf{f} \times (\mathbf{f} \times \mathbf{g}) + \nabla_\mathbf{g} \times (\mathbf{f} \times \mathbf{g})$, applying the middle-term rule for the triple vector product (1.83) gives

$$\nabla_\mathbf{f} \times (\mathbf{f} \times \mathbf{g}) = (\mathbf{g} \cdot \nabla)\mathbf{f} - \mathbf{g}(\nabla \cdot \mathbf{f}),$$
$$\nabla_\mathbf{g} \times (\mathbf{f} \times \mathbf{g}) = \mathbf{f}(\nabla \cdot \mathbf{g}) - (\mathbf{f} \cdot \nabla)\mathbf{g}.$$

Hence,

$$\nabla \times (\mathbf{f} \times \mathbf{g}) = \mathbf{f}(\nabla \cdot \mathbf{g}) - \mathbf{g}(\nabla \cdot \mathbf{f}) + (\mathbf{g} \cdot \nabla)\mathbf{f} - (\mathbf{f} \cdot \nabla)\mathbf{g}.$$

The quantities $(\mathbf{g} \cdot \nabla)\mathbf{f}$ and $(\mathbf{f} \cdot \nabla)\mathbf{g}$ are defined in (3.148).

**PROBLEM 3.62** Prove that

$$\nabla(\mathbf{f} \cdot \mathbf{g}) = \mathbf{f} \times (\nabla \times \mathbf{g}) + \mathbf{g} \times (\nabla \times \mathbf{f}) + (\mathbf{f} \cdot \nabla)\mathbf{g} + (\mathbf{g} \cdot \nabla)\mathbf{f}. \tag{3.159}$$

**Solution:** Apply the middle-term rule for the triple vector product (1.83) to $\mathbf{f} \times (\nabla \times \mathbf{g})$, where the vector function $\mathbf{f}$ is a constant. Then,

$$\mathbf{f} \times (\nabla \times \mathbf{g}) = \nabla_\mathbf{g}(\mathbf{f} \cdot \mathbf{g}) - (\mathbf{f} \cdot \nabla)\mathbf{g}. \tag{3.160}$$

Hence,

$$\nabla_\mathbf{g}(\mathbf{f} \cdot \mathbf{g}) = \mathbf{f} \times (\nabla \times \mathbf{g}) + (\mathbf{f} \cdot \nabla)\mathbf{g}, \tag{3.161}$$

and interchanging $\mathbf{f}$ and $\mathbf{g}$,

$$\nabla_\mathbf{f}(\mathbf{g} \cdot \mathbf{f}) = \nabla_\mathbf{f}(\mathbf{f} \cdot \mathbf{g}) = \mathbf{g} \times (\nabla \times \mathbf{f}) + (\mathbf{g} \cdot \nabla)\mathbf{f}. \tag{3.162}$$

Consequently, using (3.161-2),

$$\begin{aligned}\nabla(\mathbf{f} \cdot \mathbf{g}) &= \nabla_\mathbf{f}(\mathbf{f} \cdot \mathbf{g}) + \nabla_\mathbf{g}(\mathbf{f} \cdot \mathbf{g}) \\ &= \mathbf{g} \times (\nabla \times \mathbf{f}) + \mathbf{f} \times (\nabla \times \mathbf{g}) + (\mathbf{g} \cdot \nabla)\mathbf{f} + (\mathbf{f} \cdot \nabla)\mathbf{g}.\end{aligned}$$

If $\mathbf{f}$ is a vector function with continuous second derivatives, then the *curl of the curl* of $\mathbf{f}$ is

$$\text{curl}\,(\text{curl}\,\mathbf{f}) = \nabla \times (\nabla \times \mathbf{f}) = \nabla(\nabla \cdot \mathbf{f}) - \nabla^2\mathbf{f} \quad (3.163)$$
$$= \text{grad}\,(\text{div}\,\mathbf{f}) - \nabla^2\mathbf{f}.$$

**PROBLEM 3.63** Verify (3.163).

**Solution:** From the formula for the triple vector product (1.83),

$$\mathbf{A} \times (\mathbf{B} \times \mathbf{C}) = (\mathbf{A} \cdot \mathbf{C})\mathbf{B} - (\mathbf{A} \cdot \mathbf{B})\mathbf{C}; \quad [1.83]$$

then letting $\mathbf{A} = \mathbf{B} = \nabla$ and $\mathbf{C} = \mathbf{f}$,

$$\nabla \times (\nabla \times \mathbf{f}) = \nabla(\nabla \cdot \mathbf{f}) - (\nabla \cdot \nabla)\mathbf{f}$$
$$= \nabla(\nabla \cdot \mathbf{f}) - \nabla^2\mathbf{f}.$$

Rather than writing $(\nabla \cdot \mathbf{f})\nabla$, we must write $\nabla(\nabla \cdot \mathbf{f})$ so that $\nabla$ operates on $\mathbf{f}$. Then from (3.163),

$$\nabla^2\mathbf{f} = \nabla(\nabla \cdot \mathbf{f}) - \nabla \times (\nabla \times \mathbf{f}), \quad (3.164)$$

which is the formula for evaluating $\nabla^2\mathbf{f}$.

**PROBLEM 3.64** Calculate $\nabla \cdot [f(r)\mathbf{r}]$ if $\mathbf{r}$ is the position vector and $r = |\mathbf{r}|$.

**Solution:** From (3.155),

$$\nabla \cdot [f(r)\mathbf{r}] = f(r)\nabla \cdot \mathbf{r} + \mathbf{r} \cdot \nabla[f(r)],$$

and from (3.129),

$$\nabla \cdot \mathbf{r} = 3.$$

Then from (3.123–4),

$$\nabla[f(r)] = f'(r)\nabla r = f'(r)\frac{\mathbf{r}}{r} = f'(r)\,\mathbf{e}_r. \quad (3.165)$$

Hence, because $\mathbf{r} \cdot \mathbf{r} = r^2$,

$$\nabla \cdot [f(r)\mathbf{r}] = 3f(r) + \frac{f'(r)}{r}\,\mathbf{r} \cdot \mathbf{r} - 3f(r) + rf'(r). \quad (3.166)$$

**PROBLEM 3.65** Calculate $\nabla \cdot (r^{n-1}\,\mathbf{r})$.

**Solution:** Setting $f(r) = r^{n-1}$ in (3.166),

$$\nabla \cdot (r^{n-1}\,\mathbf{r}) = 3r^{n-1} + (n-1)r^{n-1}$$
$$= (n+2)r^{n-1}. \quad (3.167)$$

Setting $n = -2$ in (3.167), we obtain, for $r \neq 0$,

$$\nabla \cdot \left(\frac{\mathbf{r}}{r^3}\right) = 0. \quad (3.168)$$

Now, from (3.126), we have $\nabla(1/r) = -1/r^3\,\mathbf{r}$; hence, (3.168) indicates that for $r \neq 0$,

$$\nabla \cdot \nabla\left(\frac{1}{r}\right) = \nabla^2\left(\frac{1}{r}\right) = 0. \quad [3.137]$$

**PROBLEM 3.66** Calculate $\nabla \times [f(r)\mathbf{r}]$.

**Solution:** Using (3.156),

$$\nabla \times [f(r)\mathbf{r}] = f(r)\nabla \times \mathbf{r} + [\nabla f(r)] \times \mathbf{r}.$$

Now from (3.141), $\nabla \times \mathbf{r} = \mathbf{0}$, and from (3.165), $\nabla [f(r)] = f'(r)\mathbf{r}/r$. Hence,

$$\nabla \times [f(r)\mathbf{r}] = \frac{f'(r)}{r} \mathbf{r} \times \mathbf{r} = \mathbf{0} \tag{3.169}$$

since $\mathbf{r} \times \mathbf{r} = \mathbf{0}$ from (1.58).

**PROBLEM 3.67** Calculate $\nabla \cdot \nabla [f(r)] = \nabla^2 f(r)$.

**Solution:** From (3.165),

$$\nabla [f(r)] = \frac{f'(r)}{r} \mathbf{r}.$$

Thus, from (3.155),

$$\begin{aligned} \nabla \cdot \nabla [f(r)] &= \nabla \cdot \left[\frac{f'(r)}{r} \mathbf{r}\right] \\ &= \frac{f'(r)}{r} \nabla \cdot \mathbf{r} + \mathbf{r} \cdot \nabla \left[\frac{f'(r)}{r}\right]. \end{aligned}$$

Then from (3.129) and (3.165), we obtain $\nabla \cdot \mathbf{r} = 3$ and

$$\nabla \left[\frac{f'(r)}{r}\right] = \frac{1}{r} \frac{d}{dr} \left[\frac{f'(r)}{r}\right] \mathbf{r} = \frac{1}{r} \left[\frac{1}{r} f''(r) - \frac{1}{r^2} f'(r)\right] \mathbf{r}.$$

Thus, because $\mathbf{r} \cdot \mathbf{r} = r^2$,

$$\begin{aligned} \nabla \cdot \nabla [f(r)] &= \frac{3}{r} f'(r) + \frac{1}{r} \left[\frac{1}{r} f''(r) - \frac{1}{r^2} f'(r)\right] \mathbf{r} \cdot \mathbf{r} \\ &= \frac{2}{r} f'(r) + f''(r). \end{aligned} \tag{3.170}$$

**PROBLEM 3.68** Calculate $\nabla \cdot \nabla r^n = \nabla^2 r^n$.

**Solution:** Setting $f(r) = r^n$ in (3.170),

$$\begin{aligned} \nabla \cdot \nabla r^n = \nabla^2 r^n &= \frac{2}{r} \frac{d}{dr} r^n + \frac{d^2}{dr^2} r^n \\ &= 2nr^{n-2} + n(n-1)r^{n-2} \\ &= n(n+1)r^{n-2}. \end{aligned} \tag{3.171}$$

Setting $n = -1$ in (3.171), we have, for $r \neq 0$, $\nabla^2 \left(\frac{1}{r}\right) = 0$, which is (3.137).

**PROBLEM 3.69** Show that

$$\nabla \cdot (\phi \nabla \psi - \psi \nabla \phi) = \phi \nabla^2 \psi - \psi \nabla^2 \phi. \tag{3.172}$$

**Solution:** Setting $\mathbf{f} = \nabla \psi$ in (3.155),

$$\nabla \cdot (\phi \nabla \psi) = \phi \nabla \cdot \nabla \psi + \nabla \psi \cdot \nabla \phi = \phi \nabla^2 \psi + \nabla \psi \cdot \nabla \phi; \tag{3.173}$$

then interchanging $\phi$ and $\psi$ in (3.173),

$$\nabla \cdot (\psi \nabla \phi) = \psi \nabla^2 \phi + \nabla \phi \cdot \nabla \psi. \tag{3.174}$$

Subtracting (3.174) from (3.173) yields

$$\nabla \cdot (\phi \nabla \psi - \psi \nabla \phi) = \phi \nabla^2 \psi - \psi \nabla^2 \phi$$

since $\nabla \phi \cdot \nabla \psi = \nabla \psi \cdot \nabla \phi$.

## 3.11 Supplementary Problems

**PROBLEM 3.70** Let $\mathbf{A}(t) = t\mathbf{i} + t^2\mathbf{j} + t^3\mathbf{k}$ and $\mathbf{B}(t) = \mathbf{i} + t\mathbf{j} + (1-t)\mathbf{k}$. At $t = 1$, evaluate (a) $\mathbf{A}'(t)$, (b) $(d/dt)[\mathbf{A}(t)\cdot\mathbf{B}(t)]$, and (c) $(d/dt)[\mathbf{A}(t)\times\mathbf{B}(t)]$.
*Answer*: (a) $[1, 2, 3]$, (b) 3, and (c) $[-1, 1, 0]$.

**PROBLEM 3.71** Show that if the third derivatives of the vector function $\mathbf{f}(t)$ exist, then

(a) $\dfrac{d}{dt}[\mathbf{f}(t)\times\mathbf{f}'(t)] = \mathbf{f}(t)\times\mathbf{f}''(t)$,

(b) $\dfrac{d}{dt}[\mathbf{f}(t)\ \mathbf{f}'(t)\ \mathbf{f}''(t)] = [\mathbf{f}(t)\ \mathbf{f}'(t)\ \mathbf{f}'''(t)]$.

**PROBLEM 3.72** If $\mathbf{f}(t)\times\mathbf{f}'(t) = \mathbf{0}$, then show that $\mathbf{f}(t)$ has a fixed direction. [*Hint:* Let $\mathbf{f}(t) = f(t)\,\mathbf{e}(t)$, where $\mathbf{e}(t)$ is a unit vector. Deduce that $\mathbf{e}(t)\times\mathbf{e}'(t) = \mathbf{0}$ and $\mathbf{e}(t)\cdot\mathbf{e}'(t) = 0$.]

**PROBLEM 3.73** Verify the chain rule for derivatives (3.19).

**PROBLEM 3.74** If $\mathbf{f} = uvw\,\mathbf{i} + uw^2\mathbf{j} - v^3\mathbf{k}$ and $\mathbf{g} = u^3\mathbf{i} - uvw\,\mathbf{j} + u^2w\,\mathbf{k}$, calculate

(a) $\dfrac{\partial^2\mathbf{f}}{\partial u\,\partial v}$ at the origin,

(b) $\dfrac{\partial^2\mathbf{f}}{\partial v^2}\times\dfrac{\partial^2\mathbf{g}}{\partial u^2}$ at the point $(1, 1, 0)$.

*Answer*: (a) 0, (b) $[0, -36, 0]$.

**PROBLEM 3.75** Sketch the curves represented by the following vector functions:

(a) $\mathbf{r}(t) = \cos t\,\mathbf{i} + \sin t\,\mathbf{j} + \sin t\,\mathbf{k}$, $0 \le t \le 2\pi$;

(b) $\mathbf{r}(t) = a\cos t\,\mathbf{i} + a\sin t\,\mathbf{j} + bt\,\mathbf{k}$, $b > 0$ and $0 \le t < \infty$;

(c) $\mathbf{r}(t) = t^3\mathbf{i} + t\mathbf{j}$, $-\infty < t < \infty$.

*Answer*: (a) An ellipse, (b) a cylindrical helix.

**PROBLEM 3.76** Find the length of the curves represented by the following vector functions:

(a) $\mathbf{r}(t) = \cos t\,\mathbf{i} + \sin t\,\mathbf{j} + \sin t\,\mathbf{k}$, $0 \le t \le 2\pi$,

(b) $\mathbf{r}(t) = t\,\mathbf{i} + \sin 2\pi t\,\mathbf{j} + \cos 2\pi t\,\mathbf{k}$, $0 \le t \le 1$,

(c) $\mathbf{r}(t) = \cos 3t\,\mathbf{i} + \sin 3t\,\mathbf{j}$, $0 \le t \le 2\pi$.

*Answer*: (a) $3\pi$, (b) $\sqrt{1+4\pi^2}$, (c) $6\pi$.

**PROBLEM 3.77** Find the unit tangent vector $\mathbf{T}$ to the curves represented by the following vector functions at the points specified:

(a) $\mathbf{r}(t) = \cos t\,\mathbf{i} + \sin t\,\mathbf{j} + t\,\mathbf{k}$, at $t = \pi$;

(b) $\mathbf{r}(t) = \left(t - \dfrac{t^3}{3}\right)\mathbf{i} + t^2\mathbf{j} + \left(t + \dfrac{t^3}{3}\right)\mathbf{k}$, at $t = 1$;

(c) $\mathbf{r}(t) = a(t - \sin t)\mathbf{i} + a(1 - \cos t)\mathbf{j}$, at any point $t$.

*Answer*: (a) $\left[0, -\dfrac{1}{\sqrt{2}}, \dfrac{1}{\sqrt{2}}\right]$, (b) $\left[0, \dfrac{1}{\sqrt{2}}, \dfrac{1}{\sqrt{2}}\right]$, (c) $\left(\sin\dfrac{t}{2}\right)\mathbf{i} + \left(\cos\dfrac{t}{2}\right)\mathbf{j}$.

**PROBLEM 3.78** Find a unit normal vector $\mathbf{n}$ at (0, 0, 0) for the surface $S$ represented by $z = 3x^2 + 4y^2$.
*Answer*: $[0, 0, -1]$.

**PROBLEM 3.79** Find a unit normal vector $\mathbf{n}$ at (1, 1, 1) for the surface $S$ represented by $x^2 + y^2 - z - 1 = 0$.
*Answer*: $\left[\frac{2}{3}, \frac{2}{3}, -\frac{1}{3}\right]$.

**PROBLEM 3.80** Find a unit normal vector $\mathbf{n}$ for the surface $S$ represented by the parametric equations $x = u \cos v$, $y = u \sin v$, $z = z(u)$.

*Answer*: $\dfrac{1}{\sqrt{1 + [(z'(u)]^2}} [-z'(u) \cos v, \quad -z'(u) \sin v, \quad 1]$.

**PROBLEM 3.81** Find the directional derivative of $\phi(x, y, z) = z^2 y + y^2 z + z^2 x$ at (1, 1, 1) in the direction of $C$ represented by $\mathbf{r}(t) = t\,\mathbf{i} + t^2\mathbf{j} + t^3\mathbf{k}$.
*Answer*: $18/\sqrt{14}$.

**PROBLEM 3.82** If $\phi(x, y, z) = xy + yz + zx$, find

(a) $\nabla\phi$ at (1, 1, 3),

(b) $\dfrac{\partial\phi}{\partial s}$ at (1, 1, 3) in the direction of [1, 1, 1],

(c) the normal derivative $\dfrac{\partial\phi}{\partial n} = \nabla\phi \cdot \mathbf{n}$ at (1, 1, 3), where $\mathbf{n}$ is a unit vector normal to the surface $S$ defined by a constant $\phi(x, y, z)$.

*Answer*: (a) $[4, 4, 2]$, (b) $10/\sqrt{3}$, (c) 6.

**PROBLEM 3.83** Find the divergence and curl of $\mathbf{f} = (x - y)\mathbf{i} + (y - z)\mathbf{j} + (z - x)\mathbf{k}$ and $\mathbf{g} = (x^2 + yz)\mathbf{i} + (y^2 + zx)\mathbf{j} + (z^2 + xy)\mathbf{k}$.

*Answer*: $\nabla \cdot \mathbf{f} = 3$, $\nabla \times \mathbf{f} = [1, 1, 1]$, $\nabla \cdot \mathbf{g} = 2(x + y + z)$, and $\nabla \times \mathbf{g} = \mathbf{0}$.

**PROBLEM 3.84** If $\phi = 3x^2 - yz$ and $\mathbf{f} = 3xyz^2\mathbf{i} + 2xy^3\mathbf{j} - x^2yz\mathbf{k}$, find, at (1, –1, 1), (a) $\nabla\phi$, (b) $\nabla \cdot \mathbf{f}$, (c) $\nabla \times \mathbf{f}$, (d) $\mathbf{f} \cdot \nabla\phi$, (e) $\nabla \cdot (\phi\mathbf{f})$, (f) $\nabla \times (\phi\mathbf{f})$, and (g) $\nabla^2\phi$.
*Answer*: (a) $[6, -1, 1]$, (b) 4, (c) $[-1, -8, -5]$, (d) $-15$, (e) 1, (f) $[-3, -41, -35]$, and (g) 6.

**PROBLEM 3.85** If $\nabla \times \mathbf{f} = \mathbf{0}$, where $\mathbf{f} = (xyz)^m (x^n\mathbf{i} + y^n\mathbf{j} + z^n\mathbf{k})$, show that either $m = 0$ or $n = -1$.

**PROBLEM 3.86** For an arbitrary constant vector $\mathbf{a}$, and the position vector $\mathbf{r}$, show that

(a) $\nabla \cdot (\mathbf{a} \times \mathbf{r}) = 0$,

(b) $\nabla \times (\mathbf{a} \times \mathbf{r}) = 2\mathbf{a}$,

(c) $\nabla\left(\dfrac{\mathbf{a} \cdot \mathbf{r}}{r^3}\right) + \nabla \times \left(\dfrac{\mathbf{a} \times \mathbf{r}}{r^3}\right) = \mathbf{0}$,

(d) $\nabla\left(\mathbf{a} \cdot \nabla \dfrac{1}{r}\right) + \nabla \times \left(\mathbf{a} \times \nabla \dfrac{1}{r}\right) = \mathbf{0}$.

**PROBLEM 3.87** For any differentiable vector function $\mathbf{f}$ and the position vector $\mathbf{r}$, show that

$$\nabla \cdot (\mathbf{f} \times \mathbf{r}) = \mathbf{r} \cdot (\nabla \times \mathbf{f}).$$

**PROBLEM 3.88** Show that if $\phi$ and $\psi$ are harmonic, then $\phi + \psi$ and $c\phi$, for an arbitrary constant c, are also harmonic.

**PROBLEM 3.89** If the second derivatives of the functions $\phi$ and $\psi$ exist, then show that

(a) $\nabla^2(\phi\psi) = \phi\nabla^2\psi + 2\nabla\phi \cdot \nabla\psi + \psi\nabla^2\phi$, (b) $\nabla\left(\dfrac{\phi}{\psi}\right) = \dfrac{\psi\nabla\phi - \phi\nabla\psi}{\psi^2}$.

**PROBLEM 3.90** If $\mathbf{u}$ is a constant unit vector and $\mathbf{f}$ a differentiable vector function, show that $\mathbf{u} \cdot [\nabla(\mathbf{f} \cdot \mathbf{u}) - \nabla \times (\mathbf{f} \times \mathbf{u})] = \nabla \cdot \mathbf{f}$.

**PROBLEM 3.91** If $\mathbf{f} = 2z\,\mathbf{i} + x^2\mathbf{j} + x\mathbf{k}$ and $\phi = 2x^2y^2z^2$, find $(\mathbf{f} \times \nabla)\phi$ at the point $(1, -1, 1)$.
*Answer*: $[-8, -4, 4]$.

**PROBLEM 3.92** The vector field $\mathbf{f}$ is said to be *solenoidal* if $\mathbf{f}$ is differentiable and $\nabla \cdot \mathbf{f} = 0$; it is called *irrotational* if $\mathbf{f}$ is differentiable and $\nabla \times \mathbf{f} = \mathbf{0}$. Show that if $\mathbf{f}$ and $\mathbf{g}$ are irrotational, then $\mathbf{f} \times \mathbf{g}$ is solenoidal.

**PROBLEM 3.93** If $\phi$ and $\psi$ are scalar functions that have continuous second derivatives, then show that $\nabla\phi \times \nabla\psi$ is solenoidal.

**PROBLEM 3.94** If $\phi$ is harmonic, then show that $\nabla\phi$ is both solenoidal and irrotational.

**PROBLEM 3.95** If $c\mathbf{f} = \nabla\phi$, where c is a constant, then show that $\mathbf{f} \cdot \nabla \times \mathbf{f} = 0$.

**PROBLEM 3.96** Show that if $\mathbf{f}$ is any differentiable vector function, then

$$(\mathbf{f} \cdot \nabla)\,\mathbf{f} = \frac{1}{2}\,\nabla(\mathbf{f} \cdot \mathbf{f}) - \mathbf{f} \times (\nabla \times \mathbf{f}).$$

**PROBLEM 3.97** Show that for any differentiable scalar functions $u(x, y, z)$, $v(x, y, z)$, and $w(x, y, z)$,

$$[\nabla u\ \nabla v\ \nabla w] = \begin{vmatrix} \dfrac{\partial u}{\partial x} & \dfrac{\partial u}{\partial y} & \dfrac{\partial u}{\partial z} \\ \dfrac{\partial v}{\partial x} & \dfrac{\partial v}{\partial y} & \dfrac{\partial v}{\partial z} \\ \dfrac{\partial w}{\partial x} & \dfrac{\partial w}{\partial y} & \dfrac{\partial w}{\partial z} \end{vmatrix}$$

This is called the *Jacobian* of $u, v, w$ and is denoted by

$$J\left[\frac{(u, v, w)}{(x, y, z)}\right] = \frac{\partial(u, v, w)}{\partial(x, y, z)}.$$

**PROBLEM 3.98** Prove that a necessary and sufficient condition is that the Jacobian of $u$, $v$, $w$ vanishes for $u$, $v$, and $w$ to be *functionally dependent*; that is, $u$, $v$, $w$ satisfy the equation $F(u, v, w) = 0$.

**PROBLEM 3.99** Verify that $u = x + y$, $v = x - y + z$, and $w = (2x + z)^2 + (2y - z)^2$ are functionally dependent.

CHAPTER 4

# VECTOR INTEGRAL CALCULUS

## 4.1 Line Integrals

In Sec. 3.4, a curve $C$, for $a \leq t \leq b$, is represented by

$$\mathbf{r}(t) = x(t)\,\mathbf{i} + y(t)\,\mathbf{j} + z(t)\,\mathbf{k}, \qquad [3.38]$$

where $\mathbf{r}$ is the position vector and $t$ is any parameter. The *differential displacement vector* $d\mathbf{r}$ along $C$ is

$$d\mathbf{r} = dx\,\mathbf{i} + dy\,\mathbf{j} + dz\,\mathbf{k}. \qquad (4.1)$$

Integrals that involve differential displacement vectors $d\mathbf{r}$ are called *line integrals*. Consider the following line integrals along a curve $C$ that can be open or closed:

$$\int_C \phi\, d\mathbf{r}, \qquad (4.2)$$

$$\int_C \mathbf{f} \cdot d\mathbf{r}, \qquad (4.3)$$

$$\int_C \mathbf{f} \times d\mathbf{r}. \qquad (4.4)$$

With a scalar $\phi$, the line integral (4.2) reduces to

$$\int_C \phi\, d\mathbf{r} = \int_C \phi(dx\,\mathbf{i} + dy\,\mathbf{j} + dz\,\mathbf{k})$$

$$= \mathbf{i} \int_C \phi\, dx + \mathbf{j} \int_C \phi\, dy + \mathbf{k} \int_C \phi\, dz. \qquad (4.5)$$

To reduce (4.2), we have used the relation

$$\int_C \mathbf{i}\,\phi\, dx = \mathbf{i} \int_C \phi\, dx \quad \text{etc.,} \qquad (4.6)$$

which is permissible because $\mathbf{i}$, $\mathbf{j}$, and $\mathbf{k}$ of the rectangular coordinate system have constant magnitude and direction.

When the space curve $C$ forms a closed path, (4.2) is written as

$$\oint_C \phi\, d\mathbf{r}. \qquad (4.7)$$

In particular, if $C$ is a simple closed plane curve, and the direction of integration can be described, the symbols often used are

$$\circlearrowleft\!\!\oint_C \phi\, d\mathbf{r}, \quad \circlearrowright\!\!\oint_C \phi\, d\mathbf{r}.$$

The first integral indicates movement along the closed curve $C$ in the positive, or counterclockwise, direction; i.e., the movement along $C$ is such that its enclosed region always lies to the left. The second integral indicates movement in the negative, or clockwise, direction.

**PROBLEM 4.1** If $\phi = xy$, evaluate $\int_C \phi\, d\mathbf{r}$ from $(0,0,0)$ to $(1,1,0)$ along (a) the curve $C$ specified by $y = x^2$, $z = 0$ and (b) the straight line $C$ that joins $(0,0,0)$ and $(1,1,0)$.

**Solution:** (a) Curve $C$ can be represented parametrically by

$$x = t, \quad y = t^2, \quad z = 0, \quad 0 \le t \le 1.$$

Hence, along this path,

$$d\mathbf{r} = dx\,\mathbf{i} + dy\,\mathbf{j} + dz\,\mathbf{k} = dt\,\mathbf{i} + 2t\,dt\,\mathbf{j}$$

and $\phi = (t)(t^2) = t^3$. Then,

$$\int_{(0,0,0)}^{(1,1,0)} \phi\, d\mathbf{r} = \int_0^1 t^3(\mathbf{i} + 2t\mathbf{j})\, dt$$

$$= \mathbf{i}\int_0^1 t^3\, dt + \mathbf{j}\int_0^1 2t^4\, dt$$

$$= \frac{1}{4}\mathbf{i} + \frac{2}{5}\mathbf{j}.$$

(b) From the result of Prob. 3.15, the straight line $C$ that connects (0, 0, 0) and (1, 1, 0) can be represented parametrically by $x = t$, $y = t$, $z = 0$, $0 \le t \le 1$. Hence, along this path,

$$d\mathbf{r} = dx\,\mathbf{i} + dy\,\mathbf{j} + dz\,\mathbf{k} = dt\,\mathbf{i} + dt\,\mathbf{j}$$

and $\phi = (t)(t) = t^2$. Then,

$$\int_{(0,0,0)}^{(1,1,0)} \phi\, d\mathbf{r} = \int_0^1 t^2(\mathbf{i} + \mathbf{j})\, dt$$

$$= \mathbf{i}\int_0^1 t^2\, dt + \mathbf{j}\int_0^1 t^2\, dt$$

$$= \frac{1}{3}\mathbf{i} + \frac{1}{3}\mathbf{j}.$$

As the results of Prob. 4.1 show, the values of this type of line integral generally depend on the path of integration.

**PROBLEM 4.2** Evaluate $\oint_C d\mathbf{r}$ along the circle represented by $x^2 + y^2 = a^2$, $z = 0$.

**Solution:** From the result of Prob. 3.13, the circle of $x^2 + y^2 = a^2$, $z = 0$ can be represented parametrically by

$$x = a\cos t, \quad y = a\sin t, \quad z = 0, \qquad 0 \le t \le 2\pi.$$

Hence,

$$d\mathbf{r} = dx\,\mathbf{i} + dy\,\mathbf{j} + dz\,\mathbf{k} = -a \sin t\, dt\,\mathbf{i} + a \cos t\, dt\,\mathbf{j}.$$

Then,

$$\begin{aligned}\oint d\mathbf{r} &= \int_0^{2\pi} (-a \sin t\,\mathbf{i} + a \cos t\,\mathbf{j})\, dt \\ &= \mathbf{i}\int_0^{2\pi} -a \sin t\, dt + \mathbf{j}\int_0^{2\pi} a \cos t\, dt \\ &= \mathbf{i}\, a \cos t \Big|_0^{2\pi} + \mathbf{j}\, a \sin t \Big|_0^{2\pi} \\ &= \mathbf{i}(a - a) + \mathbf{j}(0 - 0) \\ &= \mathbf{0}. \end{aligned} \tag{4.8}$$

The line integral (4.3) is sometimes called the *scalar line integral*, or simply the *line integral*, of a vector field $\mathbf{f}$.

The line integral of $\mathbf{f}$ around a closed curve $C$ is called the *circulation* of $\mathbf{f}$ around $C$ and is

$$\text{circ}\,\mathbf{f} \equiv \oint_C \mathbf{f} \cdot d\mathbf{r}. \tag{4.9}$$

**PROBLEM 4.3** If $\mathbf{T}$ is the unit tangent vector along a curve $C$, show that

$$\int_C \mathbf{f} \cdot d\mathbf{r} = \int_C \mathbf{f} \cdot \mathbf{T}\, ds. \tag{4.10}$$

**Solution:** If, in (3.38), $t = s$ is the arc length of $C$ measured from some fixed point, then $C$ can be represented by

$$\mathbf{r}(s) = x(s)\,\mathbf{i} + y(s)\,\mathbf{j} + z(s)\,\mathbf{k}, \quad a \le s \le b. \tag{4.11}$$

From (3.68), the unit tangent vector $\mathbf{T}$ along $C$ is

$$\mathbf{T} = \frac{d\mathbf{r}}{ds}. \tag{4.12}$$

Then, from (4.12),

$$d\mathbf{r} = \frac{d\mathbf{r}}{ds}\, ds = \mathbf{T}\, ds. \tag{4.13}$$

Hence,

$$\int_C \mathbf{f} \cdot d\mathbf{r} = \int_C \mathbf{f} \cdot \frac{d\mathbf{r}}{ds}\, ds = \int_C \mathbf{f} \cdot \mathbf{T}\, ds. \tag{4.14}$$

Since the dot product $\mathbf{f} \cdot \mathbf{T}$ is equal to the component of $\mathbf{f}$ in the direction of $\mathbf{T}$, i.e., the direction of $C$, (4.10) shows that the line integral of $\mathbf{f}$ is equivalent to the integration of the tangential component of $\mathbf{f}$ along $C$ with respect to the arc length.

**PROBLEM 4.4** If $\mathbf{f} = f_1(x, y, z)\,\mathbf{i} + f_2(x, y, z)\,\mathbf{j} + f_3(x, y, z)\,\mathbf{k}$, show that

$$\int_C \mathbf{f} \cdot d\mathbf{r} = \int_C (f_1\, dx + f_2\, dy + f_3\, dz). \tag{4.15}$$

**Solution:** Since $d\mathbf{r} = dx\,\mathbf{i} + dy\,\mathbf{j} + dz\,\mathbf{k}$,

$$\mathbf{f} \cdot d\mathbf{r} = f_1\, dx + f_2\, dy + f_3\, dz,$$

and hence,

$$\int_C \mathbf{f}\cdot d\mathbf{r} = \int_C (f_1\,dx + f_2\,dy + f_3\,dz).$$

**PROBLEM 4.5** If $\mathbf{f} = x^2\mathbf{i} + y\mathbf{j} + xyz\mathbf{k}$, evaluate $\int_C \mathbf{f}\cdot d\mathbf{r}$ from $(0,0,0)$ to $(1,1,1)$ along (a) a straight line that connects these two points and (b) a path $C$, as shown in Fig. 4.1, which consists of three line segments $C_1$, $C_2$, and $C_3$ that link these two points via $(1,0,0)$ and $(1,1,0)$.

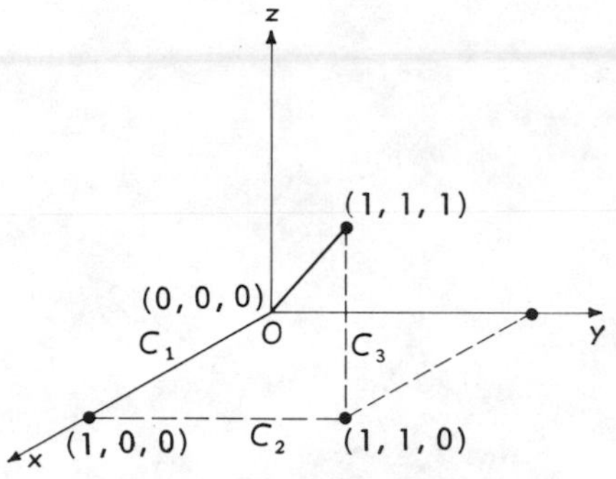


Fig. 4.1 Solution to Prob. 4.5.

**Solution:** (a) From the result of Prob. 3.15, the straight line $C$ that connects $(0,0,0)$ and $(1,1,1)$ can be represented parametrically by

$$x = t, \quad y = t, \quad z = t.$$

Hence, the curve $C$ is represented by

$$\mathbf{r} = t\mathbf{i} + t\mathbf{j} + t\mathbf{k}, \quad 0 \le t \le 1.$$

Then, along this path,

$$d\mathbf{r} = dt\,\mathbf{i} + dt\,\mathbf{j} + dt\,\mathbf{k}, \qquad \mathbf{f} = t^2\mathbf{i} + t\mathbf{j} + t^3\mathbf{k},$$

and thus,

$$\int_C \mathbf{f}\cdot d\mathbf{r} = \int_0^1 (t^2 + t + t^3)\,dt = \frac{1}{3} + \frac{1}{2} + \frac{1}{4} = \frac{13}{12}.$$

(b) In this case,

$$\int_C \mathbf{f}\cdot d\mathbf{r} = \int_{C_1} \mathbf{f}\cdot d\mathbf{r} + \int_{C_2} \mathbf{f}\cdot d\mathbf{r} + \int_{C_3} \mathbf{f}\cdot d\mathbf{r}.$$

For $C_1$, $d\mathbf{r} = dx\,\mathbf{i}$ and $\mathbf{f} = x^2\mathbf{i}$; hence,

$$\int_{C_1} \mathbf{f}\cdot d\mathbf{r} = \int_0^1 x^2\,dx = \frac{1}{3}.$$

For $C_2$, $d\mathbf{r} = dy\,\mathbf{j}$ and $\mathbf{f} = (1)^2\mathbf{i} + y\mathbf{j} = \mathbf{i} + y\mathbf{j}$; hence,

$$\int_{C_2} \mathbf{f}\cdot d\mathbf{r} = \int_0^1 y\,dy = \frac{1}{2}.$$

For $C_3$, $d\mathbf{r} = dz\,\mathbf{k}$ and $\mathbf{f} = (1)^2\mathbf{i} + (1)\mathbf{j} + (1)(1)z\mathbf{k} = \mathbf{i} + \mathbf{j} + z\mathbf{k}$; hence,

$$\int_{C_3} \mathbf{f}\cdot d\mathbf{r} = \int_0^1 z\,dz = \frac{1}{2}.$$

Thus,

$$\int_C \mathbf{f}\cdot d\mathbf{r} = \frac{1}{3} + \frac{1}{2} + \frac{1}{2} = \frac{4}{3}.$$

As the results of Prob. 4.5 show, the values of line integrals of a vector field also, in general, depend on the path of integration.

**PROBLEM 4.6** If $\mathbf{f} = x\mathbf{i} + 2y\mathbf{j} + z\mathbf{k}$, evaluate $\int_C \mathbf{f}\cdot d\mathbf{r}$ from $(0,0,0)$ to $(1,1,1)$ along (a) a straight line that connects these two points and (b) a path $C$, as shown in Fig. 4.1, which consists of three line segments $C_1$, $C_2$, and $C_3$ that link these two points via (1, 0, 0) and (1, 1, 0). (Cf., Prob. 4.5.)

**Solution:** (a) From the results of Prob. 4.5,

$$d\mathbf{r} = dt\,\mathbf{i} + dt\,\mathbf{j} + dt\,\mathbf{k}.$$

Since the parametric representation of $\mathbf{f}$ is $\mathbf{f} = t\mathbf{i} + 2t\mathbf{j} + t\mathbf{k}$, the integral is

$$\int_C \mathbf{f}\cdot d\mathbf{r} = \int_0^1 (t + 2t + t)\,dt = \int_0^1 4t\,dt = 2.$$

(b) For a path $C$, consisting of line segments $C_1$, $C_2$, and $C_3$,

$$\int_C \mathbf{f}\cdot d\mathbf{r} = \int_{C_1} \mathbf{f}\cdot d\mathbf{r} + \int_{C_2} \mathbf{f}\cdot d\mathbf{r} + \int_{C_3} \mathbf{f}\cdot d\mathbf{r}.$$

For $C_1$, $d\mathbf{r} = dx\,\mathbf{i}$ and $\mathbf{f} = x\,\mathbf{i}$; hence,

$$\int_{C_1} \mathbf{f}\cdot d\mathbf{r} = \int_0^1 x\,dx = \frac{1}{2}.$$

For $C_2$, $d\mathbf{r} = dy\,\mathbf{j}$ and $\mathbf{f} = \mathbf{i} + 2y\,\mathbf{j}$; hence,

$$\int_{C_2} \mathbf{f}\cdot d\mathbf{r} = \int_0^1 2y\,dy = 1.$$

For $C_3$, $d\mathbf{r} = dz\,\mathbf{k}$ and $\mathbf{f} = \mathbf{i} + 2\mathbf{j} + z\,\mathbf{k}$; hence,

$$\int_{C_3} \mathbf{f}\cdot d\mathbf{r} = \int_0^1 z\,dz = \frac{1}{2}.$$

Thus,

$$\int_C \mathbf{f}\cdot d\mathbf{r} = \frac{1}{2} + 1 + \frac{1}{2} = 2.$$

The result of Prob. 4.6 shows that in this case the value of the line integral is the same for two different paths joining (0, 0, 0) to (1, 1, 1). Thus, the value of the integral is 2 for *any* path joining these points. To illustrate, since

$$\int_C \mathbf{f}\cdot d\mathbf{r} = \int_C x\,dx + 2y\,dy + z\,dz,$$

$$x\,dx + 2y\,dy + z\,dz = d(x^2/2 + y^2 + z^2/2),$$

we have

$$\int_C \mathbf{f}\cdot d\mathbf{r} = \int_{(0,0,0)}^{(1,1,1)} d\left(\frac{x^2}{2} + y^2 + \frac{z^2}{2}\right)$$

$$= \frac{x^2}{2} + y^2 + \frac{z^2}{2}\bigg|_{(0,0,0)}^{(1,1,1)}$$

$$= \frac{1}{2} + 1 + \frac{1}{2}$$

$$= 2,$$

which shows that the result depends only on the points (0, 0, 0) and (1, 1, 1) and is *independent* of the path of integration.

The above discussion shows that if the integrand $f_1\,dx + f_2\,dy + f_3\,dz$ in

(4.15) is the total differential of some function, then the integral is the same for all paths that join two points. However this is not always true, and the sufficient conditions for the line integral of a vector field **f** to be independent of the path are discussed in Sec. 4.10.

**PROBLEM 4.7** Find $\oint_C \mathbf{r}\cdot d\mathbf{r}$ along the circle $C$ represented by $x^2 + y^2 = a^2$, $z = 0$.

**Solution:** Referring to Prob. 4.2, the parametric equation for the curve is

$$\mathbf{r} = a \cos t\,\mathbf{i} + a \sin t\,\mathbf{j}, \quad 0 \le t \le 2\pi.$$

Therefore, $d\mathbf{r} = -a \sin t\, dt\mathbf{i} + a \cos t\, dt\mathbf{j}$. Then

$$\mathbf{r}\cdot d\mathbf{r} = -a^2 \cos t \sin t\, dt + a^2 \sin t \cos t\, dt = 0\, dt = 0.$$

Hence,

$$\oint_C \mathbf{r}\cdot d\mathbf{r} = 0. \tag{4.16}$$

**PROBLEM 4.8** If $\mathbf{f} = f_1\mathbf{i} + f_2\mathbf{j} + f_3\mathbf{k}$, show that

$$\int_C \mathbf{f}\times d\mathbf{r} = \mathbf{i}\int_C (f_2\, dz - f_3\, dy) + \mathbf{j}\int_C (f_3\, dx - f_1\, dz) + \mathbf{k}\int_C (f_1\, dy - f_2\, dx). \tag{4.17}$$

**Solution:** From (2.27), the vector product of **f** and $d\mathbf{r}$ is

$$\mathbf{f}\times d\mathbf{r} = \begin{vmatrix} \mathbf{i} & \mathbf{j} & \mathbf{k} \\ f_1 & f_2 & f_3 \\ dx & dy & dz \end{vmatrix} = \mathbf{i}(f_2\, dz - f_3\, dy) + \mathbf{j}(f_3\, dx - f_1\, dz) + \mathbf{k}(f_1\, dy - f_2\, dx).$$

Hence, the integral is

$$\int_C \mathbf{f}\times d\mathbf{r} = \mathbf{i}\int_C (f_2\, dz - f_3\, dy) + \mathbf{j}\int_C (f_3\, dx - f_1\, dz) + \mathbf{k}\int_C (f_1\, dy - f_2\, dx).$$

**PROBLEM 4.9** Evaluate $\oint_C \mathbf{r}\times d\mathbf{r}$ along the circle represented by $x^2 + y^2 = a^2$, $z = 0$.

**Solution:** Referring to Prob. 4.2, $C$ is represented parametrically by

$$\mathbf{r} = a \cos t\,\mathbf{i} + a \sin t\,\mathbf{j}, \quad 0 \le t \le 2\pi,$$

and hence, $d\mathbf{r} = -a \sin t\, dt\,\mathbf{i} + a \cos t\, dt\,\mathbf{j}$. Thus,

$$\mathbf{r}\times d\mathbf{r} = \begin{vmatrix} \mathbf{i} & \mathbf{j} & \mathbf{k} \\ a\cos t & a \sin t & 0 \\ -a \sin t\, dt & a \cos t\, dt & 0 \end{vmatrix} = \mathbf{k}(a^2 \cos^2 t + a^2 \sin^2 t)\, dt = a^2\, dt\,\mathbf{k}.$$

Hence, integrating over $C$,

$$\oint_C \mathbf{r} \times d\mathbf{r} = \int_0^{2\pi} \mathbf{k}\, a^2\, dt = \mathbf{k}\, a^2 \int_0^{2\pi} dt = 2\pi a^2 \mathbf{k}, \tag{4.18}$$

which shows that the result is a vector in the $z$-direction with magnitude $2\pi a^2$, which is twice the area of a circle. (See Probs. 4.68 and 4.69.)

## 4.2 Surface Integrals

A *surface* $S$ is represented by

$$\mathbf{r}(u, v) = x(u, v)\,\mathbf{i} + y(u, v)\,\mathbf{j} + z(u, v)\,\mathbf{k}, \qquad [3.79]$$

where $\mathbf{r}$ is the position vector and $u$ and $v$ are parameters. (Cf., Sec. 3.5.) The differential element $d\mathbf{S}$ of the surface area is

$$d\mathbf{S} = \mathbf{r}_u \times \mathbf{r}_v\, dudv. \qquad [3.95]$$

As shown in Chap. 3, (3.95) can be written as

$$d\mathbf{S} = \mathbf{n}\, dS, \qquad [3.97]$$

where $\mathbf{n}$ is the unit vector normal to the surface at the point that corresponds to the coordinates $u$ and $v$, and

$$\mathbf{n} = \frac{\mathbf{r}_u \times \mathbf{r}_v}{|\mathbf{r}_u \times \mathbf{r}_v|}, \qquad [3.80]$$

$$dS = |\mathbf{r}_u \times \mathbf{r}_v|\, dudv. \qquad [3.96]$$

Integrals that involve the differential element $d\mathbf{S}$ of surface area are called *surface integrals*. Consider the surface integrals

$$\iint_S \phi\, d\mathbf{S}, \tag{4.19}$$

$$\iint_S \mathbf{f} \cdot d\mathbf{S}, \tag{4.20}$$

$$\iint_S \mathbf{f} \times d\mathbf{S}, \tag{4.21}$$

each of which is over a surface $S$ that can be open or closed.

If $S$ is a closed surface, the surface integrals are written as

$$\oint\!\!\oint_S \phi\, d\mathbf{S}, \quad \oint\!\!\oint_S \mathbf{f} \cdot d\mathbf{S}, \quad \oint\!\!\oint_S \mathbf{f} \times d\mathbf{S}.$$

For closed surfaces, it is usual to assume that the positive direction of the normal is directed outward from the surface.

**PROBLEM 4.10** Evaluate $\iint_S d\mathbf{S}$ over the part $z > 0$ of the sphere $x^2 + y^2 + z^2 = a^2$.

**Solution:** From the result of Prob. 3.26, the sphere $x^2 + y^2 + z^2 = a^2$ can be represented parametrically by changing $\theta$ to $u$ and $\phi$ to $v$. Thus,

$$\mathbf{r}(u, v) = a \sin u \cos v\, \mathbf{i} + a \sin u \sin v\, \mathbf{j} + a \cos u\, \mathbf{k}, \tag{4.22}$$

where $0 \le u \le \pi$, $0 \le v \le 2\pi$. The differential element $d\mathbf{S}$ of the surface area is

$$\begin{aligned} d\mathbf{S} &= \mathbf{r}_u \times \mathbf{r}_v \, dudv \\ &= a^2 \sin^2 u \cos v \, dudv \, \mathbf{i} + a^2 \sin^2 u \sin v \, dudv \, \mathbf{j} \\ &\quad + a^2 \sin u \cos u \, dudv \, \mathbf{k}. \end{aligned} \tag{4.23}$$

Since S is the part of the sphere where $z > 0$, the range of $u$ must be changed to $0 \leq u \leq \pi/2$ because $\cos u < 0$ for $\pi/2 < u \leq \pi$. Hence,

$$\begin{aligned} \iint_S d\mathbf{S} &= \int_0^{2\pi} \int_0^{\pi/2} \mathbf{r}_u \times \mathbf{r}_v \, dudv \\ &= \mathbf{i} \int_0^{2\pi} \int_0^{\pi/2} a^2 \sin^2 u \cos v \, dudv + \mathbf{j} \int_0^{2\pi} \int_0^{\pi/2} a^2 \sin^2 u \sin v \, dudv \\ &\quad + \mathbf{k} \int_0^{2\pi} \int_0^{\pi/2} \sin u \cos u \, dudv. \end{aligned}$$

Since $\int_0^{2\pi} \cos v \, dv = \int_0^{2\pi} \sin v \, dv = 0,$

$$\int_0^{2\pi} \int_0^{\pi/2} a^2 \sin^2 u \cos v \, dudv = a^2 \int_0^{2\pi} \cos v \, dv \int_0^{\pi/2} \sin^2 u \, du = 0,$$

$$\int_0^{2\pi} \int_0^{\pi/2} a^2 \sin^2 u \sin v \, dudv = a^2 \int_0^{2\pi} \sin v \, dv \int_0^{\pi/2} \sin^2 u \, du = 0,$$

$$\begin{aligned} \int_0^{2\pi} \int_0^{\pi/2} a^2 \sin u \cos u \, dudv &= a^2 \int_0^{2\pi} dv \int_0^{\pi/2} \sin u \cos u \, du \\ &= 2\pi a^2 \int_0^{\pi/2} \sin u \cos u \, du \\ &= 2\pi a^2 \int_0^{\pi/2} \sin u \, d(\sin u) \\ &= 2\pi a^2 \cdot \frac{1}{2} \sin^2 u \Big|_0^{\pi/2} \\ &= 2\pi a^2 \cdot \frac{1}{2} \\ &= \pi a^2. \end{aligned}$$

Hence,

$$\iint_S d\mathbf{S} = \pi a^2 \mathbf{k}, \tag{4.24}$$

which shows that the resultant is a vector directed in the $z$-direction with magnitude $\pi a^2$, i.e., the area surrounded by the intersection of the sphere and the xy-plane. (See Fig. 4.2.)

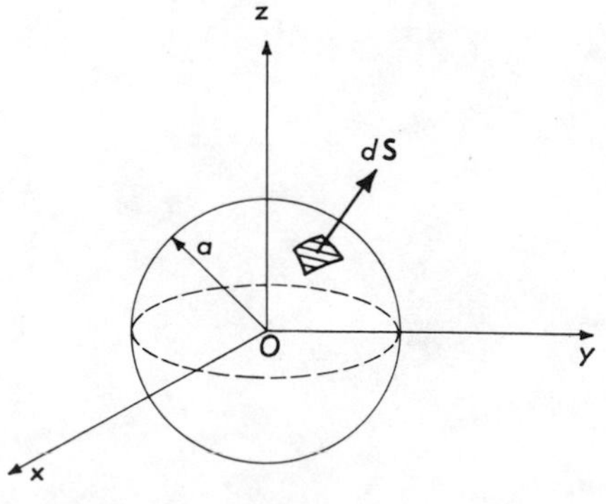


Fig. 4.2 The sphere of Prob. 4.10.

**PROBLEM 4.11** Show that, over the sphere $x^2 + y^2 + z^2 = a^2$,

$$\oiint_S d\mathbf{S} = \mathbf{0}. \tag{4.25}$$

**Solution:** If $S_1$ and $S_2$ are the parts of the sphere $x^2 + y^2 + z^2 = a^2$ where $z > 0$ and $z < 0$, respectively, then

$$\oint\!\!\oint_S d\mathbf{S} = \iint_{S_1} d\mathbf{S} + \iint_{S_2} d\mathbf{S}.$$

From the result of Prob. 4.10,

$$\iint_{S_1} d\mathbf{S} = \pi a^2 \mathbf{k}. \qquad [4.24]$$

For $S_2$, since $z < 0$, the range of $u$ in (4.22), and hence in (4.23), is $\pi/2 \le u \le \pi$. Then,

$$\iint_{S_2} d\mathbf{S} = \int_0^{2\pi} \int_{\pi/2}^{\pi} \mathbf{r}_u \times \mathbf{r}_v \, dudv,$$

and by similar calculations,

$$\int_0^{2\pi} \int_{\pi/2}^{\pi} a^2 \sin^2 u \cos v \, dudv = \int_0^{2\pi} \int_{\pi/2}^{\pi} a^2 \sin^2 u \sin v \, dudv = 0,$$

$$\int_0^{2\pi} \int_{\pi/2}^{\pi} a^2 \sin u \cos u \, dudv = 2\pi a^2 \cdot \frac{1}{2} \sin^2 u \Big|_{\pi/2}^{\pi} = 2\pi a^2 \left(-\frac{1}{2}\right) = -\pi a^2.$$

Hence,

$$\iint_{S_2} d\mathbf{S} = -\pi a^2 \mathbf{k}. \qquad (4.26)$$

Adding (4.24) and (4.26),

$$\oint\!\!\oint_S d\mathbf{S} = \pi a^2 \mathbf{k} - \pi a^2 \mathbf{k} = \mathbf{0}.$$

Relation (4.25) is true for any closed surface. (See Prob. 4.50.)

The surface integral (4.20) of a vector field $\mathbf{f}$ is called the *flux* of $\mathbf{f}$ through $S$ and is represented by

$$\iint_S \mathbf{f} \cdot d\mathbf{S}. \qquad (4.27)$$

**PROBLEM 4.12** If $S$ is represented by $\mathbf{r}(u, v)$, show that the flux of $\mathbf{f}$ through $S$ is

$$\iint_S \mathbf{f} \cdot d\mathbf{S} = \iint_{R_{uv}} [\mathbf{f}\ \mathbf{r}_u\ \mathbf{r}_v] \, dudv, \qquad (4.28)$$

where $[\mathbf{f}\ \mathbf{r}_u\ \mathbf{r}_v] = \mathbf{f} \cdot \mathbf{r}_u \times \mathbf{r}_v$ is the scalar triple product and $R_{uv}$ is the region at $(u, v)$ that corresponds to $S$.

**Solution:** The differential element of the surface area is

$$d\mathbf{S} = \mathbf{r}_u \times \mathbf{r}_v \, dudv.$$

Hence, the flux of $\mathbf{f}$ through $S$ is

$$\iint_S \mathbf{f}\cdot d\mathbf{S} = \iint_{R_{uv}} \mathbf{f}\cdot \mathbf{r}_u \times \mathbf{r}_v \, dudv = \iint_{R_{uv}} [\mathbf{f}\ \mathbf{r}_u\ \mathbf{r}_v]\, dudv.$$

**PROBLEM 4.13** If $\mathbf{f} = \cos u \cos v\,\mathbf{i} + \cos u \sin v\,\mathbf{j} - \sin u\,\mathbf{k}$, where $0 \le u \le \pi$ and $0 \le v \le 2\pi$, evaluate $\iint_S \mathbf{f}\cdot d\mathbf{S}$ over that part of the sphere $x^2 + y^2 + z^2 = a^2$ for which $z > 0$.

**Solution:** From Prob. 3.26, the components of the vector generating the surface are

$$\mathbf{r}_u = a \cos u \cos v\,\mathbf{i} + a \cos u \sin v\,\mathbf{j} - a \sin u\,\mathbf{k},$$

$$\mathbf{r}_v = -a \sin u \sin v\,\mathbf{i} + a \sin u \cos v\,\mathbf{j}.$$

According to the definition of a scalar triple product (2.53),

$$[\mathbf{f}\ \mathbf{r}_u\ \mathbf{r}_v] = \begin{vmatrix} \cos u \cos v & \cos u \sin v & -\sin u \\ a \cos u \cos v & a \cos u \sin v & -a \sin u \\ -a \sin u \sin v & a \sin u \cos v & 0 \end{vmatrix} = 0,$$

because the first and second rows of the determinant are proportional; hence, its value is zero. Consequently, from (4.28),

$$\iint_S \mathbf{f}\cdot d\mathbf{S} = 0. \tag{4.29}$$

**PROBLEM 4.14** Find $\iint_S \mathbf{r}\cdot d\mathbf{S}$, where S is the surface of the sphere $x^2 + y^2 + z^2 = a^2$.

**Solution:** At a point $(x, y, z)$ on the surface of the sphere S, the position vector $\mathbf{r} = x\mathbf{i} + y\mathbf{j} + z\mathbf{k}$ and the outer unit normal vector $\mathbf{n}$ to the surface S point directly away from the origin. Thus,

$$\mathbf{n} = \mathbf{e}_r = \frac{\mathbf{r}}{|\mathbf{r}|}. \tag{4.30}$$

Hence, for points on the surface,

$$\mathbf{r}\cdot\mathbf{n} = \mathbf{r}\cdot\frac{\mathbf{r}}{|\mathbf{r}|} = \frac{|\mathbf{r}|^2}{|\mathbf{r}|} = |\mathbf{r}| = a,$$

and since the surface area of a sphere is $4\pi a^2$ from Prob. 3.26,

$$\iint_S \mathbf{r}\cdot d\mathbf{S} = \iint_S \mathbf{r}\cdot\mathbf{n}\, dS = a \iint_S dS = a(4\pi a^2) = 4\pi a^3.$$

**PROBLEM 4.15** If $\mathbf{f} = f_1(x, y, z)\,\mathbf{i} + f_2(x, y, z)\,\mathbf{j} + f_3(x, y, z)\,\mathbf{k}$, show that the surface integral of $\mathbf{f}$ can be expressed as

$$\iint_S \mathbf{f}\cdot d\mathbf{S} = \iint_S \mathbf{f}\cdot\mathbf{n}\, dS = \pm \iint_{R_{yz}} f_1\, dydz \pm \iint_{R_{zx}} f_2\, dzdx \pm \iint_{R_{xy}} f_3\, dxdy, \tag{4.31}$$

where $R_{yz}$, $R_{zx}$, and $R_{xy}$ are the projections of S onto the $yz$-, $zx$-, and $xy$-planes, respectively, and the signs of the integrals on the right-hand side of (4.31) are determined by the signs of $(\mathbf{n}\cdot\mathbf{i})$, $(\mathbf{n}\cdot\mathbf{j})$, and $(\mathbf{n}\cdot\mathbf{k})$, respectively.

**Solution:** If $\alpha$, $\beta$, and $\gamma$ are the angles between the rectangular coordinate axes and the unit vector $\mathbf{n}$, then from the result of Prob. 2.18,

$$\mathbf{n}\cdot\mathbf{i} = \cos\alpha, \quad \mathbf{n}\cdot\mathbf{j} = \cos\beta, \quad \mathbf{n}\cdot\mathbf{k} = \cos\gamma. \qquad [2.50]$$

Hence, from (2.65), $\mathbf{n}$ can be written as

$$\begin{aligned}\mathbf{n} &= (\mathbf{n}\cdot\mathbf{i})\,\mathbf{i} + (\mathbf{n}\cdot\mathbf{j})\,\mathbf{j} + (\mathbf{n}\cdot\mathbf{k})\,\mathbf{k}\\ &= (\cos\alpha)\,\mathbf{i} + (\cos\beta)\,\mathbf{j} + (\cos\gamma)\,\mathbf{k},\end{aligned} \qquad (4.32)$$

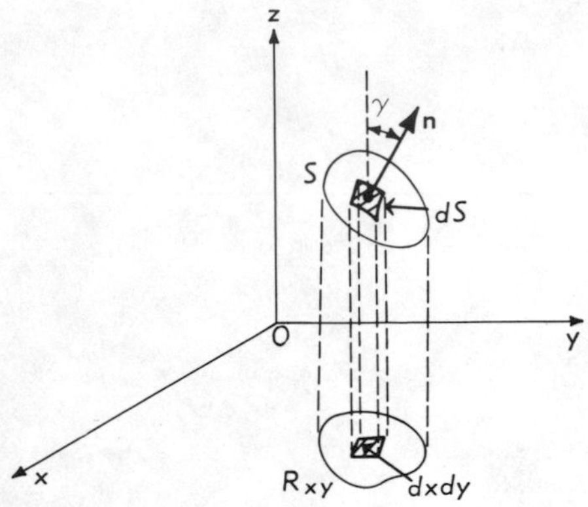


Fig. 4.3 Solution to Prob. 4.15.

and, consequently,

$$d\mathbf{S} = \mathbf{n}\,dS = (\cos\alpha)\,dS\,\mathbf{i} + (\cos\beta)\,dS\,\mathbf{j} + (\cos\gamma)\,dS\,\mathbf{k}. \qquad (4.33)$$

Now we can write (see Fig. 4.3),

$$\begin{aligned}dS\,(\mathbf{n}\cdot\mathbf{i}) &= dS\,(\cos\alpha) = \pm\,dydz,\\ dS\,(\mathbf{n}\cdot\mathbf{j}) &= dS\,(\cos\beta) = \pm\,dzdx,\\ dS\,(\mathbf{n}\cdot\mathbf{k}) &= dS\,(\cos\gamma) = \pm\,dxdy,\end{aligned}$$

where the signs are determined by those of $(\mathbf{n}\cdot\mathbf{i}) = \cos\alpha$, $(\mathbf{n}\cdot\mathbf{j}) = \cos\beta$, $(\mathbf{n}\cdot\mathbf{k}) = \cos\gamma$, respectively. Then,

$$d\mathbf{S} = \mathbf{n}\,dS = (\pm\,dydz)\,\mathbf{i} + (\pm\,dzdx)\,\mathbf{j} + (\pm\,dxdy)\,\mathbf{k}. \qquad (4.34)$$

Thus, if $\mathbf{f} = f_1\,\mathbf{i} + f_2\,\mathbf{j} + f_3\,\mathbf{k}$,

$$\iint_S \mathbf{f}\cdot d\mathbf{S} = \pm\iint_{R_{yz}} f_1\,dydz \pm \iint_{R_{zx}} f_2\,dzdx \pm \iint_{R_{xy}} f_3\,dxdy,$$

where $R_{yz}$, $R_{zx}$, and $R_{xy}$ are the projections of $S$ onto the $yz$-, $zx$-, and $xy$-planes, respectively, and the signs are determined as in (4.31).

**PROBLEM 4.16** Evaluate $\iint_S \mathbf{r}\cdot d\mathbf{S}$, where $S$ is the surface of the cube bounded by $x = 0$, $x = 1$, $y = 0$, $y = 1$, $z = 0$, $z = 1$, as shown in Fig. 4.4. The outer unit normal vector $\mathbf{n}$ and the position vector $\mathbf{r}$ of points on the surface of the cube are directed away from the origin.

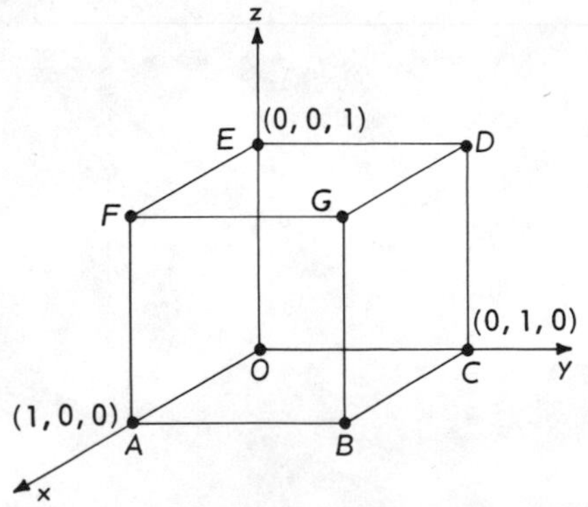


Fig. 4.4 The cube of Prob. 4.16.

**Solution:** Divide the cube into the areas $S_1$–$S_6$.

On $S_1$ for $AOCB$, $z = 0$, $\mathbf{n} = -\mathbf{k}$; hence,

$$\mathbf{r}\cdot\mathbf{n} = (x\,\mathbf{i} + y\,\mathbf{j} + z\,\mathbf{k})\cdot(-\mathbf{k}) = -z = 0.$$

On $S_2$ for $AFEO$, $y = 0$, $\mathbf{n} = -\mathbf{j}$; therefore,

$$\mathbf{r}\cdot\mathbf{n} = (x\,\mathbf{i} + y\,\mathbf{j} + z\,\mathbf{k})\cdot(-\mathbf{j}) = -y = 0.$$

On $S_3$ for $OEDC$, $z = 0$, $\mathbf{n} = -\mathbf{i}$; thus,

$$\mathbf{r}\cdot\mathbf{n} = (x\,\mathbf{i} + y\,\mathbf{j} + z\,\mathbf{k})\cdot(-\mathbf{i}) = -x = 0.$$

On $S_4$ for $AFGB$, $x = 1$, $\mathbf{n} = \mathbf{i}$; hence,

$$\mathbf{r}\cdot\mathbf{n} = (x\,\mathbf{i} + y\,\mathbf{j} + z\,\mathbf{k})\cdot(\mathbf{i}) = x = 1.$$

On $S_5$ for $BGDC$, $y = 1$, $\mathbf{n} = \mathbf{j}$; therefore,

$$\mathbf{r}\cdot\mathbf{n} = (x\,\mathbf{i} + y\,\mathbf{j} + z\,\mathbf{k})\cdot(\mathbf{j}) = y = 1.$$

On $S_6$ for $FEDG$, $z = 1$, $\mathbf{n} = \mathbf{k}$; thus,

$$\mathbf{r}\cdot\mathbf{n} = (x\mathbf{i} + y\mathbf{j} + z\mathbf{k})\cdot(\mathbf{k}) = z = 1.$$

Then, because the integrals on $S_1$–$S_3$ are zero and those on $S_4$–$S_6$, unity,

$$\iint_S \mathbf{r}\cdot d\mathbf{S} = \iint_{S_1} \mathbf{r}\cdot\mathbf{n}\,dS + \iint_{S_2} \mathbf{r}\cdot\mathbf{n}\,dS + \iint_{S_3} \mathbf{r}\cdot\mathbf{n}\,dS$$

$$+ \iint_{S_4} \mathbf{r}\cdot\mathbf{n}\,dS + \iint_{S_5} \mathbf{r}\cdot\mathbf{n}\,dS + \iint_{S_6} \mathbf{r}\cdot\mathbf{n}\,dS$$

$$= \iint_{S_4} dS + \iint_{S_5} dS + \iint_{S_6} dS$$

$$= 1 + 1 + 1$$

$$= 3.$$

**PROBLEM 4.17** If $\mathbf{f} = z\mathbf{i} + y\mathbf{j} + 2z\mathbf{k}$, evaluate $\iint_S \mathbf{f}\cdot d\mathbf{S}$, where $S$ is that part of the surface of the paraboloid $x^2 + y^2 = 1 - z$ for which $z > 0$. (See Fig. 4.5.)

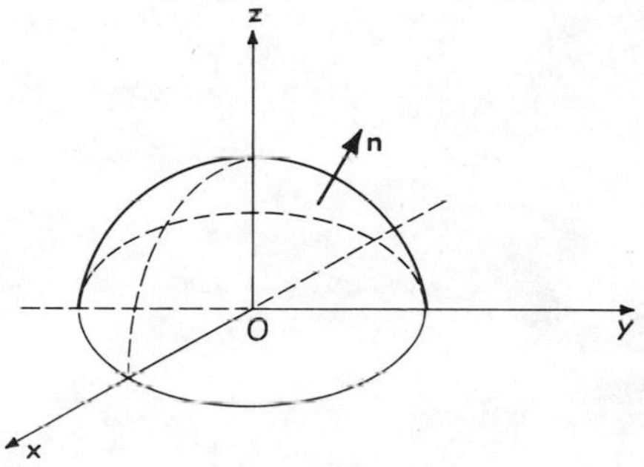

Fig. 4.5 A part of the surface of the paraboloid of Prob. 4.17.

**Solution:** In Prob. 3.31, an outer unit normal vector $\mathbf{n}$ to the surface $\phi(x, y, z) = 0$ is

$$\mathbf{n} = \frac{\nabla\phi}{|\nabla\phi|}, \qquad [3.117]$$

where $\nabla\phi$ is the gradient of $\phi$. Hence, if $\phi(x, y, z) = x^2 + y^2 + z - 1 = 0$, then from definition (3.105) of the gradient,

$$\nabla\phi = \frac{\partial\phi}{\partial x}\mathbf{i} + \frac{\partial\phi}{\partial y}\mathbf{j} + \frac{\partial\phi}{\partial z}\mathbf{k} = 2x\mathbf{i} + 2y\mathbf{j} + \mathbf{k}.$$

Hence, (3.117) becomes

$$\mathbf{n} = \frac{\nabla\phi}{|\nabla\phi|} = \frac{2x\mathbf{i} + 2y\mathbf{j} + \mathbf{k}}{(4x^2 + 4y^2 + 1)^{1/2}}.$$

The dot products of $\mathbf{n}$ with $\mathbf{i}$, $\mathbf{j}$, and $\mathbf{k}$ are

$$\mathbf{n}\cdot\mathbf{i} = \frac{2x}{(4x^2 + 4y^2 + 1)^{1/2}},$$

$$\mathbf{n}\cdot\mathbf{j} = \frac{2y}{(4x^2 + 4y^2 + 1)^{1/2}},$$

$$\mathbf{n}\cdot\mathbf{k} = \frac{1}{(4x^2 + 4y^2 + 1)^{1/2}}.$$

Thus, $\mathbf{n}\cdot\mathbf{i}$ and $\mathbf{n}\cdot\mathbf{j}$ are positive or negative *depending* upon whether $x$ and $y$ are positive or negative, while $\mathbf{n}\cdot\mathbf{k}$ is positive for all values of $x$ and $y$. Hence, if

$$\iint_S \mathbf{f}\cdot d\mathbf{S} = \iint_S \mathbf{f}\cdot\mathbf{n}\,dS = \pm\iint_{R_{yz}} f_1\,dydz \pm \iint_{R_{zx}} f_2\,dzdx \pm \iint_{R_{xy}} f_3\,dxdy \qquad [4.31]$$

is used to compute the integral, $S$ must be subdivided into two surfaces. To evaluate the first term, there must be a surface for $x > 0$ and another for $x < 0$.

Similarly, to evaluate the second term, there must be a surface for $y > 0$ and another for $y < 0$.

The first term $\iint_{R_{yz}} f_1\, dydz$ in (4.31) is evaluated as follows. For $x > 0$, $x = (1 - y^2 - z)^{1/2}$ on $S$; hence,

$$\iint_{R_{yz}} f_1\, dydz = \iint_{R_{yz}} x\, dydz$$

$$= \int_{y=-1}^{1} \int_{z=0}^{1-y^2} (1 - y^2 - z)^{1/2}\, dzdy$$

$$= \frac{2}{3} \int_{-1}^{1} (1 - y^2)^{3/2}\, dy$$

$$= \frac{2}{3} \cdot \frac{3}{8}\, \pi$$

$$= \frac{1}{4}\, \pi.$$

For $x < 0$, $x = -(1 - y^2 - z)^{1/2}$ on $S$; choosing the negative sign,

$$- \iint_{R_{yz}} f_1\, dydz = - \iint_{R_{yz}} x\, dydz$$

$$= \int_{y=-1}^{1} \int_{z=0}^{1-y^2} (1 - y^2 - z)^{1/2}\, dzdy$$

$$= \frac{1}{4}\, \pi.$$

The second term $\iint_{R_{zx}} f_2\, dzdx$ in (4.31) is evaluated as follows. For $y > 0$, $y = (1 - x^2 - z)^{1/2}$ on $S$; hence,

$$\iint_{R_{zx}} f_2\, dzdx = \iint_{R_{zx}} y\, dzdx$$

$$= \int_{x=-1}^{1} \int_{z=0}^{1-x^2} (1 - x^2 - z)^{1/2}\, dzdx$$

$$= \frac{1}{4}\, \pi$$

since the integral is the same as that for the $R_{yz}$ case. For $y < 0$, $y = -(1 - x^2 - z)^{1/2}$ on $S$; choosing the negative sign,

$$- \iint_{R_{zx}} f_2\, dzdx = - \iint_{R_{zx}} y\, dzdx$$

$$= \int_{x=-1}^{1} \int_{z=0}^{1-x^2} (1 - x^2 - z)^{1/2}\, dzdx$$

$$= \frac{1}{4}\, \pi.$$

For the third term in (4.31), since $\mathbf{n}\cdot\mathbf{k} > 0$,

$$\iint_{R_{xy}} f_3\, dxdy = \iint_{R_{xy}} 2z\, dxdy = 2\int_{x=-1}^{1}\int_{y=-\sqrt{1-x^2}}^{\sqrt{1-x^2}} (1 - x^2 - y^2)\, dydx$$

$$= 2\cdot\frac{4}{3}\int_{-1}^{1} (1 - x^2)^{3/2}\, dx$$

$$= \frac{8}{3}\cdot\frac{3}{8}\pi$$

$$= \pi.$$

Adding the above results for all three terms in (4.31) yields

$$\iint_S \mathbf{f}\cdot d\mathbf{S} = \left(\frac{1}{4}\pi + \frac{1}{4}\pi\right) + \left(\frac{1}{4}\pi + \frac{1}{4}\pi\right) + \pi = 2\pi.$$

**PROBLEM 4.18** If $S$ is represented by $z = z(x, y)$, show that the flux of $\mathbf{f}$ through $S$ is

$$\iint_S \mathbf{f}\cdot d\mathbf{S} = \iint_S \mathbf{f}\cdot\mathbf{n}\, dS$$

$$= \iint_{R_{xy}} \mathbf{f}\cdot\mathbf{n}\sec\gamma\, dxdy$$

$$= \iint_{R_{xy}} \mathbf{f}\cdot\frac{\mathbf{n}}{\mathbf{n}\cdot\mathbf{k}}\, dxdy, \tag{4.35}$$

where $\sec\gamma = \dfrac{1}{\mathbf{n}\cdot\mathbf{k}} = \left[\left(\dfrac{\partial z}{\partial x}\right)^2 + \left(\dfrac{\partial z}{\partial y}\right)^2 + 1\right]^{1/2}$.

**Solution:** If $S$ is represented by $z = z(x, y)$, then from Prob. 3.24, the unit normal vector is

$$\mathbf{n} = \frac{-\dfrac{\partial z}{\partial x}\mathbf{i} - \dfrac{\partial z}{\partial y}\mathbf{j} + \mathbf{k}}{\left[\left(\dfrac{\partial z}{\partial x}\right)^2 + \left(\dfrac{\partial z}{\partial y}\right)^2 + 1\right]^{1/2}}. \qquad [3.89]$$

Hence, if $\gamma$ is the angle between $\mathbf{n}$ and $\mathbf{k}$,

$$\mathbf{n}\cdot\mathbf{k} = \cos\gamma = \frac{1}{\sec\gamma} = \frac{1}{\left[\left(\dfrac{\partial z}{\partial x}\right)^2 + \left(\dfrac{\partial z}{\partial y}\right)^2 + 1\right]^{1/2}}. \tag{4.36}$$

Next, from (3.103), the differential element $dS$ of the surface area $S$ is

$$dS = \left[\left(\frac{\partial z}{\partial x}\right)^2 + \left(\frac{\partial z}{\partial y}\right)^2 + 1\right]^{1/2} dxdy$$

$$= \sec\gamma\, dxdy$$

$$= \frac{1}{(\mathbf{n}\cdot\mathbf{k})}\, dxdy. \tag{4.37}$$

Hence, the flux of $\mathbf{f}$ through $S$ is

$$\iint_S \mathbf{f}\cdot d\mathbf{S} = \iint_S \mathbf{f}\cdot\mathbf{n}\, dS$$

$$= \iint_{R_{xy}} \mathbf{f}\cdot\mathbf{n} \sec\gamma\, dxdy$$

$$= \iint_{R_{xy}} \mathbf{f}\cdot\frac{\mathbf{n}}{\mathbf{n}\cdot\mathbf{k}}\, dxdy.$$

**PROBLEM 4.19** If $\mathbf{f} = z\mathbf{i} + y\mathbf{j} + 2z\mathbf{k}$, use (4.35) to evaluate $\iint_S \mathbf{f}\cdot d\mathbf{S}$, where $S$ is that part of the surface of the paraboloid $x^2 + y^2 = 1 - z$ for which $z > 0$. (Cf., Prob. 4.17 and Fig. 4.5.)

**Solution:** Since $S$ is represented by $z = 1 - x^2 - y^2$ with $z > 0$, the unit normal vector from (3.89) is

$$\mathbf{n} = \frac{-\dfrac{\partial z}{\partial x}\mathbf{i} - \dfrac{\partial z}{\partial y}\mathbf{j} + \mathbf{k}}{\left[\left(\dfrac{\partial z}{\partial x}\right)^2 + \left(\dfrac{\partial z}{\partial y}\right)^2 + 1\right]^{1/2}}$$

$$= \frac{2x\mathbf{i} + 2y\mathbf{j} + \mathbf{k}}{(4x^2 + 4y^2 + 1)^{1/2}}.$$

Now,

$$\mathbf{n}\cdot\mathbf{k} = \frac{1}{(4x^2 + 4y^2 + 1)^{1/2}},$$

and

$$\mathbf{f}\cdot\mathbf{n} = \frac{1}{(4x^2 + 4y^2 + 1)^{1/2}}[(x)(2x) + (y)(2y) + (2z)1] = \frac{2x^2 + 2y^2 + 2z}{(4x^2 + 4y^2 + 1)^{1/2}}.$$

Thus, according to (4.35),

$$\iint_S \mathbf{f}\cdot d\mathbf{S} = \iint_{R_{xy}} \frac{2x^2 + 2y^2 + 2z}{(2x^2 + 4y^2 + 1)^{1/2}}(4x^2 + 4y^2 + 1)^{1/2}\, dxdy$$

$$= \iint_{R_{xy}} [2x^2 + 2y^2 + 2(1 - x^2 - y^2)]\, dxdy$$

$$= 2\int_{x=-1}^{1}\int_{y=-\sqrt{1-x^2}}^{\sqrt{1-x^2}} dxdy$$

$$= 4\int_{-1}^{1}(1 - x^2)^{1/2}\, dx$$

$$= 4\cdot\frac{\pi}{2}$$

$$= 2\pi.$$

**PROBLEM 4.20** Evaluate $\iint_S \mathbf{r}\times d\mathbf{S}$, where $S$ is the surface of the cube bounded by $x = 0$, $x = 1$, $y = 0$, $y = 1$, $z = 0$, $z = 1$, and $\mathbf{r}$ is the position vector and $\mathbf{n}$ is the unit normal vector having outward direction. (Cf., Prob. 4.16 and Fig. 4.4.)

**Solution:** Referring to Fig. 4.4, we have on $S_1$ for $AOCB$, $\mathbf{n} = -\mathbf{k}$, $d\mathbf{S} = \mathbf{n}\,dxdy = -dxdy\,\mathbf{k}$; hence,

$$\mathbf{r} \times \mathbf{n} = (x\,\mathbf{i} + y\,\mathbf{j} + z\,\mathbf{k}) \times (-\mathbf{k}) = -y\,\mathbf{i} + x\,\mathbf{j}.$$

Thus,

$$\iint_{S_1} \mathbf{r} \times d\mathbf{S} = \int_0^1 \int_0^1 (-y\,\mathbf{i} + x\,\mathbf{j})\,dxdy$$

$$= -\mathbf{i}\int_0^1 \int_0^1 y\;dydx + \mathbf{j}\int_0^1 \int_0^1 x\;dxdy$$

$$= -\frac{1}{2}\,\mathbf{i} + \frac{1}{2}\,\mathbf{j}.$$

On $S_2$ for $AFEO$, $\mathbf{n} = -\mathbf{j}$, $d\mathbf{S} = \mathbf{n}\,dzdx = -dzdx\,\mathbf{j}$; therefore,

$$\mathbf{r} \times \mathbf{n} = (x\,\mathbf{i} + y\,\mathbf{j} + z\,\mathbf{k}) \times (-\mathbf{j}) = z\,\mathbf{i} - x\,\mathbf{k}.$$

Hence,

$$\iint_{S_2} \mathbf{r} \times d\mathbf{S} = \int_0^1 \int_0^1 (z\,\mathbf{i} - x\,\mathbf{k})\,dzdx$$

$$= \mathbf{i}\int_0^1 \int_0^1 z\;dzdx - \mathbf{k}\int_0^1 \int_0^1 x\;dxdz$$

$$= \frac{1}{2}\,\mathbf{i} - \frac{1}{2}\,\mathbf{k}.$$

On $S_3$ for $OEDC$, $\mathbf{n} = -\mathbf{i}$, $d\mathbf{S} = \mathbf{n}\,dydz = -dydz\,\mathbf{i}$; thus,

$$\mathbf{r} \times \mathbf{n} = (x\,\mathbf{i} + y\,\mathbf{j} + z\,\mathbf{k}) \times (-\mathbf{i}) = -z\,\mathbf{j} + y\,\mathbf{k}.$$

Hence,

$$\iint_{S_3} \mathbf{r} \times d\mathbf{S} = \int_0^1 \int_0^1 (-z\,\mathbf{j} + y\,\mathbf{k})\;dydz$$

$$= -\mathbf{j}\int_0^1 \int_0^1 z\;dzdy + \mathbf{k}\int_0^1 \int_0^1 y\;dydz$$

$$= -\frac{1}{2}\,\mathbf{j} + \frac{1}{2}\,\mathbf{k}.$$

On $S_4$ for $AFGB$, $\mathbf{n} = \mathbf{i}$, $d\mathbf{S} = \mathbf{n}\,dydz = dydz\,\mathbf{i}$; hence,

$$\mathbf{r} \times \mathbf{n} = (x\,\mathbf{i} + y\,\mathbf{j} + z\,\mathbf{k}) \times \mathbf{i} = z\,\mathbf{j} - y\,\mathbf{k}.$$

Thus,

$$\iint_{S_4} \mathbf{r} \times d\mathbf{S} = \int_0^1 \int_0^1 (z\,\mathbf{i} - y\,\mathbf{k})\;dydz = \frac{1}{2}\,\mathbf{j} - \frac{1}{2}\,\mathbf{k}.$$

On $S_5$ for $BGDC$, $\mathbf{n} = \mathbf{j}$, $d\mathbf{S} = \mathbf{n}\,dzdx = dzdz\,\mathbf{j}$; thus,

$$\mathbf{r} \times \mathbf{n} = (x\,\mathbf{i} + y\,\mathbf{j} + z\,\mathbf{k}) \times \mathbf{j} = -z\,\mathbf{i} + x\,\mathbf{k}.$$

Hence,

$$\iint_{S_5} \mathbf{r} \times d\mathbf{S} = \int_0^1 \int_0^1 (-z\,\mathbf{i} + x\,\mathbf{k})\, dzdx = -\frac{1}{2}\,\mathbf{i} + \frac{1}{2}\,\mathbf{k}.$$

On $S_6$ for $FEDG$, $\mathbf{n} = \mathbf{k}$, $d\mathbf{S} = \mathbf{n}\, dxdy = dxdy\, \mathbf{k}$; therefore,

$$\mathbf{r} \times \mathbf{n} = (x\,\mathbf{i} + y\,\mathbf{j} + z\,\mathbf{k})\, x\,\mathbf{k} = y\,\mathbf{i} - x\,\mathbf{j}.$$

Hence,

$$\iint_{S_6} \mathbf{r} \times d\mathbf{S} = \int_0^1 \int_0^1 (y\,\mathbf{i} - x\,\mathbf{j})\, dxdy = \frac{1}{2}\,\mathbf{i} - \frac{1}{2}\,\mathbf{j}.$$

Adding all the above results yields

$$\iint_S \mathbf{r} \times d\mathbf{S} = \mathbf{0}. \tag{4.38}$$

**PROBLEM 4.21** Evaluate $\iint_S \mathbf{r} \times d\mathbf{S}$, where $S$ is the closed spherical surface represented by $x^2 + y^2 + z^2 = a^2$.

**Solution:** From Prob. 4.14, the outer unit normal vector $\mathbf{n}$ at $S$ is

$$\mathbf{n} = \mathbf{e}_r = \frac{\mathbf{r}}{|\mathbf{r}|} = \frac{\mathbf{r}}{a}.$$

Thus, from (1.58), $\mathbf{r} \times \mathbf{n} = (1/a)\,\mathbf{r} \times \mathbf{r} = \mathbf{0}$. Hence,

$$\iint_S \mathbf{r} \times d\mathbf{S} = \iint_S \mathbf{r} \times \mathbf{n}\, dS = \mathbf{0}. \tag{4.39}$$

## 4.3 Volume Integrals

Since the *element of volume* $dV$ is a scalar, consider two *volume integrals* over a region $R$:

$$\iiint_R \phi\, dV, \tag{4.40}$$

$$\iiint_R \mathbf{f}\, dV. \tag{4.41}$$

In the rectangular coordinate system,

$$dV = dxdydz, \tag{4.42}$$

and (4.40) can be rewritten as

$$\iiint_R \phi(x, y, z)\, dxdydz, \tag{4.43}$$

which is the ordinary triple integral of $\phi(x, y, z)$ over the region $R$. Setting $\phi(x, y, z) = 1$, the volume $V$ of the region $R$ is

$$V = \iiint_R dV = \iiint_R dxdydz. \tag{4.44}$$

If $\mathbf{f} = f_1\,\mathbf{i} + f_2\,\mathbf{j} + f_3\,\mathbf{k}$, then (4.41) can be resolved into its components; i.e.,

$$\iiint_R \mathbf{f}\,dV = \mathbf{i}\iiint_R f_1\,dV + \mathbf{j}\iiint_R f_2\,dV + \mathbf{k}\iiint_R f_3\,dV. \tag{4.45}$$

**PROBLEM 4.22** Evaluate $\iiint_R \nabla\cdot\mathbf{r}\,dV$, where $R$ is any region with volume $V$ and $\mathbf{r}$ is the position vector.

**Solution:** From (3.129), $\nabla\cdot\mathbf{r} = 3$. Hence, using (4.44),

$$\iiint_R \nabla\cdot\mathbf{r}\,dV = \iiint_R 3\,dV = 3\iiint_R dV = 3V. \tag{4.46}$$

**PROBLEM 4.23** Evaluate $\iiint_R \nabla\times\mathbf{f}\,dV$ if $\mathbf{f} = y\mathbf{i} - x\mathbf{j}$ and $R$ is any space region with volume $V$.

**Solution:** By (3.138), the curl of $\mathbf{f}$ is

$$\nabla\times\mathbf{f} = \begin{vmatrix} \mathbf{i} & \mathbf{j} & \mathbf{k} \\ \dfrac{\partial}{\partial x} & \dfrac{\partial}{\partial y} & \dfrac{\partial}{\partial z} \\ y & -x & 0 \end{vmatrix} = -2\mathbf{k}.$$

Hence,

$$\iiint_R \nabla\times\mathbf{f}\,dV = -2\mathbf{k}\iiint_R dV = -2V\mathbf{k}.$$

## 4.4 Alternate Definitions of the Gradient, Divergence, and Curl

The *gradient* of a scalar function $\phi$, written as grad $\phi$ or $\nabla\phi$, is defined as

$$\nabla\phi = \frac{\partial\phi}{\partial x}\mathbf{i} + \frac{\partial\phi}{\partial y}\mathbf{j} + \frac{\partial\phi}{\partial z}\mathbf{k}. \tag{3.105}$$

The *divergence* of $\mathbf{f}$, written div $\mathbf{f}$ or $\nabla\cdot\mathbf{f}$, can be defined by

$$\nabla\cdot\mathbf{f} = \lim_{\Delta V\to 0}\frac{1}{\Delta V}\oiint_S \mathbf{f}\cdot d\mathbf{S}, \tag{4.47}$$

where $\Delta V$ is the volume of the region $R$ bounded by a closed surface $S$. The volume $\Delta V$ always contains the point at which the divergence $\nabla\cdot\mathbf{f}$ is to be evaluated as $\Delta V$ approaches zero.

The *curl* of $\mathbf{f}$, written curl $\mathbf{f}$ or $\nabla\times\mathbf{f}$, can be defined as

$$\text{or } \nabla\times\mathbf{f} = \mathbf{n}_{max}\lim_{\Delta S\to 0}\frac{1}{\Delta S}\oint_C \mathbf{f}\cdot d\mathbf{r}, \tag{4.48}$$

where $\Delta S$ is the surface bounded by a simple closed curve $C$ and $\mathbf{n}_{max}$ is the unit normal vector associated with $\Delta\mathbf{S}$ such that the orientation of the plane of $\Delta\mathbf{S}$ will give a maximum value of

$$\frac{1}{\Delta S}\oint_C \mathbf{f}\cdot d\mathbf{r}. \tag{4.49}$$

The curl $\nabla \times \mathbf{f}$ of $\mathbf{f}$ is also defined by its component in a particular direction; i.e., the component of $\nabla \times \mathbf{f}$ in the $\mathbf{n}$ direction is

$$\mathbf{n}\cdot(\nabla \times \mathbf{f}) = \lim_{\Delta S \to 0} \frac{1}{\Delta S}\oint_C \mathbf{f}\cdot d\mathbf{r}, \tag{4.50}$$

where $\Delta S$ is a surface bounded by a simple closed curve $C$ and $\mathbf{n}$ is the unit normal vector associated with $\Delta \mathbf{S}$, that is, $\Delta \mathbf{S} = \mathbf{n}\,\Delta S$.

As in definition (4.47) of $\nabla \cdot \mathbf{f}$, $\Delta S$ contains the point at which the curl $\nabla \times \mathbf{f}$ is to be evaluated as $\Delta S$ approaches zero.

**PROBLEM 4.24** Give the physical interpretation of $\nabla \cdot \mathbf{f}$ as defined by (4.47).

**Solution:** In (4.27), the surface integral $\iint_S \mathbf{f}\cdot d\mathbf{S}$ is defined as the flux of $\mathbf{f}$ passing through the surface $S$. Then $\oiint_S \mathbf{f}\cdot d\mathbf{S}$ is the total net outflow flux of $\mathbf{f}$ through the closed surface $S$. Hence, (4.47) shows that the divergence of $\mathbf{f}$ at a point $P$ is the limit of the net outflow flux per unit volume as $S$ shrinks to the point $P$.

If the small volume that surrounds $P$ contains a *source* or *sink* of a vector field $\mathbf{f}$, then the flux of $\mathbf{f}$ will diverge from or converge to $P$, depending on whether $\nabla \cdot \mathbf{f}$ is positive or negative. Hence, $\nabla \cdot \mathbf{f}$ can be considered a measure of vector *source* or *sink* strength at $P$.

**PROBLEM 4.25** Using (4.47), derive the formula for $\nabla \cdot \mathbf{f}$ as given by (3.127).

**Solution:** If the point $(x, y, z)$ at the center of a small rectangular parallelepiped has edges $\Delta x$, $\Delta y$, and $\Delta z$, as shown in Fig. 4.6, then $\Delta V = \Delta x \Delta y \Delta z$. If $\mathbf{f} = f_1\,\mathbf{i} + f_2\,\mathbf{j} + f_3\,\mathbf{k}$, then

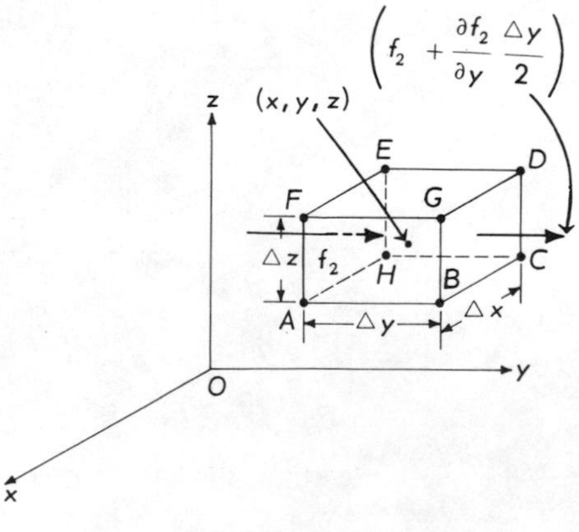


Fig. 4.6 Solution to Prob. 4.25.

on $S_1$ for $AFGB$, $\mathbf{n} = \mathbf{i}$, $d\mathbf{S} = dydz\,\mathbf{i}$,
on $S_2$ for $FEDG$, $\mathbf{n} = -\mathbf{i}$, $d\mathbf{S} = -dydz\,\mathbf{i}$,
on $S_3$ for $BGDC$, $\mathbf{n} = \mathbf{j}$, $d\mathbf{S} = dzdx\,\mathbf{j}$,
on $S_4$ for $AFEH$, $\mathbf{n} = -\mathbf{j}$, $d\mathbf{S} = -dzdx\,\mathbf{j}$,
on $S_5$ for $FEDG$, $\mathbf{n} = \mathbf{k}$, $d\mathbf{S} = dxdy\,\mathbf{k}$,
on $S_6$ for $AHGB$, $\mathbf{n} = -\mathbf{k}$, $d\mathbf{S} = -dxdy\,\mathbf{k}$.

Hence, ignoring the differential contributions of higher order,

$$\iint_{S_1} \mathbf{f}\cdot d\mathbf{S} = \left(f_1 + \frac{\partial f_1}{\partial x}\frac{\Delta x}{2}\right)\Delta y \Delta z,$$

$$\iint_{S_2} \mathbf{f}\cdot d\mathbf{S} = -\left(f_1 - \frac{\partial f_1}{\partial x}\frac{\Delta x}{2}\right)\Delta y \Delta z,$$

$$\iint_{S_3} \mathbf{f}\cdot d\mathbf{S} = \left(f_2 + \frac{\partial f_2}{\partial y}\frac{\Delta y}{2}\right)\Delta z \Delta x,$$

$$\iint_{S_4} \mathbf{f}\cdot d\mathbf{S} = -\left(f_2 - \frac{\partial f_2}{\partial y}\frac{\Delta y}{2}\right)\Delta z \Delta x,$$

$$\iint_{S_5} \mathbf{f}\cdot d\mathbf{S} = \left(f_3 + \frac{\partial f_3}{\partial z}\frac{\Delta z}{2}\right)\Delta x \Delta y,$$

$$\iint_{S_6} \mathbf{f}\cdot d\mathbf{S} = -\left(f_3 - \frac{\partial f_3}{\partial z}\frac{\Delta z}{2}\right)\Delta x \Delta y.$$

Adding all the above results yields

$$\oiint_S \mathbf{f}\cdot d\mathbf{S} = \left(\frac{\partial f_1}{\partial x} + \frac{\partial f_2}{\partial y} + \frac{\partial f_3}{\partial z}\right)\Delta x \Delta y \Delta z = \left(\frac{\partial f_1}{\partial x} + \frac{\partial f_2}{\partial y} + \frac{\partial f_3}{\partial z}\right)\Delta V.$$

Hence, by (4.47),

$$\nabla\cdot\mathbf{f} = \lim_{\Delta V\to 0} \oiint_S \mathbf{f}\cdot d\mathbf{S} = \frac{\partial f_1}{\partial x} + \frac{\partial f_2}{\partial y} + \frac{\partial f_3}{\partial z}. \qquad [3.127]$$

**PROBLEM 4.26** Give the physical interpretation of $\nabla\times\mathbf{f}$ as defined by (4.48).

**Solution:** The integral on the right of (4.48) or (4.49), i.e., $\oint_C \mathbf{f}\cdot\mathbf{r}$, is the *circulation* of **f** around $C$ defined in (4.9). Hence, (4.48) shows that the magnitude of $\nabla\times\mathbf{f}$ at a point $P$ is the limit of the circulation per unit area as the curve $C$ shrinks to the point $P$, i.e., the intensity of circulation at $P$. In general, the circulation of **f** around $C$ depends on the orientation of the plane of $C$. The direction of $\nabla\times\mathbf{f}$ is the direction in which maximum circulation occurs.

**PROBLEM 4.27** Using (4.50), derive the definition of the curl of **f** as the cross product of $\nabla$ and **f** as given by (3.138). Ignore the higher order terms.

**Solution:** If a rectangle $EFGH$ about the point $(x, y, z)$ has sides $\Delta y$ and $\Delta z$, as shown in Fig. 4.7, then $\Delta\mathbf{S} = \mathbf{i}\,\Delta S = \mathbf{i}\,\Delta y\Delta z$. If $\mathbf{f} = f_1\mathbf{i} + f_2\mathbf{j} + f_3\mathbf{k}$, then

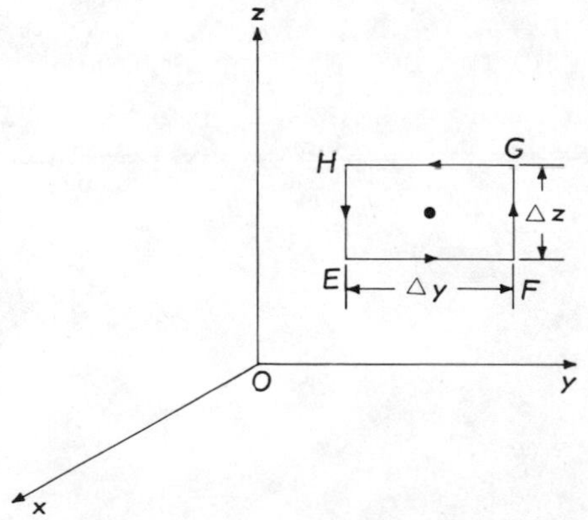

Fig. 4.7 Solution to Prob. 4.27.

for side $EF$, $d\mathbf{r} = dy\,\mathbf{j}$, $$\int_{EF} \mathbf{f}\cdot d\mathbf{r} = \left(f_2 - \frac{\partial f_2}{\partial z}\frac{\Delta z}{2}\right)\Delta y,$$

for side $FG$, $d\mathbf{r} = dz\,\mathbf{k}$, $$\int_{FG} \mathbf{f}\cdot d\mathbf{r} = \left(f_3 + \frac{\partial f_3}{\partial y}\frac{\Delta y}{2}\right)\Delta z,$$

for side $GH$, $d\mathbf{r} = -dy\,\mathbf{j}$, $$\int_{GH} \mathbf{f}\cdot d\mathbf{r} = -\left(f_2 + \frac{\partial f_2}{\partial z}\frac{\Delta z}{2}\right)\Delta y,$$

for side $HE$, $d\mathbf{r} = -dz\,\mathbf{k}$, $$\int_{HE} \mathbf{f}\cdot d\mathbf{r} = -\left(f_3 - \frac{\partial f_3}{\partial y}\frac{\Delta y}{2}\right)\Delta z.$$

Adding all the above results yields

$$\oint_C \mathbf{f}\cdot d\mathbf{r} = \left(\frac{\partial f_3}{\partial y} - \frac{\partial f_2}{\partial z}\right)\Delta y\Delta z = \left(\frac{\partial f_3}{\partial y} - \frac{\partial f_2}{\partial z}\right)\Delta S.$$

Hence, from (4.50),

$$\mathbf{i}\cdot(\nabla\times\mathbf{f}) = \lim_{\Delta S\to 0}\frac{1}{\Delta S}\int_C \mathbf{f}\cdot d\mathbf{r} = \left(\frac{\partial f_3}{\partial y} - \frac{\partial f_2}{\partial z}\right). \tag{4.51}$$

By similar integration around rectangles in the *zx*- and *xy*-planes, or by simple cyclic permutation of $x$, $y$, $z$ and 1, 2, 3,

$$\mathbf{j}\cdot(\nabla\times\mathbf{f}) = \left(\frac{\partial f_1}{\partial z} - \frac{\partial f_3}{\partial x}\right), \tag{4.52}$$

$$\mathbf{k}\cdot(\nabla\times\mathbf{f}) = \left(\frac{\partial f_2}{\partial x} - \frac{\partial f_1}{\partial y}\right). \tag{4.53}$$

Since for an arbitrary vector $\mathbf{A}$, by (2.65), $\mathbf{A} = (\mathbf{A}\cdot\mathbf{i})\mathbf{i} + (\mathbf{A}\cdot\mathbf{j})\mathbf{j} + (\mathbf{A}\cdot\mathbf{k})\mathbf{k}$, we obtain (3.138):

$$\nabla\times\mathbf{f} = \left(\frac{\partial f_3}{\partial y} - \frac{\partial f_2}{\partial z}\right)\mathbf{i} + \left(\frac{\partial f_1}{\partial z} - \frac{\partial f_3}{\partial x}\right)\mathbf{j} + \left(\frac{\partial f_2}{\partial x} - \frac{\partial f_1}{\partial y}\right)\mathbf{k}$$

$$= \begin{vmatrix} \mathbf{i} & \mathbf{j} & \mathbf{k} \\ \dfrac{\partial}{\partial x} & \dfrac{\partial}{\partial y} & \dfrac{\partial}{\partial z} \\ f_1 & f_2 & f_3 \end{vmatrix}. \tag{4.54}$$

Alternative definitions of $\nabla\phi$, $\nabla\cdot\mathbf{f}$, and $\nabla\times\mathbf{f}$ are

$$\nabla\phi = \lim_{\Delta V\to 0}\frac{1}{\Delta V}\oiint_S d\mathbf{S}\,\phi, \tag{4.55}$$

$$\nabla\cdot\mathbf{f} = \lim_{\Delta V\to 0}\frac{1}{\Delta V}\oiint_S d\mathbf{S}\cdot\mathbf{f}, \qquad [4.47]$$

$$\nabla\times\mathbf{f} = \lim_{\Delta V\to 0}\frac{1}{\Delta V}\oiint_S d\mathbf{S}\times\mathbf{f}, \tag{4.56}$$

where $\Delta V$ is the volume of the region $R$ bounded by a closed surface $S$.

**PROBLEM 4.28** Show that (4.55) is consistent with the definition of $\nabla\phi$ given by (3.105). Ignore the higher order terms.

**Solution:** Follow the procedure of Prob. 4.25 and use the same notations. (Cf., Fig. 4.6.) Thus,

$$\iint_{S_1} d\mathbf{S}\,\phi = \mathbf{i}\left(\phi + \frac{\partial\phi}{\partial x}\frac{\Delta x}{2}\right)\Delta y\Delta z,$$

$$\iint_{S_2} d\mathbf{S}\,\phi = -\mathbf{i}\left(\phi - \frac{\partial\phi}{\partial x}\frac{\Delta x}{2}\right)\Delta y\Delta z,$$

$$\iint_{S_3} d\mathbf{S}\,\phi = \mathbf{j}\left(\phi + \frac{\partial\phi}{\partial y}\frac{\Delta y}{2}\right)\Delta z\Delta x,$$

$$\iint_{S_4} d\mathbf{S}\,\phi = -\mathbf{j}\left(\phi - \frac{\partial\phi}{\partial y}\frac{\Delta y}{2}\right)\Delta z\Delta x,$$

$$\iint_{S_5} d\mathbf{S}\,\phi = \mathbf{k}\left(\phi + \frac{\partial\phi}{\partial z}\frac{\Delta z}{2}\right)\Delta x\Delta y,$$

$$\iint_{S_6} d\mathbf{S}\,\phi = -\mathbf{k}\left(\phi - \frac{\partial\phi}{\partial z}\frac{\Delta z}{2}\right)\Delta x\Delta y.$$

Adding all the above results yields

$$\oiint_S d\mathbf{S}\,\phi = \left[\mathbf{i}\left(\frac{\partial\phi}{\partial x}\right) + \mathbf{j}\left(\frac{\partial\phi}{\partial y}\right) + \mathbf{k}\left(\frac{\partial\phi}{\partial z}\right)\right]\Delta x\Delta y\Delta z$$

$$= \left[\mathbf{i}\left(\frac{\partial\phi}{\partial x}\right) + \mathbf{j}\left(\frac{\partial\phi}{\partial y}\right) + \mathbf{k}\left(\frac{\partial\phi}{\partial z}\right)\right]\Delta V.$$

Hence, by (4.55), we obtain (3.105):

$$\nabla\phi = \lim_{\Delta V\to 0}\frac{1}{\Delta V}\oiint d\mathbf{S}\,\phi = \mathbf{i}\frac{\partial\phi}{\partial x} + \mathbf{j}\frac{\partial\phi}{\partial y} + \mathbf{k}\frac{\partial\phi}{\partial z}.$$

**PROBLEM 4.29** Show that (4.56) is consistent with the definition of $\nabla\times\mathbf{f}$ given by (3.138). Ignore the higher order terms.

**Solution:** Follow the procedure of Prob. 4.25 and use the same notations. (Cf., Fig. 4.6.) We have for the surface $S_1$,

$$\iint_{S_1} d\mathbf{S}\times\mathbf{f} = \iint_{S_1} \mathbf{i}\times(f_1\mathbf{i} + f_2\mathbf{j} + f_3\mathbf{k})\,dydz$$

$$= \iint_{S_1} (\mathbf{k}\,f_2 - \mathbf{j}\,f_3)\,dydz$$

$$= \mathbf{k}\left(f_2 + \frac{\partial f_2}{\partial x}\frac{\Delta x}{2}\right)\Delta y\Delta z - \mathbf{j}\left(f_3 + \frac{\partial f_3}{\partial x}\frac{\Delta x}{2}\right)\Delta y\Delta z.$$

Similarly, for the other five surfaces,

$$\iint_{S_2} d\mathbf{S}\times\mathbf{f} = -\mathbf{k}\left(f_2 - \frac{\partial f_2}{\partial x}\frac{\Delta x}{2}\right)\Delta y\Delta z + \mathbf{j}\left(f_3 - \frac{\partial f_3}{\partial x}\frac{\Delta x}{2}\right)\Delta y\Delta z,$$

$$\iint_{S_3} d\mathbf{S}\times\mathbf{f} = -\mathbf{k}\left(f_1 + \frac{\partial f_1}{\partial y}\frac{\Delta y}{2}\right)\Delta z\Delta x + \mathbf{i}\left(f_3 + \frac{\partial f_3}{\partial y}\frac{\Delta y}{2}\right)\Delta z\Delta x,$$

$$\iint_{S_4} d\mathbf{S}\times\mathbf{f} = \mathbf{k}\left(f_1 - \frac{\partial f_1}{\partial y}\frac{\Delta y}{2}\right)\Delta z\Delta x - \mathbf{i}\left(f_3 - \frac{\partial f_3}{\partial y}\frac{\Delta y}{2}\right)\Delta z\Delta x,$$

$$\iint_{S_5} d\mathbf{S}\times\mathbf{f} = \mathbf{j}\left(f_1 + \frac{\partial f_1}{\partial z}\frac{\Delta z}{2}\right)\Delta x\Delta y - \mathbf{i}\left(f_2 + \frac{\partial f_2}{\partial z}\frac{\Delta z}{2}\right)\Delta x\Delta y,$$

$$\iint_{S_6} d\mathbf{S}\times\mathbf{f} = -\mathbf{j}\left(f_1 - \frac{\partial f_1}{\partial z}\frac{\Delta z}{2}\right)\Delta x\Delta y + \mathbf{i}\left(f_2 - \frac{\partial f_2}{\partial z}\frac{\Delta z}{2}\right)\Delta x\Delta y.$$

Adding all the above results yields

$$\oiint_S d\mathbf{S} \times \mathbf{f} = \left[\mathbf{i}\left(\frac{\partial f_3}{\partial y} - \frac{\partial f_2}{\partial z}\right) + \mathbf{j}\left(\frac{\partial f_1}{\partial z} - \frac{\partial f_3}{\partial x}\right) + \mathbf{k}\left(\frac{\partial f_2}{\partial x} - \frac{\partial f_1}{\partial y}\right)\right] \Delta x \Delta y \Delta z$$

$$= \left[\mathbf{i}\left(\frac{\partial f_3}{\partial y} - \frac{\partial f_2}{\partial z}\right) + \mathbf{j}\left(\frac{\partial f_1}{\partial z} - \frac{\partial f_3}{\partial x}\right) + \mathbf{k}\left(\frac{\partial f_2}{\partial x} - \frac{\partial f_1}{\partial y}\right)\right] \Delta V.$$

Hence, by (4.56), we obtain (3.138):

$$\nabla \times \mathbf{f} = \lim_{\Delta V \to 0} \oiint_S d\mathbf{S} \times \mathbf{f} = \mathbf{i}\left(\frac{\partial f_3}{\partial y} - \frac{\partial f_2}{\partial z}\right) + \mathbf{j}\left(\frac{\partial f_1}{\partial z} - \frac{\partial f_3}{\partial x}\right) + \mathbf{k}\left(\frac{\partial f_2}{\partial x} - \frac{\partial f_1}{\partial y}\right).$$

**PROBLEM 4.30** Find an equivalent integral representation of the $\nabla$ operator.

**Solution:** From (4.55–6), $\nabla$ is represented by

$$\nabla = \lim_{\Delta V \to 0} \frac{1}{\Delta V} \oiint_S d\mathbf{S}. \tag{4.57}$$

## 4.5 Divergence Theorem or Gauss' Theorem

The definition of divergence,

$$\operatorname{div} \mathbf{f} = \lim_{\Delta V \to 0} \frac{1}{\Delta V} \oiint_S \mathbf{f} \cdot d\mathbf{S}, \qquad [4.47]$$

gives the value of div **f** at a point.

The *divergence theorem*, or *Gauss' theorem*, is obtained by extending (4.47) to a finite region. If **f** is a continuous vector function in a region $R$ with volume $V$ and bounded by a closed surface $S$, then

$$\iiint_R \nabla \cdot \mathbf{f}\, dV = \oiint_S \mathbf{f} \cdot d\mathbf{S}. \tag{4.58}$$

This theorem has a special consequence, called Green's theorem. This theorem is also referred to as Green's theorem for space because its two dimensional form is Green's theorem for a plane. [See Sec. 4.6 and (4.112).]

**PROBLEM 4.31** Verify the divergence theorem (4.58).

**Solution:** Consider a finite closed surface $S$ that encloses a region $R$ with volume $V$. Divide $R$ into $N$ subregions of volumes $\Delta V_1, \Delta V_2, \cdots, \Delta V_N$. At point $(x_i, y_i, z_i)$ within $\Delta V_i$, where $i = 1, 2, \cdots, N$, the divergence definition (4.47) gives $\nabla \cdot \mathbf{f} = \frac{1}{\Delta V_i} \oiint_{\Delta S_i} \mathbf{f} \cdot d\mathbf{S} + \varepsilon_i$, where $\varepsilon_i \longrightarrow 0$ as $\Delta V_i \longrightarrow 0$. Thus,

$$\nabla \cdot \mathbf{f}\, \Delta V_i = \oiint_{\Delta S_i} \mathbf{f} \cdot d\mathbf{S} + \varepsilon_i \Delta V_i. \tag{4.59}$$

The sum of the entire volume $V$ is

$$\sum_{i=1}^{N} \nabla \cdot \mathbf{f}\, \Delta V_i = \sum_{i=1}^{N} \oiint_{\Delta S_i} \mathbf{f} \cdot d\mathbf{S} + \sum_{i=1}^{N} \varepsilon_i \Delta V_i.$$

Now consider the limit of this expression as $N \longrightarrow \infty$. The surface boundary $\Delta S_i$ of each $\Delta V_i$ consists of numerous segments that are either part of the boundary $S$ or two adjacent subregions. The surface integrals for the adjacent boundary surfaces cancel out since the outer normals have opposite directions over the common boundary surface. Thus only the surface integral over $S$ is left. Also, by the definition of a multiple integral,

$$\lim_{N\to\infty} \sum_{i=1}^{N} \nabla \cdot \mathbf{f}\, \Delta V_i = \iiint_R \nabla \cdot \mathbf{f}\, dV.$$

Because

$$\lim_{N\to\infty} \sum_{i=1}^{N} \oiint_{\Delta S_i} \mathbf{f} \cdot d\mathbf{S} = \oiint_S \mathbf{f} \cdot d\mathbf{S},$$

we have

$$\iiint_R \nabla \cdot \mathbf{f}\, dV = \oiint_S \mathbf{f} \cdot d\mathbf{S} + \lim_{N\to\infty} \sum_{i=1}^{N} \varepsilon_i\, \Delta V_i. \tag{4.60}$$

For the second term on the right-hand side of (4.60),

$$\left| \sum_{i=1}^{N} \varepsilon_i \Delta V_i \right| \leq \sum_{i=1}^{N} |\, \varepsilon_i \,|\, \Delta V_i \leq |\, \varepsilon_m \,| \sum_{i=1}^{N} \Delta V_i = |\, \varepsilon_m \,|\, V,$$

where $\varepsilon_m = \max \varepsilon_i$. However, $\varepsilon_m \longrightarrow 0$ as $N \longrightarrow \infty$ and $\Delta V_i \longrightarrow 0$. Hence,

$$\lim_{N\to\infty} \sum_{i=1}^{N} \varepsilon_i\, \Delta V_i \longrightarrow 0.$$

Thus, taking limits,

$$\iiint_R \nabla \cdot \mathbf{f}\, dV = \oiint_S \mathbf{f} \cdot d\mathbf{S}.$$

**PROBLEM 4.32** Give the physical interpretation of the divergence theorem (4.58).

**Solution:** As shown in Prob. 4.24, the divergence of a vector field $\mathbf{f}$ at a given point is the density of outward flux flow from that point. The divergence, or Gauss', theorem (4.58) states that the total outward flux flow from a closed surface $S$ equals the integral of the divergence throughout the region $R$ bounded by $S$.

**PROBLEM 4.33** Show that if $\mathbf{r}$ is the position vector, then

$$\oiint_S \mathbf{r} \cdot d\mathbf{S} = 3V, \tag{4.61}$$

where $V$ is the volume of the region $R$ bounded by closed surface $S$.

**Solution:** The divergence $\nabla \cdot \mathbf{r}$ is

$$\nabla \cdot \mathbf{r} = \frac{\partial x}{\partial x} + \frac{\partial y}{\partial y} + \frac{\partial z}{\partial z} = 3. \qquad [3.129]$$

Thus applying Gauss' theorem (4.58),

$$\oiint_S \mathbf{r}\cdot d\mathbf{S} = \iiint_R \nabla\cdot\mathbf{r}\,dV = 3\iiint_R dV = 3V.$$

**PROBLEM 4.34** Using (4.61), find $\iint_S \mathbf{r}\cdot d\mathbf{S}$ for the surface $S$ of a sphere $x^2 + y^2 + z^2 = a^2$. (Cf., Prob. 4.14.)

**Solution:** The volume $V$ of a sphere with radius $a$ is $V = (4/3)\pi a^3$. Hence, by (4.61),

$$\oiint_S \mathbf{r}\cdot d\mathbf{S} = 3\cdot\frac{4}{3}\,\pi a^3 = 4\pi a^3.$$

**PROBLEM 4.35** Using (4.61), evaluate $\iint_S \mathbf{r}\cdot d\mathbf{S}$, where $\mathbf{S}$ is the surface of a cube bounded by $x = 0$, $x = 1$, $y = 0$, $y = 1$, $z = 0$, $z = 1$, as shown in Fig. 4.4. The outer unit normal vector $\mathbf{n}$ and the position vector $\mathbf{r}$ of points on the surface of the cube are directed away from the origin. (Cf., Prob. 4.16.)

**Solution:** Since the volume of the cube is 1, then by (4.61),

$$\oiint_S \mathbf{r}\cdot d\mathbf{S} = 3V = 3\cdot 1 = 3.$$

**PROBLEM 4.36** Show that

$$\iiint_R \frac{1}{r^2}\,dV = \oiint_S \frac{\mathbf{r}\cdot d\mathbf{S}}{r^2}, \tag{4.62}$$

where $S$ encloses the region $R$, $\mathbf{r}$ is the position vector, and $|\mathbf{r}| = r$.

**Solution:** From (3.167),

$$\nabla\cdot[r^{n-1}\,\mathbf{r}] = (n+2)\,r^{n-1}.$$

If $n = -1$,

$$\nabla\cdot\left(\frac{\mathbf{r}}{r^2}\right) = (-1+2)\,r^{-2} = \frac{1}{r^2}. \tag{4.63}$$

Hence, applying the divergence theorem (4.58),

$$\iiint_R \nabla\cdot\left(\frac{\mathbf{r}}{r^2}\right)dV = \iiint_R \frac{1}{r^2}\,dV = \oiint_S \frac{\mathbf{r}\cdot d\mathbf{S}}{r^2}.$$

**PROBLEM 4.37** Show that, for any closed surface $S$,

$$\oiint_S \nabla\times\mathbf{f}\cdot d\mathbf{S} = 0. \tag{4.64}$$

**Solution:** By (4.58),

$$\oiint_S \nabla\times\mathbf{f}\cdot d\mathbf{S} = \iiint_R \nabla\cdot(\nabla\times\mathbf{f})\,dV. \tag{4.65}$$

But from (3.143), $\nabla\cdot(\nabla\times\mathbf{f}) = 0$; hence,

$$\oiint_S \nabla \times \mathbf{f} \cdot d\mathbf{S} = 0.$$

**PROBLEM 4.38** If $\mathbf{f} = P(x, y, z)\mathbf{i} + Q(x, y, z)\mathbf{j} + R(x, y, z)\mathbf{k}$ and $R$ is the region bounded by a closed surface $S$, show that the divergence theorem (4.58) expressed in rectangular coordinates is

$$\iiint_R \left(\frac{\partial P}{\partial x} + \frac{\partial Q}{\partial y} + \frac{\partial R}{\partial z}\right) dxdydz = \oiint_S (P\ dydz + Q\ dzdx + R\ dxdy). \quad (4.66)$$

**Solution:** If we write

$$\mathbf{f} = P\mathbf{i} + Q\mathbf{j} + R\mathbf{k},$$

$$\mathbf{n} = \cos\alpha\ \mathbf{i} + \cos\beta\ \mathbf{j} + \cos\gamma\ \mathbf{k},$$

then, in general, for any surface S,

$$\mathbf{n}\cdot\mathbf{i}\ dS = \cos\alpha\ dS = dydz,$$

$$\mathbf{n}\cdot\mathbf{j}\ dS = \cos\beta\ dS = dzdx,$$

$$\mathbf{n}\cdot\mathbf{k}\ dS = \cos\gamma\ dS = dxdy.$$

(Cf., Prob. 4.15.) Since the divergence of $\mathbf{f}$ is

$$\nabla\cdot\mathbf{f} = \frac{\partial P}{\partial x} + \frac{\partial Q}{\partial y} + \frac{\partial R}{\partial z},$$

$$\iiint_R \nabla\cdot\mathbf{f}\ dV = \iiint_R \left(\frac{\partial P}{\partial x} + \frac{\partial Q}{\partial y} + \frac{\partial R}{\partial z}\right) dxdydz.$$

Again,

$$\oiint_S \mathbf{f}\cdot d\mathbf{S} = \oiint_S (P\mathbf{i} + Q\mathbf{j} + R\mathbf{k})\cdot\mathbf{n}\ dS$$

$$= \oiint_S (P\cos\alpha + Q\cos\beta + R\cos\gamma)\ dS$$

$$= \oiint_S (P\ dydz + Q\ dzdx + R\ dxdy)$$

Hence, (4.58) reduces to

$$\iiint_R \left(\frac{\partial P}{\partial x} + \frac{\partial Q}{\partial y} + \frac{\partial R}{\partial z}\right) dxdydz = \oiint_S (P\ dydz + Q\ dzdx + R\ dxdy).$$

**PROBLEM 4.39** Using the divergence theorem (4.66), evaluate

$$I = \iint_S x\ dydz + y\ dzdx + 2z\ dxdy,$$

where $S$ is a closed surface that consists of the surface of the paraboloid $x^2 + y^2 = 1 - z$, $0 < z < 1$, and the disc $x^2 + y^2 \leq 1$, $z = 0$, as shown in Fig. 4.8. (Cf., Prob. 4.17.)

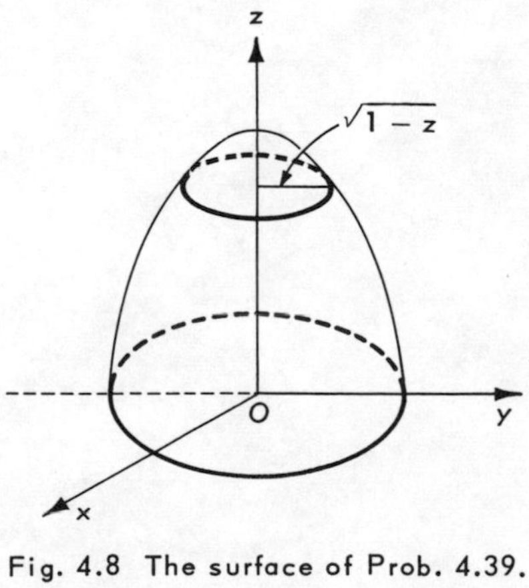

Fig. 4.8 The surface of Prob. 4.39.

**Solution:** From divergence theorem expressed in rectangular coordinates (4.66),

$$I = \iiint_R \left[\frac{\partial x}{\partial x} + \frac{\partial y}{\partial y} + \frac{\partial (2z)}{\partial z}\right] dxdydz = \iiint 4\, dxdydz$$

$$= 4 \iiint_R dV$$

$$= 4 \int_0^1 \pi (1 - z)\, dz$$

$$= 4\left(\pi - \frac{\pi}{2}\right)$$

$$= 2\pi,$$

which is the same result obtained in Prob. 4.17. Note that the contribution from the disc $x^2 + y^2 \leq 1$, $z = 0$ is zero, since on this disc $\mathbf{n} = -\mathbf{k}$ and $\mathbf{f} \cdot \mathbf{n}\big|_{z=0} = -2z\big|_{z=0} = 0$.

**PROBLEM 4.40** Using the divergence theorem (4.66), evaluate

$$I = \iint_S (x^3\, dydz + x^2 y\, dzdx + x^2 z\, dxdy),$$

where $S$ is the closed surface that consists of the cylinder $x^2 + y^2 = a^2$, $0 \leq z \leq b$, and the circular discs $x^2 + y^2 \leq a^2$, $z = 0$ and $x^2 + y^2 \leq a^2$, $z = b$, as shown in Fig. 4.9.

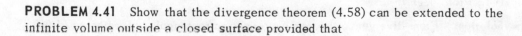

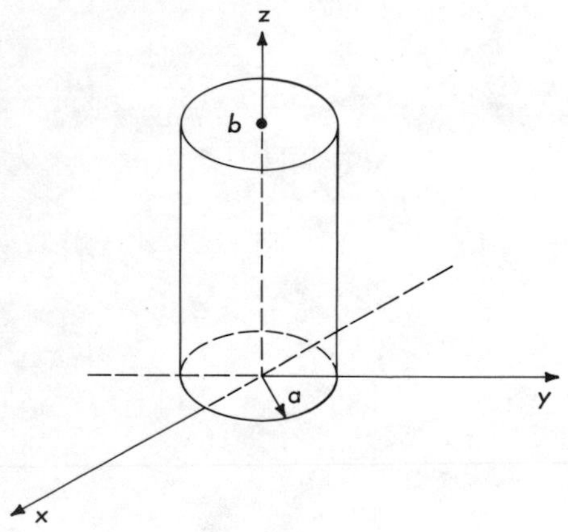

Fig. 4.9 The surface of Prob. 4.40.

**Solution:** From the divergence theorem (4.66),

$$I = \iiint_R \left(\frac{\partial x^3}{\partial x} + \frac{\partial x^2 y}{\partial y} + \frac{\partial x^2 z}{\partial z}\right) dxdydz$$

$$= 5 \iiint_R x^2\, dxdydz$$

$$= 5 \int_0^b \int_{-a}^{a} \int_{-\sqrt{a^2-y^2}}^{\sqrt{a^2-y^2}} x^2\, dxdydz$$

$$= 5 \cdot 4 \int_0^b \int_0^a \int_0^{\sqrt{a^2-y^2}} x^2\, dxdydz$$

$$= 20 \int_0^b \int_0^a \frac{1}{3} (a^2 - y^2)^{3/2}\, dydz$$

$$= \frac{20b}{3} \int_0^a (a^2 - y^2)^{3/2}\, dy$$

$$= \frac{20b}{3} \cdot \frac{3}{16} \pi a^4$$

$$= \frac{5}{4} \pi a^4 b.$$

**PROBLEM 4.41** Show that the divergence theorem (4.58) can be extended to the infinite volume outside a closed surface provided that

$$\lim_{r\to\infty} r^2\,|\mathbf{f}| = 0, \tag{4.67}$$

where $r$ is the distance from the origin to any point in space.

**Solution:** Let a closed surface $S$ be bounded by a sphere $S_r$ of radius $r$ with its center at the origin. If $\mathbf{f}$ is a vector field in a region $R$ bounded by $S$ and $S_r$, then, applying the divergence theorem (4.58),

$$\iiint_R \nabla\cdot\mathbf{f}\,dV = \oiint_S \mathbf{f}\cdot d\mathbf{S} + \oiint_{S_r} \mathbf{f}\cdot d\mathbf{S}. \tag{4.68}$$

(See Fig. 4.10.) From the Cauchy-Schwartz inequality (1.45), $|\mathbf{f}\cdot\mathbf{n}| \le |\mathbf{f}|$; then,

$$\left|\iint_S \mathbf{f}\cdot d\mathbf{S}\right| = \left|\iint_S \mathbf{f}\cdot\mathbf{n}\,dS\right| \le \iint_S |\mathbf{f}\cdot\mathbf{n}|\,dS \le \iint_S |\mathbf{f}|\,dS.$$

Hence, if $|\mathbf{f}| \le \varepsilon/r^2$ at all points on $S_r$,

$$\left|\oiint_{S_r} \mathbf{f}\cdot d\mathbf{S}\right| \le \oiint_{S_r} |\mathbf{f}|\,dS \le \frac{\varepsilon}{r^2}\oiint_{S_r} dS = 4\pi\varepsilon$$

since $\oiint_{S_r} dS = 4\pi r^2$. Thus, if $\lim_{r\to\infty} r^2\,|\mathbf{f}| = 0$,

$$\lim_{r\to\infty}\oiint_{S_r} \mathbf{f}\cdot d\mathbf{S} = 0,$$

from which

$$\iiint_R \nabla\cdot\mathbf{f}\,dV = \oiint_S \mathbf{f}\cdot d\mathbf{S}.$$

Note that in this surface integral, the normal is pointed inward.

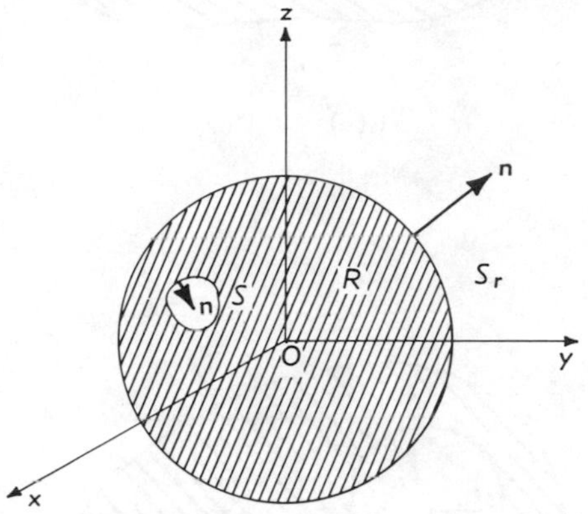

Fig. 4.10 The closed surface of Prob. 4.41.

In Fig. 4.11, $\mathbf{r}$ is the position vector that represents a point $P$ on the surface $S$. The *solid angle* $d\Omega$ subtended at the origin $O$ by an element $dS$ of the surface $S$ is defined as

$$d\Omega = \frac{\mathbf{r}\cdot d\mathbf{S}}{r^3}. \tag{4.69}$$

The total solid angle $\Omega$ subtended by $S$ is

$$\Omega = \iint_S \frac{\mathbf{r}\cdot d\mathbf{S}}{r^3}. \tag{4.70}$$

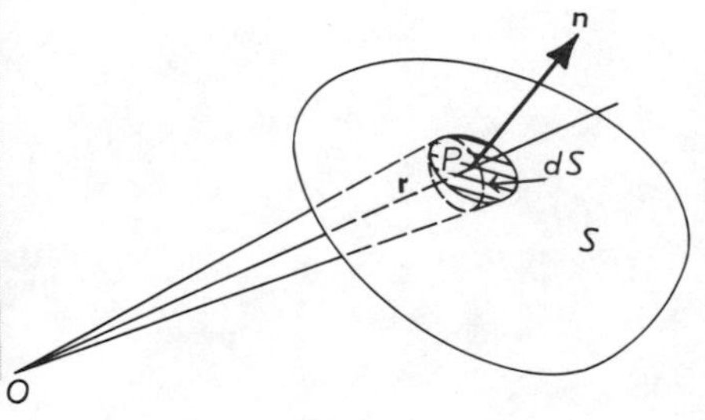

Fig. 4.11 Solid angle.

**PROBLEM 4.42** Show that the total solid angle subtended by a closed surface $S$ at the origin $O$ is zero if $O$ lies outside the region $R$ bounded by $S$, and that it is $4\pi$ if $O$ lies inside $R$.

**Solution:** From the divergence theorem (4.58),

$$\oiint_S \frac{\mathbf{r}\cdot d\mathbf{S}}{r^3} = \iiint_R \nabla\cdot\left(\frac{\mathbf{r}}{r^3}\right) dV.$$

However, by (3.168), $\nabla\cdot(\mathbf{r}/r^3) = 0$ within $R$ if $r \ne 0$. Now if $O$ lies outside $R$,

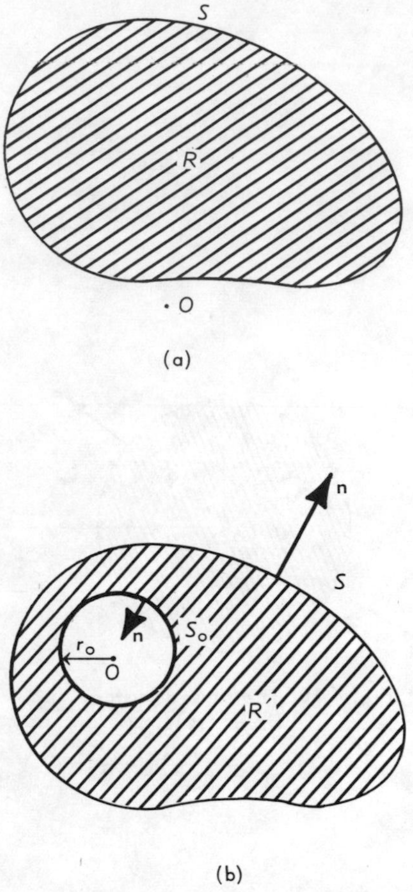


Fig. 4.12 Solution to Prob. 4.42.

then $r \neq 0$, as shown in Fig. 4.12(a). Hence, when $O$ lies outside $R$, the total solid angle subtended by $S$ is

$$\Omega = \oint\!\!\oint_S \frac{\mathbf{r} \cdot d\mathbf{S}}{r^3} = 0. \tag{4.71}$$

If $O$ lies inside $R$, we construct a small sphere $S_O$ of radius $r_O$ and consider the region $R'$ bounded by $S$ and $S_O$, as shown in Fig. 4.12(b). If we apply the divergence theorem (4.58),

$$\oint\!\!\oint_{S+S_O} \frac{\mathbf{r} \cdot d\mathbf{S}}{r^3} = \iint_S \frac{\mathbf{r} \cdot d\mathbf{S}}{r^3} + \iint_{S_O} \frac{\mathbf{r} \cdot d\mathbf{S}}{r^3} = \iiint_{R'} \nabla \cdot \left(\frac{\mathbf{r}}{r^3}\right) dV = 0$$

since $r \neq 0$ within $R'$. Thus,

$$\oint\!\!\oint_S \frac{\mathbf{r} \cdot d\mathbf{S}}{r^3} = -\oint\!\!\oint_{S_O} \frac{\mathbf{r} \cdot d\mathbf{S}}{r^3}.$$

At points on $S_O$, $r = r_O$ and the positive or outward normal is directed toward $O$, that is, $\mathbf{n} = -\mathbf{r}/r_O$; hence,

$$\begin{aligned}\oint\!\!\oint_{S_O} \frac{\mathbf{r} \cdot d\mathbf{S}}{r^3} &= \iint_{S_O} \frac{\mathbf{r} \cdot \mathbf{n}\, dS}{r^3} \\ &= -\oint\!\!\oint_{S_O} \frac{dS}{r_O^2} \\ &= -\frac{1}{r_O^2} \oint\!\!\oint_{S_O} dS \\ &= -\frac{1}{r_O^2}\, 4\pi r_O^2 \\ &= -4\pi;\end{aligned}$$

and when $O$ is inside $R$, the total angle subtended by $S$ is

$$\Omega = \oint\!\!\oint_S \frac{\mathbf{r} \cdot d\mathbf{S}}{r^3} = -\oint\!\!\oint_{S_O} \frac{\mathbf{r} \cdot d\mathbf{S}}{r^3} = -(-4\pi) = 4\pi. \tag{4.72}$$

## 4.6 Green's Theorems

*Green's first theorem* or *identity* states that if $\phi$ and $\psi$ are scalar functions that have continuous second derivatives in a region $R$ bounded by a closed surface $S$, then

$$\iiint_R (\phi \nabla^2 \psi + \nabla\phi \cdot \nabla\psi)\, dV = \oint\!\!\oint_S \phi \nabla\psi \cdot d\mathbf{S}. \tag{4.73}$$

*Green's second theorem* or *identity* states that if $\phi$ and $\psi$ are scalar functions that have continuous second derivatives in a region $R$ bounded by a closed surface $S$, then

$$\iiint_R (\phi \nabla^2 \psi - \psi \nabla^2 \phi)\, dV = \oint\!\!\oint_S (\phi \nabla\psi - \psi \nabla\phi) \cdot d\mathbf{S}. \tag{4.74}$$

These theorems or identities are derived from the divergence theorem (4.58) by using a suitable vector function.

*Green's third theorem* or *identity* states that if $\mathbf{f}(\nabla \cdot \mathbf{g})$ and $\mathbf{f} \times (\nabla \times \mathbf{g})$ are vector functions that have continuous second derivatives in a region $R$ bounded by a closed surface $S$, then

$$\iiint_R [\mathbf{f} \cdot \nabla^2 \mathbf{g} - \mathbf{g} \cdot \nabla^2 \mathbf{f}]\, dV$$

$$= \oiint_S [\mathbf{f} \times (\nabla \times \mathbf{g}) + \mathbf{f}(\nabla \cdot \mathbf{g}) - \mathbf{g} \times (\nabla \times \mathbf{f}) - \mathbf{g}(\nabla \cdot \mathbf{f})] \cdot d\mathbf{S}, \quad (4.75)$$

where $\nabla^2 \mathbf{f} = \nabla(\nabla \cdot \mathbf{f}) - \nabla \times (\nabla \times \mathbf{f})$ from (3.164).

This theorem is equivalent to the Green's second theorem (4.74) that relates two scalars.

**PROBLEM 4.43** Verify Green's first theorem (4.73).

**Solution:** Using the vector identity, $\nabla \cdot (\phi \mathbf{f}) = \phi \nabla \cdot \mathbf{f} + \mathbf{f} \cdot \nabla \phi$, where $\mathbf{f} = \nabla \psi$,

$$\nabla \cdot (\phi \nabla \psi) = \phi \nabla \cdot \nabla \psi + \nabla \psi \cdot \nabla \phi = \phi \nabla^2 \psi + \nabla \phi \cdot \nabla \psi. \quad (4.76)$$

Integrating over the region $R$,

$$\iiint_R \nabla \cdot (\phi \nabla \psi)\, dV = \iiint_R (\phi \nabla^2 \psi + \nabla \phi \cdot \nabla \psi)\, dV. \quad (4.77)$$

Applying the divergence theorem (4.58),

$$\iiint_R \nabla \cdot (\phi \nabla \psi)\, dV = \oiint_S \phi \nabla \psi \cdot d\mathbf{S}. \quad (4.78)$$

Thus,

$$\iiint_R (\phi \nabla^2 \psi + \nabla \phi \cdot \nabla \psi)\, dV = \oiint_S \phi \nabla \psi \cdot d\mathbf{S}.$$

From the definition of the directional derivative (3.98), i.e., $\partial \phi / \partial s = \text{grad}\, \phi \cdot \mathbf{T}$,

$$\phi \nabla \psi \cdot d\mathbf{S} = \phi \nabla \psi \cdot \mathbf{n}\, dS = \phi \frac{\partial \psi}{\partial n}\, dS, \quad (4.79)$$

where $\partial \psi / \partial n$ is the *normal derivative*. Hence, (4.73) can be written as

$$\iiint_R (\phi \nabla^2 \psi + \nabla \phi \cdot \nabla \psi)\, dV = \oiint_S \phi \frac{\partial \psi}{\partial n}\, dS. \quad (4.80)$$

**PROBLEM 4.44** Verify Green's second theorem (4.74).

**Solution:** Interchanging $\phi$ and $\psi$ in (4.73),

$$\iiint_R (\psi \nabla^2 \phi + \nabla \psi \cdot \nabla \phi)\, dV = \oiint_S \psi \nabla \phi \cdot d\mathbf{S}. \quad (4.81)$$

Then by subtracting (4.81) from (4.73),

$$\iiint_R (\phi \nabla^2 \psi - \psi \nabla^2 \phi)\, dV = \oint\!\!\!\oint_S (\phi \nabla \psi - \psi \nabla \phi) \cdot d\mathbf{S}. \qquad [4.74]$$

From (4.79),

$$\nabla \psi \cdot d\mathbf{S} = \frac{\partial \psi}{\partial n}\, dS, \qquad \nabla \phi \cdot d\mathbf{S} = \frac{\partial \phi}{\partial n}\, dS;$$

hence, (4.74) can be written as

$$\iiint_R (\phi \nabla^2 \psi - \psi \nabla^2 \phi)\, dV = \oint\!\!\!\oint_S \left(\phi \frac{\partial \psi}{\partial n} - \psi \frac{\partial \phi}{\partial n}\right) dS. \qquad (4.82)$$

**PROBLEM 4.45** If $\psi$ is harmonic in a region $R$ enclosed by $S$, then prove that

$$\oint\!\!\!\oint_S \nabla \psi \cdot d\mathbf{S} = \oint\!\!\!\oint_S \frac{\partial \psi}{\partial n}\, dS = 0. \qquad (4.83)$$

**Solution:** If we set $\phi = 1$ in Green's first theorem (4.73),

$$\oint\!\!\!\oint_S \nabla \psi \cdot d\mathbf{S} = \iiint_R \nabla^2 \psi\, dV \qquad (4.84)$$

since $\nabla(1) = \mathbf{0}$. Since $\psi$ is harmonic, then by Laplace's equation (3.133), $\nabla^2 \psi = 0$. Hence, (4.84) reduces to

$$\oint\!\!\!\oint_S \nabla \psi \cdot d\mathbf{S} = \oint\!\!\!\oint_S \nabla \psi \cdot \mathbf{n}\, dS = \oint\!\!\!\oint_S \frac{\partial \psi}{\partial n}\, dS = 0.$$

**PROBLEM 4.46** If $\phi$ and $\psi$ are harmonic in a region $R$ enclosed by $S$, then prove that

$$\oint\!\!\!\oint_S (\phi \nabla \psi - \psi \nabla \phi) \cdot d\mathbf{S} = \oint\!\!\!\oint_S \left(\phi \frac{\partial \psi}{\partial n} - \psi \frac{\partial \phi}{\partial n}\right) dS = 0. \qquad (4.85)$$

**Solution:** If $\phi$ and $\psi$ are harmonic, then by Laplace's equation (3.133), we have $\nabla^2 \phi = \nabla^2 \psi = 0$. Thus, by Green's second theorem (4.74),

$$\oint\!\!\!\oint_S (\phi \nabla \psi - \psi \nabla \phi) \cdot d\mathbf{S} = \iiint_R (\phi \nabla^2 \psi - \psi \nabla^2 \phi)\, dV = 0.$$

**PROBLEM 4.47** Derive Green's third theorem (4.75).

**Solution:** Applying the divergence theorem (4.58) to the vectors $\mathbf{f}(\nabla \cdot \mathbf{g})$ and $\mathbf{f} \times (\nabla \times \mathbf{g})$,

$$\iiint_R \nabla \cdot [\mathbf{f}(\nabla \cdot \mathbf{g})]\, dV = \oint\!\!\!\oint_S \mathbf{f}(\nabla \cdot \mathbf{g}) \cdot d\mathbf{S}, \qquad (4.86)$$

$$\iiint_R \nabla \cdot [\mathbf{f} \times (\nabla \times \mathbf{g})]\, dV = \oint\!\!\!\oint_S \mathbf{f} \times (\nabla \times \mathbf{g}) \cdot d\mathbf{S}. \qquad (4.87)$$

From the vector identifies (3.155) and (3.157),

$$\nabla \cdot [\mathbf{f}(\nabla \cdot \mathbf{g})] = (\nabla \cdot \mathbf{g})(\nabla \cdot \mathbf{f}) + \mathbf{f} \cdot \nabla(\nabla \cdot \mathbf{g}), \qquad (4.88)$$

$$\nabla \cdot [\mathbf{f} \times (\nabla \times \mathbf{g})] = (\nabla \times \mathbf{g}) \cdot (\nabla \times \mathbf{f}) \quad \mathbf{f} \cdot \nabla \times (\nabla \times \mathbf{g}). \qquad (4.89)$$

Hence,

$$\iiint_R \nabla\cdot[\mathbf{f}(\nabla\cdot\mathbf{g})]\,dV = \iiint_R [(\nabla\cdot\mathbf{g})(\nabla\cdot\mathbf{f}) + \mathbf{f}\cdot\nabla(\nabla\cdot\mathbf{g})]\,dV, \tag{4.90}$$

$$\iiint_R \nabla\cdot[\mathbf{f}\times(\nabla\times\mathbf{g})]\,dV = \iiint_R [(\nabla\times\mathbf{g})\cdot(\nabla\times\mathbf{f}) - \mathbf{f}\cdot\nabla\times(\nabla\times\mathbf{g})]\,dV. \tag{4.91}$$

Interchanging the roles of **f** and **g** and subtracting,

$$\iiint_R [\mathbf{f}\cdot\nabla(\nabla\cdot\mathbf{g}) - \mathbf{g}\cdot\nabla(\nabla\cdot\mathbf{f})]\,dV = \oint\!\!\oint_S [\mathbf{f}(\nabla\cdot\mathbf{g}) - \mathbf{g}(\nabla\cdot\mathbf{f})]\cdot d\mathbf{S}, \tag{4.92}$$

$$\iiint_R [\mathbf{f}\cdot\nabla\times(\nabla\times\mathbf{g}) - \mathbf{g}\cdot\nabla\times(\nabla\times\mathbf{f})]\,dV$$

$$= -\oint\!\!\oint_S [\mathbf{f}\times(\nabla\times\mathbf{g}) - \mathbf{g}\times(\nabla\times\mathbf{f})]\cdot d\mathbf{S}. \tag{4.93}$$

Adding (4.92) and (4.93) and using

$$\nabla^2\mathbf{f} = \nabla(\nabla\cdot\mathbf{f}) - \nabla\times(\nabla\times\mathbf{f}), \qquad [3.164]$$

we obtain

$$\iiint_R (\mathbf{f}\cdot\nabla^2\mathbf{g} - \mathbf{g}\cdot\nabla^2\mathbf{f})\,dV =$$

$$\oint\!\!\oint_S [\mathbf{f}\times(\nabla\times\mathbf{g}) + \mathbf{f}(\nabla\cdot\mathbf{g}) - \mathbf{g}\times(\nabla\times\mathbf{f}) - \mathbf{g}(\nabla\cdot\mathbf{f})]\cdot d\mathbf{S}. \qquad [4.75]$$

## 4.7 Volume-to-Surface Integral Transformations

The *divergence theorem* (4.58) represents a volume-to-surface integral transformation involving the divergence of a vector; i.e.,

$$\iiint_R \nabla\cdot\mathbf{f}\,dV = \oint\!\!\oint_S d\mathbf{S}\cdot\mathbf{f}. \qquad [4.58]$$

By extending the definitions of the gradient and a curl of a vector to finite volumes, we obtain the following theorems:

The *gradient theorem* states that if $\phi$ is a continuous scalar function in a region $R$ bounded by a closed surface $S$, then

$$\iiint_R \nabla\phi\,dV = \oint\!\!\oint_S d\mathbf{S}\,\phi. \tag{4.94}$$

The *curl theorem* states that if **f** is a continuous vector function in a region $R$ bounded by a closed surface $S$, then

$$\iiint_R \nabla\times\mathbf{f}\,dV = \oint\!\!\oint_S d\mathbf{S}\times\mathbf{f}. \tag{4.95}$$

Note that the theorems (4.58) and (4.94–5) can be stated as

$$\iiint_R \nabla * a\, dV = \oiint_S d\mathbf{S} * a, \tag{4.96}$$

where $a$ is any scalar or vector quantity, and the star (*) represents any acceptable form of multiplication, i.e., the dot, cross, or simple product.

**PROBLEM 4.48** Prove the gradient theorem (4.94).

**Solution:** Let $\mathbf{f} = \phi\mathbf{a}$, where $\mathbf{a}$ is any constant vector. Applying the divergence theorem (4.58),

$$\iiint_R \nabla\cdot(\phi\,\mathbf{a})\,dV = \oiint_S \phi\,\mathbf{a}\cdot d\mathbf{S}. \tag{4.97}$$

But by (3.155),

$$\nabla\cdot(\phi\,\mathbf{a}) = \phi\nabla\cdot\mathbf{a} + \mathbf{a}\cdot\nabla\phi.$$

Since $\mathbf{a}$ is a constant, $\nabla\cdot\mathbf{a} = 0$; hence,

$$\nabla\cdot(\phi\,\mathbf{a}) = \mathbf{a}\cdot\nabla\phi.$$

Thus, (4.97) can be written as

$$\mathbf{a}\cdot\left(\iiint_R \nabla\phi\, dV - \oiint_S \phi\, d\mathbf{S}\right) = 0. \tag{4.98}$$

Since $\mathbf{a}$ is any constant vector, the expression in parentheses vanishes, and (4.94) is proved.

**PROBLEM 4.49** Prove the curl theorem (4.95).

**Solution:** If $\mathbf{a}$ is any constant vector and we replace $\mathbf{f}$ in (4.58) by $\mathbf{f}\times\mathbf{a}$, then

$$\iiint_R \nabla\cdot(\mathbf{f}\times\mathbf{a})\,dV = \oiint_S (\mathbf{f}\times\mathbf{a})\cdot d\mathbf{S}. \tag{4.99}$$

But by (3.157),

$$\nabla\cdot(\mathbf{f}\times\mathbf{a}) = \mathbf{a}\cdot(\nabla\times\mathbf{f}) - \mathbf{f}\cdot(\nabla\times\mathbf{a}).$$

Since $\mathbf{a}$ is constant, $\nabla\times\mathbf{a} = \mathbf{0}$; hence,

$$\nabla\cdot(\mathbf{f}\times\mathbf{a}) = \mathbf{a}\cdot(\nabla\times\mathbf{f}).$$

From the permutation rule of the triple scalar product (1.77) or (2.53),

$$\mathbf{f}\times\mathbf{a}\cdot d\mathbf{S} = \mathbf{a}\cdot d\mathbf{S}\times\mathbf{f}.$$

Thus, (4.99) can be written as

$$\mathbf{a}\cdot\left(\iiint_R \nabla\times\mathbf{F}\, dV - \oiint_S d\mathbf{S}\times\mathbf{f}\right) = 0. \tag{4.100}$$

Again, because $\mathbf{a}$ is any constant vector, the expression in parentheses vanishes, and (4.95) is proved.

**PROBLEM 4.50** Show that for a closed surface $S$,

$$\oiint_S d\mathbf{S} = \mathbf{0}. \tag{4.101}$$

**Solution:** By the gradient theorem (4.94),

$$\oiint_S \phi \, d\mathbf{S} = \iiint_R \nabla\phi \, dV.$$

If $\phi = 1$, then $\nabla\phi = \mathbf{0}$; hence,

$$\oiint_S d\mathbf{S} = \mathbf{0}.$$

**PROBLEM 4.51** Using the integral representation (4.57) of $\nabla$, i.e., $\nabla = \lim_{\Delta V \to 0} \frac{1}{\Delta V} \oiint_S d\mathbf{S}$, show that

$$\nabla \cdot (\phi \mathbf{f}) = \phi \nabla \cdot \mathbf{f} + \mathbf{f} \cdot \nabla\phi. \qquad [3.155]$$

**Solution:** Let the values of $\phi$ and $\mathbf{f}$ at some fixed point $P_0$ be $\phi_0$ and $\mathbf{f}_0$, and let $\Delta V$ be a small region about $P_0$. On the surface $S$ that bounds $\Delta V$ the values of $\phi$ and $\mathbf{f}$ are $\phi = \phi_0 + \Delta\phi$, $\mathbf{f} = \mathbf{f}_0 + \Delta\mathbf{f}$. Using (4.57),

$$\begin{aligned}
\nabla \cdot (\phi \mathbf{f}) &= \lim_{\Delta V \to 0} \frac{1}{\Delta V} \oiint_S d\mathbf{S} \cdot (\phi \mathbf{f}) \\
&= \lim_{\Delta V \to 0} \frac{1}{\Delta V} \oiint_S d\mathbf{S} \cdot (\phi_0 + \Delta\phi) \mathbf{f} \\
&= \lim_{\Delta V \to 0} \frac{1}{\Delta V} \left[ \phi_0 \oiint_S d\mathbf{S} \cdot \mathbf{f} + \oiint_S d\mathbf{S} \cdot (\Delta\phi) \mathbf{f} \right] \\
&= \lim_{\Delta V \to 0} \frac{1}{\Delta V} \left[ \phi_0 \oiint_S d\mathbf{S} \cdot \mathbf{f} + \oiint_S d\mathbf{S} \cdot (\phi - \phi_0)(\mathbf{f}_0 + \Delta\mathbf{f}) \right] \\
&= \lim_{\Delta V \to 0} \frac{1}{\Delta V} \left( \phi_0 \oiint_S d\mathbf{S} \cdot \mathbf{f} + \mathbf{f}_0 \cdot \oiint_S d\mathbf{S}\, \phi - \phi_0 \mathbf{f}_0 \cdot \oiint_S d\mathbf{S} \right. \\
&\qquad \left. + \oiint_S d\mathbf{S} \cdot \Delta\phi \Delta\mathbf{f} \right). \qquad (4.102)
\end{aligned}$$

But, from the result of Prob. 4.50,

$$\oiint_S d\mathbf{S} = \mathbf{0}. \qquad [4.101]$$

Since the last integral $\oiint_S d\mathbf{S} \cdot \Delta\phi\Delta\mathbf{f}$ is a higher order term, it can be neglected in the limit. Then, at the point $P_0$,

$$\begin{aligned}
\nabla \cdot (\phi \mathbf{f}) &= \lim_{\Delta V \to 0} \frac{1}{\Delta V} \left( \phi_0 \oiint_S d\mathbf{S} \cdot \mathbf{f} + \mathbf{f}_0 \cdot \oiint_S d\mathbf{S}\, \phi \right) \\
&= \phi_0 \lim_{\Delta V \to 0} \frac{1}{\Delta V} \oiint_S d\mathbf{S} \cdot \mathbf{f} + \mathbf{f} \cdot \left( \lim_{\Delta V \to 0} \frac{1}{\Delta V} \oiint_S d\mathbf{S}\, \phi \right) \\
&= \phi \nabla \cdot \mathbf{f} + \mathbf{f} \cdot \nabla\phi,
\end{aligned}$$

where all expressions are evaluated at the point $P_0$. Since $P_0$ is arbitrary, (3.155) is proved.

**PROBLEM 4.52** If $\mathbf{r}$ is a position vector, show that for a closed surface $S$,

$$\oiint_S \mathbf{r} \times d\mathbf{S} = \mathbf{0}. \tag{4.103}$$

**Solution:** By the curl theorem (4.95),

$$\oiint_S d\mathbf{S} \times \mathbf{r} = \iiint_R \nabla \times \mathbf{r}\, dV.$$

But by (3.141), $\nabla \times \mathbf{r} = \mathbf{0}$; hence,

$$\oiint_S \mathbf{r} \times d\mathbf{S} = -\oiint_S d\mathbf{S} \times \mathbf{r} = \mathbf{0}.$$

## 4.8 Stokes' Theorem

*Stokes' Theorem* states that if $S$ is a surface bounded by a simple closed curve $C$ and $\mathbf{f}$ is a vector function that has continuous first partial derivatives on $S$ and $C$, then

$$\iint_S \nabla \times \mathbf{f} \cdot d\mathbf{S} = \oint_C \mathbf{f} \cdot d\mathbf{r}. \tag{4.104}$$

**PROBLEM 4.53** Prove Stokes' theorem (4.104).

**Solution:** Consider a surface $S$ bounded by a simple closed curve $C$. Divide $S$ into $N$ subregions so small that they can be considered to be planar with areas $\Delta S_1, \Delta S_2, \cdots, \Delta S_N$. At points $(x_i, y_i, z_i)$ within $\Delta S_i$, definition (4.50) of the curl gives

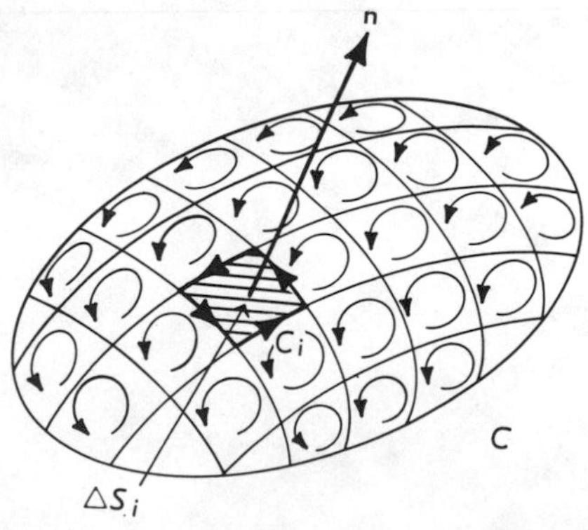


Fig. 4.13 Proof of Stoke's theorem.

$$\mathbf{n} \cdot \nabla \times \mathbf{f}\, \Delta S_i = \oint_{C_i} \mathbf{f} \cdot d\mathbf{r} + \varepsilon_i\, \Delta S_i, \tag{4.105}$$

where $\varepsilon_i \longrightarrow 0$ as $\Delta S_i \longrightarrow 0$, and $\mathbf{n}$ is the unit normal vector associated with $\Delta \mathbf{S}_i$. (See Fig. 4.13.) Summation over the entire surface $S$ yields

$$\sum_{i=1}^{N} \mathbf{n} \cdot \nabla \times \mathbf{f}\, \Delta S_i = \sum_{i=1}^{N} \oint_{C_i} \mathbf{f} \cdot d\mathbf{r} + \sum_{i=1}^{N} \varepsilon_i\, \Delta S_i.$$

Now consider the limit of this expression as $N \longrightarrow \infty$. The boundary $C_i$ of each $\Delta S_i$ consists of a number of pieces that are either part of the boundary $C$ or part of the boundaries of the two adjacent subregions. The line integrals along the adjacent boundary curves cancel, since the $d\mathbf{r}$ vectors are directed in opposite directions; thus, leaving only the line integral along $C$. Hence,

$$\lim_{N\to\infty} \sum_{i=1}^{N} \mathbf{n} \cdot \nabla \times \mathbf{f}\, \Delta S_i = \iint_S \mathbf{n} \cdot \nabla \times \mathbf{f}\, dS = \iint_S \nabla \times \mathbf{f} \cdot d\mathbf{S},$$

$$\lim_{N\to\infty} \sum_{i=1}^{N} \oint_{C_i} \mathbf{f} \cdot d\mathbf{r} = \oint_C \mathbf{f} \cdot d\mathbf{r}.$$

Thus, as $N \longrightarrow \infty$,

$$\iint_S \nabla \times \mathbf{f} \cdot d\mathbf{S} = \oint_C \mathbf{f} \cdot d\mathbf{r} + \lim_{N \to \infty} \sum_{i=1}^{N} \varepsilon_i \, \Delta S_i. \tag{4.106}$$

For the remaining term,

$$\left| \sum_{i=1}^{N} \varepsilon_i \, \Delta S_i \right| \leq \sum_{i=1}^{N} |\varepsilon_i| \, \Delta S_i \leq |\varepsilon_m| \sum_{i=1}^{N} \Delta S_i = |\varepsilon_m| \, S,$$

where $\varepsilon_m = \max \varepsilon_i$. But, $\varepsilon_m \longrightarrow 0$ as $N \longrightarrow \infty$, $\Delta S_i \longrightarrow 0$. Hence,

$$\lim_{N \to \infty} \sum_{i=1}^{N} \varepsilon_i \, \Delta S_i \longrightarrow 0.$$

Thus, in the limit,

$$\iint_S \nabla \times \mathbf{f} \cdot d\mathbf{S} = \oint_C \mathbf{f} \cdot d\mathbf{r}.$$

**PROBLEM 4.54** Give the physical interpretation of Stokes' theorem.

**Solution:** The curl of a vector field **f** is the intensity of circulation at a point for **f** (see Prob. 4.26). Stokes' theorem (4.104) states that the total circulation around a closed curve $C$ is equal to the flux of curl **f** through a surface $S$ enclosed by $C$.

**PROBLEM 4.55** Show that if **r** is the position vector, then

$$\oint_C \mathbf{r} \cdot d\mathbf{r} = 0. \tag{4.107}$$

**Solution:** From (3.141), $\nabla \times \mathbf{r} = \mathbf{0}$. Hence, by Stokes' theorem (4.104),

$$\oint_C \mathbf{r} \cdot d\mathbf{r} = \iint_S \nabla \times \mathbf{r} \cdot d\mathbf{S} = 0.$$

**PROBLEM 4.56** Using Stokes' theorem (4.104), show that, for any closed surface $S$,

$$\oiint_S \nabla \times \mathbf{f} \cdot d\mathbf{S} = 0.$$

**Solution:** Let a closed curve $C$ divide a closed surface $S$ into two regions $S_1$ and $S_2$, as shown in Fig. 4.14. Applying Stokes' theorem (4.104) to both $S_1$ and $S_2$,

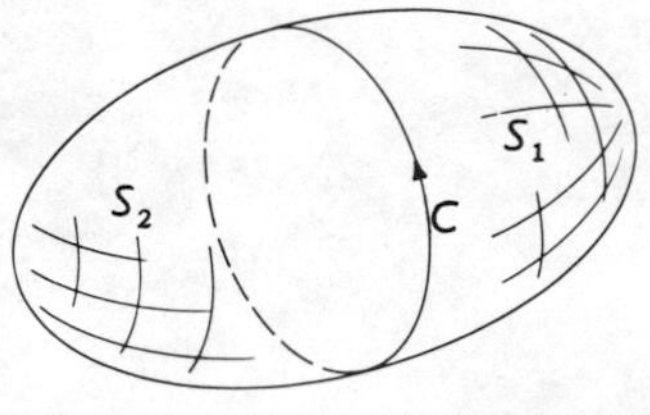

Fig. 4.14 Solution to Prob. 4.56.

$$\iint_{S_1} \nabla \times \mathbf{f} \cdot d\mathbf{S} = \oint_C \mathbf{f} \cdot d\mathbf{r},$$

$$\iint_{S_2} \nabla \times \mathbf{f} \cdot d\mathbf{S} = \oint_C \mathbf{f} \cdot d\mathbf{r} = -\oint_C \mathbf{f} \cdot d\mathbf{r}.$$

Hence, for the closed surface $S$,

$$\oiint_S \nabla \times \mathbf{f} \cdot d\mathbf{S} = \iint_{S_1} \nabla \times \mathbf{f} \cdot d\mathbf{S} + \iint_{S_2} \nabla \times \mathbf{f} \cdot d\mathbf{S}$$

$$= \oint_C \mathbf{f} \cdot d\mathbf{r} + \oint_C \mathbf{f} \cdot d\mathbf{r}$$

$$= 0.$$

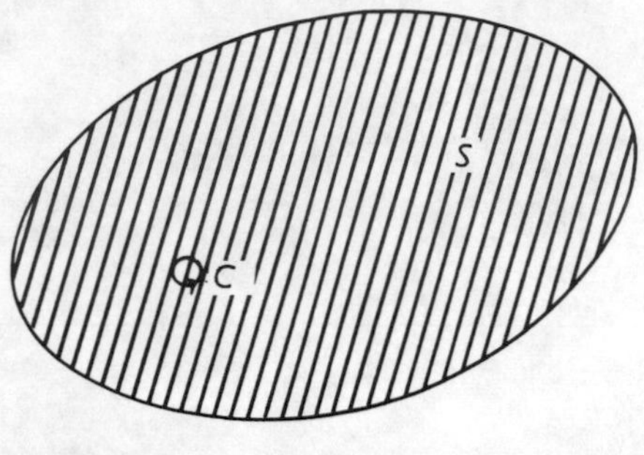


Fig. 4.15 Alternate solution to Prob. 4.56.

**Alternate Solution:** Consider an almost closed surface $S$ with a small opening bounded by a simple closed curve $C$, as shown in Fig. 4.15. Applying Stokes' theorem (4.104),

$$\iint_S \nabla \times \mathbf{f} \cdot d\mathbf{S} = \oint_C \mathbf{f} \cdot d\mathbf{r}.$$

Now let the small opening become smaller and smaller so that in the limit it shrinks to a point. Then the surface becomes a closed surface and the line integral goes to zero. Hence,

$$\oiint_S \nabla \times \mathbf{f} \cdot d\mathbf{S} = 0.$$

**PROBLEM 4.57** If $C$ is a closed curve, show that

$$\oint_C \nabla\phi \cdot d\mathbf{r} = 0. \tag{4.108}$$

**Solution:** By Stokes' theorem,

$$\oint_C \nabla\phi \cdot d\mathbf{r} = \iint_S \nabla \times (\nabla\phi) \cdot d\mathbf{S}, \qquad [4.104]$$

where $S$ is the surface enclosed by $C$. But from (3.142), $\nabla \times \nabla\phi = \mathbf{0}$; hence, (4.108) is proved.

**PROBLEM 4.58** Show that $\nabla \times \mathbf{f} = \mathbf{0}$ is a necessary and sufficient condition for $\oint_C \mathbf{f} \cdot d\mathbf{r} = 0$ around any closed curve $C$.

**Solution:** For the sufficiency condition, $\nabla \times \mathbf{f} = \mathbf{0}$; then by Stokes' theorem (4.104),

$$\oint_C \mathbf{f} \cdot d\mathbf{r} = \iint_S (\nabla \times \mathbf{f}) \cdot d\mathbf{S} = 0.$$

For the necessary condition, assume that $\oint_C \mathbf{f} \cdot d\mathbf{r} = 0$ for any closed curve $C$ and that $\nabla \times \mathbf{f} \neq \mathbf{0}$ at some point $P$. Then if $\nabla \times \mathbf{f}$ is continuous, there is some region about $P$ where $\nabla \times \mathbf{f} \neq \mathbf{0}$. Choose a small plane surface $S$ in this region and a unit normal vector to $S$ parallel to $\nabla \times \mathbf{f}$, that is, $\nabla \times \mathbf{f} \cong a\mathbf{n}$, where $a > 0$. If $C$ is the boundary of $S$, then by Stokes' theorem (4.104),

$$\oint_C \mathbf{f} \cdot d\mathbf{r} = \iint_S \nabla \times \mathbf{f} \cdot d\mathbf{S} \cong \iint_S a\,\mathbf{n} \cdot \mathbf{n}\, dS = a \iint_S dS = aS > 0,$$

which contradicts the assumption that $\oint_C \mathbf{f} \cdot d\mathbf{r} = 0$.

*Stokes' theorem* for rectangular coordinates states that if $\mathbf{f} = P\mathbf{i} + Q\mathbf{j} + R\mathbf{k}$, then

$$\oint_C P\,dx + Q\,dy + R\,dz = \iint_S \left(\frac{\partial R}{\partial y} - \frac{\partial Q}{\partial z}\right) dydz + \left(\frac{\partial P}{\partial z} - \frac{\partial R}{\partial x}\right) dzdx + \left(\frac{\partial Q}{\partial x} - \frac{\partial P}{\partial y}\right) dxdy. \tag{4.109}$$

**PROBLEM 4.59** Verify (4.109).

**Solution:** If $\mathbf{f} = P\mathbf{i} + Q\mathbf{j} + R\mathbf{k}$, then $\mathbf{f}\cdot d\mathbf{r} = P\,dx + Q\,dy + R\,dz$ and

$$\nabla \times \mathbf{f} = \begin{vmatrix} \mathbf{i} & \mathbf{j} & \mathbf{k} \\ \dfrac{\partial}{\partial x} & \dfrac{\partial}{\partial y} & \dfrac{\partial}{\partial z} \\ P & Q & R \end{vmatrix} = \left(\frac{\partial R}{\partial y} - \frac{\partial Q}{\partial z}\right)\mathbf{i} + \left(\frac{\partial P}{\partial z} - \frac{\partial R}{\partial x}\right)\mathbf{j} + \left(\frac{\partial Q}{\partial x} - \frac{\partial P}{\partial y}\right)\mathbf{k}.$$

Now as in Prob. 4.38,

$$\begin{aligned}\iint_S \nabla \times \mathbf{f}\cdot d\mathbf{S} &= \iint_S \nabla \times \mathbf{f}\cdot\mathbf{n}\,dS \\ &= \iint_S \left[\left(\frac{\partial R}{\partial y} - \frac{\partial Q}{\partial z}\right)\mathbf{i} + \left(\frac{\partial P}{\partial z} - \frac{\partial R}{\partial x}\right)\mathbf{j} + \left(\frac{\partial Q}{\partial x} - \frac{\partial P}{\partial y}\right)\mathbf{k}\right]\cdot\mathbf{n}\,dS \\ &= \iint_S \left[\left(\frac{\partial R}{\partial y} - \frac{\partial Q}{\partial z}\right)\cos\alpha + \left(\frac{\partial P}{\partial z} - \frac{\partial R}{\partial x}\right)\cos\beta + \left(\frac{\partial Q}{\partial x} - \frac{\partial P}{\partial y}\right)\cos\gamma\right] dS \\ &= \iint_S \left(\frac{\partial R}{\partial y} - \frac{\partial Q}{\partial z}\right) dydz + \left(\frac{\partial P}{\partial z} - \frac{\partial R}{\partial x}\right) dzdx + \left(\frac{\partial Q}{\partial x} - \frac{\partial P}{\partial y}\right) dxdy.\end{aligned}$$

Hence, Stokes' theorem (4.104) reduces to

$$\oint_C P\,dx + Q\,dy + R\,dz = \iint_S \left(\frac{\partial R}{\partial y} - \frac{\partial Q}{\partial z}\right) dydz + \left(\frac{\partial P}{\partial z} - \frac{\partial R}{\partial x}\right) dzdx + \left(\frac{\partial Q}{\partial x} - \frac{\partial P}{\partial y}\right) dxdy. \qquad [4.109]$$

**PROBLEM 4.60** If $\mathbf{f} = 4y\mathbf{i} + x\mathbf{j} + 2z\mathbf{k}$, evaluate $I = \iint_S \nabla \times \mathbf{f}\cdot d\mathbf{S}$ over the hemisphere $x^2 + y^2 + z^2 = a^2$, $z \geq 0$.

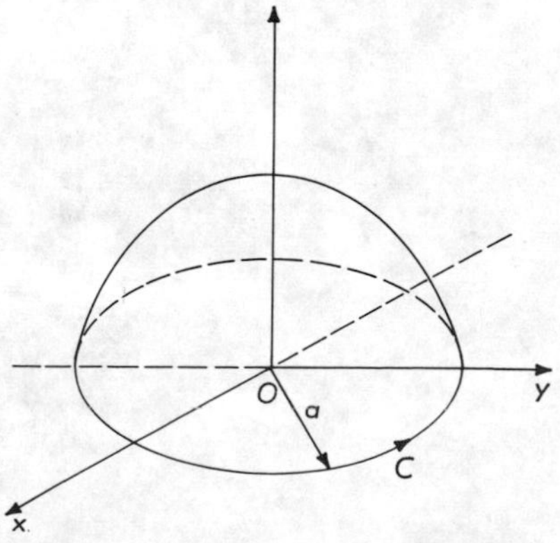


Fig. 4.16 The hemisphere of Prob. 4.60.

**Solution:** Since $I$ is in the form of the surface integral in Stokes' theorem (4.104),

$$I = \oint_C \mathbf{f}\cdot d\mathbf{r} = \oint_C 4y\,dx + x\,dy + 2z\,dz,$$

where $C$ is the circle $x^2 + y^2 = a^2$, $z = 0$, directed as shown in Fig. 4.16.

The parametric representation of $C$ (Prob. 3.13) is $x = a\cos t$, $y = a\sin t$, $z = 0$, where $0 \leq t \leq 2\pi$. Then $dx = -a\sin t\,dt$, $dy = a\cos t\,dt$, $dz = 0$. Hence,

$$I = \int_0^{2\pi} 4\,(a \sin t)(-a \sin t\, dt) + (a \cos t)(a \cos t\, dt)$$

$$= a^2 \int_0^{2\pi} (-4 \sin^2 t + \cos^2 t)\, dt$$

$$= a^2 \int_0^{2\pi} (1 - 5 \sin^2 t)\, dt$$

$$= a^2 \int_0^{2\pi} \left[1 - 5 \cdot \frac{1}{2}(1 - \cos 2t)\right] dt$$

$$= a^2 \int_0^{2\pi} \left(-\frac{3}{2} + \frac{5}{2} \cos 2t\right) dt$$

$$= -3a^2 \pi.$$

*Green's theorem for a plane* states that if $P$, $Q$, $\partial P/\partial y$, and $\partial Q/\partial x$ are continuous in a region $R$ in the $xy$-plane bounded by a closed curve $C$, then

$$\oint_C P\, dx + Q\, dy = \iint_R \left(\frac{\partial Q}{\partial x} - \frac{\partial P}{\partial y}\right) dxdy. \tag{4.110}$$

Equation (4.110) can also be expressed in vector form; i.e., if $\mathbf{f} = P\mathbf{i} + Q\mathbf{j}$, then

$$\oint_C \mathbf{f} \cdot d\mathbf{r} = \iint_R \nabla \times \mathbf{f} \cdot \mathbf{k}\, dxdy. \tag{4.111}$$

**PROBLEM 4.61** Verify Green's theorem (4.110) for a plane.

**Solution:** If $\mathbf{f} = P\mathbf{i} + Q\mathbf{j}$ and $d\mathbf{S} = \mathbf{k}\, dxdy$, then (4.110) follows directly from Stokes' theorem (4.104).

Alternatively, (4.110) is a special case of (4.109) with $R = 0$. Now if $\mathbf{f} = P\mathbf{i} + Q\mathbf{j}$, then

$$\nabla \times \mathbf{f} = \begin{vmatrix} \mathbf{i} & \mathbf{j} & \mathbf{k} \\ \dfrac{\partial}{\partial x} & \dfrac{\partial}{\partial y} & \dfrac{\partial}{\partial z} \\ P & Q & 0 \end{vmatrix} = -\frac{\partial Q}{\partial z}\mathbf{i} + \frac{\partial P}{\partial z}\mathbf{j} + \left(\frac{\partial Q}{\partial x} - \frac{\partial P}{\partial y}\right)\mathbf{k},$$

$$\mathbf{f} \cdot d\mathbf{r} = P\, dx + Q\, dy,$$

$$\nabla \times \mathbf{f} \cdot d\mathbf{S} = \nabla \times \mathbf{f} \cdot \mathbf{k}\, dxdy = \left(\frac{\partial Q}{\partial x} - \frac{\partial P}{\partial y}\right) dxdy.$$

Hence, by Stokes' theorem (4.104),

$$\oint_C P\, dx + Q\, dy = \iint_R \left(\frac{\partial Q}{\partial x} - \frac{\partial P}{\partial y}\right) dxdy.$$

**PROBLEM 4.62** Show that Green's theorem (4.110) for a plane can also be expressed as

$$\oint_C \mathbf{f} \cdot \mathbf{n}\, ds = \iint_R \nabla \cdot \mathbf{f}\, dxdy, \tag{4.112}$$

where $\mathbf{f} = Q\mathbf{i} - P\mathbf{j}$, $\mathbf{n}$ is the outward unit normal vector to $C$, as shown in Fig. 4.17, and $s$ is the arc length.

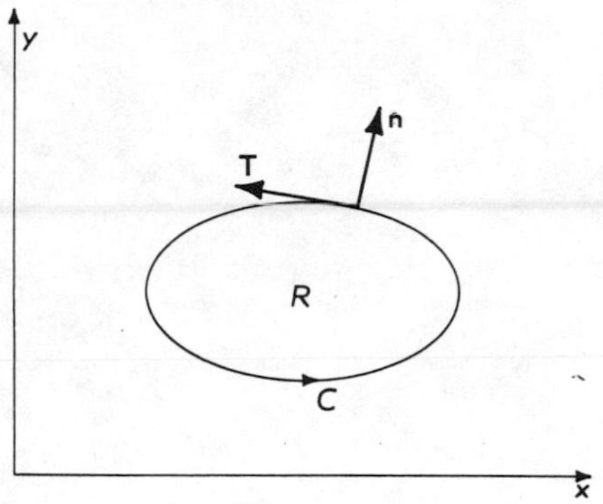


Fig. 4.17 Green's theorem of a plane.

**Solution:** From (3.107), the unit tangent vector $\mathbf{T}$ to $C$ is

$$\mathbf{T} = \frac{d\mathbf{r}}{ds} = \frac{dx}{ds}\mathbf{i} + \frac{dy}{ds}\mathbf{j}.$$

Now, from Fig. 4.17,

$$\mathbf{n} = \mathbf{T} \times \mathbf{k} = \left(\frac{dx}{ds}\mathbf{i} + \frac{dy}{ds}\mathbf{j}\right) \times \mathbf{k} = \frac{dy}{ds}\mathbf{i} - \frac{dx}{ds}\mathbf{j}.$$

Accordingly,

$$\mathbf{f}\cdot\mathbf{n} = (Q\mathbf{i} - P\mathbf{j})\cdot\left(\frac{dy}{ds}\mathbf{i} - \frac{dx}{ds}\mathbf{j}\right) = Q\frac{dy}{ds} + P\frac{dx}{ds}.$$

Thus,

$$\oint_C \mathbf{f}\cdot\mathbf{n}\, ds = \oint_C \left(Q\frac{dy}{ds} + P\frac{dx}{ds}\right) ds = \oint_C P\,dx + Q\,dy.$$

Next,

$$\nabla\cdot\mathbf{f} = \frac{\partial Q}{\partial x} + \frac{\partial(-P)}{\partial y} = \frac{\partial Q}{\partial x} - \frac{\partial P}{\partial y}.$$

Hence, Green's theorem (4.110) for a plane can be expressed as

$$\oint_C \mathbf{f}\cdot\mathbf{n}\, ds = \iint_R \nabla\cdot\mathbf{f}\, dxdy.$$

**PROBLEM 4.63** Show that the area $A$ of a region $R$ in the xy-plane bounded by a simple closed curve $C$ is

$$A = \oint_C x\,dy = \oint_C -y\,dx = \frac{1}{2}\oint_C x\,dy - y\,dx. \qquad (4.113)$$

**Solution:** If $P(x, y) = 0$ and $Q(x, y) = x$ in (4.110), then

$$\oint_C x\,dy = \iint_R dxdy = A.$$

If we let $P = -y$ and $Q = 0$ in (4.110), then

$$\oint_C -y\,dx = \iint_R dxdy = A.$$

Adding the above results, we obtain $A = \frac{1}{2}\oint x\,dy - y\,dx$. If we let $P = -y$ and $Q = x$ in (4.110),

$$\oint_C (-y)\,dx + x\,dy = \oint_C x\,dy - y\,dx = \iint_R \left[\frac{\partial x}{\partial x} - \frac{\partial(-y)}{\partial y}\right] dxdy$$

$$= 2\iint_R dxdy$$

$$= 2A.$$

Hence,

$$A = \frac{1}{2}\oint x\, dy - y\, dx.$$

**PROBLEM 4.64** Determine the area $A$ of a region $R$ bounded by an ellipse $C$ whose major and minor axes are $2a$ and $2b$, respectively.

**Solution:** The equation of an ellipse $C$ having a major axis $2a$ and a minor axis $2b$ is

$$\frac{x^2}{a^2} + \frac{y^2}{b^2} = 1, \qquad z = 0.$$

Hence, $C$ can be represented parametrically by

$$x = a \cos t, \qquad y = b \sin t, \qquad z = 0, \qquad 0 \le t \le 2\pi.$$

Then, $dx = -a \sin t\, dt$, $dy = b \cos t\, dt$. Hence, by (4.112),

$$\begin{aligned} A &= \frac{1}{2}\oint x\, dy - y\, dx \\ &= \frac{1}{2}\int_0^{2\pi} (a \cos t)(b \cos t\, dt) - (b \sin t)(-a \sin t\, dt) \\ &= \frac{1}{2}\int_0^{2\pi} ab(\cos^2 t + \sin^2 t)\, dt \\ &= \frac{1}{2}\, ab \int_0^{2\pi} dt \\ &= \pi ab. \end{aligned}$$

## 4.9 Surface-to-Line Integral Transformations

Stokes' theorem (4.104) represents a surface-to-line integral transformation involving the curl of a vector; i.e.,

$$\iint_S \nabla \times \mathbf{f} \cdot d\mathbf{S} = \oint_C \mathbf{f} \cdot d\mathbf{r}. \qquad [4.104]$$

Since

$$\iint_S \nabla \times \mathbf{f} \cdot d\mathbf{S} = \iint_S d\mathbf{S} \cdot \nabla \times \mathbf{f} = \iint_S (d\mathbf{S} \times \nabla) \cdot \mathbf{f},$$

Stokes' theorem can be stated as

$$\iint_S (d\mathbf{S} \times \nabla) \cdot \mathbf{f} = \oint d\mathbf{r} \cdot \mathbf{f}. \qquad (4.114)$$

By extending the definitions of the curl of the gradient and the curl of the curl to finite surfaces, we obtain the following theorems:

If $S$ is a finite surface bounded by a simple closed curve $C$ and $\phi$ is a scalar function with continuous derivatives, then

$$\iint_S d\mathbf{S} \times \nabla\phi = \oint_C \phi\, d\mathbf{r}. \qquad (4.115)$$

If $S$ is a finite surface bounded by a closed curve $C$ and $\mathbf{f}$ is a vector function with continuous derivatives, then

$$\iint_S (d\mathbf{S} \times \nabla) \times \mathbf{f} = \oint_C d\mathbf{r} \times \mathbf{f}. \tag{4.116}$$

Note that the theorems (4.104) and (4.115–6) can be stated as

$$\iint_S (d\mathbf{S} \times \nabla) * \alpha = \oint_C d\mathbf{r} * \alpha, \tag{4.117}$$

where $\alpha$ is any scalar or vector quantity and the star (*) represents any acceptable form of multiplication, i.e., the dot, cross, or simple product.

**PROBLEM 4.65** Verify (4.115).

**Solution:** Let $\mathbf{f} = \phi\,\mathbf{a}$, where $\mathbf{a}$ is any constant vector. Applying Stokes' theorem (4.104),

$$\iint_S \nabla \times (\phi\,\mathbf{a}) \cdot d\mathbf{S} = \oint_C \phi\,\mathbf{a} \cdot d\mathbf{r}. \tag{4.118}$$

From (3.156),

$$\nabla \times (\phi\,\mathbf{a}) = \phi \nabla \times \mathbf{a} - \mathbf{a} \times \nabla\phi.$$

Since $\mathbf{a}$ is a constant vector, $\nabla \times \mathbf{a} = \mathbf{0}$; hence,

$$\nabla \times (\phi\,\mathbf{a}) = \nabla\phi \times \mathbf{a}.$$

From the permutation rule of the triple scalar product (1.77),

$$\iint_S (\nabla\phi \times \mathbf{a}) \cdot d\mathbf{S} = \iint_S \mathbf{a} \cdot d\mathbf{S} \times \nabla\phi.$$

Hence, (4.118) reduces to

$$\mathbf{a} \cdot \iint_S d\mathbf{S} \times \nabla\phi = \mathbf{a} \cdot \oint_C \phi\, d\mathbf{r},$$

or

$$\mathbf{a} \cdot \left( \iint_S d\mathbf{S} \times \nabla\phi - \oint_C \phi\, d\mathbf{r} \right) = 0. \tag{4.119}$$

Since $\mathbf{a}$ is any constant vector, the expression in parentheses vanishes and (4.115) is proved.

**PROBLEM 4.66** Verify (4.116).

**Solution:** If $\mathbf{a}$ is any constant vector and we replace $\mathbf{f}$ in (4.104) by $\mathbf{f} \times \mathbf{a}$,

$$\iint_S \nabla \times (\mathbf{f} \times \mathbf{a}) \cdot d\mathbf{S} = \oint_C (\mathbf{f} \times \mathbf{a}) \cdot d\mathbf{r}. \tag{4.120}$$

From (3.158),

$$\nabla \times (\mathbf{f} \times \mathbf{a}) = \mathbf{f}(\nabla \cdot \mathbf{a}) - \mathbf{a}(\nabla \cdot \mathbf{f}) + (\mathbf{a} \cdot \nabla)\mathbf{f} - (\mathbf{f} \cdot \nabla)\,\mathbf{a}.$$

Since $\mathbf{a}$ is a constant vector, $\nabla \cdot \mathbf{a} = 0$ and $(\mathbf{f} \cdot \nabla)\,\mathbf{a} = \mathbf{0}$; hence,

$$\nabla \times (\mathbf{f} \times \mathbf{a}) = (\mathbf{a} \cdot \nabla)\mathbf{f} - \mathbf{a}(\nabla \cdot \mathbf{f}). \tag{4.121}$$

Thus,

$$\iint_S \nabla \times (\mathbf{f} \times \mathbf{a}) \cdot d\mathbf{S} = \iint_S [(\mathbf{a} \cdot \nabla)\mathbf{f} \cdot d\mathbf{S} - \mathbf{a} \cdot d\mathbf{S}(\nabla \cdot \mathbf{f})]$$

$$= \mathbf{a} \cdot \iint_S [\nabla_{\mathbf{f}}(\mathbf{f} \cdot d\mathbf{S}) - d\mathbf{S}(\nabla \cdot \mathbf{f})],$$

where $\nabla_{\mathbf{f}}$ indicates that $\nabla$ operates only on **f**.

Applying the middle-term rule for the triple vector product (1.98) to $(d\mathbf{S} \times \nabla) \times \mathbf{f}$,

$$(d\mathbf{S} \times \nabla) \times \mathbf{f} = \nabla_{\mathbf{f}}(\mathbf{f} \cdot d\mathbf{S}) - d\mathbf{S}(\nabla \cdot \mathbf{f}), \tag{4.122}$$

and we can write

$$\iint_S \nabla \times (\mathbf{f} \times \mathbf{a}) \cdot d\mathbf{S} = \mathbf{a} \cdot \iint_S (d\mathbf{S} \times \nabla) \times \mathbf{f}.$$

From the permutation rule of the triple scalar product (1.77),

$$\oint_C (\mathbf{f} \times \mathbf{a}) \cdot d\mathbf{r} = \oint_C \mathbf{a} \cdot (d\mathbf{r} \times \mathbf{f}) = \mathbf{a} \cdot \oint_C d\mathbf{r} \times \mathbf{f}.$$

Hence, (4.120) reduces to

$$\mathbf{a} \cdot \iint_S (d\mathbf{S} \times \nabla) \times \mathbf{f} = \mathbf{a} \cdot \oint_C d\mathbf{r} \times \mathbf{f},$$

or

$$\mathbf{a} \cdot \left( \iint_S (d\mathbf{S} \times \nabla) \times \mathbf{f} - \oint_C d\mathbf{r} \times \mathbf{f} \right) = 0. \tag{4.123}$$

Since **a** is any constant vector, the expression in parentheses vanishes and (4.116) is proved.

**PROBLEM 4.67** Prove that if **r** is a position vector, then

$$\oint_C d\mathbf{r} = \mathbf{0}. \tag{4.124}$$

**Solution:** From (4.115),

$$\oint_C \phi \, d\mathbf{r} = \iint_S d\mathbf{S} \times \nabla\phi.$$

If $\phi = 1$, then $\nabla\phi = \mathbf{0}$; hence,

$$\oint_C d\mathbf{r} = \mathbf{0}.$$

**PROBLEM 4.68** Show that, by integrating around a closed curve $C$ in the $xy$-plane,

$$\left| \oint_C \mathbf{r} \times d\mathbf{r} \right| = 2A, \tag{4.125}$$

where **r** is the position vector and $A$ is the area enclosed by the curve $C$.

**Solution:** If $\mathbf{f} = \mathbf{r}$ and $d\mathbf{S} = \mathbf{k}\, dxdy$ in (4.116),

$$\oint_C d\mathbf{r} \times \mathbf{r} = \iint_S (\mathbf{k} \times \nabla) \times \mathbf{r}\, dxdy.$$

Since $\nabla \cdot \mathbf{r} = 3$ from (3.129), using (4.122),

$$(\mathbf{k} \times \nabla) \times \mathbf{r} = \nabla(\mathbf{k} \cdot \mathbf{r}) - \mathbf{k}(\nabla \cdot \mathbf{r}) = \nabla(z) - 3\mathbf{k} = \mathbf{k} - 3\mathbf{k} = -2\mathbf{k}.$$

Hence,

$$\oint_C \mathbf{r} \times d\mathbf{r} = -\oint_C d\mathbf{r} \times \mathbf{r} = 2\mathbf{k} \iint_S dxdy = 2A\mathbf{k}, \tag{4.126}$$

and $\left| \oint_C \mathbf{r} \times d\mathbf{r} \right| = 2A.$

**PROBLEM 4.69** If $S$ is an open surface bounded by a simple closed curve $C$, show that

$$\oint_C \mathbf{r} \times d\mathbf{r} = 2 \iint_S d\mathbf{S}. \tag{4.127}$$

**Solution:** If in Stokes' theorem (4.104) $\mathbf{f} = \mathbf{r} \times \mathbf{a}$, where $\mathbf{a}$ is a constant vector, then

$$\oint_C (\mathbf{r} \times \mathbf{a}) \cdot d\mathbf{r} = \iint_S \nabla \times (\mathbf{r} \times \mathbf{a}) \cdot d\mathbf{S}. \tag{4.128}$$

Since $\mathbf{a}$ is a constant vector, we have from (4.121),

$$\nabla \times (\mathbf{r} \times \mathbf{a}) = (\mathbf{a} \cdot \nabla)\mathbf{r} - \mathbf{a}(\nabla \cdot \mathbf{r}).$$

Now from (3.141) and (3.121), since

$$(\mathbf{a} \cdot \nabla)\mathbf{r} = \mathbf{a},$$

$$\nabla \cdot \mathbf{r} = 3,$$

we have

$$\nabla \times (\mathbf{r} \times \mathbf{a}) = \mathbf{a} - 3\mathbf{a} = -2\mathbf{a}.$$

Also, by the permutation rule of the triple scalar product (1.77), $(\mathbf{r} \times \mathbf{a}) \cdot d\mathbf{r} = -\mathbf{a} \cdot (\mathbf{r} \times d\mathbf{r})$. Hence, (4.128) can be written as

$$\mathbf{a} \cdot \oint_C \mathbf{r} \times d\mathbf{r} = 2\mathbf{a} \cdot \iint_S d\mathbf{S}.$$

Since $\mathbf{a}$ is any constant vector,

$$\oint_C \mathbf{r} \times d\mathbf{r} = 2 \iint_S d\mathbf{S}.$$

Note that (4.18), i.e.,

$$\oint_C \mathbf{r} \times d\mathbf{r} = \int_0^{2\pi} \mathbf{k}\, a^2\, dt = \mathbf{k}\, a^2 \int_0^{2\pi} dt = 2\pi a^2 \mathbf{k},$$

and (4.125) are the special cases of (4.127). They are relevant to (4.127) because twice the integral of $d\mathbf{S}$ over the surface $S$ is equal to the line integral of

$\mathbf{r} \times d\mathbf{r}$ around the boundary of $S$, which is independent of the point chosen for the origin of the position vector $\mathbf{r}$ and of the surface $S$ bounded by $C$.

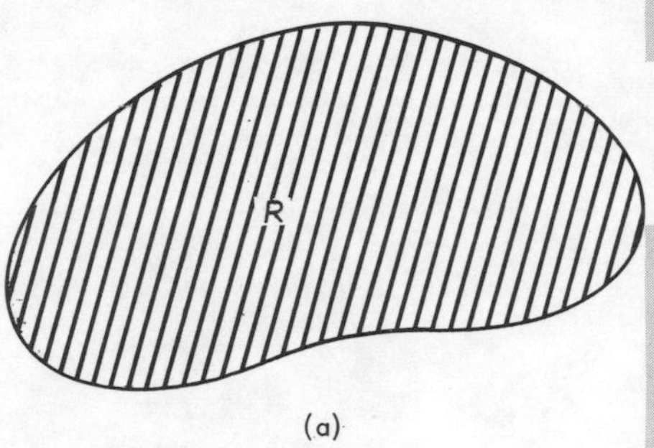


Fig. 4.18a A simply connected region.

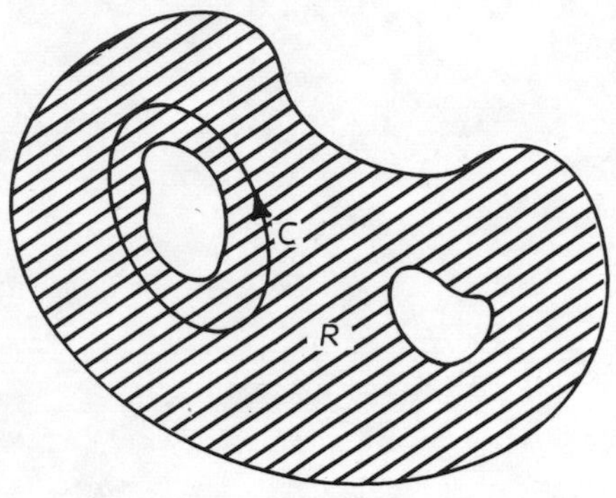


Fig. 4.18b A region that is not simply connected.

## 4.10 Irrotational and Solenoidal Fields

A region $R$ is said to be *connected* if any two points of $R$ can be joined by an arc where every point on the arc belongs to $R$.

A region $R$ is said to be *simply connected* if every closed curve in $R$ can be continuously shrunk to a point in $R$. The region $R$ in Fig. 4.18(a) is simply connected. However, the region $R$ in Fig. 4.18(b) is not simply connected because the closed curve $C$ that surrounds one of the "holes" cannot be continuously shrunk to a point without leaving $R$.

A scalar potential function $\phi$ is a single-valued function for which a continuous vector field $\mathbf{f}$ in a simply connected region satisfies

$$\mathbf{f} = \nabla\phi. \tag{4.129}$$

**PROBLEM 4.70** Show that the necessary and sufficient condition for the line integral $\int_P^Q \mathbf{f}\cdot d\mathbf{r}$ to be independent of the path of integration from the point $P$ to the point $Q$ is that the continuous vector field $\mathbf{f}$ satisfy (4.129).

**Solution:** To prove the sufficiency, assume that $\mathbf{f} = \nabla\phi$. Then by (3.120),

$$\mathbf{f}\cdot d\mathbf{r} = \nabla\phi\cdot d\mathbf{r} = d\phi,$$

and hence,

$$\int_P^Q \mathbf{f}\cdot d\mathbf{r} = \int_P^Q d\phi = \phi(Q) - \phi(P). \tag{4.130}$$

If $\phi$ is single-valued, the right-hand side of (4.130) has a definite value that depends only on the end points $P$ and $Q$ and not on the path.

To prove the necessity, assume that $\int_P^Q \mathbf{f}\cdot d\mathbf{r}$ is independent of the path of integration. Let

$$\phi(Q) = \int_P^Q \mathbf{f}\cdot d\mathbf{r},$$

where $P$ is a fixed point and $Q$ is a variable point in $R$. Since the line integral is independent of the path, $Q$ moves along a curve through $P$ on which the unit tangent vector $\mathbf{T}$ is continuous. (See Fig. 4.19.) Along this curve,

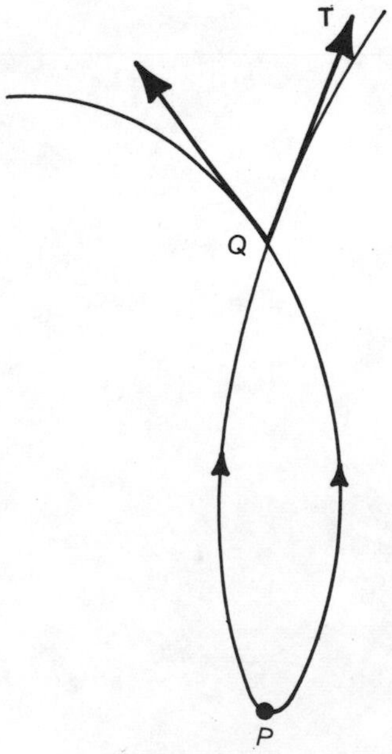


Fig. 4.19 Solution to Prob. 4.70.

$$\phi = \int_P^Q \mathbf{f}\cdot d\mathbf{r} = \int_P^Q \mathbf{f}\cdot\frac{d\mathbf{r}}{ds}\,ds = \int_P^Q \mathbf{f}\cdot\mathbf{T}\,ds$$

is a function of the arc length $s$. Thus,

$$\frac{\partial\phi}{\partial s} = \mathbf{f}\cdot\frac{d\mathbf{r}}{ds} = \mathbf{f}\cdot\mathbf{T}. \tag{4.131}$$

The curve $PQ$ could be chosen to have any given direction at $Q$. Hence, (4.131) shows that $\phi$ has a continuous directional derivative in any direction. But

$$\frac{\partial\phi}{\partial s} = \nabla\phi\cdot\mathbf{T}. \qquad [3.106]$$

Now comparing (4.131) and (3.106),

$$(\mathbf{f} - \nabla\phi) \cdot \mathbf{T} = 0. \tag{4.132}$$

Since (4.132) holds for every direction of **T**,

$$\mathbf{f} - \nabla\phi = \mathbf{0}, \quad \text{or} \quad \mathbf{f} = \nabla\phi. \qquad [4.129]$$

**PROBLEM 4.71** If $\mathbf{f} = \nabla\phi$ everywhere in a simply connected region $R$, and $C$ is any closed curve in $R$, show that

$$\oint_C \mathbf{f} \cdot d\mathbf{r} = 0. \tag{4.133}$$

**Solution:** If $\mathbf{f} = \nabla\phi$ everywhere in $R$, then from Prob. 4.70, the line integral $\int_C \mathbf{f} \cdot d\mathbf{r}$ is independent of the path of integration. If the path of integration is closed, then $P = Q$ in (4.130). Thus,

$$\oint_C \mathbf{f} \cdot d\mathbf{r} = \oint_C \nabla\phi \cdot d\mathbf{r} = \int_P^P d\phi = \phi(P) - \phi(P) = 0.$$

This problem was solved in Prob. 4.57 by applying Stokes' theorem (4.104). Note that (4.133) is valid only when $\phi$ is a single-valued function and $R$ is simply connected. If $R$ is not simply connected, then it is possible to have $\mathbf{f} = \nabla\phi$, and the circulation of **f** around a closed path C in a region $R$ may not be zero; i.e., we can have $\oint_C \mathbf{f} \cdot d\mathbf{r} \neq 0$. Problem 4.72 illustrates this point.

**PROBLEM 4.72** Let $\mathbf{f} = -\dfrac{y}{x^2 + y^2}\mathbf{i} + \dfrac{x}{x^2 + y^2}\mathbf{j}$. (a) Show that **f** can be expressed as $\nabla\phi$, where $\phi = \tan^{-1}(y/x)$. (b) Evaluate

$$I = \oint_C \mathbf{f} \cdot d\mathbf{r}$$

if C is a circle of radius $a$ on the $xy$-plane when its center is at the origin and when it is at $(\alpha, \beta, 0)$ with $\alpha^2 + \beta^2 > a^2$.

**Solution:** (a) Since $\phi = \tan^{-1}(y/x)$,

$$\begin{aligned}
\nabla\phi &= \frac{\partial}{\partial x}\left[\tan^{-1}\left(\frac{y}{x}\right)\right]\mathbf{i} + \frac{\partial}{\partial y}\left[\tan^{-1}\left(\frac{y}{x}\right)\right]\mathbf{i} \\
&= \frac{1}{1 + \left(\frac{y}{x}\right)^2}\left(\frac{-y}{x^2}\right)\mathbf{i} + \frac{1}{1 + \left(\frac{y}{x}\right)^2}\left(\frac{1}{x}\right)\mathbf{j} \\
&= \frac{-y}{x^2 + y^2}\mathbf{i} + \frac{x}{x^2 + y^2}\mathbf{j} \\
&= \mathbf{f}.
\end{aligned}$$

(b) When the center of C is at the origin,

$$I = \oint_C \mathbf{f} \cdot d\mathbf{r} = \oint_C \nabla\phi \cdot d\mathbf{r} = \oint_C d\phi = \oint_C d\left[\tan^{-1}\left(\frac{y}{x}\right)\right].$$

The parametric representation for C is

$$x = a\cos t, \quad y = a\sin t, \quad z = 0.$$

Thus,

$$I = \int_0^{2\pi} d\left[\tan^{-1}\left(\frac{y}{x}\right)\right] = \int_0^{2\pi} d[\tan^{-1}(\tan t)] = \int_0^{2\pi} dt = 2\pi \neq 0.$$

The result is not zero because the region defined for which $\mathbf{f} = \nabla\phi$ is not a simply connected region, since $\phi = \tan^{-1}(y/x)$ is not defined at the origin, and the region is punctured at the origin.

When the center of $C$ is at $(\alpha, \beta, 0)$, its parametric representation is

$$x = \alpha + a\cos t, \quad y = \beta + a\sin t, \quad z = 0.$$

Hence,

$$I = \int_0^{2\pi} d\left[\tan^{-1}\left(\frac{y}{x}\right)\right] = \tan^{-1}\left(\frac{\beta + a\sin t}{\alpha + a\cos t}\right)\Bigg|_0^{2\pi} = 0.$$

**PROBLEM 4.73** If $R$ is a simply connected region, show that the necessary and sufficient condition for $\nabla \times \mathbf{f} = \mathbf{0}$ is that $\mathbf{f} = \nabla\phi$ when $\mathbf{f}$ has continuous derivatives.

**Solution:** If $\mathbf{f} = \nabla\phi$,

$$\nabla \times \mathbf{f} = \nabla \times \nabla\phi = \mathbf{0}. \qquad [3.142]$$

On the other hand, if $\nabla \times \mathbf{f} = \mathbf{0}$, then from the solution to Prob. 4.58, or Stokes' theorem (4.104),

$$\oint_C \mathbf{f} \cdot d\mathbf{r} = 0$$

for every simple closed curve $C$ in $R$. From the solution to Prob. 4.71, this indicates that the line integral of $\mathbf{f}$ is independent of the path of integration and that $\mathbf{f}$ can be expressed as $\mathbf{f} = \nabla\phi$.

Problem 4.73 provides a simple test of whether a vector field $\mathbf{f}$ is the gradient of a scalar field $\phi$. This is illustrated in Prob. 4.74.

**PROBLEM 4.74** Two vector fields are given by $\mathbf{f} = 3y^2\mathbf{i} + z\mathbf{j} + 2y\mathbf{k}$ and $\mathbf{g} = yz\mathbf{i} + xz\mathbf{j} + xy\mathbf{k}$. Determine whether these vector fields are the gradients of scalar fields.

**Solution:** Since $\mathbf{f} = 3y^2\mathbf{i} + z\mathbf{j} + 2y\mathbf{k}$,

$$\nabla \times \mathbf{f} = \begin{vmatrix} \mathbf{i} & \mathbf{j} & \mathbf{k} \\ \dfrac{\partial}{\partial x} & \dfrac{\partial}{\partial y} & \dfrac{\partial}{\partial z} \\ 3y^2 & z & 2y \end{vmatrix}$$

$$= \mathbf{i} - 6y\mathbf{j}$$

$$\neq \mathbf{0}.$$

Therefore, $\mathbf{f}$ is not the gradient of a scalar field.

Since $\mathbf{g} = yz\mathbf{i} + xz\mathbf{j} + xy\mathbf{k}$,

$$\nabla \times \mathbf{g} = \begin{vmatrix} \mathbf{i} & \mathbf{j} & \mathbf{k} \\ \dfrac{\partial}{\partial x} & \dfrac{\partial}{\partial y} & \dfrac{\partial}{\partial z} \\ yz & xz & xy \end{vmatrix}$$

$$= (x - x)\mathbf{i} + (y - y)\mathbf{j} + (z - z)\mathbf{k}$$

$$= \mathbf{0}.$$

Hence, **g** is the gradient of a scalar field. Note that $\mathbf{g} = \nabla(xyz + \text{constant})$.

**PROBLEM 4.75** If, in a simply connected region $R$, $\nabla \times \mathbf{f} = \nabla \times \mathbf{g}$, prove that

$$\mathbf{f} = \mathbf{g} + \nabla\phi.$$

**Solution:** Since $\nabla \times \mathbf{f} = \nabla \times \mathbf{g}$,

$$\nabla \times (\mathbf{f} - \mathbf{g}) = \mathbf{0}.$$

Then, from the result of Prob. 4.73,

$$\mathbf{f} - \mathbf{g} = \nabla\phi,$$

and hence,

$$\mathbf{f} = \mathbf{g} + \nabla\phi. \tag{4.134}$$

A vector field **f** is said to be *irrotational* in a region $R$ if

$$\nabla \times \mathbf{f} = \mathbf{0} \tag{4.135}$$

everywhere in $R$. From the results of Probs. 4.70–2, we conclude that for a vector field **f** to be irrotational in a simply connected region $R$, any of the following three conditions is necessary and sufficient:

(1) $\nabla \times \mathbf{f} \equiv \mathbf{0}$;

(2) **f** is the gradient of a scalar field; i.e., $\mathbf{f} = \nabla\phi$;

(3) for every simple closed curve $C$ in $R$, $\oint_C \mathbf{f} \cdot d\mathbf{r} = 0$.

**PROBLEM 4.76** Show that if there exists a scalar $\lambda \neq 0$ such that $\lambda\mathbf{f}$ is irrotational, then

$$\mathbf{f} \cdot \nabla \times \mathbf{f} = 0. \tag{4.136}$$

**Solution:** If $\lambda\mathbf{f}$ is irrotational, there is a scalar function $\phi$ such that

$$\lambda\mathbf{f} = \nabla\phi.$$

Taking the curl of both sides,

$$\nabla \times (\lambda\mathbf{f}) = \nabla \times (\nabla\phi) = \mathbf{0}.$$

But by (3.156),

$$\nabla \times (\lambda\mathbf{f}) = \lambda\nabla \times \mathbf{f} + \nabla\lambda \times \mathbf{f} = \mathbf{0}$$

or

$$\lambda\nabla \times \mathbf{f} = -\nabla\lambda \times \mathbf{f} = \mathbf{f} \times \nabla\lambda.$$

If we dot product both sides with **f**, we obtain (by Prob. 2.21)

$$\lambda\mathbf{f} \cdot \nabla \times \mathbf{f} = \mathbf{f} \cdot \mathbf{f} \times \nabla\lambda = 0.$$

Since $\lambda$ is not zero,

$$\mathbf{f} \cdot \nabla \times \mathbf{f} = 0.$$

Note that the converse is also true.

A vector field **f** is said to be *solenoidal* if, everywhere in a region $R$,

$$\nabla \cdot \mathbf{f} = 0. \tag{4.137}$$

**PROBLEM 4.77** Show that a vector $\mathbf{f}$, which is the curl of another vector $\mathbf{A}$, is solenoidal.

**Solution:** If $\mathbf{f} = \nabla \times \mathbf{A}$, then by (3.143),

$$\nabla \cdot \mathbf{f} = \nabla \cdot (\nabla \times \mathbf{A}) = 0;$$

hence, $\mathbf{f}$ is solenoidal.

A *vector potential function* $\mathbf{A}$ in a specific region $R^*$ is a vector field for which a solenoidal vector field $\mathbf{f}$ satisfies

$$\mathbf{f} = \nabla \times \mathbf{A}. \tag{4.138}$$

There is no unique $\mathbf{A}$ for which (4.138) holds because

$$\nabla \times (\mathbf{A} + \nabla\psi) = \nabla \times \mathbf{A} + \nabla \times \nabla\psi = \nabla \times \mathbf{A}.$$

(Cf., Prob. 3.50.) The region $R^*$ is a *generalization* of a simply connected region, i.e., a region in which every closed surface $S$ in $R$ must bound a volume $V$ also in $R$.

Hence, if a solenoidal field $\mathbf{f}$ is in the region $R^*$, then from the result of Prob. 4.77 and the divergence theorem (4.58), $\mathbf{f}$ has the following properties:

(a) $\nabla \cdot \mathbf{f} = 0$;

(b) $\mathbf{f}$ is the curl of a vector; i.e., $\mathbf{f} = \nabla \times \mathbf{A}$;

(c) for every closed surface $S$ in $R$, $\displaystyle\oiint_S \mathbf{f} \cdot d\mathbf{S} = 0.$

**PROBLEM 4.78** If $\mathbf{f}$ is a solenoidal vector field, show that there exists a vector potential function $\mathbf{A}$ such that

$$\mathbf{f} = \nabla \times \mathbf{A}. \qquad [4.138]$$

**Solution:** The existence of $\mathbf{A}$ is demonstrated by actually calculating it. Let $\mathbf{f} = f_1\mathbf{i} + f_2\mathbf{j} + f_3\mathbf{k}$ and $\mathbf{A} = A_1\mathbf{i} + A_2\mathbf{j} + A_3\mathbf{k}$. Now we need to show that there exist scalar functions $A_1$, $A_2$, and $A_3$ such that

$$\mathbf{f} = \nabla \times \mathbf{A},$$

or

$$f_1 = \frac{\partial A_3}{\partial y} - \frac{\partial A_2}{\partial z}, \tag{4.139a}$$

$$f_2 = \frac{\partial A_1}{\partial z} - \frac{\partial A_3}{\partial x}, \tag{4.139b}$$

$$f_3 = \frac{\partial A_2}{\partial x} - \frac{\partial A_1}{\partial y}. \tag{4.139c}$$

To find any $\mathbf{A}$, assume that $A_1 = 0$; then,

$$f_1 = \frac{\partial A_3}{\partial y} - \frac{\partial A_2}{\partial z}, \tag{4.140a}$$

$$f_2 = -\frac{\partial A_3}{\partial x}, \tag{4.140b}$$

$$f_3 = \frac{\partial A_2}{\partial x}. \tag{4.140c}$$

Integration gives

$$A_2 = \int_{x_0}^{x} f_3\, dx + g_2(y, z),$$

$$A_3 = -\int_{x_0}^{x} f_2\, dx + g_3(y, z),$$

where $g_2$ and $g_3$ are arbitrary functions of $y$ and $z$ but not of $x$. The difference of the partial derivatives of $A_3$ and $A_2$ is

$$\frac{\partial A_3}{\partial y} - \frac{\partial A_2}{\partial z} = -\int_{x_0}^{x} \left(\frac{\partial f_2}{\partial y} + \frac{\partial f_3}{\partial z}\right) dx + \frac{\partial g_3}{\partial y} - \frac{\partial g_2}{\partial z}.$$

Since $\mathbf{f}$ is solenoidal, $\nabla \cdot \mathbf{f} = 0$ or

$$\frac{\partial f_1}{\partial x} = -\left(\frac{\partial f_2}{\partial y} + \frac{\partial f_3}{\partial z}\right).$$

Hence,

$$\frac{\partial A_3}{\partial y} - \frac{\partial A_2}{\partial z} = \int_{x_0}^{x} \frac{\partial f_1}{\partial x}\, dx + \frac{\partial g_3}{\partial z} - \frac{\partial g_2}{\partial z}$$

$$= f_1(x, y, z) - f_1(x_0, y, z) + \frac{\partial g_3}{\partial z} - \frac{\partial g_2}{\partial z}.$$

To satisfy (4.140a),

$$f_1 = f_1(x, y, z) - f_1(x_0, y, z) + \frac{\partial g_3}{\partial y} - \frac{\partial g_2}{\partial z}. \tag{4.141}$$

Since by assumption, $g_2$ and $g_3$ are arbitrary functions of $y$ and $z$, (4.141) is satisfied if

$$g_2 = 0, \tag{4.142}$$

$$g_3 = \int_{y_0}^{y} f_1(x_0, y, z)\, dy, \tag{4.143}$$

where $y_0$ is a constant. Hence, with $g_2$ and $g_3$ given by (4.142) and (4.143), we can construct $\mathbf{A}$ as

$$\mathbf{A} = \mathbf{j} \int_{x_0}^{x} f_3(x, y, z)\, dx + \mathbf{k}\left[\int_{y_0}^{y} f_1(x_0, y, z)\, dy - \int_{x_0}^{x} f_2(x, y, z)\, dx\right]. \tag{4.144}$$

In this proof, several arbitrary selections have been made, and also note that the region $R^*$ in which $\mathbf{A}$ was constructed has been assumed to be a rectangular parallelepiped.

**PROBLEM 4.79** If $\phi$ and $\psi$ are scalars with continuous second partial derivatives in a region $R$, show that

$$\mathbf{f} = \nabla\phi \times \nabla\psi \tag{4.145}$$

is solenoidal in $R$.

**Solution:** By (3.157) and (3.142),

$$
\begin{aligned}
\nabla \cdot \mathbf{f} &= \nabla \cdot (\nabla \phi \times \nabla \psi) \\
&= \nabla \psi \cdot [\nabla \times (\nabla \phi)] - \nabla \phi \cdot [\nabla \times (\nabla \psi)] \\
&= 0.
\end{aligned}
$$

Hence, $\mathbf{f}$ is solenoidal.

The *uniqueness theorem* states that a vector $\mathbf{f}$ is uniquely determined in a region $R$ enclosed by a surface $S$ if the normal component of $\mathbf{f}$ is specified on $S$ and if $\nabla \cdot \mathbf{f}$ and $\nabla \times \mathbf{f}$ are specified through $R$.

**PROBLEM 4.80** Prove the uniqueness theorem.

**Solution:** We prove this theorem by contradiction. Assume that $\mathbf{f}$ and $\mathbf{g}$ are two vectors that satisfy the given conditions; i.e., if $\mathbf{n}$ is the unit normal vector to $S$,

$$
\nabla \cdot \mathbf{f} = \nabla \cdot \mathbf{g}, \quad \nabla \times \mathbf{f} = \nabla \times \mathbf{g} \qquad \text{in } R,
$$

$$
\mathbf{f} \cdot \mathbf{n} = \mathbf{g} \cdot \mathbf{n} \qquad \text{on } S.
$$

Then letting $\mathbf{h} = \mathbf{f} - \mathbf{g}$,

$$
\left.
\begin{aligned}
\nabla \cdot \mathbf{h} &= \nabla \cdot \mathbf{f} - \nabla \cdot \mathbf{g} = 0 \\
\nabla \times \mathbf{h} &= \nabla \times \mathbf{f} - \nabla \times \mathbf{g} = \mathbf{0}
\end{aligned}
\right\} \quad \text{in } R, \tag{4.146}
$$

$$
\mathbf{h} \cdot \mathbf{n} = \mathbf{f} \cdot \mathbf{n} - \mathbf{g} \cdot \mathbf{n} = 0 \qquad \text{on } S. \tag{4.147}
$$

Since $\nabla \times \mathbf{h} = \mathbf{0}$, the vector $\mathbf{h}$ is irrotational; i.e., if $\phi$ is a scalar function,

$$
\mathbf{h} = \nabla \phi. \tag{4.148}
$$

Now,

$$
\nabla \cdot \mathbf{h} = \nabla \cdot (\nabla \phi) = \nabla^2 \phi = 0 \qquad \text{in } R, \tag{4.149}
$$

$$
\mathbf{h} \cdot \mathbf{n} = \nabla \phi \cdot \mathbf{n} = \frac{\partial \phi}{\partial n} = 0 \qquad \text{on } S. \tag{4.150}
$$

Next, setting $\psi = \phi$ in (4.80),

$$
\iiint_R (\phi \nabla^2 \phi + \nabla \phi \cdot \nabla \phi)\, dV = \oiint_S \phi \frac{\partial \phi}{\partial n}\, dS \tag{4.151}
$$

or

$$
\iiint_R \phi \nabla^2 \phi \, dV + \iiint_R |\nabla \phi|^2 \, dV = \oiint_S \phi \frac{\partial \phi}{\partial n}\, dS. \tag{4.152}
$$

According to the conditions (4.149–50), (4.152) reduces to

$$
\iiint_R |\nabla \phi|^2 \, dV = 0. \tag{4.153}
$$

But since the integrand $|\nabla \phi|^2$ is nonnegative, $|\nabla \phi|^2 = 0$; i.e.,

$$
\mathbf{h} = \nabla \phi = \mathbf{0}. \tag{4.154}
$$

Hence, $\mathbf{f} = \mathbf{g}$, which contradicts our original assumption that $\mathbf{f}$ and $\mathbf{g}$ are distinct. Therefore the theorem is proved.

## 4.11 Supplementary Problems

**PROBLEM 4.81** Evaluate $\int_C \phi d\mathbf{r}$ for $\phi = x^3y + 2y$ from (1, 1, 0) to (2, 4, 0) along (a) the parabola $y = x^2$, $z = 0$, and (b) the straight line joining (1, 1,0) and (2, 4, 0).
*Answer:* (a) [91/6, 359/7, 0], (b) [143/10, 429/10, 0].

**PROBLEM 4.82** Evaluate $\int_C \mathbf{f}\cdot d\mathbf{r}$ for $\mathbf{f} = y\mathbf{i} + (x+z)^2\mathbf{j} + (x-z)^2\mathbf{k}$ from (0, 0, 0) to (2, 4, 0) along (a) the parabola $y = x^2$, $z = 0$, and (b) the straight line $y = 2x$.
*Answer:* (a) 32/3, (b) 28/3.

**PROBLEM 4.83** Evaluate $\int_C \mathbf{f}\cdot d\mathbf{r}$ for $\mathbf{f} = 2xy^2\mathbf{i} + 2(x^2y + y)\mathbf{j}$ from (0, 0, 0) to (2, 4, 0) along (a) the parabola $y = x^2$, $z = 0$, and (b) the straight line $y = 2x$.
*Answer:* (a) 80, (b) 80.

**PROBLEM 4.84** Evaluate $\int_C \mathbf{f}\cdot d\mathbf{r}$ for $\mathbf{f} = 3x\mathbf{i} + (2xz - y)\mathbf{j} + z\mathbf{k}$ from (0, 0, 0) to (2, 1, 3) along (a) the curve of $x = 2t^2$, $y = t$, $z = 4t^2 - t$, where $0 \le t \le 1$, and (b) the straight line from (0, 0, 0) to (2, 1, 3).
*Answer:* (a) 71/5, (b) 16.

**PROBLEM 4.85** Evaluate $\int_C \mathbf{f}\times d\mathbf{r}$ for $\mathbf{f} = y\mathbf{i} + x\mathbf{j}$ from (0, 0, 0) to (3, 9, 0) along the curve given by $y = x^3/3$, $z = 0$.
*Answer:* [0, 0, 36].

**PROBLEM 4.86** If $\mathbf{a}$ is a constant vector, show that $\oint \mathbf{a}\cdot d\mathbf{r} = 0$, and $\oint \mathbf{a}\times d\mathbf{r} = \mathbf{0}$.

**PROBLEM 4.87** If $\mathbf{f} = x\mathbf{i} + y\mathbf{j} + z\mathbf{k}$, evaluate $\iint_S \mathbf{f}\cdot d\mathbf{S}$, where $S$ is the cylindrical surface represented by $\mathbf{r} = \cos u\,\mathbf{i} + \sin u\,\mathbf{j} + v\mathbf{k}$, $0 \le u \le 2\pi$, $0 \le v \le 1$, $d\mathbf{S} = \mathbf{n}\,dS$, and $\mathbf{n}$ is the outer unit normal vector.
*Answer:* $2\pi$.

**PROBLEM 4.88** If $\mathbf{f} = 4xz\mathbf{i} + xyz^2\mathbf{j} + 3z\mathbf{k}$, evaluate $\iint_S \mathbf{f}\cdot d\mathbf{S}$, where $S$ is the surface bounded by $z^2 = x^2 + y^2$, $z = 0$, $z = 4$, $d\mathbf{S} = \mathbf{n}\,dS$, and $\mathbf{n}$ is the outer unit normal vector.
*Answer:* 320.

**PROBLEM 4.89** If $\mathbf{f} = (y+z)\mathbf{i} + (z+x)\mathbf{j} + (x+y)\mathbf{k}$ and $S$ is the surface of the cube bounded by $x = 0$, $y = 0$, $z = 0$, $x = 1$, $y = 1$, $z = 1$, evaluate (a) $\iint_S \mathbf{f}\,dS$, (b) $\iint_S \mathbf{f}\cdot d\mathbf{S}$, and (c) $\iint_S \mathbf{f}\times d\mathbf{S}$.
*Answer:* (a) [6, 6, 6], (b) 0, (c) $\mathbf{0}$.

**PROBLEM 4.90** Evaluate $\iiint\limits_R \mathbf{r}\, dV$, where $\mathbf{r}$ is the position vector and $R$ is the region bounded by the surfaces $x = 0$, $y = 0$, $y = 6$, $z = 4$, and $z = x^2$.
*Answer*: $[24, 96, 384/5]$.

**PROBLEM 4.91** Using the equivalent integral representation (4.57) of $\nabla$, verify that $\nabla \times (\phi \mathbf{f}) = \phi \nabla \times \mathbf{f} + (\nabla \phi) \times \mathbf{f}$.

**PROBLEM 4.92** Show that if $\mathbf{f} = \nabla \phi$ and $\nabla \cdot \mathbf{f} = 0$ for a region $R$ bounded by $S$, then

$$\iiint\limits_R |\mathbf{f}|^2\, dV = \oiint\limits_S \phi \mathbf{f} \cdot d\mathbf{S}.$$

**PROBLEM 4.93** Evaluate $\oiint\limits_S (a^2x^2 + b^2y^2 + c^2z^2)^{-1/2}\, dS$ over the surface of the ellipsoid $ax^2 + by^2 + cz^2 = 1$.
*Answer*: $4\pi/\sqrt{abc}$.

**PROBLEM 4.94** If $\mathbf{f} = ax\mathbf{i} + by\mathbf{j} + cz\mathbf{k}$, evaluate $\oiint\limits_S \mathbf{f} \cdot d\mathbf{S}$ over any closed surface $S$ that encloses a region of volume $V$.
*Answer*: $(a + b + c)V$.

**PROBLEM 4.95** If $\mathbf{f} = y\mathbf{i} + x\mathbf{j} + z^2\mathbf{k}$, evaluate $\iiint\limits_R \nabla \cdot \mathbf{f}\, dV$, where $R$ is the region bounded by $z = (1 - x^2 - y^2)^{1/2}$, and $z = 0$.
*Answer*: $\pi/2$.

**PROBLEM 4.96** If $\mathbf{f} = u(x, y)\mathbf{i} + v(x, y)\mathbf{j}$, prove that

$$\oint\limits_C \mathbf{f} \times d\mathbf{r} = \mathbf{k} \iint\limits_S \nabla \cdot \mathbf{f}\, dxdy,$$

where $C$ is a closed curve in the $xy$-plane that bounds a region $S$.
[*Hint:* Apply the divergence theorem (4.58) to $\mathbf{f}$ over a cylinder of base $S$ with $z = 1$.]

**PROBLEM 4.97** Show that the volume enclosed by any closed surface $S$ is

$$V = \frac{1}{6} \oiint\limits_S \nabla(r^2) \cdot d\mathbf{S}.$$

**PROBLEM 4.98** Using the divergence theorem (4.66), evaluate

$$\iint\limits_S x\, dydz + y\, dzdx + z\, dxdy,$$

where $S$ is the surface of the sphere $x^2 + y^2 + z^2 = 1$, and $\mathbf{n}$ is the outer unit normal vector.
*Answer*: $4\pi$.

**PROBLEM 4.99** Let $S$ be the boundary surface of a region $R$ whose volume is $V$ in space, and let $\mathbf{n}$ be its outer unit normal vector. Prove that

$$V = \iint_S x\,dydz = \iint_S y\,dzdx = \iint_S z\,dxdy$$

$$= \frac{1}{3}\iint_S x\,dydz + y\,dzdx + z\,dxdy$$

$$= \frac{1}{3}\oiint_S \mathbf{r}\cdot d\mathbf{S}.$$

**PROBLEM 4.100** If there exists $h(x, y, z)$ such that $\nabla^2\phi = h\phi$ and $\nabla^2\psi = h\psi$ in a region $R$ bounded by $S$, prove that

$$\oiint_S (\phi\nabla\psi - \psi\nabla\phi)\cdot d\mathbf{S} = 0.$$

**PROBLEM 4.101** If $\phi$ is harmonic in a region $R$ bounded by $S$, show that

$$\oiint_S \phi\nabla\phi\cdot d\mathbf{S} = \iiint_R |\nabla\phi|^2\,dV.$$

**PROBLEM 4.102** Show that

$$\iiint_R \mathbf{f}\cdot\nabla\phi\,dV = \oiint_S \phi\mathbf{f}\cdot d\mathbf{S} - \iiint_R \phi\nabla\cdot\mathbf{f}\,dV.$$

**PROBLEM 4.103** Prove that

$$5\iiint_R r^4\mathbf{r}\,dV - \oiint_S r^5\,d\mathbf{S}.$$

**PROBLEM 4.104** If $\mathbf{a}$ is an arbitrary constant vector and $V$ is the volume of a region $R$ bounded by $S$, prove that

$$\oiint_S \mathbf{n}\times(\mathbf{a}\times\mathbf{r})\,dS = 2V\,\mathbf{a}.$$

**PROBLEM 4.105** If $\mathbf{f} = (x^2 + y^2)y\mathbf{i} - (x^2 + y^2)x\mathbf{j} + (a^3 + z^3)\mathbf{k}$, evaluate $\oint_C \mathbf{f}\cdot d\mathbf{r}$ where $C$ is the circle $x^2 + y^2 = a^2$, $z = 0$.
*Answer*: $-2\pi a^4$.

**PROBLEM 4.106** If $\mathbf{f} = (x^2 + y^2 - 4)\mathbf{i} + 3xy\,\mathbf{j} + (2xz + z^2)\mathbf{k}$, evaluate $\iint_S \nabla\times\mathbf{f}\cdot d\mathbf{S}$, where $S$ is the surface defined by $z = 4 - (x^2 + y^2)$, and $\mathbf{n}$ is the outer unit normal vector.
*Answer*: $-4\pi$.

**PROBLEM 4.107** The sphere $x^2 + y^2 + z^2 = a^2$ intersects the positive $x$-, $y$-, and $z$-axes at $A$, $B$, and $C$, respectively. The simple closed curve $C$ consists of the three circular arcs $AB$, $BC$, and $CA$. If $\mathbf{f} = (y+z)\mathbf{i} + (z+x)\mathbf{j} + (x+z)\mathbf{k}$, evaluate $\oint_C \mathbf{f} \cdot d\mathbf{r}$ directly.

[*Hint:* Use Stokes' theorem (4.104) to verify this line integral by evaluating a surface integral over (a) the surface $ABC$ of the octant of the sphere in the positive quadrant, and (b) the three quadrants of the circular arcs in the coordinate planes.]
*Answer*: $-\frac{1}{4}\pi \mathbf{a}^2$.

**PROBLEM 4.108** By Stokes' theorem (4.104), prove that $\nabla \times (\nabla \phi) = \mathbf{0}$.

**PROBLEM 4.109** Prove that

$$\oint_C \phi \nabla \psi \cdot d\mathbf{r} = \iint_S \nabla \phi \times \nabla \psi \cdot d\mathbf{S}.$$

**PROBLEM 4.110** Using Green's theorem (4.110) for a plane, evaluate

$$I = \oint_C (3x + 4y)\, dx + (2x - 3y)\, dy,$$

where $C$ is the circle $x^2 + y^2 = 4$.
*Answer*: $-8\pi$.

**PROBLEM 4.111** Using Green's theorem for a plane (4.110), evaluate

$$I = \oint_C ay\, dx + bx\, dy,$$

where $a$ and $b$ are arbitrary constants and $C$ is an arbitrary closed regular curve.
*Answer*: $(b-a)A$, where $A$ is the area of the region bounded by $C$.

**PROBLEM 4.112** By changing variables from $(x, y)$ to $(u, v)$ according to the transformation $x = x(u, v)$, $y = y(u, v)$, show that the area $A$ of a simply connected region $R$ bounded by a closed regular curve $C$ is

$$A = \iint_R \frac{\partial(x, y)}{\partial(u, v)}\, dudv = \iint_R J\left[\frac{(x, y)}{(u, v)}\right] dudv,$$

where the Jacobian of the transformation is

$$J\left[\frac{(x, y)}{(u, v)}\right] = \frac{\partial(x, y)}{\partial(u, v)} = \begin{vmatrix} \dfrac{\partial x}{\partial u} & \dfrac{\partial y}{\partial u} \\ \dfrac{\partial x}{\partial v} & \dfrac{\partial y}{\partial v} \end{vmatrix}.$$

**PROBLEM 4.113** Show that

$$\iint_S d\mathbf{S} \times \mathbf{r} = \frac{1}{2} \oint_C r^2\, d\mathbf{r}.$$

**PROBLEM 4.114** Show that

$$\iint_S \frac{\mathbf{r}}{r^3} \times d\mathbf{S} = \oint_C \frac{d\mathbf{r}}{r}.$$

**PROBLEM 4.115** Establish the independence of the path of integration and evaluate

(a) $\displaystyle\int_{(1,-1)}^{(4,2)} \frac{y\,dx - x\,dy}{x^2},$

(b) $\displaystyle\int_{(0,1,0)}^{(\pi,0,1)} \sin x\,dx + y^2\,dy + e^z\,dz.$

*Answer*: (a) $-3/2$, (b) $e + 2/3$.

**PROBLEM 4.116** If $C$ is the curve $x^2 + y^2 = a^2$, prove that

$$\oint_C (\cos x \sinh y - xy^2)\,dx + (\sin x \cosh y + x^2 y)\,dy = 0.$$

**PROBLEM 4.117** Find a scalar potential function $\phi$ for the vector field

$$\mathbf{f} = (y + z \cos xz)\,\mathbf{i} + x\,\mathbf{j} + (x \cos xz)\,\mathbf{k}.$$

*Answer*: $\phi = yx + \sin xz + k$, where $k$ is an arbitrary constant.

**PROBLEM 4.118** Show that a constant vector $\mathbf{a}$ has a scalar potential $\phi = \mathbf{a} \cdot \mathbf{r}$ and a vector potential $\mathbf{A} = (\mathbf{a} \times \mathbf{r})/2$.

**PROBLEM 4.119** Consider any vector field $\mathbf{f}$ such that $\nabla \cdot \mathbf{f} = \rho$ and $\nabla \times \mathbf{f} = \mathbf{c}$. The scalar $\rho$ and the vector $\mathbf{c}$ are given functions of $x$, $y$, and $z$, and $\rho$ can be interpreted as a source density and $\mathbf{c}$, as a circulation density. Show that if both source and circulation densities vanish at infinity, the vector field $\mathbf{f}$ can be expressed as the sum of two parts, one irrotational and the other solenoidal. (This is called *Helmholtz' theorem*.)

**PROBLEM 4.120** Show that if $\phi$ is harmonic in a simply connected region whose boundary is the closed curve $C$, then

$$\oint_C \nabla\phi \cdot \mathbf{n}\,ds = 0,$$

where $\mathbf{n}$ is the outer unit normal vector to $C$.
[*Hint:* Use (4.112).]

**PROBLEM 4.121** If $\mathbf{h} = \frac{1}{2} \nabla \times \mathbf{g}$, and $\mathbf{g} = \nabla \times \mathbf{f}$, show that

$$\frac{1}{2} \iiint_R \mathbf{g}^2\,dV = \frac{1}{2} \oiint_S (\mathbf{f} \times \mathbf{g}) \cdot d\mathbf{S} + \iiint_R \mathbf{f} \cdot \mathbf{h}\,dV,$$

where $R$ is the region bounded by a closed surface $S$.

# 5 CHAPTER CURVILINEAR ORTHOGONAL COORDINATES

So far in our vector analysis, we have restricted ourselves almost completely to a rectangular (or Cartesian) coordinate system, which offers the unique advantage that all three base vectors **i**, **j**, **k** are constant vectors. However, it is often useful to employ other coordinate systems. In this chapter, we shall develop expressions for the gradient, divergence, and curl in these other coordinate systems.

## 5.1 Curvilinear Coordinates

The *transformation* between the coordinates of a point $(x, y, z)$ in the Cartesian coordinate system and those of a point $(u, v, w)$ in space is defined by

$$x = x(u, v, w), \quad y = y(u, v, w), \quad z = z(u, v, w). \tag{5.1}$$

The transformation (5.1) is *single-valued* and its *Jacobian* is

$$J = \frac{\partial(x, y, z)}{\partial(u, v, w)} = \begin{vmatrix} \dfrac{\partial x}{\partial u} & \dfrac{\partial x}{\partial v} & \dfrac{\partial x}{\partial w} \\ \dfrac{\partial y}{\partial u} & \dfrac{\partial y}{\partial v} & \dfrac{\partial y}{\partial w} \\ \dfrac{\partial z}{\partial u} & \dfrac{\partial z}{\partial v} & \dfrac{\partial z}{\partial w} \end{vmatrix} \neq 0. \tag{5.2}$$

From calculus, (5.1) can be locally solved uniquely for $u$, $v$, $w$ in terms of $x$, $y$, $z$; that is,

$$u = u(x, y, z), \quad v = v(x, y, z), \quad w = w(x, y, z). \tag{5.3}$$

Hence, any point $(x, y, z)$ in space has unique corresponding coordinates $(u, v, w)$.

*Coordinate surfaces* are families of surfaces obtained by setting the coordinates equal to a constant; e.g., if $c_1$, $c_2$, $c_3$ are constants, then three families of surfaces are

$$u(x, y, z) = c_1, \quad v(x, y, z) = c_2, \quad w(x, y, z) = c_3.$$

Thus, if $v$ and $w$ are constant, (5.1) represents the *u-curve*; similarly, we have *v-curves and w-curves*; these three curves are referred to as *coordinate curves*. Since the three coordinate curves are generally not straight lines, as in the rectangular coordinate system, such coordinate systems are called *curvilinear coordinates*.

In the rectangular coordinate system, a set of mutually orthogonal base vectors is **i**, **j**, **k**, as shown in Chap. 2. Similarly, we can introduce a set of *base* *vectors* appropriate for curvilinear coordinate systems. In the most general case, at each point $P$ in space there are two sets of base vectors (cf., Fig. 5.1). The first set is the set of unit vectors $\mathbf{e}_u$, $\mathbf{e}_v$, $\mathbf{e}_w$ tangent at $P$ to the coordinate curves through $P$. The second is the set of unit vectors $\mathbf{e}_U$, $\mathbf{e}_V$, $\mathbf{e}_W$ normal at $P$ to the coordinate surfaces through $P$.

The unit vectors $\mathbf{e}_u$, $\mathbf{e}_v$, $\mathbf{e}_w$ (or $\mathbf{e}_U$, $\mathbf{e}_V$, $\mathbf{e}_W$) generally vary in orientation from point to point.

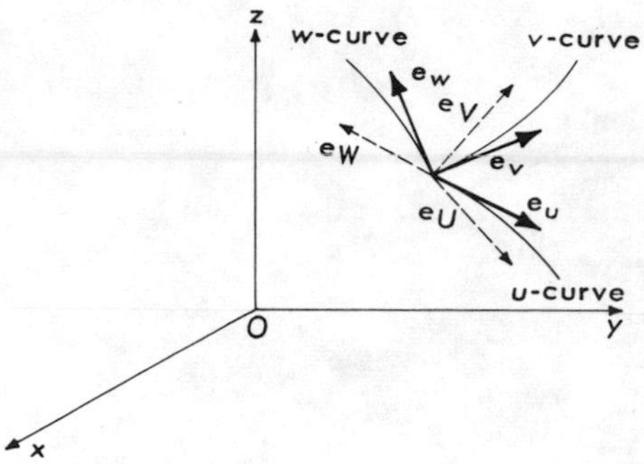


Fig. 5.1 Base vectors for general curvilinear coordinates.

**PROBLEM 5.1** Show that if $\mathbf{r} = x\mathbf{i} + y\mathbf{j} + z\mathbf{k}$, the three unit vectors $\mathbf{e}_u$, $\mathbf{e}_v$, $\mathbf{e}_w$ at $P$ tangent to the coordinate $u$-, $v$-, $w$-curves can be expressed as

$$\mathbf{e}_u = \frac{1}{h_u}\frac{\partial \mathbf{r}}{\partial u}, \quad \mathbf{e}_v = \frac{1}{h_v}\frac{\partial \mathbf{r}}{\partial v}, \quad \mathbf{e}_w = \frac{1}{h_w}\frac{\partial \mathbf{r}}{\partial w}, \tag{5.4}$$

where

$$h_u = \left|\frac{\partial \mathbf{r}}{\partial u}\right|, \quad h_v = \left|\frac{\partial \mathbf{r}}{\partial v}\right|, \quad h_w = \left|\frac{\partial \mathbf{r}}{\partial w}\right|. \tag{5.5}$$

**Solution:** If $\mathbf{r}$ is the position vector from the origin of a rectangular coordinate system to the point $P(x, y, z)$, then $\mathbf{r} = x\mathbf{i} + y\mathbf{j} + z\mathbf{k} = \mathbf{r}(x, y, z)$. Using (5.1), $\mathbf{r}$ can also be expressed as a function of $u$, $v$, and $w$; i.e.,

$$\mathbf{r} = \mathbf{r}(u, v, w),$$

where $(u, v, w)$ are curvilinear coordinates of $P$. If $v$ and $w$ are constant, then (5.1) is the parametric equation of the $u$-curve, with parameter $u$. Hence, according to (3.40), a tangent vector at $P$ to the $u$-curve is $\partial\mathbf{r}/\partial u$. Similarly, $\partial\mathbf{r}/\partial v$ and $\partial\mathbf{r}/\partial w$ are tangent at $P$ to the $v$- and $w$-curves, respectively.

In general, $\left|\frac{\partial \mathbf{r}}{\partial u}\right|$, $\left|\frac{\partial \mathbf{r}}{\partial v}\right|$, and $\left|\frac{\partial \mathbf{r}}{\partial w}\right|$ are not equal to unity. Hence, if $h_u = \left|\frac{\partial \mathbf{r}}{\partial u}\right|$, $h_v = \left|\frac{\partial \mathbf{r}}{\partial v}\right|$, $h_w = \left|\frac{\partial \mathbf{r}}{\partial w}\right|$,

$$\mathbf{e}_u = \frac{1}{h_u}\frac{\partial \mathbf{r}}{\partial u}, \quad \mathbf{e}_v = \frac{1}{h_v}\frac{\partial \mathbf{r}}{\partial v}, \quad \mathbf{e}_w = \frac{1}{h_w}\frac{\partial \mathbf{r}}{\partial w}.$$

Note that $h_u$, $h_v$, and $h_w$ are, in general, functions of $u$, $v$, $w$, and $h_u \neq 0$, $h_v \neq 0$, and $h_w \neq 0$; hence, $\mathbf{e}_u$, $\mathbf{e}_v$, and $\mathbf{e}_w$ are also functions of $u$, $v$, and $w$.

**PROBLEM 5.2** Show that the three unit vectors $\mathbf{e}_U$, $\mathbf{e}_V$, $\mathbf{e}_W$ normal at $P$ to the coordinate $u$-, $v$-, $w$-surfaces, respectively, can be expressed as

$$\mathbf{e}_U = \frac{1}{H_u}\nabla u, \quad \mathbf{e}_V = \frac{1}{H_v}\nabla v, \quad \mathbf{e}_W = \frac{1}{H_w}\nabla w, \tag{5.6}$$

where

$$H_u = |\nabla u|, \quad H_v = |\nabla v|, \quad H_w = |\nabla w|. \tag{5.7}$$

**Solution:** From the result of Prob. 3.31, we see that the vector $\nabla u$ is perpendicular to the surface $u(x, y, z) = c_1$ at $P$. Similarly, $\nabla v$ and $\nabla w$ are normal to the $v$- and $w$-surfaces, respectively. Hence, if

$$H_u = |\nabla u|, \quad H_v = |\nabla v|, \quad H_w = |\nabla w|,$$

we obtain

$$\mathbf{e}_U = \frac{1}{H_u}\nabla u, \quad \mathbf{e}_V = \frac{1}{H_v}\nabla v, \quad \mathbf{e}_W = \frac{1}{H_w}\nabla w.$$

Sets $\mathbf{a}_1$, $\mathbf{a}_2$, $\mathbf{a}_3$ and $\mathbf{b}_1$, $\mathbf{b}_2$, $\mathbf{b}_3$ are reciprocal sets of vectors if

$$\mathbf{a}_m \cdot \mathbf{b}_n = \delta_{mn}, \tag{1.109}$$

where $\delta_{mn}$ is the Kronecker delta. From Sec. 1.8, for reciprocal sets of vectors,

$$\mathbf{b}_1 = \frac{\mathbf{a}_2 \times \mathbf{a}_3}{[\mathbf{a}_1\,\mathbf{a}_2\,\mathbf{a}_3]}, \quad \mathbf{b}_2 = \frac{\mathbf{a}_3 \times \mathbf{a}_1}{[\mathbf{a}_1\,\mathbf{a}_2\,\mathbf{a}_3]}, \quad \mathbf{b}_3 = \frac{\mathbf{a}_1 \times \mathbf{a}_2}{[\mathbf{a}_1\,\mathbf{a}_2\,\mathbf{a}_3]}, \tag{1.114}$$

$$\mathbf{a}_1 = \frac{\mathbf{b}_2 \times \mathbf{b}_3}{[\mathbf{b}_1\,\mathbf{b}_2\,\mathbf{b}_3]}, \quad \mathbf{a}_2 = \frac{\mathbf{b}_3 \times \mathbf{b}_1}{[\mathbf{b}_1\,\mathbf{b}_2\,\mathbf{b}_3]}, \quad \mathbf{a}_3 = \frac{\mathbf{b}_1 \times \mathbf{b}_2}{[\mathbf{b}_1\,\mathbf{b}_2\,\mathbf{b}_3]}, \tag{1.115}$$

$$[\mathbf{a}_1\,\mathbf{a}_2\,\mathbf{a}_3] = \frac{1}{[\mathbf{b}_1\,\mathbf{b}_2\,\mathbf{b}_3]}. \tag{1.122}$$

**PROBLEM 5.3** Show that $\partial\mathbf{r}/\partial u$, $\partial\mathbf{r}/\partial v$, $\partial\mathbf{r}/\partial w$ and $\nabla u$, $\nabla v$, $\nabla w$ are reciprocal sets of vectors.

**Solution:** Since

$$\begin{aligned} u &= u(x, y, z) \\ &= u[x(u, v, w),\ y(u, v, w),\ z(u, v, w)], \end{aligned} \tag{5.8}$$

differentiating with respect to $u$ yields

$$\frac{\partial u}{\partial x}\frac{\partial x}{\partial u} + \frac{\partial u}{\partial y}\frac{\partial y}{\partial u} + \frac{\partial u}{\partial z}\frac{\partial z}{\partial u} = 1. \tag{5.9}$$

Since $\dfrac{\partial \mathbf{r}}{\partial u} = \dfrac{\partial x}{\partial u}\mathbf{i} + \dfrac{\partial y}{\partial u}\mathbf{j} + \dfrac{\partial z}{\partial u}\mathbf{k}$ and $\nabla u = \dfrac{\partial u}{\partial x}\mathbf{i} + \dfrac{\partial u}{\partial y}\mathbf{j} + \dfrac{\partial u}{\partial z}\mathbf{k}$, we can write (5.9) as

$$\frac{\partial \mathbf{r}}{\partial u} \cdot \nabla u = 1. \tag{5.10}$$

Similarly,

$$\frac{\partial \mathbf{r}}{\partial v} \cdot \nabla v = 1, \quad \frac{\partial \mathbf{r}}{\partial w} \cdot \nabla w = 1. \tag{5.11}$$

Now, differentiating (5.8) with respect to $v$,

$$\frac{\partial u}{\partial x}\frac{\partial x}{\partial v} + \frac{\partial u}{\partial y}\frac{\partial y}{\partial v} + \frac{\partial u}{\partial z}\frac{\partial z}{\partial v} = 0,$$

or

$$\frac{\partial \mathbf{r}}{\partial v} \cdot \nabla u = 0. \tag{5.12}$$

Similarly,

$$\frac{\partial \mathbf{r}}{\partial w} \cdot \nabla u = 0, \quad \frac{\partial \mathbf{r}}{\partial u} \cdot \nabla v = 0, \quad \frac{\partial \mathbf{r}}{\partial w} \cdot \nabla v = 0, \quad \frac{\partial \mathbf{r}}{\partial u} \cdot \nabla w = 0, \quad \frac{\partial \mathbf{r}}{\partial v} \cdot \nabla w = 0. \tag{5.13}$$

If $u = q_1$, $v = q_2$, $w = q_3$, then (5.10–3) can be summarized as

$$\frac{\partial \mathbf{r}}{\partial q_m} \cdot (\nabla q_n) = \delta_{mn}, \tag{5.14}$$

where $\delta_{mn}$ is the Kronecker delta. Hence, by the definition (1.109) of reciprocal sets of vectors, we conclude that $\partial\mathbf{r}/\partial u$, $\partial\mathbf{r}/\partial v$, $\partial\mathbf{r}/\partial w$ and $\nabla u$, $\nabla v$, $\nabla w$ are reciprocal sets of vectors.

**PROBLEM 5.4** Show that

$$\frac{\partial \mathbf{r}}{\partial u} = \frac{1}{\alpha}\nabla v \times \nabla w, \quad \frac{\partial \mathbf{r}}{\partial v} = \frac{1}{\alpha}\nabla w \times \nabla u, \quad \frac{\partial \mathbf{r}}{\partial w} = \frac{1}{\alpha}\nabla u \times \nabla v, \tag{5.15}$$

$$\nabla u = \frac{1}{\beta}\left(\frac{\partial \mathbf{r}}{\partial v} \times \frac{\partial \mathbf{r}}{\partial w}\right), \quad \nabla v = \frac{1}{\beta}\left(\frac{\partial \mathbf{r}}{\partial w} \times \frac{\partial \mathbf{r}}{\partial u}\right), \quad \nabla w = \frac{1}{\beta}\left(\frac{\partial \mathbf{r}}{\partial u} \times \frac{\partial \mathbf{r}}{\partial v}\right), \tag{5.16}$$

where

$$\alpha = [\nabla u \, \nabla v \, \nabla w] = \nabla u \cdot \nabla v \times \nabla w, \tag{5.17}$$

$$\beta = \left[\frac{\partial \mathbf{r}}{\partial u}\,\frac{\partial \mathbf{r}}{\partial v}\,\frac{\partial \mathbf{r}}{\partial w}\right] = \frac{\partial \mathbf{r}}{\partial u} \cdot \frac{\partial \mathbf{r}}{\partial v} \times \frac{\partial \mathbf{r}}{\partial w} = \frac{1}{\alpha}. \tag{5.18}$$

**Solution:** Since the vectors $\partial \mathbf{r}/\partial u$, $\partial \mathbf{r}/\partial v$, $\partial \mathbf{r}/\partial w$ and $\nabla u$, $\nabla v$, $\nabla w$ form reciprocal sets of vectors, the results of Sec. 1.9 can be applied. Hence (5.15–6) follow directly from (1.114–5). The relation (5.18) follows from (1.122).

## 5.2 Orthogonal Curvilinear Coordinates

A curvilinear coordinate system is called *orthogonal* if the coordinate curves are everywhere orthogonal. In this case, the three vectors $\mathbf{e}_u$, $\mathbf{e}_v$, $\mathbf{e}_w$ are mutually orthogonal at every point; i.e.,

$$\mathbf{e}_u \cdot \mathbf{e}_v = \mathbf{e}_v \cdot \mathbf{e}_w = \mathbf{e}_w \cdot \mathbf{e}_u = 0. \tag{5.19}$$

We shall also assume that $\mathbf{e}_u$, $\mathbf{e}_v$, $\mathbf{e}_w$ form a right-handed system; i.e.,

$$[\mathbf{e}_u \, \mathbf{e}_v \, \mathbf{e}_w] = 1. \tag{5.20}$$

**PROBLEM 5.5** If a system of curvilinear coordinates is orthogonal, show that

$$\mathbf{e}_u = \mathbf{e}_U, \quad \mathbf{e}_v = \mathbf{e}_V, \quad \mathbf{e}_w = \mathbf{e}_W. \tag{5.21}$$

**Solution:** From Prob. 5.3, we know that $\mathbf{e}_u$, $\mathbf{e}_v$, $\mathbf{e}_w$ and $\mathbf{e}_U$, $\mathbf{e}_V$, $\mathbf{e}_W$ are reciprocal sets of vectors. Now, the orthonormal system $\mathbf{e}_u$, $\mathbf{e}_v$, $\mathbf{e}_w$ satisfies

$$\mathbf{e}_u = \mathbf{e}_v \times \mathbf{e}_w, \quad \mathbf{e}_v = \mathbf{e}_w \times \mathbf{e}_u, \quad \mathbf{e}_w = \mathbf{e}_u \times \mathbf{e}_v. \tag{5.22}$$

Hence, by Probs. 5.2 and 5.4, we have the result (5.21).

**PROBLEM 5.6** In an orthogonal curvilinear coordinate system, show that

(a) $$h_u = \frac{1}{H_u}, \quad h_v = \frac{1}{H_v}, \quad h_w = \frac{1}{H_w}, \tag{5.23}$$

(b) $$\mathbf{e}_u = h_u \nabla u, \quad \mathbf{e}_v = h_v \nabla v, \quad \mathbf{e}_w = h_w \nabla w, \tag{5.24}$$

(c) $$[\nabla u \, \nabla v \, \nabla w] = \nabla u \cdot \nabla v \times \nabla w = \frac{1}{h_u h_v h_w}. \tag{5.25}$$

**Solution:** (a) By (5.4) and (5.6), and because of (5.10),

$$\mathbf{e}_u \cdot \mathbf{e}_U = \left(\frac{1}{h_u}\frac{\partial \mathbf{r}}{\partial u}\right) \cdot \left(\frac{1}{H_u}\nabla u\right) = \frac{1}{h_u H_u}\left(\frac{\partial \mathbf{r}}{\partial u} \cdot \nabla u\right) = \frac{1}{h_u H_u}. \tag{5.26}$$

In an orthogonal system, by (5.21),

$$\frac{1}{h_u H_u} = \mathbf{e}_u \cdot \mathbf{e}_U = \mathbf{e}_u \cdot \mathbf{e}_u = 1.$$

Hence, $h_u = 1/H_u$. Similarly, we can have $h_v = 1/H_v$, $h_w = 1/H_w$.

(b) From (5.21), (5.6), and (5.23),

$$\mathbf{e}_u = \mathbf{e}_U = \frac{1}{H_u}\nabla u = h_u \nabla u,$$

$$\mathbf{e}_v = \mathbf{e}_V = \frac{1}{H_v}\nabla v = h_v \nabla v,$$

$$\mathbf{e}_w = \mathbf{e}_W = \frac{1}{H_w}\nabla w = h_w \nabla w.$$

(c) By (5.24),

$$\nabla u = \frac{1}{h_u}\mathbf{e}_u, \quad \nabla v = \frac{1}{h_v}\mathbf{e}_v, \quad \nabla w = \frac{1}{h_w}\mathbf{e}_w. \tag{5.27}$$

Hence, because of (5.20),

$$[\nabla u \nabla v \nabla w] = \nabla u \cdot \nabla v \times \nabla w$$

$$= \frac{1}{h_u h_v h_w}\mathbf{e}_u \cdot \mathbf{e}_v \times \mathbf{e}_w$$

$$= \frac{1}{h_u h_v h_w}.$$

*Scale factors* or *metrical coefficients* are the quantities $h_u$, $h_v$, $h_w$ because the differential coefficients $du$, $dv$, $dw$ must be multiplied by them to obtain arc lengths. The scale factors depend on the coordinates and have dimension. But their product with the differential coordinates have the dimension of length.

**PROBLEM 5.7** In an orthogonal curvilinear coordinate system, if $s_u$, $s_v$, $s_w$ represent arc lengths along the $u$-, $v$-, $w$-curves, show that

(a) $$ds_u = h_u\, du, \quad ds_v = h_v\, dv, \quad ds_w = h_w\, dw, \tag{5.28}$$

(b) $$(ds)^2 = (h_u\, du)^2 + (h_v\, dv)^2 + (h_w\, dw)^2, \tag{5.29}$$

(c) $$dV = h_u h_v h_w\, du dv dw, \tag{5.30}$$

where $ds$ represents the infinitesimal arc length between the points $(u, v, w)$ and $(u + du, v + dv, w + dw)$, and $dV$ is the volume element.

**Solution:** (a) Using the arc lengths $s_u$, $s_v$, $s_w$,

$$\frac{\partial \mathbf{r}}{\partial u} = \frac{\partial \mathbf{r}}{\partial s_u}\frac{ds_u}{du}, \quad \frac{\partial \mathbf{r}}{\partial v} = \frac{\partial \mathbf{r}}{\partial s_v}\frac{ds_v}{dv}, \quad \frac{\partial \mathbf{r}}{\partial w} = \frac{\partial \mathbf{r}}{\partial s_w}\frac{ds_w}{ds}. \tag{5.31}$$

The unit tangent vector to curve $C$ of arc length $s$ at any point $P$ is the derivative of the radius vector $\mathbf{r}$ to $P$ with respect to $s$. Thus,

$$\frac{\partial \mathbf{r}}{\partial s_u} = \mathbf{e}_u, \quad \frac{\partial \mathbf{r}}{\partial s_v} = \mathbf{e}_v, \quad \frac{\partial \mathbf{r}}{\partial s_w} = \mathbf{e}_w. \tag{5.32}$$

Hence, from (5.31) and (5.4),

$$\frac{\partial \mathbf{r}}{\partial u} = \frac{ds_u}{du}\mathbf{e}_u = h_u \mathbf{e}_u, \quad \frac{\partial \mathbf{r}}{\partial v} = \frac{ds_v}{dv}\mathbf{e}_v = h_v \mathbf{e}_v, \quad \frac{\partial \mathbf{r}}{\partial w} = \frac{ds_w}{dw}\mathbf{e}_w = h_w \mathbf{e}_w. \tag{5.33}$$

Hence,

$$h_u = \frac{ds_u}{du}, \quad h_v = \frac{ds_v}{dv}, \quad h_w = \frac{ds_w}{dw}, \tag{5.34}$$

or

$$ds_u = h_u\,du, \quad ds_v = h_v\,dv, \quad ds_w = h_w\,dw.$$

Thus, the differential coordinates $du$, $dv$, $dw$ must be multiplied by $h_u$, $h_v$, $h_w$ to obtain arc lengths.

(b) Because of (5.33),

$$d\mathbf{r} = \frac{\partial \mathbf{r}}{\partial u}du + \frac{\partial \mathbf{r}}{\partial v}dv + \frac{\partial \mathbf{r}}{\partial w}dw = h_u\,du\,\mathbf{e}_u + h_v\,dv\,\mathbf{e}_v + h_w\,dw\,\mathbf{e}_w. \tag{5.35}$$

Hence, the arc length $ds$ between the points $(u, v, w)$ and $(u + du, v + dv, w + dw)$ is

$$ds^2 = d\mathbf{r}\cdot d\mathbf{r} = (h_u\,du)^2 + (h_v\,dv)^2 + (h_w\,dw)^2$$

since $\mathbf{e}_u$, $\mathbf{e}_v$, $\mathbf{e}_w$ form an orthonormal basis.

(c) The differential element of volume is a parallelepiped, three sides of which are the vectors

$$\frac{\partial \mathbf{r}}{\partial u}du = h_u\,du\,\mathbf{e}_u, \quad \frac{\partial \mathbf{r}}{\partial v}dv = h_v\,dv\,\mathbf{e}_v, \quad \frac{\partial \mathbf{r}}{\partial w}dw = h_w\,dw\,\mathbf{e}_w.$$

Hence, the volume element $dV$ is

$$\begin{aligned} dV &= (h_u\,du\,\mathbf{e}_u)\cdot[(h_v\,dv\,\mathbf{e}_v)\times(h_w\,dw\,\mathbf{e}_w)] \\ &= [\mathbf{e}_u\,\mathbf{e}_v\,\mathbf{e}_w]\,h_u h_v h_w\,du dv dw \\ &= h_u h_v h_w\,du dv dw. \end{aligned}$$

In the cylindrical coordinate system, the variables $u$, $v$, and $w$ are usually referred to as $\rho$, $\phi$, and $z$. This more familiar notation is used in Sec. 5.4. For the present, however, the neutral coordinates $u$, $v$, and $w$ are used to illustrate the preceding general theory.

**PROBLEM 5.8** The cylindrical coordinate system is defined by the transformation

$$x = u\cos v, \quad y = u\sin v, \quad z = w. \tag{5.36}$$

The ranges of $u$, $v$, and $w$ are given by $u \geq 0$, $0 \leq v < 2\pi$ and $-\infty < w < \infty$.

(a) Determine $h_u$, $h_v$, $h_w$ and the vectors $\mathbf{e}_u$, $\mathbf{e}_v$, $\mathbf{e}_w$. (b) Find $H_u$, $H_v$, $H_w$ and the vectors $\mathbf{e}_U$, $\mathbf{e}_V$, $\mathbf{e}_W$. (c) Prove that the cylindrical coordinate system is orthogonal.

**Solution:** By (5.2), the Jacobian of the transformation is

$$J = \frac{\partial(x, y, z)}{\partial(u, v, w)} = \begin{vmatrix} \cos v & -u\sin v & 0 \\ \sin v & u\cos v & 0 \\ 0 & 0 & 1 \end{vmatrix} = u(\cos^2 v + \sin^2 v) = u, \tag{5.37}$$

which is not zero except on the $z$-axis. The inverse transformation is

$$u = (x^2 + y^2)^{1/2}, \quad v = \tan^{-1}\left(\frac{y}{x}\right), \quad w = z. \tag{5.38}$$

(a) Since the position vector is

$$\mathbf{r} = u\cos v\,\mathbf{i} + u\sin v\,\mathbf{j} + w\,\mathbf{k},$$

its partial derivatives are

$$\frac{\partial \mathbf{r}}{\partial u} = \cos v\,\mathbf{i} + \sin v\,\mathbf{j}, \quad \frac{\partial \mathbf{r}}{\partial v} = -u\sin v\,\mathbf{i} + u\cos v\,\mathbf{j}, \quad \frac{\partial \mathbf{r}}{\partial w} = \mathbf{k}.$$

Hence, the scale factors are

$$h_u = \left|\frac{\partial \mathbf{r}}{\partial u}\right| = (\cos^2 v + \sin^2 v)^{1/2} = 1,$$

$$h_v = \left|\frac{\partial \mathbf{r}}{\partial v}\right| = [(-u \sin v)^2 + (u \cos v)^2]^{1/2} = u,$$

$$h_w = \left|\frac{\partial \mathbf{r}}{\partial w}\right| = 1,$$

and the base vectors are

$$\mathbf{e}_u = \frac{1}{h_u}\frac{\partial \mathbf{r}}{\partial u} = \cos v\,\mathbf{i} + \sin v\,\mathbf{j},$$

$$\mathbf{e}_v = \frac{1}{h_v}\frac{\partial \mathbf{r}}{\partial v} = -\sin v\,\mathbf{i} + \cos v\,\mathbf{j},$$

$$\mathbf{e}_w = \frac{1}{h_w}\frac{\partial \mathbf{r}}{\partial w} = \mathbf{k}.$$

(b) From the inverse transformation (5.38),

$$\nabla u = \frac{1}{(x^2 + y^2)^{1/2}}(x\,\mathbf{i} + y\,\mathbf{j}), \qquad \nabla v = \frac{1}{(x^2 + y^2)}(-y\,\mathbf{i} + x\,\mathbf{j}), \qquad \nabla w = \mathbf{k}.$$

Hence, the scale factors are

$$H_u = |\nabla u| = 1 = \frac{1}{h_u},$$

$$H_v = |\nabla v| = \frac{1}{(x^2 + y^2)^{1/2}} = \frac{1}{u} = \frac{1}{h_v},$$

$$H_w = |\nabla w| = 1 = \frac{1}{h_w},$$

and the base vectors are

$$\begin{aligned}\mathbf{e}_U = \frac{1}{H_u}\nabla u &= \frac{1}{(x^2 + y^2)^{1/2}}(x\,\mathbf{i} + y\,\mathbf{j})\\ &= \frac{1}{u}(u \cos v\,\mathbf{i} + u \sin v\,\mathbf{j})\\ &= \cos v\,\mathbf{i} + \sin v\,\mathbf{j}\\ &= \mathbf{e}_u,\end{aligned}$$

$$\begin{aligned}\mathbf{e}_V = \frac{1}{H_v}\nabla v &= (x^2 + y^2)^{1/2}\frac{1}{(x^2 + y^2)}(-y\,\mathbf{i} + x\,\mathbf{j})\\ &= \frac{1}{(x^2 + y^2)^{1/2}}(-y\mathbf{i} + x\mathbf{j})\\ &= \frac{1}{u}(-u \sin v\,\mathbf{i} + u \cos v\,\mathbf{j})\\ &= -\sin v\,\mathbf{i} + \cos v\,\mathbf{j}\\ &= \mathbf{e}_v,\end{aligned}$$

$$\mathbf{e}_W = \frac{1}{H_w}\nabla w = \mathbf{k} = \mathbf{e}_w.$$

(c) Dotting $\mathbf{e}_u$, $\mathbf{e}_v$, and $\mathbf{e}_w$ between themselves,

$$\mathbf{e}_u \cdot \mathbf{e}_v = (\cos v)(-\sin v) + (\sin v)(\cos v) = 0,$$

$$\mathbf{e}_v \cdot \mathbf{e}_w = (-\sin v)(0) + (\cos v)(0) + (0)(1) = 0,$$

$$\mathbf{e}_w \cdot \mathbf{e}_u = (0)(\cos v) + (0)(\sin v) + (1)(0) = 0.$$

Hence, $\mathbf{e}_u$, $\mathbf{e}_v$, $\mathbf{e}_w$ are mutually orthogonal.

In the spherical coordinate system, the variables $u$, $v$, and $w$ are usually referred to as $r$, $\theta$, and $\phi$. This more familiar notation is used in Sec. 5.4. For the present, however, the neutral coordinates $u$, $v$, and $w$ are used to illustrate the preceding theory.

**PROBLEM 5.9** The spherical coordinate system is defined by the transformation

$$x = u \sin v \cos w, \quad y = u \sin v \sin w, \quad z = u \cos v, \tag{5.39}$$

where $u \geq 0$, $0 \leq v < \pi$, $0 \leq w < 2\pi$.

(a) Find $h_u$, $h_v$, $h_w$ and $\mathbf{e}_u$, $\mathbf{e}_v$, $\mathbf{e}_w$. (b) Determine $H_u$, $H_v$, $H_w$ and $\mathbf{e}_U$, $\mathbf{e}_V$, $\mathbf{e}_W$. (c) Prove that the spherical coordinate system is orthogonal.

**Solution:** By (5.2), the Jacobian of the transformation is

$$J = \frac{\partial(x, y, z)}{\partial(u, v, w)} = \begin{vmatrix} \sin v \cos w & u \cos v \cos w & -u \sin v \sin w \\ \sin v \sin w & u \cos v \sin w & u \sin v \cos w \\ \cos v & -u \sin v & 0 \end{vmatrix}$$

$$= u^2 \sin v, \tag{5.40}$$

which is nonzero everywhere but the $z$-axis. The inverse transformation is

$$u = (x^2 + y^2 + z^2)^{1/2}, \quad v = \tan^{-1}\left[\frac{(x^2 + y^2)^{1/2}}{z}\right], \quad w = \tan^{-1}\left(\frac{y}{x}\right). \tag{5.41}$$

(a) Since the position vector is

$$\mathbf{r} = u \sin v \cos w\, \mathbf{i} + u \sin v \sin w\, \mathbf{j} + u \cos v\, \mathbf{k},$$

its partial derivatives are

$$\frac{\partial \mathbf{r}}{\partial u} = \sin v \cos w\, \mathbf{i} + \sin v \sin w\, \mathbf{j} + \cos v\, \mathbf{k},$$

$$\frac{\partial \mathbf{r}}{\partial v} = u \cos v \cos w\, \mathbf{i} + u \cos v \sin w\, \mathbf{j} - u \sin v\, \mathbf{k},$$

$$\frac{\partial \mathbf{r}}{\partial w} = -u \sin v \sin w\, \mathbf{i} + u \sin v \cos w\, \mathbf{j}.$$

Hence, the scale factors are

$$h_u = \left|\frac{\partial \mathbf{r}}{\partial u}\right| = [(\sin v \cos w)^2 + (\sin v \sin w)^2 + (\cos v)^2]^{1/2} = 1,$$

$$h_v = \left|\frac{\partial \mathbf{r}}{\partial v}\right| = u[(\cos v \cos w)^2 + (\cos v \sin w)^2 + (-\sin v)^2]^{1/2} = u,$$

$$h_w = \left|\frac{\partial \mathbf{r}}{\partial w}\right| = u[(-\sin v \sin w)^2 + (\sin v \cos w)^2]^{1/2} = u \sin v,$$

and the base vectors are

$$\mathbf{e}_u = \frac{1}{h_u}\frac{\partial \mathbf{r}}{\partial u} = \sin v \cos w\, \mathbf{i} + \sin v \sin w\, \mathbf{j} + \cos v\, \mathbf{k},$$

$$\mathbf{e}_v = \frac{1}{h_v}\frac{\partial \mathbf{r}}{\partial v} = \cos v \cos w\, \mathbf{i} + \cos v \sin w\, \mathbf{j} - \sin v\, \mathbf{k},$$

$$\mathbf{e}_w = \frac{1}{h_w}\frac{\partial \mathbf{r}}{\partial w} = -\sin w\, \mathbf{i} + \cos w\, \mathbf{j}.$$

(b) From (5.41),

$$\nabla u = \frac{1}{(x^2+y^2+z^2)^{1/2}}(x\,\mathbf{i} + y\,\mathbf{j} + z\,\mathbf{k}),$$

$$\nabla v = \frac{1}{(x^2+y^2)^{1/2}\,(x^2+y^2+z^2)}\left[zx\,\mathbf{i} + zy\,\mathbf{j} - (x^2+y^2)\mathbf{k}\right],$$

$$\nabla w = \frac{1}{(x^2+y^2)}(-y\,\mathbf{i} + x\,\mathbf{j}).$$

Hence, the scale factors are

$$H_u = |\nabla u| = 1 = \frac{1}{h_u},$$

$$H_u = |\nabla v| = \frac{1}{(x^2+y^2+z^2)^{1/2}} = \frac{1}{u} = \frac{1}{h_v},$$

$$H_w = |\nabla w| = \frac{1}{(x^2+y^2)^{1/2}} = \frac{1}{u \sin v} = \frac{1}{h_w},$$

and the base vectors are

$$\mathbf{e}_U = \frac{1}{H_u}\nabla u = \frac{1}{(x^2+y^2+z^2)^{1/2}}(x\,\mathbf{i} + y\,\mathbf{j} + z\,\mathbf{k})$$

$$= \sin v \cos w\, \mathbf{i} + \sin v \sin w\, \mathbf{j} + \cos v\, \mathbf{k}$$

$$= \mathbf{e}_u,$$

$$\mathbf{e}_V = \frac{1}{H_v}\nabla v = \frac{1}{(x^2+y^2)^{1/2}\,(x^2+y^2+z^2)^{1/2}}\left[zx\,\mathbf{i} + zy\,\mathbf{j} - (x^2+y^2)\mathbf{k}\right]$$

$$= \cos v \cos w\, \mathbf{i} + \cos v \sin w\, \mathbf{j} - \sin v\, \mathbf{k}$$

$$= \mathbf{e}_v,$$

$$\mathbf{e}_W = \frac{1}{H_w}\nabla w = \frac{1}{(x^2+y^2)^{1/2}}(-y\,\mathbf{i} + x\,\mathbf{j})$$

$$= -\sin w\, \mathbf{i} + \cos w\, \mathbf{j}$$

$$= \mathbf{e}_w.$$

(c) Dotting $\mathbf{e}_u$, $\mathbf{e}_v$, and $\mathbf{e}_w$ between themselves,

$$\mathbf{e}_u \cdot \mathbf{e}_v = \sin v \cos v \cos^2 w + \sin v \cos v \sin^2 w - \cos v \sin v = 0,$$

$$\mathbf{e}_v \cdot \mathbf{e}_w = -\cos v \cos w \sin w + \cos v \sin w \cos w = 0,$$

$$\mathbf{e}_w \cdot \mathbf{e}_u = -\sin w \sin v \cos w + \cos w \sin v \sin w = 0.$$

Hence, $\mathbf{e}_u$, $\mathbf{e}_v$, $\mathbf{e}_w$ are mutually orthogonal.

**PROBLEM 5.10** Using the relation

$$(ds)^2 = (dx)^2 + (dy)^2 + (dz)^2 = (h_u\,du)^2 + (h_v\,dv)^2 + (h_w\,dw)^2, \tag{5.42}$$

find the scale factors $h_u$, $h_v$, $h_w$ in (a) cylindrical coordinates, (b) spherical coordinates.

**Solution:** (a) From (5.36),

$$dx = \cos v\, du - u \sin v\, dv,$$

$$dy = \sin v\, du + u \cos v\, dv,$$

$$dz = dw.$$

Thus,

$$\begin{aligned}(dx)^2 + (dy)^2 + (dz)^2 &= \cos^2 v\,(du)^2 + u^2 \sin^2 v (dv)^2 - 2\,u \sin v \cos v\, dudv \\ &\quad + \sin^2 v (du)^2 + u^2 \cos^2 v (dv)^2 + 2u \sin v \cos v\, dudv \\ &\quad + (dw)^2 \\ &= (\sin^2 v + \cos^2 v)\,(du)^2 + u^2 (\sin^2 v + \cos^2 v)\,(dv)^2 + (dw)^2 \\ &= (du)^2 + (u\, dv)^2 + (dw)^2 \\ &= (h_u\, du)^2 + (h_v\, dv)^2 + (h_w\, dw)^2.\end{aligned}$$

Hence, $h_u = 1$, $h_v = u$, $h_w = 1$.

(b) From (5.39),

$$dx = \sin v \cos w\, du + u \cos v \cos w\, dv - u \sin v \sin w\, dw,$$

$$dy = \sin v \sin w\, du + u \cos v \sin w\, dv + u \sin v \cos w\, dw,$$

$$dz = \cos v\, du - u \sin v\, dv.$$

Thus,

$$\begin{aligned}&(dx)^2 + (dy)^2 + (dz)^2 \\ &\quad = \sin^2 v \cos^2 w\,(du)^2 + u^2 \cos^2 v \cos^2 w\,(dv)^2 + u^2 \sin^2 v \sin^2 w\,(dw)^2 \\ &\qquad + 2u \sin v \cos v \cos^2 w\, dudv - 2u^2 \sin v \cos v \sin w \cos w\, dvdw \\ &\qquad - 2u \sin^2 v \sin w \cos w\, dwdu \\ &\qquad + \sin^2 v \sin^2 w\,(du)^2 + u^2 \cos^2 v \sin^2 w\,(dv)^2 + u^2 \sin^2 v \cos^2 w\,(dw)^2 \\ &\qquad + 2u \sin v \cos v \sin^2 w\, dudv + 2u^2 \sin v \cos v \sin w \cos w\, dvdw \\ &\qquad + 2u \sin^2 v \sin w \cos w\, dwdu \\ &\qquad + \cos^2 v (du)^2 + u^2 \sin^2 v (dv)^2 - 2u \sin v \cos v\, dudv \\ &\quad = [\sin^2 v (\cos^2 w + \sin^2 w) + \cos^2 v]\,(du)^2 \\ &\qquad + u^2 [\cos^2 v (\cos^2 w + \sin^2 w) + \sin^2 v]\,(dv)^2 \\ &\qquad + u^2 \sin^2 v (\sin^2 w + \cos^2 w)\,(dw)^2 \\ &\quad = (du)^2 + (u\, dv)^2 + (u \sin v\, dw)^2 \\ &\quad = (h_u\, du)^2 + (h_v\, dv)^2 + (h_w\, dw)^2.\end{aligned}$$

Hence, $h_u = 1$, $h_v = u$, $h_w = u \sin v$. Note that (5.42) is true only for orthogonal coordinates.

## 5.3 Gradient, Divergence, and Curl in Orthogonal Curvilinear Coordinates

If $\psi = \psi(u, v, w)$ is a scalar function, the *gradient* in orthogonal curvilinear coordinates is

$$\nabla\psi = \frac{\partial\psi}{\partial u}\nabla u + \frac{\partial\psi}{\partial v}\nabla v + \frac{\partial\psi}{\partial w}\nabla w, \tag{5.43}$$

$$\nabla\psi = \frac{1}{h_u}\frac{\partial\psi}{\partial u}\mathbf{e}_u + \frac{1}{h_v}\frac{\partial\psi}{\partial v}\mathbf{e}_v + \frac{1}{h_w}\frac{\partial\psi}{\partial w}\mathbf{e}_w. \tag{5.44}$$

If $\mathbf{f} = f_u\mathbf{e}_u + f_v\mathbf{e}_v + f_w\mathbf{e}_w$ is a vector in the basis $\mathbf{e}_u, \mathbf{e}_v, \mathbf{e}_w$, then the *divergence* in the orthogonal curvilinear coordinates is

$$\nabla\cdot\mathbf{f} = \frac{1}{h_u h_v h_w}\left[\frac{\partial}{\partial u}(h_v h_w f_u) + \frac{\partial}{\partial v}(h_w h_u f_v) + \frac{\partial}{\partial w}(h_u h_v f_w)\right]. \tag{5.45}$$

The *Laplacian* of the scalar function $\psi$ is

$$\nabla^2\psi = \nabla\cdot(\nabla\psi) = \frac{1}{h_u h_v h_w}\left[\frac{\partial}{\partial u}\left(\frac{h_v h_w}{h_u}\frac{\partial\psi}{\partial u}\right) + \frac{\partial}{\partial v}\left(\frac{h_w h_u}{h_v}\frac{\partial\psi}{\partial v}\right) + \frac{\partial}{\partial w}\left(\frac{h_u h_v}{h_w}\frac{\partial\psi}{\partial w}\right)\right]. \tag{5.46}$$

The *curl* of the vector function **f** is

$$\nabla\times\mathbf{f} = \frac{1}{h_v h_w}\left[\frac{\partial}{\partial v}(h_w f_w) - \frac{\partial}{\partial w}(h_v f_v)\right]\mathbf{e}_u + \frac{1}{h_w h_u}\left[\frac{\partial}{\partial w}(h_u f_u) - \frac{\partial}{\partial u}(h_w f_w)\right]\mathbf{e}_v + \frac{1}{h_u h_v}\left[\frac{\partial}{\partial u}(h_v f_v) - \frac{\partial}{\partial v}(h_u f_u)\right]\mathbf{e}_w. \tag{5.47}$$

**PROBLEM 5.11** Verify (5.43).

**Solution:** The gradient in the rectangular coordinates is

$$\nabla\psi = \frac{\partial\psi}{\partial x}\mathbf{i} + \frac{\partial\psi}{\partial y}\mathbf{j} + \frac{\partial\psi}{\partial z}\mathbf{k}. \qquad [3.110]$$

If $\psi = \psi(u, v, w) = \psi[u(x, y, z), v(x, y, z), w(x, y, z)]$, then

$$\frac{\partial\psi}{\partial x} = \frac{\partial\psi}{\partial u}\frac{\partial u}{\partial x} + \frac{\partial\psi}{\partial v}\frac{\partial v}{\partial x} + \frac{\partial\psi}{\partial w}\frac{\partial w}{\partial x},$$

$$\frac{\partial\psi}{\partial y} = \frac{\partial\psi}{\partial u}\frac{\partial u}{\partial y} + \frac{\partial\psi}{\partial v}\frac{\partial v}{\partial y} + \frac{\partial\psi}{\partial w}\frac{\partial w}{\partial y},$$

$$\frac{\partial\psi}{\partial z} = \frac{\partial\psi}{\partial u}\frac{\partial u}{\partial z} + \frac{\partial\psi}{\partial v}\frac{\partial v}{\partial z} + \frac{\partial\psi}{\partial w}\frac{\partial w}{\partial z}.$$

Hence,

$$\begin{aligned}\nabla\psi &= \frac{\partial\psi}{\partial u}\left(\frac{\partial u}{\partial x}\mathbf{i} + \frac{\partial u}{\partial y}\mathbf{j} + \frac{\partial u}{\partial z}\mathbf{k}\right) + \frac{\partial\psi}{\partial v}\left(\frac{\partial v}{\partial x}\mathbf{i} + \frac{\partial v}{\partial y}\mathbf{j} + \frac{\partial v}{\partial z}\mathbf{k}\right) \\ &\quad + \frac{\partial\psi}{\partial w}\left(\frac{\partial w}{\partial x}\mathbf{i} + \frac{\partial w}{\partial y}\mathbf{j} + \frac{\partial w}{\partial z}\mathbf{k}\right) \\ &= \frac{\partial\psi}{\partial u}\nabla u + \frac{\partial\psi}{\partial v}\nabla v + \frac{\partial\psi}{\partial w}\nabla w. \qquad [5.43]\end{aligned}$$

**PROBLEM 5.12** Verify (5.44).

**Solution:** Substituting

$$\nabla u = \frac{1}{h_u}\,\mathbf{e}_u, \quad \nabla v = \frac{1}{h_v}\,\mathbf{e}_v, \quad \nabla w = \frac{1}{h_w}\,\mathbf{e}_w \qquad [5.27]$$

in (5.43),

$$\nabla \psi = \frac{1}{h_u}\frac{\partial \psi}{\partial u}\,\mathbf{e}_u + \frac{1}{h_v}\frac{\partial \psi}{\partial v}\,\mathbf{e}_v + \frac{1}{h_w}\frac{\partial \psi}{\partial w}\,\mathbf{e}_w.$$

**PROBLEM 5.13** Verify (5.45).

**Solution:** We know that $\mathbf{e}_u$, $\mathbf{e}_v$, $\mathbf{e}_w$ form a right-handed orthonormal basis. Using (5.24),

$$\left.\begin{aligned} \mathbf{e}_u &= \mathbf{e}_v \times \mathbf{e}_w = h_v h_w\, \nabla v \times \nabla w, \\ \mathbf{e}_v &= \mathbf{e}_w \times \mathbf{e}_u = h_w h_u\, \nabla w \times \nabla u, \\ \mathbf{e}_w &= \mathbf{e}_u \times \mathbf{e}_v = h_u h_v\, \nabla u \times \nabla v. \end{aligned}\right\} \qquad (5.48)$$

Thus,

$$\begin{aligned} \mathbf{f} &= f_u\,\mathbf{e}_u + f_v\,\mathbf{e}_v + f_w\,\mathbf{e}_w \\ &= h_v h_w f_u\, \nabla v \times \nabla w + h_w h_u f_v\, \nabla w \times \nabla u + h_u h_v f_w\, \nabla u \times \nabla v. \end{aligned} \qquad (5.49)$$

Since

$$\nabla \cdot (\phi\,\mathbf{f}) = \phi \nabla \cdot \mathbf{f} + \mathbf{f} \cdot \nabla \phi, \qquad [3.155]$$

we have

$$\begin{aligned} \nabla \cdot (f_u\,\mathbf{e}_u) &= \nabla \cdot (h_v h_w f_u\, \nabla v \times \nabla w) \\ &= h_v h_w f_u\, \nabla \cdot (\nabla v \times \nabla w) + (\nabla v \times \nabla w) \cdot \nabla (h_v h_w f_u). \end{aligned} \qquad (5.50)$$

Again because

$$\nabla \cdot (\mathbf{f} \times \mathbf{g}) = \mathbf{g} \cdot (\nabla \times \mathbf{f}) - \mathbf{f} \cdot (\nabla \times \mathbf{g}), \qquad [3.157]$$

and using $\nabla \times (\nabla \phi) = \mathbf{0}$ from (3.142),

$$\nabla \cdot (\nabla v \times \nabla w) = \nabla w \cdot (\nabla \times \nabla v) - \nabla v \cdot (\nabla \times \nabla w) = 0.$$

Next, by (5.44) and (5.48),

$$\nabla (h_v h_w f_u) = \frac{1}{h_u}\frac{\partial}{\partial u}(h_v h_w f_u)\,\mathbf{e}_u + \frac{1}{h_v}\frac{\partial}{\partial v}(h_v h_w f_u)\,\mathbf{e}_v + \frac{1}{h_w}\frac{\partial}{\partial w}(h_v h_w f_u)\,\mathbf{e}_w,$$

$$\nabla v \times \nabla w = \frac{1}{h_v h_w}\,\mathbf{e}_u.$$

Since $\mathbf{e}_u \cdot \mathbf{e}_u = 1$ and $\mathbf{e}_u \cdot \mathbf{e}_v = \mathbf{e}_u \cdot \mathbf{e}_w = 0$, taking the dot product yields

$$(\nabla v \times \nabla w) \cdot \nabla (h_v h_w f_u) = \frac{1}{h_u h_v h_w}\frac{\partial}{\partial u}(h_v h_w f_u).$$

Thus,

$$\nabla \cdot (f_u\,\mathbf{e}_u) = \frac{1}{h_u h_v h_w}\frac{\partial}{\partial u}(h_v h_w f_u). \qquad (5.51)$$

Similarly (or by cyclic changes of indices),

$$\nabla \cdot (f_v\,\mathbf{e}_v) = \frac{1}{h_u h_v h_w}\frac{\partial}{\partial v}(h_w h_u f_v), \qquad (5.52)$$

$$\nabla \cdot (f_w \mathbf{e}_w) = \frac{1}{h_u h_v h_w} \frac{\partial}{\partial w} (h_u h_v h_w). \tag{5.53}$$

Adding (5.51–3), we obtain (5.45).

**PROBLEM 5.14** Verify (5.46).

**Solution:** Applying (5.45) to the vector $\nabla \psi$, given by (5.44), i.e., substituting

$$f_u = \frac{1}{h_u} \frac{\partial \psi}{\partial u}, \quad f_v = \frac{1}{h_v} \frac{\partial \psi}{\partial v}, \quad f_w = \frac{1}{h_w} \frac{\partial \psi}{\partial w}$$

into (5.45), we obtain (5.46).

**PROBLEM 5.15** Verify (5.47).

**Solution:** Using (5.24),

$$\begin{aligned} \mathbf{f} &= f_u \mathbf{e}_u + f_v \mathbf{e}_v + f_w \mathbf{e}_w \\ &= h_u f_u \nabla u + h_v f_v \nabla v + h_w f_w \nabla w. \end{aligned} \tag{5.54}$$

Since

$$\nabla \times (\phi \mathbf{f}) = \phi \nabla \times \mathbf{f} + (\nabla \phi) \times \mathbf{f} \qquad [3.156]$$

and $\nabla \times \nabla u = \mathbf{0}$,

$$\begin{aligned} \nabla \times (f_u \mathbf{e}_u) &= \nabla \times (h_u f_u \nabla u) \\ &= (h_u f_u) \nabla \times \nabla u + \nabla (h_u f_u) \times \nabla u \\ &= \nabla (h_u f_u) \times \nabla u. \end{aligned} \tag{5.55}$$

Now, using (5.44) and (5.27),

$$\begin{aligned} \nabla (h_u f_u) \times \nabla u = {} & \frac{1}{h_u^2} \frac{\partial}{\partial u} (h_u f_u) \mathbf{e}_u \times \mathbf{e}_u + \frac{1}{h_u h_v} \frac{\partial}{\partial v} (h_u f_u) \mathbf{e}_v \times \mathbf{e}_u \\ & + \frac{1}{h_w h_u} \frac{\partial}{\partial w} (h_u f_u) \mathbf{e}_w \times \mathbf{e}_u. \end{aligned}$$

Because $\mathbf{e}_u$, $\mathbf{e}_v$, $\mathbf{e}_w$ form a right-handed orthonormal basis,

$$\mathbf{e}_u \times \mathbf{e}_u = \mathbf{0}, \quad \mathbf{e}_v \times \mathbf{e}_u = -\mathbf{e}_w, \quad \mathbf{e}_w \times \mathbf{e}_u = \mathbf{e}_v,$$

and hence,

$$\begin{aligned} \nabla \times (f_u \mathbf{e}_u) &= \nabla (h_u f_u) \times \nabla u \\ &= \frac{1}{h_w h_u} \frac{\partial}{\partial w} (h_u f_u) \mathbf{e}_v - \frac{1}{h_u h_v} \frac{\partial}{\partial v} (h_u f_u) \mathbf{e}_w. \end{aligned} \tag{5.56}$$

Similarly, or by cyclic changes in indices,

$$\nabla \times (f_v \mathbf{e}_v) = \frac{1}{h_u h_v} \frac{\partial}{\partial u} (h_v f_v) \mathbf{e}_w - \frac{1}{h_v h_w} \frac{\partial}{\partial w} (h_v f_v) \mathbf{e}_u, \tag{5.57}$$

$$\nabla \times (f_w \mathbf{e}_w) = \frac{1}{h_v h_w} \frac{\partial}{\partial v} (h_w f_w) \mathbf{e}_u - \frac{1}{h_w h_u} \frac{\partial}{\partial u} (h_w f_w) \mathbf{e}_v. \tag{5.58}$$

Adding (5.56–8), we obtain (5.47).

Note that (5.47) can also be written as

$$\nabla \times \mathbf{f} = \frac{1}{h_u h_v h_w} \begin{vmatrix} h_u \mathbf{e}_u & h_v \mathbf{e}_v & h_w \mathbf{e}_w \\ \dfrac{\partial}{\partial u} & \dfrac{\partial}{\partial v} & \dfrac{\partial}{\partial w} \\ h_u f_u & h_v f_v & h_w f_w \end{vmatrix}. \tag{5.59}$$

**PROBLEM 5.16** Using the definition of divergence given by

$$\nabla \cdot \mathbf{f} = \lim_{\Delta V \to 0} \frac{1}{\Delta V} \oiint_S \mathbf{f} \cdot d\mathbf{S}, \qquad [4.47]$$

derive (5.45).

**Solution:** Let the point $P(u, v, w)$ be at the center of the curvilinear volume element $dV$, as shown in Fig. 5.2, and let

$$dV = h_u h_v h_w \, du dv dw. \qquad [5.30]$$

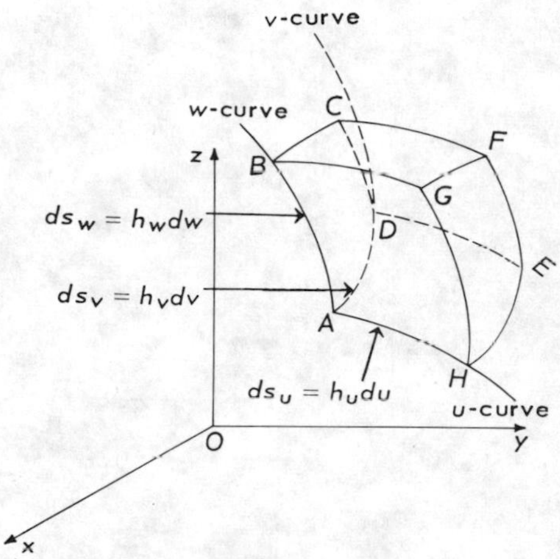


Fig. 5.2 Curvilinear volume element.

If $\mathbf{f} = f_u \mathbf{e}_u + f_v \mathbf{e}_v + f_w \mathbf{e}_w$, then the flux for the outward normal through surface $ABCD$ for constant $u$ is

$$-f_u h_v h_w \, dv dw + \frac{1}{2} \frac{\partial}{\partial u} (f_u h_v h_w) \, du dv dw, \tag{5.60}$$

and through surface $EFGH$ it is

$$f_u h_v h_w \, dv dw + \frac{1}{2} \frac{\partial}{\partial u} (f_u h_v h_w) \, du dv dw. \tag{5.61}$$

(We ignore infinitesimals of higher order.) Adding (5.60) and (5.61), the net outflow of the flux through the two surfaces, for constant $u$, is

$$\frac{\partial}{\partial u} (f_u h_v h_w) \, du dv dw. \tag{5.62}$$

Adding-in the similar results for the other two pairs of surfaces,

$$\oiint_S \mathbf{f} \cdot d\mathbf{S} = \left[ \frac{\partial}{\partial u} (f_u h_v h_w) + \frac{\partial}{\partial v} (f_v h_w h_u) + \frac{\partial}{\partial w} (f_w h_u h_v) \right] du dv dw. \tag{5.63}$$

Dividing (5.63) by $dV$, given in (5.30), yields

$$\nabla \cdot \mathbf{f} = \frac{1}{h_u h_v h_w} \left[ \frac{\partial}{\partial u} (f_u h_v h_w) + \frac{\partial}{\partial v} (f_v h_w h_u) + \frac{\partial}{\partial w} (f_w h_u h_v) \right]. \qquad [5.45]$$

**PROBLEM 5.17** Using the definition of curl given by

$$\mathbf{n} \cdot (\nabla \times \mathbf{f}) = \lim_{\Delta S \to 0} \frac{1}{\Delta S} \oint_C \mathbf{f} \cdot d\mathbf{r}, \qquad [4.50]$$

derive (5.47).

**Solution:** Let $\mathbf{f} = f_u \mathbf{e}_u + f_v \mathbf{e}_v + f_w \mathbf{e}_w$ and first calculate $\mathbf{e}_u \cdot (\nabla \times \mathbf{f})$. Consider a closed curve $C_u$ $(ADCB)$ lying in the surface $u$ = constant, as shown in Fig. 5.3. The surface element $dS$ enclosed by $C_u$ is

$$dS = h_v h_w \, dv dw. \tag{5.64}$$

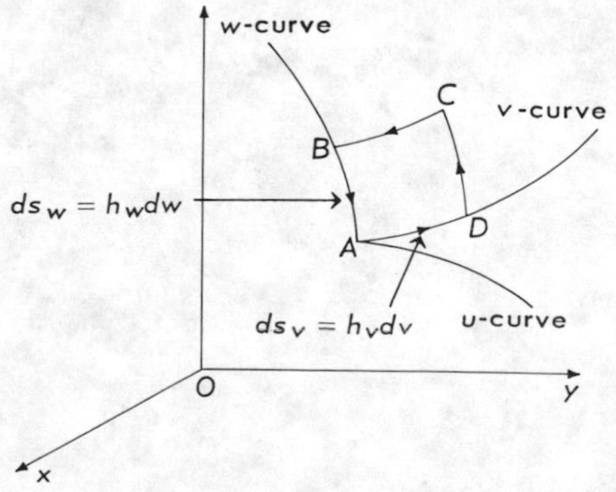


Fig. 5.3 Curvilinear surface element.

The circulation around the closed curve $C_u$ is

$$\oint_{C_u} \mathbf{f} \cdot d\mathbf{r} = \int_A^D \mathbf{f} \cdot d\mathbf{r} + \int_D^C \mathbf{f} \cdot d\mathbf{r} + \int_C^B \mathbf{f} \cdot d\mathbf{r} + \int_B^A \mathbf{f} \cdot d\mathbf{r}.$$

Ignoring infinitesimals of higher order,

$$\int_A^D \mathbf{f}\cdot d\mathbf{r} = f_v h_v \, dv,$$

$$\int_D^C \mathbf{f}\cdot d\mathbf{r} = \left[f_w h_w + \frac{\partial}{\partial v}(f_w h_w)\, dv\right] dw,$$

$$\int_C^B \mathbf{f}\cdot d\mathbf{r} = -\left[f_v h_v + \frac{\partial}{\partial w}(f_v h_v)\, dw\right] dv,$$

$$\int_B^A \mathbf{f}\cdot d\mathbf{r} = -f_w h_w \, dw.$$

Adding these results yields

$$\oint_{C_u} \mathbf{f}\cdot d\mathbf{r} = \left[\frac{\partial}{\partial v}(f_w h_w) - \frac{\partial}{\partial w}(f_v h_v)\right] dvdw. \tag{5.65}$$

Dividing (5.65) by $dS$, given in (5.64),

$$\mathbf{e}_u \cdot (\nabla \times \mathbf{f}) = \frac{1}{h_v h_w}\left[\frac{\partial}{\partial v}(f_w h_w) - \frac{\partial}{\partial w}(f_v h_v)\right]. \tag{5.66}$$

By cyclic permutation of the indices, the remaining two components of $\nabla \times \mathbf{f}$ are obtained. Consequently,

$$\begin{aligned}\nabla \times \mathbf{f} = {} & \frac{1}{h_v h_w}\left[\frac{\partial}{\partial v}(f_w h_w) - \frac{\partial}{\partial w}(f_v h_v)\right]\mathbf{e}_u \\ & + \frac{1}{h_w h_u}\left[\frac{\partial}{\partial w}(f_u h_u) - \frac{\partial}{\partial u}(f_w h_w)\right]\mathbf{e}_v \\ & + \frac{1}{h_u h_v}\left[\frac{\partial}{\partial u}(f_v h_v) - \frac{\partial}{\partial v}(f_u h_u)\right]\mathbf{e}_w. \end{aligned} \tag{5.47}$$

## 5.4 Special Coordinate Systems

### 5.4a Rectangular Cartesian Coordinates (x, y, z)

Since $u = x$, $v = y$, $w = z$ for the rectangular coordinates, the scale factors are

$$h_u = h_x = 1, \quad h_v = h_y = 1, \quad h_w = h_z = 1. \tag{5.67}$$

The coordinate surfaces for these coordinates are

$$x = \text{const}, \quad y = \text{const}, \quad z = \text{const}.$$

Let $\psi = \psi(x, y, z)$ and $\mathbf{f} = f_1\mathbf{i} + f_2\mathbf{j} + f_3\mathbf{k}$. Then from (3.110), (3.127), (3.138), and (3.132), the gradient of $\phi$, the divergence and curl of $\mathbf{f}$, and the Laplacian of $\psi$ are

$$\nabla\psi = \frac{\partial\psi}{\partial x}\mathbf{i} + \frac{\partial\psi}{\partial y}\mathbf{j} + \frac{\partial\psi}{\partial z}\mathbf{k}, \tag{5.68}$$

$$\nabla\cdot\mathbf{f} = \frac{\partial f_1}{\partial x} + \frac{\partial f_2}{\partial y} + \frac{\partial f_3}{\partial z}, \tag{5.69}$$

$$\nabla \times \mathbf{f} = \begin{vmatrix} \mathbf{i} & \mathbf{j} & \mathbf{k} \\ \dfrac{\partial}{\partial x} & \dfrac{\partial}{\partial y} & \dfrac{\partial}{\partial z} \\ f_1 & f_2 & f_3 \end{vmatrix}, \tag{5.70}$$

$$\nabla^2 \psi = \frac{\partial^2 \psi}{\partial x^2} + \frac{\partial^2 \psi}{\partial y^2} + \frac{\partial^2 \psi}{\partial z^2}. \tag{5.71}$$

### 5.4b Circular Cylindrical Coordinates ($\rho$, $\phi$, $z$)

Since $u = \rho$, $v = \phi$, $w = z$ with $0 \le \rho < \infty$, $0 \le \phi < 2\pi$, $-\infty < z < \infty$ for the circular cylindrical coordinates, from Fig. 5.4, the transformation from the rectangular to the cylindrical coordinates is

$$x = \rho \cos \phi, \quad y = \rho \sin \phi, \quad z = z. \tag{5.72}$$

The coordinate surface for the circular cylinders having the $z$-axis as a common axis is

$$\rho = (x^2 + y^2)^{1/2} = \text{const};$$

for the half-plane through the $z$-axis,

$$\phi = \tan^{-1}\left(\frac{y}{x}\right) = \text{const},$$

and for the plane parallel to the $xy$-plane,

$$z = \text{const}.$$

From the results of Prob. 5.8, the scale factors are

$$h_u = h_\rho = 1, \quad h_v = h_\phi = \rho, \quad h_w = h_z = 1. \tag{5.73}$$

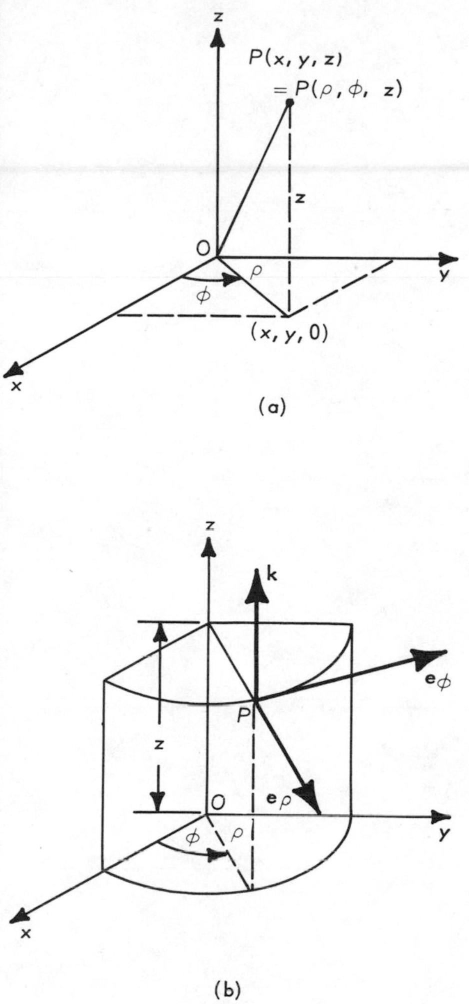


Fig. 5.4 Circular cylindrical coordinates.

**PROBLEM 5.18** For circular cylindrical coordinates $(\rho, \phi, z)$, if $\psi = \psi(\rho, \phi, z)$, $\mathbf{f} = f_\rho \mathbf{e}_\rho + f_\phi \mathbf{e}_\phi + f_3 \mathbf{k}$, evaluate (a) $(ds)^2$, (b) $dV$, (c) $\nabla\psi$, (d) $\nabla \cdot \mathbf{f}$, (e) $\nabla \times \mathbf{f}$, (f) $\nabla^2\psi$.

**Solution:** From (5.29), (5.30), (5.44), (5.45), (5.59), and (5.46),

(a) $$(ds)^2 = (d\rho)^2 + (\rho\, d\phi)^2 + (dz)^2; \tag{5.74}$$

(b) $$dV = \rho\, d\rho d\phi dz; \tag{5.75}$$

(c) $$\nabla\psi = \frac{\partial\psi}{\partial\rho}\mathbf{e}_\rho + \frac{1}{\rho}\frac{\partial\psi}{\partial\phi}\mathbf{e}_\phi + \frac{\partial\psi}{\partial z}\mathbf{k}; \tag{5.76}$$

(d) $$\nabla \cdot \mathbf{f} = \frac{1}{\rho}\frac{\partial}{\partial\rho}(\rho f_\rho) + \frac{1}{\rho}\frac{\partial f_\phi}{\partial\phi} + \frac{\partial f_3}{\partial z}; \tag{5.77}$$

(e) $$\nabla \times \mathbf{f} = \frac{1}{\rho}\begin{vmatrix} \mathbf{e}_\rho & \rho\mathbf{e}_\phi & \mathbf{k} \\ \dfrac{\partial}{\partial\rho} & \dfrac{\partial}{\partial\phi} & \dfrac{\partial}{\partial z} \\ f_\rho & f_\phi & f_3 \end{vmatrix} \tag{5.78}$$

$$= \frac{1}{\rho}\left(\frac{\partial f_3}{\partial\phi} - \frac{\partial f_\phi}{\partial z}\right)\mathbf{e}_\rho + \left(\frac{\partial f_\rho}{\partial z} - \frac{\partial f_3}{\partial\rho}\right)\mathbf{e}_\phi + \frac{1}{\rho}\left(\frac{\partial f_\phi}{\partial\rho} - \frac{\partial f_\rho}{\partial\phi}\right)\mathbf{k}; \tag{5.79}$$

(f) $$\nabla^2\psi = \frac{1}{\rho}\frac{\partial}{\partial\rho}\left(\rho\frac{\partial\psi}{\partial\rho}\right) + \frac{1}{\rho^2}\frac{\partial^2\psi}{\partial\phi^2} + \frac{\partial^2\psi}{\partial z^2}. \tag{5.80}$$

**PROBLEM 5.19** Find the relationships between **i**, **j**, **k** of the rectangular Cartesian coordinate system and $\mathbf{e}_\rho$, $\mathbf{e}_\phi$, **k** of the circular cylindrical coordinate system.

**Solution:** From the results of Prob. 5.8,

$$\mathbf{e}_\rho = \cos\phi\,\mathbf{i} + \sin\phi\,\mathbf{j}, \tag{5.81a}$$

$$\mathbf{e}_\phi = -\sin\phi\,\mathbf{i} + \cos\phi\,\mathbf{j}, \tag{5.81b}$$

$$\mathbf{k} = \mathbf{k}. \tag{5.81c}$$

From (2.70),

$$\mathbf{e}_\rho = (\mathbf{e}_\rho\cdot\mathbf{i})\,\mathbf{i} + (\mathbf{e}_\rho\cdot\mathbf{j})\,\mathbf{j} + (\mathbf{e}_\rho\cdot\mathbf{k})\,\mathbf{k}, \tag{5.82a}$$

$$\mathbf{e}_\phi = (\mathbf{e}_\phi\cdot\mathbf{i})\,\mathbf{i} + (\mathbf{e}_\phi\cdot\mathbf{j})\,\mathbf{j} + (\mathbf{e}_\phi\cdot\mathbf{k})\,\mathbf{k}. \tag{5.82b}$$

Comparing (5.81) and (5.82),

$$\begin{aligned} &\mathbf{e}_\rho\cdot\mathbf{i} = \cos\phi, \quad \mathbf{e}_\rho\cdot\mathbf{j} = \sin\phi, \quad \mathbf{e}_\rho\cdot\mathbf{k} = 0, \\ &\mathbf{e}_\phi\cdot\mathbf{i} = -\sin\phi, \quad \mathbf{e}_\phi\cdot\mathbf{j} = \cos\phi, \quad \mathbf{e}_\phi\cdot\mathbf{k} = 0. \end{aligned} \tag{5.83}$$

Table 5.1 shows the results of (5.83) in tabular form.

TABLE 5.1 Relationship Between Rectangular and Cylindrical Base Vectors

| · | **i** | **j** | **k** |
|---|---|---|---|
| $\mathbf{e}_\rho$ | $\cos\phi$ | $\sin\phi$ | 0 |
| $\mathbf{e}_\phi$ | $-\sin\phi$ | $\cos\phi$ | 0 |
| **k** | 0 | 0 | 1 |

Note that (5.83) can also be obtained from Fig. 5.4, by applying the definition of the dot product (1.25).

Using (5.83), **i**, **j**, **k** in terms of $\mathbf{e}_\rho$, $\mathbf{e}_\phi$, **k** are

$$\begin{aligned} \mathbf{i} &= (\mathbf{i}\cdot\mathbf{e}_\rho)\,\mathbf{e}_\rho + (\mathbf{i}\cdot\mathbf{e}_\phi)\,\mathbf{e}_\phi + (\mathbf{i}\cdot\mathbf{k})\,\mathbf{k} \\ &= \cos\phi\,\mathbf{e}_\rho - \sin\phi\,\mathbf{e}_\phi, \end{aligned} \tag{5.84a}$$

$$\begin{aligned} \mathbf{j} &= (\mathbf{j}\cdot\mathbf{e}_\rho)\,\mathbf{e}_\rho + (\mathbf{j}\cdot\mathbf{e}_\phi)\,\mathbf{e}_\phi + (\mathbf{j}\cdot\mathbf{k})\,\mathbf{k} \\ &= \sin\phi\,\mathbf{e}_\rho + \cos\phi\,\mathbf{e}_\phi, \end{aligned} \tag{5.84b}$$

$$\mathbf{k} = \mathbf{k}. \tag{5.84c}$$

Using matrix notation, the transformations between **i**, **j**, **k** and $\mathbf{e}_\rho$, $\mathbf{e}_\phi$, **k**, (5.81) and (5.84), can be written, respectively, as

$$\begin{bmatrix} \mathbf{e}_\rho \\ \mathbf{e}_\phi \\ \mathbf{k} \end{bmatrix} = \begin{bmatrix} \cos\phi & \sin\phi & 0 \\ -\sin\phi & \cos\phi & 0 \\ 0 & 0 & 1 \end{bmatrix} \begin{bmatrix} \mathbf{i} \\ \mathbf{j} \\ \mathbf{k} \end{bmatrix}, \tag{5.85}$$

$$\begin{bmatrix} \mathbf{i} \\ \mathbf{j} \\ \mathbf{k} \end{bmatrix} = \begin{bmatrix} \cos\phi & -\sin\phi & 0 \\ \sin\phi & \cos\phi & 0 \\ 0 & 0 & 1 \end{bmatrix} \begin{bmatrix} \mathbf{e}_\rho \\ \mathbf{e}_\phi \\ \mathbf{k} \end{bmatrix}. \tag{5.86}$$

It must be emphasized that the unit vectors $\mathbf{e}_\rho$, $\mathbf{e}_\phi$ vary in direction from point to point.

**PROBLEM 5.20** If

$$\mathbf{f} = f_1\,\mathbf{i} + f_2\,\mathbf{j} + f_3\,\mathbf{k} = f_\rho \mathbf{e}_\rho + f_\phi \mathbf{e}_\phi + f_3\,\mathbf{k}, \tag{5.87}$$

find the relationship between $f_1$, $f_2$, $f_3$ and $f_\rho$, $f_\phi$, $f_3$.

**Solution:** Using (5.84),

$$\begin{aligned}\mathbf{f} &= f_1\,\mathbf{i} + f_2\,\mathbf{j} + f_3\,\mathbf{k}\\ &= f_1(\cos\phi\ \mathbf{e}_\rho - \sin\phi\ \mathbf{e}_\phi) + f_2(\sin\phi\ \mathbf{e}_\rho + \cos\phi\ \mathbf{e}_\phi) + f_3\,\mathbf{k}\\ &= (f_1\cos\phi + f_2\sin\phi)\,\mathbf{e}_\rho + (-f_1\sin\phi + f_2\cos\phi)\,\mathbf{e}_\phi + f_3\,\mathbf{k}.\end{aligned} \tag{5.88}$$

Since $\mathbf{f} = f_\rho \mathbf{e}_\rho + f_\phi \mathbf{e}_\phi + f_3\,\mathbf{k}$, comparing coefficients yields

$$f_\rho = f_1\cos\phi + f_2\sin\phi, \tag{5.89a}$$

$$f_\phi = -f_1\sin\phi + f_2\cos\phi, \tag{5.89b}$$

$$f_3 = f_3. \tag{5.89c}$$

Similarly, using (5.81),

$$\begin{aligned}\mathbf{f} &= f_\rho\,\mathbf{e}_\rho + f_\phi\,\mathbf{e}_\phi + f_3\,\mathbf{k}\\ &= f_\rho(\cos\phi\ \mathbf{i} + \sin\phi\ \mathbf{j}) + f_\phi(-\sin\phi\ \mathbf{i} + \cos\phi\ \mathbf{j}) + f_3\,\mathbf{k}\\ &= (f_\rho\cos\phi - f_\phi\sin\phi)\,\mathbf{i} + (f_\rho\sin\phi + f_\phi\cos\phi)\,\mathbf{j} + f_3\,\mathbf{k}.\end{aligned}$$

Again, because $\mathbf{f} = f_1\,\mathbf{i} + f_2\,\mathbf{j} + f_3\,\mathbf{k}$, comparing coefficients yields

$$f_1 = f_\rho\cos\phi - f_\phi\sin\phi, \tag{5.90a}$$

$$f_2 = f_\rho\sin\phi + f_\phi\cos\phi, \tag{5.90b}$$

$$f_3 = f_3. \tag{5.90c}$$

In matrix notation, (5.89) and (5.90) can be respectively expressed as

$$\begin{bmatrix} f_\rho \\ f_\phi \\ f_3 \end{bmatrix} = \begin{bmatrix} \cos\phi & \sin\phi & 0 \\ -\sin\phi & \cos\phi & 0 \\ 0 & 0 & 1 \end{bmatrix} \begin{bmatrix} f_1 \\ f_2 \\ f_3 \end{bmatrix}, \tag{5.91}$$

$$\begin{bmatrix} f_1 \\ f_2 \\ f_3 \end{bmatrix} = \begin{bmatrix} \cos\phi & -\sin\phi & 0 \\ \sin\phi & \cos\phi & 0 \\ 0 & 0 & 1 \end{bmatrix} \begin{bmatrix} f_\rho \\ f_\phi \\ f_3 \end{bmatrix}. \tag{5.92}$$

Comparing (5.85) and (5.91), and (5.86) and (5.92), we observe that the transformations of the base vectors and the components of a vector have the same matrix.

**PROBLEM 5.21** Transform $\mathbf{f} = x\,\mathbf{i} + y\,\mathbf{j} + z\,\mathbf{k}$ into circular cylindrical coordinates.

**Solution:** Since $f_1 = x$, $f_2 = y$, and $f_3 = z$, from (5.89),

$$f_\rho = f_1\cos\phi + f_2\sin\phi = x\cos\phi + y\sin\phi,$$

$$f_\phi = -f_1\sin\phi + f_2\cos\phi = -x\sin\phi + y\cos\phi,$$

$$f_3 = f_3 = z.$$

Substituting $x = \rho\cos\phi$ and $y = \rho\sin\phi$,

$$f_\rho = \rho\cos^2\phi + \rho\sin^2\phi = \rho(\cos^2\phi + \sin^2\phi) = \rho,$$

$$f_\phi = -\rho\cos\phi\sin\phi + \rho\sin\phi\cos\phi = 0,$$

$$f_3 = z.$$

Hence, $\mathbf{f} = \rho\,\mathbf{e}_\rho + z\,\mathbf{k}$.

**Alternate Solution:** Using (5.84),

$$\begin{aligned}\mathbf{f} &= x\mathbf{i} + y\mathbf{j} + z\mathbf{k}\\ &= x(\cos\phi\,\mathbf{e}_\rho - \sin\phi\,\mathbf{e}_\phi) + y(\sin\phi\,\mathbf{e}_\rho + \cos\phi\,\mathbf{e}_\phi) + z\mathbf{k}\\ &= (x\cos\phi + y\sin\phi)\mathbf{e}_\rho + (-x\sin\phi + y\cos\phi)\mathbf{e}_\phi + z\mathbf{k}.\end{aligned}$$

Substituting $x = \rho\cos\phi$ and $y = \rho\sin\phi$,

$$\begin{aligned}f &= \rho(\cos^2\phi + \sin^2\phi)\mathbf{e}_\rho + (-\rho\cos\phi\sin\phi + \rho\sin\phi\cos\phi)\mathbf{e}_\phi + z\mathbf{k}\\ &= \rho\,\mathbf{e}_\rho + z\mathbf{k}.\end{aligned}$$

**PROBLEM 5.22** Transform $\mathbf{f} = \dfrac{1}{\rho}\mathbf{e}_\rho$ into rectangular Cartesian coordinates.

**Solution:** Since $f_\rho = 1/\rho$, $f_\phi = 0$, and $f_3 = 0$, from (5.90),

$$f_1 = f_\rho\cos\phi - f_\phi\sin\phi = \frac{1}{\rho}\cos\phi,$$

$$f_2 = f_\rho\sin\phi + f_\phi\cos\phi = \frac{1}{\rho}\sin\phi,$$

$$f_3 = f_3 = 0.$$

Substituting $\rho = (x^2+y^2)^{1/2}$, $\cos\phi = \dfrac{x}{\rho} = \dfrac{x}{(x^2+y^2)^{1/2}}$, and $\sin\phi = \dfrac{y}{\rho} = \dfrac{y}{(x^2+y^2)^{1/2}}$,

$$f_1 = \frac{x}{\rho^2} = \frac{x}{x^2+y^2}, \quad f_2 = \frac{y}{\rho^2} = \frac{y}{x^2+y^2}.$$

Hence,

$$\mathbf{f} = \frac{x}{(x^2+y^2)}\mathbf{i} + \frac{y}{(x^2+y^2)}\mathbf{j}.$$

**Alternate Solution:** Using (5.81),

$$\mathbf{f} = \frac{1}{\rho}\mathbf{e}_\rho = \frac{1}{\rho}(\cos\phi\,\mathbf{i} + \sin\phi\,\mathbf{j}) = \frac{\cos\phi}{\rho}\mathbf{i} + \frac{\sin\phi}{\rho}\mathbf{j}.$$

Hence, substituting $\cos\phi = x/\rho$, $\sin\phi = y/\rho$, and $\rho^2 = x^2 + y^2$,

$$f = \frac{x}{\rho^2}\mathbf{i} + \frac{y}{\rho^2}\mathbf{j} = \frac{x}{x^2+y^2}\mathbf{i} + \frac{y}{x^2+y^2}\mathbf{j}.$$

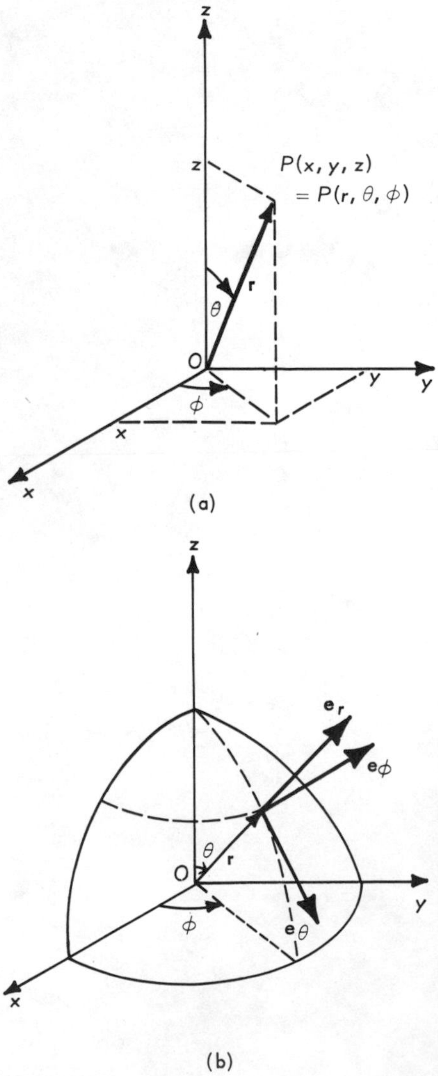


Fig. 5.5 Spherical coordinates.

### 5.4c Spherical Coordinates $(r, \theta, \phi)$

Since $u = r$, $v = \theta$, $w = \phi$ with $0 \le r < \infty$, $0 \le \theta \le \pi$, $0 \le \phi < 2\pi$, from Fig. 5.5, the *transformation* from the rectangular to the spherical coordinates is

$$x = r\sin\theta\cos\phi, \quad y = r\sin\theta\sin\phi, \quad z = r\cos\theta. \tag{5.93}$$

The *coordinate surface* for the concentric spheres centered at the origin is

$$r = (x^2+y^2+z^2)^{1/2} = \text{const},$$

for circular cones centered on the $z$-axis and with vertices at the origin it is

$$\theta = \cos^{-1}\left[\frac{z}{(x^2+y^2+z^2)^{1/2}}\right] = \text{const},$$

and for the half-plane through the $z$-axis it is

$$\phi = \tan^{-1}\left(\frac{y}{x}\right) = \text{const.}$$

From the results of Prob. 5.9, the scale factors are

$$h_u = h_r = 1, \quad h_v = h_\theta = r, \quad h_w = h_\phi = r\sin\theta. \tag{5.94}$$

**PROBLEM 5.23** For spherical coordinates $(r, \theta, \phi)$, if $\psi = \psi(r, \theta, \phi)$ and $\mathbf{f} = f_r\mathbf{e}_r + f_\theta\mathbf{e}_\theta + f_\phi\mathbf{e}_\phi$, evaluate (a) $(ds)^2$, (b) $dV$, (c) $\nabla\psi$, (d) $\nabla\cdot\mathbf{f}$, (e) $\nabla\times\mathbf{f}$, (f) $\nabla^2\psi$.

**Solution:** From (5.29), (5.30), (5.44), (5.45), (5.46), and (5.59),

(a)
$$(ds)^2 = (dr)^2 + (r\,d\theta)^2 + (r\sin\theta\,d\phi)^2; \tag{5.95}$$

(b)
$$dV = r^2\sin\theta\,dr d\theta d\phi;$$

(c)
$$\nabla\psi = \frac{\partial\psi}{\partial r}\mathbf{e}_r + \frac{1}{r}\frac{\partial\psi}{\partial\theta}\mathbf{e}_\theta + \frac{1}{r\sin\theta}\frac{\partial\psi}{\partial\phi}\mathbf{e}_\phi; \tag{5.96}$$

(d)
$$\nabla\cdot\mathbf{f} = \frac{1}{r^2\sin\theta}\left[\sin\theta\frac{\partial}{\partial r}(r^2 f_r) + r\frac{\partial}{\partial\theta}(\sin\theta\, f_\theta) + r\frac{\partial f_\phi}{\partial\phi}\right]$$

$$= \frac{1}{r^2}\frac{\partial}{\partial r}(r^2 f_r) + \frac{1}{r\sin\theta}\frac{\partial}{\partial\theta}(\sin\theta\, f_\theta) + \frac{1}{r\sin\theta}\frac{\partial f_\phi}{\partial\phi}; \tag{5.97}$$

(e)
$$\nabla\times\mathbf{f} = \frac{1}{r^2\sin\theta}\begin{vmatrix} \mathbf{e}_r & r\mathbf{e}_\theta & r\sin\theta\,\mathbf{e}_\phi \\ \dfrac{\partial}{\partial r} & \dfrac{\partial}{\partial\theta} & \dfrac{\partial}{\partial\phi} \\ f_r & rf_\theta & r\sin\theta\, f_\phi \end{vmatrix}, \tag{5.98}$$

or hence,

$$\nabla\times\mathbf{f} = \frac{1}{r\sin\theta}\left[\frac{\partial}{\partial\theta}(\sin\theta\, f_\phi) - \frac{\partial f_\theta}{\partial\phi}\right]\mathbf{e}_r + \frac{1}{r}\left[\frac{1}{\sin\theta}\frac{\partial f_r}{\partial\phi} - \frac{\partial}{\partial r}(rf_\phi)\right]\mathbf{e}_\theta$$

$$+ \frac{1}{r}\left[\frac{\partial}{\partial r}(rf_\theta) - \frac{\partial f_r}{\partial\theta}\right]\mathbf{e}_\phi; \tag{5.99}$$

(f)
$$\nabla^2\psi = \frac{1}{r^2\sin\theta}\left[\sin\theta\frac{\partial}{\partial r}\left(r^2\frac{\partial\psi}{\partial r}\right) + \frac{\partial}{\partial\theta}\left(\sin\theta\frac{\partial\psi}{\partial\theta}\right) + \frac{1}{\sin\theta}\frac{\partial^2\psi}{\partial\phi^2}\right]$$

$$= \frac{1}{r^2}\frac{\partial}{\partial r}\left(r^2\frac{\partial\psi}{\partial r}\right) + \frac{1}{r^2\sin\theta}\frac{\partial}{\partial\theta}\left(\sin\theta\frac{\partial\psi}{\partial\theta}\right) + \frac{1}{r^2\sin^2\theta}\frac{\partial^2\psi}{\partial\phi^2}. \tag{5.100}$$

**PROBLEM 5.24** Using (5.96–100), derive

(a)
$$\nabla f(r) = f'(r)\,\mathbf{e}_r, \tag{3.165}$$

(b)
$$\nabla\cdot[f(r)\mathbf{r}] = 3f(r) + rf'(r), \tag{3.166}$$

(c)
$$\nabla\times[f(r)\mathbf{r}] = \mathbf{0}, \tag{3.169}$$

(d)
$$\nabla^2 f(r) = \frac{2}{r}f'(r) + f''(r). \tag{3.170}$$

**Solution:** (a) From (5.96),

$$\nabla f(r) = \frac{\partial f(r)}{\partial r}\mathbf{e}_r = f'(r)\mathbf{e}_r.$$

(b) Since $\mathbf{r} = r\,\mathbf{e}_r$ and $f(r)\mathbf{r} = rf(r)\,\mathbf{e}_r$, then from (5.97),

$$\begin{aligned}\nabla \cdot [f(r)\mathbf{r}] &= \nabla \cdot [rf(r)\mathbf{e}_r] \\ &= \frac{1}{r^2}\frac{\partial}{\partial r}[r^3 f(r)] \\ &= \frac{1}{r^2}[3r^2 f(r) + r^3 f'(r)] \\ &= 3f(r) + rf'(r).\end{aligned}$$

(c) From (5.98),

$$\begin{aligned}\nabla \times [f(r)\mathbf{r}] &= \nabla \times [rf(r)\mathbf{e}_r] \\ &= \frac{1}{r^2 \sin\theta}\begin{vmatrix} \mathbf{e}_r & r\mathbf{e}_\theta & r\sin\theta\,\mathbf{e}_\phi \\ \dfrac{\partial}{\partial r} & \dfrac{\partial}{\partial \theta} & \dfrac{\partial}{\partial \phi} \\ rf(r) & 0 & 0 \end{vmatrix} \\ &= \mathbf{0}.\end{aligned}$$

(d) From (5.100),

$$\begin{aligned}\nabla^2 f(r) &= \frac{1}{r^2}\frac{\partial}{\partial r}\left(r^2 \frac{\partial f(r)}{\partial r}\right) \\ &= \frac{1}{r^2}\frac{d}{dr}[r^2 f'(r)] \\ &= \frac{1}{r^2}[2rf'(r) + r^2 f''(r)] \\ &= \frac{2}{r}f'(r) + f''(r).\end{aligned}$$

**PROBLEM 5.25** Find the relationships between **i**, **j**, **k** of the rectangular Cartesian coordinate system and $\mathbf{e}_r$, $\mathbf{e}_\theta$, $\mathbf{e}_\phi$ of the spherical coordinate system.

**Solution:** From the results of Prob. 5.9,

$$\mathbf{e}_r = \sin\theta\cos\phi\,\mathbf{i} + \sin\theta\sin\phi\,\mathbf{j} + \cos\theta\,\mathbf{k}, \tag{5.101a}$$

$$\mathbf{e}_\theta = \cos\theta\cos\phi\,\mathbf{i} + \cos\theta\sin\phi\,\mathbf{j} - \sin\theta\,\mathbf{k}, \tag{5.101b}$$

$$\mathbf{e}_\phi = -\sin\phi\,\mathbf{i} + \cos\phi\,\mathbf{j}. \tag{5.101c}$$

From (2.70),

$$\mathbf{e}_r = (\mathbf{e}_r\cdot\mathbf{i})\mathbf{i} + (\mathbf{e}_r\cdot\mathbf{j})\mathbf{j} + (\mathbf{e}_r\cdot\mathbf{k})\mathbf{k}, \tag{5.102a}$$

$$\mathbf{e}_\theta = (\mathbf{e}_\theta\cdot\mathbf{i})\mathbf{i} + (\mathbf{e}_\theta\cdot\mathbf{j})\mathbf{j} + (\mathbf{e}_\theta\cdot\mathbf{k})\mathbf{k}, \tag{5.102b}$$

$$\mathbf{e}_\phi = (\mathbf{e}_\phi\cdot\mathbf{i})\mathbf{i} + (\mathbf{e}_\phi\cdot\mathbf{j})\mathbf{j} + (\mathbf{e}_\phi\cdot\mathbf{k})\mathbf{k}. \tag{5.102c}$$

Comparing (5.101) and (5.102),

$$\begin{aligned}&\mathbf{e}_r\cdot\mathbf{i} = \sin\theta\cos\phi, \quad \mathbf{e}_r\cdot\mathbf{j} = \sin\theta\sin\phi, \quad \mathbf{e}_r\cdot\mathbf{k} = \cos\theta, \\ &\mathbf{e}_\theta\cdot\mathbf{i} = \cos\theta\cos\phi, \quad \mathbf{e}_\theta\cdot\mathbf{j} = \cos\theta\sin\phi, \quad \mathbf{e}_\theta\cdot\mathbf{k} = -\sin\theta, \\ &\mathbf{e}_\phi\cdot\mathbf{i} = -\sin\phi, \quad \mathbf{e}_\phi\cdot\mathbf{j} = \cos\phi, \quad \mathbf{e}_\phi\cdot\mathbf{k} = 0.\end{aligned} \tag{5.103}$$

The results of (5.103) are tabulated in Table 5.2. The relations (5.103) can also be obtained from Fig. 5.5 by applying the definition of the dot product (1.25).

TABLE 5.2 Relationship Between Rectangular and Spherical Base Vectors

| $\cdot$ | $\mathbf{i}$ | $\mathbf{j}$ | $\mathbf{k}$ |
|---|---|---|---|
| $\mathbf{e}_r$ | $\sin\theta\cos\phi$ | $\sin\theta\sin\phi$ | $\cos\theta$ |
| $\mathbf{e}_\theta$ | $\cos\theta\cos\phi$ | $\cos\theta\sin\phi$ | $-\sin\theta$ |
| $\mathbf{e}_\phi$ | $-\sin\phi$ | $\cos\phi$ | $0$ |

Using (5.103), we can now express $\mathbf{i}$, $\mathbf{j}$, $\mathbf{k}$ in terms of $\mathbf{e}_r$, $\mathbf{e}_\theta$, $\mathbf{e}_\phi$; i.e.,

$$\begin{aligned}\mathbf{i} &= (\mathbf{i}\cdot\mathbf{e}_r)\mathbf{e}_r + (\mathbf{i}\cdot\mathbf{e}_\theta)\mathbf{e}_\theta + (\mathbf{i}\cdot\mathbf{e}_\phi)\mathbf{e}_\phi \\ &= \sin\theta\cos\phi\,\mathbf{e}_r + \cos\theta\cos\phi\,\mathbf{e}_\theta - \sin\phi\,\mathbf{e}_\phi,\end{aligned} \tag{5.104a}$$

$$\begin{aligned}\mathbf{j} &= (\mathbf{j}\cdot\mathbf{e}_r)\mathbf{e}_r + (\mathbf{j}\cdot\mathbf{e}_\theta)\mathbf{e}_\theta + (\mathbf{j}\cdot\mathbf{e}_\phi)\mathbf{e}_\phi \\ &= \sin\theta\sin\phi\,\mathbf{e}_r + \cos\theta\sin\phi\,\mathbf{e}_\theta + \cos\phi\,\mathbf{e}_\phi,\end{aligned} \tag{5.104b}$$

$$\begin{aligned}\mathbf{k} &= (\mathbf{k}\cdot\mathbf{e}_r)\mathbf{e}_r + (\mathbf{k}\cdot\mathbf{e}_\theta)\mathbf{e}_\theta + (\mathbf{k}\cdot\mathbf{e}_\phi)\mathbf{e}_\phi \\ &= \cos\theta\,\mathbf{e}_r - \sin\theta\,\mathbf{e}_\theta.\end{aligned} \tag{5.104c}$$

Note that the unit vectors $\mathbf{e}_r$, $\mathbf{e}_\theta$, $\mathbf{e}_\phi$ vary in direction from point to point while the unit vectors $\mathbf{i}$, $\mathbf{j}$, $\mathbf{k}$ maintain their fixed directions.

In matrix notation, the transformations between $\mathbf{i}$, $\mathbf{j}$, $\mathbf{k}$ and $\mathbf{e}_r$, $\mathbf{e}_\theta$, $\mathbf{e}_\phi$, (5.101) and (5.104), can be written, respectively, as

$$\begin{bmatrix}\mathbf{e}_r\\ \mathbf{e}_\theta\\ \mathbf{e}_\phi\end{bmatrix} = \begin{bmatrix}\sin\theta\cos\phi & \sin\theta\sin\phi & \cos\theta\\ \cos\theta\cos\phi & \cos\theta\sin\phi & -\sin\theta\\ -\sin\phi & \cos\phi & 0\end{bmatrix}\begin{bmatrix}\mathbf{i}\\ \mathbf{j}\\ \mathbf{k}\end{bmatrix}, \tag{5.105}$$

$$\begin{bmatrix}\mathbf{i}\\ \mathbf{j}\\ \mathbf{k}\end{bmatrix} = \begin{bmatrix}\sin\theta\cos\phi & \cos\theta\cos\phi & -\sin\phi\\ \sin\theta\sin\phi & \cos\theta\sin\phi & \cos\phi\\ \cos\theta & -\sin\theta & 0\end{bmatrix}\begin{bmatrix}\mathbf{e}_r\\ \mathbf{e}_\theta\\ \mathbf{e}_\phi\end{bmatrix}. \tag{5.106}$$

**PROBLEM 5.26** Find the relationships between $f_1$, $f_2$, $f_3$ and $f_r$, $f_\theta$, $f_\phi$ if

$$\mathbf{f} = f_1\mathbf{i} + f_2\mathbf{j} + f_3\mathbf{k} = f_r\mathbf{e}_r + f_\theta\mathbf{e}_\theta + f_\phi\mathbf{e}_\phi. \tag{5.107}$$

**Solution:** Using (5.104),

$$\begin{aligned}\mathbf{f} &= f_1\mathbf{i} + f_2\mathbf{j} + f_3\mathbf{k}\\ &= f_1(\sin\theta\cos\phi\,\mathbf{e}_r + \cos\theta\cos\phi\,\mathbf{e}_\theta - \sin\phi\,\mathbf{e}_\phi)\\ &\quad + f_2(\sin\theta\sin\phi\,\mathbf{e}_r + \cos\theta\sin\phi\,\mathbf{e}_\theta + \cos\phi\,\mathbf{e}_\phi)\\ &\quad + f_3(\cos\theta\,\mathbf{e}_r - \sin\theta\,\mathbf{e}_\theta)\\ &= (f_1\sin\theta\cos\phi + f_2\sin\theta\sin\phi + f_3\cos\theta)\mathbf{e}_r\\ &\quad + (f_1\cos\theta\cos\phi + f_2\cos\theta\sin\phi - f_3\sin\theta)\mathbf{e}_\theta\\ &\quad + (-f_1\sin\phi + f_2\cos\phi)\mathbf{e}_\phi.\end{aligned} \tag{5.108}$$

Since $\mathbf{f} = f_r\mathbf{e}_r + f_\theta\mathbf{e}_\theta + f_\phi\mathbf{e}_\phi$, comparing coefficients yields

$$f_r = f_1\sin\theta\cos\phi + f_2\sin\theta\sin\phi + f_3\cos\theta, \tag{5.109a}$$

$$f_\theta = f_1\cos\theta\cos\phi + f_2\cos\theta\sin\phi - f_3\sin\theta, \tag{5.109b}$$

$$f_\phi = -f_1\sin\phi + f_2\cos\phi. \tag{5.109c}$$

Similarly, using (5.101),

$$\begin{aligned}
\mathbf{f} &= f_r \mathbf{e}_r + f_\theta \mathbf{e}_\theta + f_\phi \mathbf{e}_\phi \\
&= f_r (\sin\theta\cos\phi\,\mathbf{i} + \sin\theta\sin\phi\,\mathbf{j} + \cos\theta\,\mathbf{k}) \\
&\quad + f_\theta(\cos\theta\cos\phi\,\mathbf{i} + \cos\theta\sin\phi\,\mathbf{j} - \sin\theta\,\mathbf{k}) \\
&\quad + f_\phi(-\sin\phi\,\mathbf{i} + \cos\phi\,\mathbf{j}) \\
&= (f_r \sin\theta\cos\phi + f_\theta\cos\theta\cos\phi - f_\phi\sin\phi)\mathbf{i} \\
&\quad + (f_r\sin\theta\sin\phi + f_\theta\cos\theta\sin\phi + f_\phi\cos\phi)\mathbf{j} \\
&\quad + (f_r\cos\theta - f_\theta\sin\theta)\mathbf{k}.
\end{aligned}$$

Again, because $\mathbf{f} = f_1\mathbf{i} + f_2\mathbf{j} + f_3\mathbf{k}$, comparing coefficients yields

$$f_1 = f_r\sin\theta\cos\phi + f_\theta\cos\theta\cos\phi - f_\phi\sin\phi, \tag{5.110a}$$

$$f_2 = f_r\sin\theta\sin\phi + f_\theta\cos\theta\sin\phi + f_\phi\cos\phi, \tag{5.110b}$$

$$f_3 = f_r\cos\theta - f_\theta\sin\theta. \tag{5.110c}$$

In matrix notation, the transformations (5.109) and (5.110) can be respectively expressed as

$$\begin{bmatrix} f_r \\ f_\theta \\ f_\phi \end{bmatrix} = \begin{bmatrix} \sin\theta\cos\phi & \sin\theta\sin\phi & \cos\theta \\ \cos\theta\cos\phi & \cos\theta\sin\phi & -\sin\theta \\ -\sin\phi & \cos\phi & 0 \end{bmatrix} \begin{bmatrix} f_1 \\ f_2 \\ f_3 \end{bmatrix}, \tag{5.111}$$

$$\begin{bmatrix} f_1 \\ f_2 \\ f_3 \end{bmatrix} = \begin{bmatrix} \sin\theta\cos\phi & \cos\theta\cos\phi & -\sin\phi \\ \sin\theta\sin\phi & \cos\theta\sin\phi & \cos\phi \\ \cos\theta & -\sin\theta & 0 \end{bmatrix} \begin{bmatrix} f_r \\ f_\theta \\ f_\phi \end{bmatrix}. \tag{5.112}$$

Again, note that the transformations of the base vectors and the components of a vector have the same matrix.

**PROBLEM 5.27** Transform $\mathbf{f} = x\mathbf{i} + y\mathbf{j} + z\mathbf{k}$ to spherical coordinates.

**Solution:** Since $f_1 = x$, $f_2 = y$, $f_3 = z$, from (5.109) or (5.111),

$$\begin{aligned}
f_r &= x\sin\theta\cos\phi + y\sin\theta\sin\phi + z\cos\theta, \\
f_\theta &= x\cos\theta\cos\phi + y\cos\theta\sin\phi - z\sin\theta, \\
f_\phi &= -x\sin\phi + y\cos\phi.
\end{aligned}$$

Substituting $x = r\sin\theta\cos\phi$, $y = r\sin\theta\sin\phi$, and $z = r\cos\theta$,

$$\begin{aligned}
f_r &= r\sin^2\theta\cos^2\phi + r\sin^2\theta\sin^2\phi + r\cos^2\theta \\
&= r\sin^2\theta(\cos^2\phi + \sin^2\phi) + r\cos^2\theta = r(\sin^2\theta + \cos^2\theta) \\
&= r, \\
f_\theta &= r\sin\theta\cos\theta\cos^2\phi + r\sin\theta\cos\theta\sin^2\phi - r\cos\theta\sin\theta \\
&= r\sin\theta\cos\theta(\cos^2\phi + \sin^2\phi - 1) \\
&= 0, \\
f_\phi &= -r\sin\theta\sin\phi\cos\phi + r\sin\theta\sin\phi\cos\phi \\
&= 0.
\end{aligned}$$

Hence, $\mathbf{f} = f_r\mathbf{e}_r = r\,\mathbf{e}_r$.

**PROBLEM 5.28** Transform $\mathbf{f} = \dfrac{1}{r\sin\theta}\mathbf{e}_\phi$ to rectangular coordinates.

**Solution:** Using (5.101c),

$$\mathbf{f} = \frac{1}{r \sin\theta}\,\mathbf{e}_\phi = \frac{1}{r \sin\theta}(-\sin\phi\,\mathbf{i} + \cos\phi\,\mathbf{j}) = -\frac{\sin\phi}{r\sin\theta}\,\mathbf{i} + \frac{\cos\phi}{r\sin\theta}\,\mathbf{j}.$$

Now from $x = r\sin\theta\cos\phi$, $y = r\sin\theta\sin\phi$, and $z = r\cos\theta$,

$$\sin\phi = \frac{y}{r\sin\theta}, \quad \cos\phi = \frac{x}{r\sin\theta}, \quad x^2 + y^2 = r^2\sin^2\theta.$$

Hence,

$$\mathbf{f} = -\frac{y}{r^2\sin^2\theta}\,\mathbf{i} + \frac{x}{r^2\sin^2\theta}\,\mathbf{j} = -\frac{y}{x^2+y^2}\,\mathbf{i} + \frac{x}{x^2+y^2}\,\mathbf{j}.$$

**PROBLEM 5.29** Find the relationships between $\mathbf{e}_\rho$, $\mathbf{e}_\phi$, $\mathbf{k}$ of the circular cylindrical coordinate system and $\mathbf{e}_r$, $\mathbf{e}_\theta$, $\mathbf{e}_\phi$ of the spherical coordinate system.

**Solution:** Substituting (5.84) into (5.101),

$$\begin{aligned}\mathbf{e}_r &= \sin\theta\cos\phi(\cos\phi\,\mathbf{e}_\rho - \sin\phi\,\mathbf{e}_\phi) + \sin\theta\sin\phi(\sin\phi\,\mathbf{e}_\rho + \cos\phi\,\mathbf{e}_\phi)\\ &\quad + \cos\theta\,\mathbf{k}\\ &= \sin\theta(\cos^2\phi + \sin^2\phi)\mathbf{e}_\rho + (-\sin\theta\cos\phi\sin\phi + \sin\theta\sin\phi\cos\phi)\mathbf{e}_\phi\\ &\quad + \cos\theta\,\mathbf{k}\\ &= \sin\theta\,\mathbf{e}_\rho + \cos\theta\,\mathbf{k}, \qquad (5.113a)\end{aligned}$$

$$\begin{aligned}\mathbf{e}_\theta &= \cos\theta\cos\phi(\cos\phi\,\mathbf{e}_\rho - \sin\phi\,\mathbf{e}_\phi)\\ &\quad + \cos\theta\sin\phi(\sin\phi\,\mathbf{e}_\rho + \cos\phi\,\mathbf{e}_\phi) - \sin\theta\,\mathbf{k}\\ &= \cos\theta(\cos^2\phi + \sin^2\phi)\mathbf{e}_\rho + (-\cos\theta\cos\phi\sin\phi + \cos\theta\sin\phi\cos\phi)\mathbf{e}_\phi\\ &\quad - \sin\theta\,\mathbf{k}\\ &= \cos\theta\,\mathbf{e}_\rho - \sin\theta\,\mathbf{k}, \qquad (5.113b)\end{aligned}$$

$$\begin{aligned}\mathbf{e}_\phi &= -\sin\phi(\cos\phi\,\mathbf{e}_\rho - \sin\phi\,\mathbf{e}_\phi) + \cos\phi(\sin\phi\,\mathbf{e}_\rho + \cos\phi\,\mathbf{e}_\phi)\\ &= (-\sin\phi\cos\phi + \cos\phi\sin\phi)\mathbf{e}_\rho + (\sin^2\phi + \cos^2\phi)\mathbf{e}_\phi\\ &= \mathbf{e}_\phi. \qquad (5.113c)\end{aligned}$$

Similarly, by substituting (5.104) into (5.81),

$$\mathbf{e}_\rho = \sin\theta\,\mathbf{e}_r + \cos\theta\,\mathbf{e}_\theta, \qquad (5.114a)$$

$$\mathbf{e}_\phi = \mathbf{e}_\phi, \qquad (5.114b)$$

$$\mathbf{k} = \cos\theta\,\mathbf{e}_r - \sin\theta\,\mathbf{e}_\theta. \qquad (5.114c)$$

Using matrix notation, (5.113) and (5.114) can be respectively expressed as

$$\begin{bmatrix}\mathbf{e}_r\\ \mathbf{e}_\theta\\ \mathbf{e}_\phi\end{bmatrix} = \begin{bmatrix}\sin\theta & 0 & \cos\theta\\ \cos\theta & 0 & -\sin\theta\\ 0 & 1 & 0\end{bmatrix}\begin{bmatrix}\mathbf{e}_\rho\\ \mathbf{e}_\phi\\ \mathbf{k}\end{bmatrix}, \qquad (5.115)$$

$$\begin{bmatrix}\mathbf{e}_\rho\\ \mathbf{e}_\phi\\ \mathbf{k}\end{bmatrix} = \begin{bmatrix}\sin\theta & \cos\theta & 0\\ 0 & 0 & 1\\ \cos\theta & -\sin\theta & 0\end{bmatrix}\begin{bmatrix}\mathbf{e}_r\\ \mathbf{e}_\theta\\ \mathbf{e}_\phi\end{bmatrix}. \qquad (5.116)$$

Equations (5.115–6) can also easily be obtained by simple matrix product operations using (5.105), (5.86) and (5.85), (5.106), respectively.

## 5.5 Supplementary Problems

**PROBLEM 5.30** Show that the Jacobian

$$J\left(\frac{x, y, z}{u, v, w}\right) = h_u h_v h_w,$$

and thus, that the volume element $dV$ given by

$$dV = J\left(\frac{x, y, z}{u, v, w}\right) dudvdw$$

is $h_u h_v h_w \, dudvdw$, in agreement with (5.30).

**PROBLEM 5.31** Using curvilinear coordinates and the vector identity

$$\nabla \cdot \nabla \mathbf{f} = \nabla^2 \mathbf{f} = \nabla(\nabla \cdot \mathbf{f}) - \nabla \times (\nabla \times \mathbf{f}), \qquad [3.164]$$

obtain the curvilinear form of the vector Laplacian $\nabla^2 \mathbf{f}$.

**PROBLEM 5.32** Show that the *volume-integral* definition of the operator $\nabla$ given by

$$\nabla\{\ \} = \lim_{\Delta V \to 0} \frac{1}{\Delta V} \oiint_S \mathbf{n}\{\ \}\, dS \qquad [4.57]$$

leads to the expression

$$\nabla\{\ \} = \frac{1}{h_u h_v h_w}\left[\frac{\partial}{\partial u}(h_v h_w \mathbf{e}_u\{\ \}) + \frac{\partial}{\partial v}(h_w h_u \mathbf{e}_v\{\ \}) + \frac{\partial}{\partial w}(h_u h_v \mathbf{e}_w\{\ \})\right].$$

**PROBLEM 5.33** Using the form of the $\nabla$ operator given in Prob. 5.32, find $\nabla\psi$, $\nabla \cdot \mathbf{f}$, and $\nabla \times \mathbf{f}$; also show that they reduce to (5.44), (5.45), and (5.47), respectively.

**PROBLEM 5.34** In circular cylindrical coordinates $(\rho, \phi, z)$, if vector field $\mathbf{f}$ is

$$\mathbf{f}(\rho, \phi) = f_\rho(\rho, \phi)\, \mathbf{e}_\rho + f_\phi(\rho, \phi)\, \mathbf{e}_\phi,$$

show that $\nabla \times \mathbf{f}$ has only a $z$-component.

**PROBLEM 5.35** Transform $\mathbf{f} = \dfrac{x}{y}\,\mathbf{i}$ to circular cylindrical coordinates.

*Answer*: $\cos\phi \cot\phi\, \mathbf{e}_\rho - \cos\phi\, \mathbf{e}_\phi$.

**PROBLEM 5.36** Transform $\mathbf{f} = \rho\, \mathbf{e}_\rho + \rho\, \mathbf{e}_\phi$ to rectangular coordinates.
*Answer*: $(x - y)\,\mathbf{i} + (x + y)\,\mathbf{j}$.

**PROBLEM 5.37** Show that the following three forms, in spherical coordinates, of $\nabla^2\psi(r)$ are equivalent:

(a) $$\frac{1}{r^2}\frac{d}{dr}\left[r^2 \frac{d\psi(r)}{dr}\right],$$

(b) $$\frac{1}{r}\frac{d^2}{dr^2}[r\psi(r)],$$

(c) $$\frac{d^2\psi(r)}{dr^2} + \frac{2}{r}\frac{d\psi(r)}{dr}.$$

**PROBLEM 5.38** Transform $\mathbf{f} = \frac{1}{r}\mathbf{e}_r$ to rectangular coordinates.

*Answer:* $\frac{x}{x^2+y^2+z^2}\mathbf{i} + \frac{y}{x^2+y^2+z^2}\mathbf{j} + \frac{z}{x^2+y^2+z^2}\mathbf{k}.$

**PROBLEM 5.39** For the *elliptic cylindrical coordinates* $(u, v, z)$, the transformation between the coordinates $(x, y, z)$ and $(u, v, z)$ is given by $x = a\cosh u \cos v$, $y = a \sinh u \sin v$, $z = z$, where $a$ is a constant.

(a) Show that the families of coordinate surfaces are:

(1) elliptic cylinders, $u = \text{const}$, $0 \le u < \infty$;

(2) hyperbolic cylinders, $v = \text{const}$, $0 \le v < 2\pi$;

(3) planes parallel to the $xy$-plane, $z = \text{const}$, $-\infty < z < \infty$.

(b) Is this system orthogonal?

(c) Find the scale factors.

*Answer:* (b) Yes. (c) $h_u = a(\sinh^2 u + \sin^2 v)^{\frac{1}{2}}$, $h_v = a(\sinh^2 u + \sin^2 v)^{\frac{1}{2}}$, $h_z = 1$.

**PROBLEM 5.40** For the *parabolic cylindrical coordinates* $(\xi, \eta, z)$, the transformation between the coordinates $(x, y, z)$ and $(\xi, \eta, z)$ is given by $x = \xi\eta$, $y = \frac{1}{2}(\eta^2 - \xi^2)$, $z = z$.

(a) Show that the families of coordinate surfaces are:

(1) parabolic cylinders, $\xi = \text{const}$, $-\infty < \xi < \infty$;

(2) parabolic cylinders, $\eta = \text{const}$, $0 \le \eta < \infty$;

(3) plane parallel to the $xy$-plane, $z = \text{const}$, $-\infty < z < \infty$.

(b) Find the scale factors.

*Answer:* (b) $h_\xi = (\xi^2 + \eta^2)^{\frac{1}{2}}$, $h_\eta = (\xi^2 + \eta^2)^{\frac{1}{2}}$, $h_z = 1$.

**PROBLEM 5.41** For the *prolate spheroidal coordinates* $(u, v, \phi)$, the transformation between the coordinates $(x, y, z)$ and $(u, v, \phi)$ is $x = a \sinh u \sin v \cos \phi$, $y = a \sinh u \sin v \sin \phi$, $z = a \cosh u \cos v$, where $a$ is a constant.

(a) Show that the families of coordinate surfaces are:

(1) prolate spheroids, $u = \text{const}$, $0 \le u < \infty$;

(2) hyperboloids or two sheets, $v = \text{const}$, $0 \le v \le \pi$;

(3) half-plane through the $z$-axis, $\phi = \text{const}$, $0 \le \phi < 2\pi$.

(b) Find the scale factors.

*Answer:* (b) $h_u = a(\sinh^2 u + \sin^2 v)^{\frac{1}{2}} = a(\cosh^2 u - \cos^2 v)^{\frac{1}{2}}$,

$h_v = a(\sinh^2 u + \sin^2 v)^{\frac{1}{2}}$,

$h_\phi = a \sinh u \sin v$.

**PROBLEM 5.42** For the *oblate spheroidal coordinates* $(u, v, \phi)$, the transformation between the coordinates $(x, y, z)$ and $(u, v, \phi)$ is $x = a\cosh u \cos v \cos \phi$, $y = a \cosh u \cos v \sin \phi$, $z = a \sinh u \sin v$, where $a$ is a constant.

(a) Show that the families of coordinate surfaces are:

(1) oblate spheroids, $u = \text{const}$, $0 \le u < \infty$;

(2) hyperboloids of one sheet, $v = \text{const}$, $-\frac{\pi}{2} \le v \le \frac{\pi}{2}$;

(3) half-planes through the $z$-axis, $\phi = \text{const}$, $0 \le \phi < 2\pi$.

(b) Find the scale factors.

*Answer:* (b) $h_u = a(\sinh^2 u + \sin^2 v)^{\frac{1}{2}} = a(\cosh^2 u - \cos^2 v)^{\frac{1}{2}}$,

$h_v = a(\sinh^2 u + \sin^2 v)^{\frac{1}{2}}$,

$h_\phi = a \cosh u \cos v$.

**PROBLEM 5.43** For *parabolic coordinates* $(\xi, \eta, \phi)$, the transformation equations are given by $x = \xi\eta \cos \phi$, $y = \xi\eta \sin \phi$, $z = \frac{1}{2}(\eta^2 - \xi^2)$.

(a) Show that the families of coordinate surfaces are:

(1) paraboloids about the positive $z$-axis, $\xi = \text{const}$, $0 \leq \xi < \infty$;

(2) paraboloids about the negative $z$-axis, $\eta = \text{const}$, $0 \leq \eta < \infty$;

(3) half-planes through the $z$-axis, $\phi = \text{const}$, $0 \leq \phi < 2\pi$.

(b) Find the scale factors.

(c) Show that $\mathbf{e}_\xi \times \mathbf{e}_\eta = -\mathbf{e}_\phi$.

*Answer*: (b) $h_\xi = (\xi^2 + \eta^2)^{1/2}$, $h_\eta = (\xi^2 + \eta^2)^{1/2}$, $h_\phi = \xi\eta$.

**PROBLEM 5.44** Verify that in cylindrical coordinates,

$$\nabla \ln \rho = \nabla \times (\mathbf{k}\phi).$$

**PROBLEM 5.45** Verify the following relations in spherical coordinates:

(a) $\nabla \dfrac{1}{r} = \nabla \times (\cos\theta\, \nabla\phi)$; (b) $\nabla\phi = \nabla \times (r\nabla\theta/\sin\theta)$.

**PROBLEM 5.46** Using the matrix multiplication method, derive (5.115-6) from (5.85-6) and (5.105-6).

**PROBLEM 5.47** Express $\partial/\partial x$, $\partial/\partial y$, $\partial/\partial z$ in spherical coordinates.

*Answer:*

$$\frac{\partial}{\partial x} = \sin\theta\cos\phi\frac{\partial}{\partial r} + \cos\theta\cos\phi\frac{1}{r}\frac{\partial}{\partial\theta} - \frac{\sin\phi}{r\sin\theta}\frac{\partial}{\partial\phi},$$

$$\frac{\partial}{\partial y} = \sin\theta\sin\phi\frac{\partial}{\partial r} + \cos\theta\sin\phi\frac{1}{r}\frac{\partial}{\partial\theta} + \frac{\cos\phi}{r\sin\theta}\frac{\partial}{\partial\phi},$$

$$\frac{\partial}{\partial z} = \cos\theta\frac{\partial}{\partial r} - \sin\theta\frac{1}{r}\frac{\partial}{\partial\theta}.$$

**PROBLEM 5.48** In Sec. 3.5,

$$x = x(u, v), \quad y = y(u, v), \quad z = z(u, v) \qquad [3.78]$$

is interpreted as parametric equations of a surface $S$ in space. They can be considered as a special case of (5.1), in which $w$ is a constant; the surface $S$ then corresponds to a surface $w(x, y, z) = \text{const}$. The curvilinear coordinates on $S$ are $u$ and $v$. Let $\mathbf{r} = x\mathbf{i} + y\mathbf{j} + z\mathbf{k}$.

(a) Show that the curves $u = \text{const}$, $v = \text{const}$ intersect at right angles, so that the coordinates are orthogonal, if and only if

$$\frac{\partial x}{\partial u}\frac{\partial x}{\partial v} + \frac{\partial y}{\partial u}\frac{\partial y}{\partial v} + \frac{\partial z}{\partial u}\frac{\partial z}{\partial v} = 0.$$

(b) Show that the element of an arc on a curve $u = u(t)$, $v = v(t)$ on $S$ is

$$ds^2 = E\,du^2 + 2F\,du dv + G\,dv^2,$$

$$E = |\partial\mathbf{r}/\partial u|^2, \quad F = (\partial\mathbf{r}/\partial u)\cdot(\partial\mathbf{r}/\partial v), \quad G = |\partial\mathbf{r}/\partial v|^2.$$

(c) Show that the coordinates are othogonal when

$$ds^2 = E\,du^2 + G\,dv^2.$$

(d) Show that the area of the surface $S$ is

$$S = \iint_{R_{uv}} \sqrt{EG - F^2}\, du dv.$$

# 6 CHAPTER

# APPLICATIONS TO GEOMETRY

## 6.1 Applications to Plane and Space Geometry

In this section we prove some well-known theorems of plane and space geometry by vector methods.

**PROBLEM 6.1** Prove that the line segment that connects the midpoints of two sides of a triangle is parallel to and one-half the length of the third side.

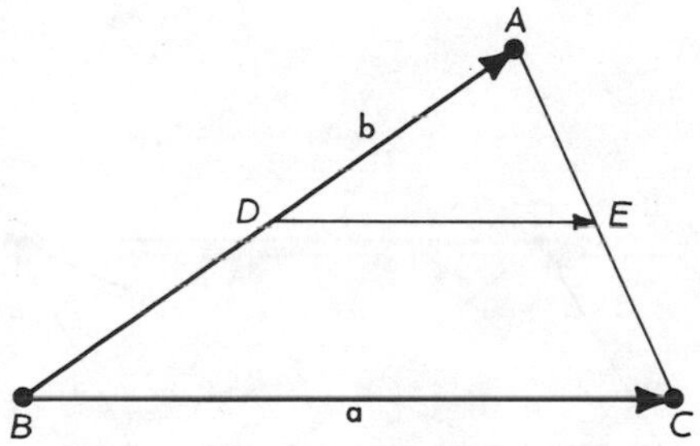


Fig. 6.1 The triangle of Prob. 6.1.

**Solution:** In the triangle $ABC$ shown in Fig. 6.1, $D$ and $E$ are the midpoints of the sides $BA$ and $CA$. If $\overrightarrow{BC} = \mathbf{a}$ and $\overrightarrow{BA} = \mathbf{b}$, then from the definition of addition of vectors and that of the negative of a vector,

$$\overrightarrow{CA} = \overrightarrow{CB} + \overrightarrow{BA} = -\mathbf{a} + \mathbf{b} = \mathbf{b} - \mathbf{a}.$$

Now, $\overrightarrow{BD} = \frac{1}{2}\mathbf{b}$ and $\overrightarrow{CE} = \frac{1}{2}\overrightarrow{CA} = \frac{1}{2}(\mathbf{b} - \mathbf{a})$. Hence, the line segment that joins $D$ and $E$ is

$$\begin{aligned}\overrightarrow{DE} &= \overrightarrow{BE} - \overrightarrow{BD}\\ &= \overrightarrow{BC} + \overrightarrow{CE} - \overrightarrow{BD}\\ &= \mathbf{a} + \frac{1}{2}(\mathbf{b} - \mathbf{a}) - \frac{1}{2}\mathbf{b}\\ &- \frac{1}{2}\mathbf{a}\\ &= \frac{1}{2}\overrightarrow{BC},\end{aligned}$$

which shows that $\overrightarrow{DE}$ is parallel to and has one-half the magnitude of $\overrightarrow{BC}$.

**PROBLEM 6.2** Prove that the medians of a triangle meet at a point that divides each median into the ratio 2 : 1.

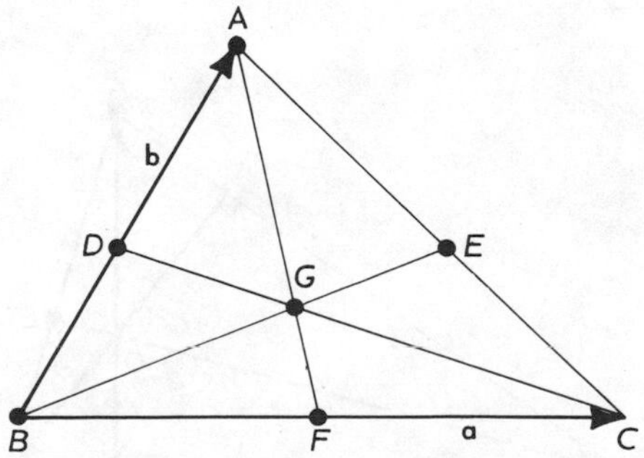


Fig. 6.2 The triangle of Prob. 6.2.

**Solution:** In the triangle $ABC$ shown in Fig. 6.2, $\overrightarrow{BC} = \mathbf{a}$ and $\overrightarrow{BA} = \mathbf{b}$. Then from the definitions of vector addition and that of the negative of a vector, $CA = \mathbf{b} - \mathbf{a}$. Now let the medians $AF$ and $BE$ intersect at $G$. Then,

$$\overrightarrow{BE} = \overrightarrow{BC} + \overrightarrow{CE} = \mathbf{a} + \frac{1}{2}(\mathbf{b} - \mathbf{a}) = \frac{1}{2}(\mathbf{a} + \mathbf{b}).$$

Because $G$ lies on the median $BE$, there exists a scalar $m$ such that

$$\overrightarrow{BG} = m\overrightarrow{BE} = \frac{m}{2}(\mathbf{a} + \mathbf{b}).$$

Because

$$\overrightarrow{FA} = \overrightarrow{FB} + \overrightarrow{BA} = -\frac{1}{2}\,\mathbf{a} + \mathbf{b} = \mathbf{b} - \frac{1}{2}\,\mathbf{a}$$

and $G$ lies on the median $FA$, there exists a scalar $n$ such that

$$\overrightarrow{FG} = n\overrightarrow{FA} = n\left(\mathbf{b} - \frac{1}{2}\,\mathbf{a}\right).$$

But $\overrightarrow{BG} = \overrightarrow{BF} + \overrightarrow{FG}$; i.e.,

$$\frac{m}{2}\,(\mathbf{a} + \mathbf{b}) = \frac{1}{2}\,\mathbf{a} + n\left(\mathbf{b} - \frac{1}{2}\,\mathbf{a}\right),$$

or, on simplification,

$$\frac{1}{2}\,(m + n - 1)\,\mathbf{a} + \left(\frac{m}{2} - n\right)\mathbf{b} = \mathbf{0}.$$

Since $\mathbf{a}$ and $\mathbf{b}$ are linearly independent,

$$\frac{1}{2}\,(m + n - 1) = 0, \quad \frac{m}{2} - n = 0.$$

Solving for $m$ and $n$, we obtain $m = 2/3$ and $n = 1/3$. Thus, $\overrightarrow{BG} = \frac{2}{3}\overrightarrow{BE}$ and $\overrightarrow{FG} = \frac{1}{3}\overrightarrow{FA}$, from which it follows that $G$ is a point that divides $AF$ and $BE$ into the ratio 2:1.

Similarly, it can be shown that the point of intersection $G$ of the medians $AF$ and $CD$ divides them into the ratio 2:1.

**PROBLEM 6.3** Prove that the diagonals of a parallelogram bisect each other.

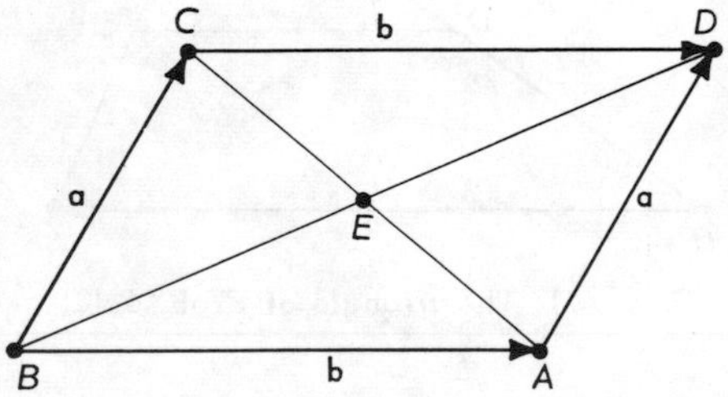

Fig. 6.3 The parallelogram of Prob. 6.3.

**Solution:** In the parallelogram $ABCD$ shown in Fig. 6.3, $\overrightarrow{BC} = \mathbf{a}$ and $\overrightarrow{BA} = \mathbf{b}$. Then $\overrightarrow{AD} = \overrightarrow{BC} = \mathbf{a}$, $\overrightarrow{CD} = \overrightarrow{BA} = \mathbf{b}$. Hence,

$$\overrightarrow{BD} = \overrightarrow{BC} + \overrightarrow{CD} = \mathbf{a} + \mathbf{b}, \qquad \overrightarrow{CA} = \overrightarrow{CB} + \overrightarrow{BA} = -\mathbf{a} + \mathbf{b} = \mathbf{b} - \mathbf{a}.$$

If $E$ is the midpoint of $BD$, then $\overrightarrow{BE} = \frac{1}{2}\,\overrightarrow{BD} = \frac{1}{2}\,(\mathbf{a} + \mathbf{b})$. Since $\overrightarrow{CA} = \mathbf{b} - \mathbf{a}$,

$$\overrightarrow{CE} = \overrightarrow{CB} + \overrightarrow{BE} = -\mathbf{a} + \frac{1}{2}\,(\mathbf{a} + \mathbf{b}) = \frac{1}{2}\,(\mathbf{b} - \mathbf{a}) = \frac{1}{2}\,\overrightarrow{CA}.$$

Hence, $E$ is the midpoint of both $BD$ and $CA$.

**PROBLEM 6.4** Prove that the altitudes of a triangle are concurrent.

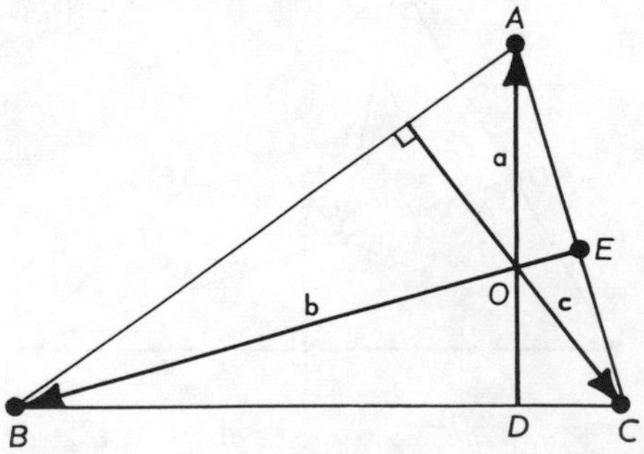

Fig. 6.4 The triangle of Prob. 6.4.

**Solution:** Let the altitudes $AD$, $BE$ of the triangle $ABC$, shown in Fig. 6.4, meet at $O$. If $\overrightarrow{OA} = \mathbf{a}$, $\overrightarrow{OB} = \mathbf{b}$, and $\overrightarrow{OC} = \mathbf{c}$, then

$$\overrightarrow{BC} = \mathbf{c} - \mathbf{b}, \quad \overrightarrow{AC} = \mathbf{c} - \mathbf{a}, \quad \overrightarrow{BA} = \mathbf{a} - \mathbf{b}.$$

Since $\overrightarrow{OA} \perp \overrightarrow{BC}$, $\overrightarrow{OA} \cdot \overrightarrow{BC} = 0$; i.e.,

$$\mathbf{a}\cdot(\mathbf{c} - \mathbf{b}) = 0, \quad \text{or} \quad \mathbf{a}\cdot\mathbf{c} = \mathbf{a}\cdot\mathbf{b}.$$

Similarly, because $\overrightarrow{OB} \perp \overrightarrow{AC}$, $\overrightarrow{OB} \cdot \overrightarrow{AC} = 0$; i.e.,

$$\mathbf{b}\cdot(\mathbf{c} - \mathbf{a}) = 0 \quad \text{or} \quad \mathbf{b}\cdot\mathbf{c} = \mathbf{b}\cdot\mathbf{a}.$$

Since the dot product is commutative, $\mathbf{b}\cdot\mathbf{a} = \mathbf{a}\cdot\mathbf{b}$. Hence,

$$\mathbf{a}\cdot\mathbf{c} = \mathbf{b}\cdot\mathbf{c} \quad \text{or} \quad (\mathbf{a} - \mathbf{b})\cdot\mathbf{c} = 0,$$

which implies that $\mathbf{OC} \perp \mathbf{BA}$. Hence the altitude from $C$ to $AB$ passes through $O$. Thus the altitudes are concurrent.

**PROBLEM 6.5** In the tetrahedron $OABC$, shown in Fig. 6.5, the edge $OA$ is perpendicular to the edge $BC$, and the edge $OB$ is perpendicular to $CA$. Show that the edge $OC$ is perpendicular to the edge $AB$.

**Solution:** In the tetrahedron $OABC$, if $\overrightarrow{OA} = \mathbf{a}$, $\overrightarrow{OB} = \mathbf{b}$, and $\overrightarrow{OC} = \mathbf{c}$, then $\overrightarrow{AB} = \mathbf{b} - \mathbf{a}$, $\overrightarrow{BC} = \mathbf{c} - \mathbf{b}$, and $\overrightarrow{CA} = \mathbf{a} - \mathbf{c}$. Since $\overrightarrow{OA} \perp \overrightarrow{BC}$,

$$\mathbf{a} \cdot (\mathbf{c} - \mathbf{b}) = 0, \quad \text{or} \quad \mathbf{a} \cdot \mathbf{c} = \mathbf{a} \cdot \mathbf{b}.$$

Similarly, $\overrightarrow{OB} \perp \overrightarrow{CA}$, implies

$$\mathbf{b} \cdot (\mathbf{a} - \mathbf{c}) = 0, \quad \text{or} \quad \mathbf{b} \cdot \mathbf{a} = \mathbf{b} \cdot \mathbf{c}.$$

Because of the commutativity of the scalar product, $\mathbf{a} \cdot \mathbf{b} = \mathbf{b} \cdot \mathbf{a}$, and hence,

$$\mathbf{a} \cdot \mathbf{c} = \mathbf{b} \cdot \mathbf{c} \quad \text{or} \quad \mathbf{c} \cdot (\mathbf{b} - \mathbf{a}) = 0,$$

which implies $\overrightarrow{OC} \perp \overrightarrow{AB}$.

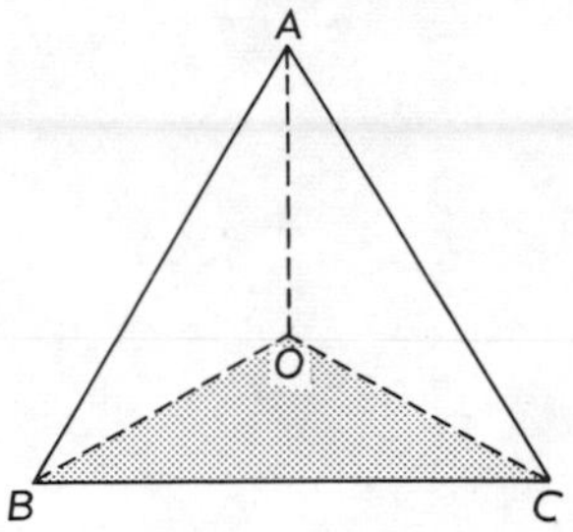

Fig. 6.5 The tetrahedron of Prob. 6.5.

**PROBLEM 6.6** Prove that an angle inscribed in a semicircle is a right angle.

**Solution:** Let $\measuredangle\, ACB$ be any angle inscribed in a semicircle with center at $O$ and radius $OA = OB = OC = r$. (See Fig. 6.6.) If $\overrightarrow{OA} = \mathbf{a}$ and $\overrightarrow{OC} = \mathbf{c}$, then

$$\overrightarrow{OB} = -\mathbf{a}, \quad \overrightarrow{BC} = \mathbf{a} + \mathbf{c}, \quad \overrightarrow{AC} = -\mathbf{a} + \mathbf{c} = \mathbf{c} - \mathbf{a}.$$

Since $a^2 = c^2 = r^2$,

$$\overrightarrow{AC} \cdot \overrightarrow{BC} = (\mathbf{c} - \mathbf{a}) \cdot (\mathbf{a} + \mathbf{c}) = \mathbf{c} \cdot \mathbf{a} - \mathbf{a} \cdot \mathbf{a} = c^2 - a^2 = 0.$$

Hence, **AC** and **BC** are perpendicular; i.e., $\measuredangle\, BCA$ is a right angle.

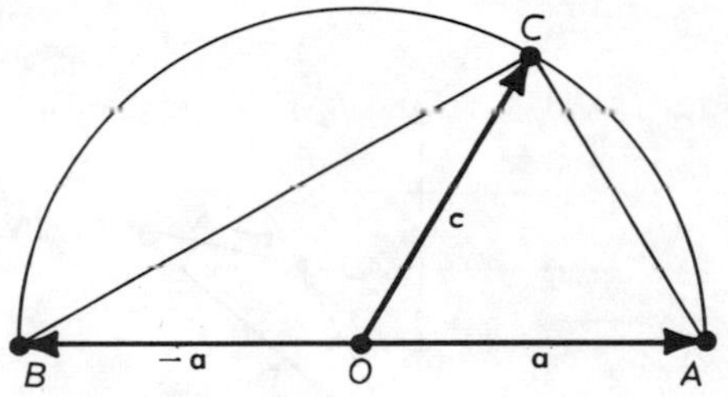

Fig. 6.6 Solution to Prob. 6.6.

*Apollonius' Theorem* states that in a triangle $ABC$ if $AD$ is the median of the side $BC$, then

$$\overline{AB}^2 + \overline{AC}^2 = 2\,\overline{AD}^2 + \frac{1}{2}\,\overline{BC}^2.$$

**PROBLEM 6.7** Prove Apollonius' theorem.

**Solution:** In the triangle $ABC$ shown in Fig. 6.7, let $\overrightarrow{AB} = \mathbf{b}$ and $\overrightarrow{AC} = \mathbf{c}$. Then $\overrightarrow{AD} = \frac{1}{2}(\mathbf{b} + \mathbf{c})$ and $\overrightarrow{BC} = \mathbf{c} - \mathbf{b}$. Hence,

$$\overline{AD}^2 = \overrightarrow{AD} \cdot \overrightarrow{AD} = \frac{1}{4}(\mathbf{b} + \mathbf{c}) \cdot (\mathbf{b} + \mathbf{c}) = \frac{1}{4}(b^2 + c^2 + 2\,\mathbf{b} \cdot \mathbf{c}),$$

$$\overline{BC}^2 = \overrightarrow{BC} \cdot \overrightarrow{BC} = (\mathbf{c} - \mathbf{b}) \cdot (\mathbf{c} - \mathbf{b}) = c^2 + b^2 - 2\,\mathbf{b} \cdot \mathbf{c}.$$

Thus,

$$2\overline{AD}^2 + \frac{1}{2}\,\overline{BC}^2 = \frac{1}{2}(b^2 + c^2 + 2\,\mathbf{b} \cdot \mathbf{c}) + \frac{1}{2}(c^2 + b^2 - 2\,\mathbf{b} \cdot \mathbf{c})$$

$$= b^2 + c^2$$

$$= \overline{AB}^2 + \overline{AC}^2.$$

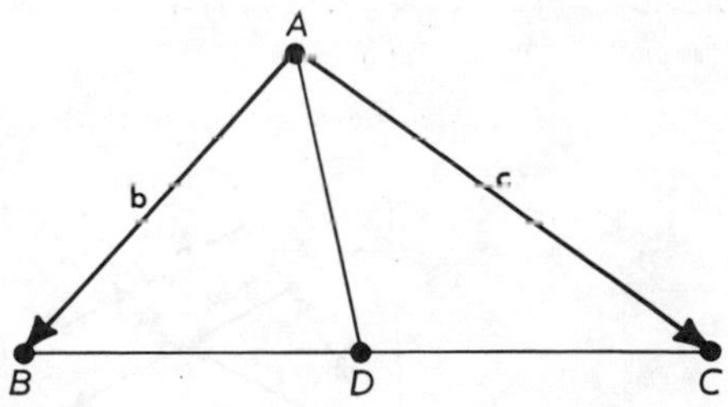

Fig. 6.7 Proof of Apollonius' theorem.

**PROBLEM 6.8** Prove that the line that joins the vertex of an isosceles triangle to the midpoint of its base is perpendicular to the base.

**Solution:** In the isosceles triangle $ABC$ shown in Fig. 6.8, let $\overrightarrow{OC} = \mathbf{a}$, $\overrightarrow{OA} = \mathbf{c}$, and $O$ is the midpoint of the base $BC$. Then,

$$\overrightarrow{OB} = -\mathbf{a}, \quad \overrightarrow{AC} = \overrightarrow{AO} + \overrightarrow{OC} = \mathbf{a} - \mathbf{c}, \quad \overrightarrow{BA} = \overrightarrow{BO} + \overrightarrow{OA} = \mathbf{a} + \mathbf{c}.$$

Now,

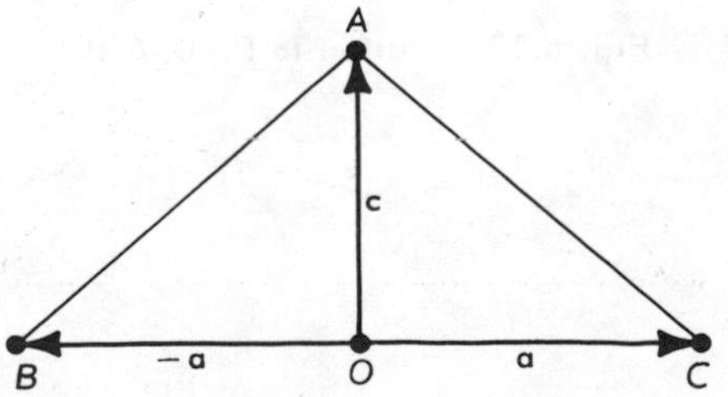

Fig. 6.8 Solution to Prob. 6.8.

$$\overline{AC}^2 = \overrightarrow{AC} \cdot \overrightarrow{AC} = (\mathbf{a} - \mathbf{c}) \cdot (\mathbf{a} - \mathbf{c}) = a^2 + c^2 - 2\,\mathbf{a} \cdot \mathbf{c},$$
$$\overline{AB}^2 = \overrightarrow{AB} \cdot \overrightarrow{AB} = (\mathbf{a} + \mathbf{c}) \cdot (\mathbf{a} + \mathbf{c}) = a^2 + c^2 + 2\,\mathbf{a} \cdot \mathbf{c}.$$

Since $\overline{AC} = \overline{AB}$, we have $\overline{AC}^2 = \overline{AB}^2$; i.e.,

$$a^2 + c^2 - 2\,\mathbf{a} \cdot \mathbf{c} = a^2 + c^2 + 2\,\mathbf{a} \cdot \mathbf{c}.$$

Thus, on simplification,

$$4\,\mathbf{a} \cdot \mathbf{c} = 0 \quad \text{or} \quad \mathbf{a} \cdot \mathbf{c} = 0.$$

Hence, $\mathbf{a} \perp \mathbf{c}$; i.e., $OA$ is perpendicular to $BC$.

## 6.2 Applications to Analytic Geometry

In this section, the equation of a plane and some distance formulas are derived by vector methods.

**PROBLEM 6.9** Show that the equation of the line that is parallel to the vector $\mathbf{B}$ and that passes through a point whose position vector is $\mathbf{A}$ is

$$(\mathbf{r} - \mathbf{A}) \times \mathbf{B} = \mathbf{0}, \tag{6.1}$$

where $\mathbf{r}$ is the position vector of any point on the line.

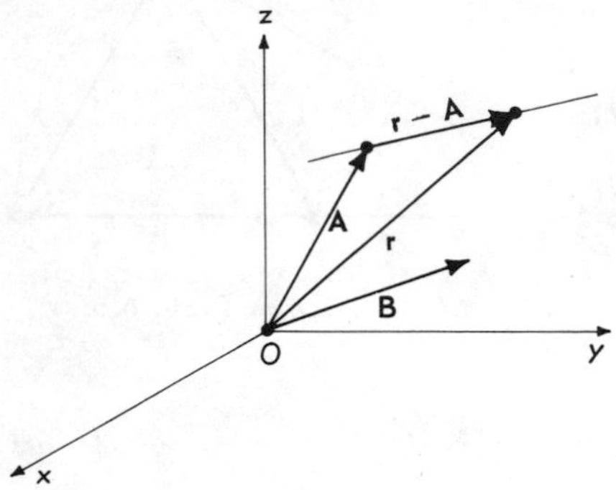


Fig. 6.9 Solution to Prob. 6.9.

**Solution:** From Prob. 3.14 and Fig. 6.9, the equation of a line that is parallel to a nonzero vector $\mathbf{B}$ and that passes through a point whose position vector is $\mathbf{A}$ is

$$\mathbf{r} - \mathbf{A} = t\mathbf{B},$$

for some parameter $t$.

Since the cross product of a vector with a scalar multiple of itself is the zero vector, it follows from (3.43) that

$$(\mathbf{r} - \mathbf{A}) \times \mathbf{B} = t\mathbf{B} \times \mathbf{B} = \mathbf{0}.$$

Conversely, if $(\mathbf{r} - \mathbf{A}) \times \mathbf{B} = \mathbf{0}$, then $\mathbf{r} - \mathbf{A}$ is parallel to $\mathbf{B}$, so that $\mathbf{r} - \mathbf{A} = t\mathbf{B}$, for some parameter $t$.

**PROBLEM 6.10** Show that the equation of a line that passes through two points whose position vectors are $\mathbf{A}$ and $\mathbf{B}$ is

$$(\mathbf{r} - \mathbf{A}) \times (\mathbf{B} - \mathbf{A}) = \mathbf{0}, \tag{6.2}$$

where $\mathbf{r}$ is the position vector of any point on this line.

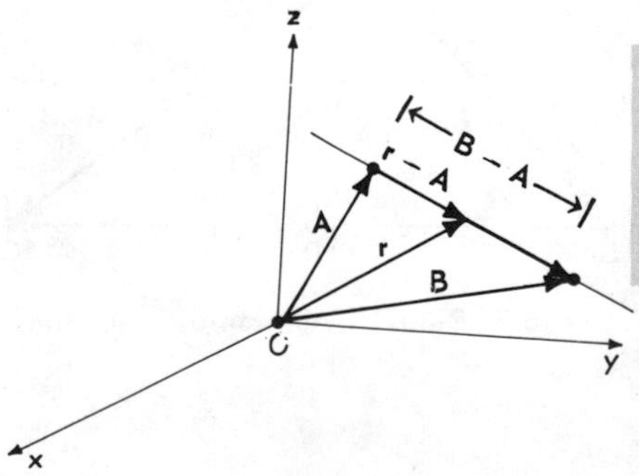


Fig. 6.10 Solution to Prob. 6.10.

**Solution:** From Fig. 6.10, it is required to find the equation of the line that passes through the point, which has the position vector $\mathbf{A}$, and that is parallel to $\mathbf{B} - \mathbf{A}$. From Prob. 6.9, the required equation is (6.2).

**PROBLEM 6.11** Show that if the two straight lines represented by $(\mathbf{r} - \mathbf{A}) \times \mathbf{B} = \mathbf{0}$ and $(\mathbf{r} - \mathbf{C}) \times \mathbf{D} = \mathbf{0}$ intersect, then $(\mathbf{A} - \mathbf{C}) \cdot \mathbf{B} \times \mathbf{D} = 0$.

**Solution:** The general equations of the two straight lines (6.1–2) can be rewritten as $\mathbf{r} = \mathbf{A} + t\mathbf{B}$ and $\mathbf{r} = \mathbf{C} + s\mathbf{D}$. Now if the straight lines intersect, there exist scalars $s$ and $t$ such that

$$\mathbf{A} + t\mathbf{B} = \mathbf{C} + s\mathbf{D}.$$

Now take the dot product of both sides with $\mathbf{B} \times \mathbf{D}$ to obtain

$$(\mathbf{A} + t\mathbf{B}) \cdot (\mathbf{B} \times \mathbf{D}) = (\mathbf{C} + s\mathbf{D}) \cdot (\mathbf{B} \times \mathbf{D}).$$

Since, by (1.71), $\mathbf{B}\cdot\mathbf{B}\times\mathbf{D}=\mathbf{D}\cdot\mathbf{B}\times\mathbf{D}=0$,

$$\mathbf{A}\cdot\mathbf{B}\times\mathbf{D}=\mathbf{C}\cdot\mathbf{B}\times\mathbf{D}.$$

Hence,

$$(\mathbf{A}-\mathbf{C})\cdot\mathbf{B}\times\mathbf{D}=0. \tag{6.3}$$

**PROBLEM 6.12** In Fig. 6.11 the arbitrary points $P$ and $Q$ are specified by the position vectors $\mathbf{r}_0$ and $\mathbf{A}$, relative to the point $O$. Show that the distance $d$ from $P$ to a line that is parallel to $B$ and passes through $Q$ is

$$d=\frac{|(\mathbf{r}_0-\mathbf{A})\times\mathbf{B}|}{B}, \tag{6.4}$$

where $B=|\mathbf{B}|$.

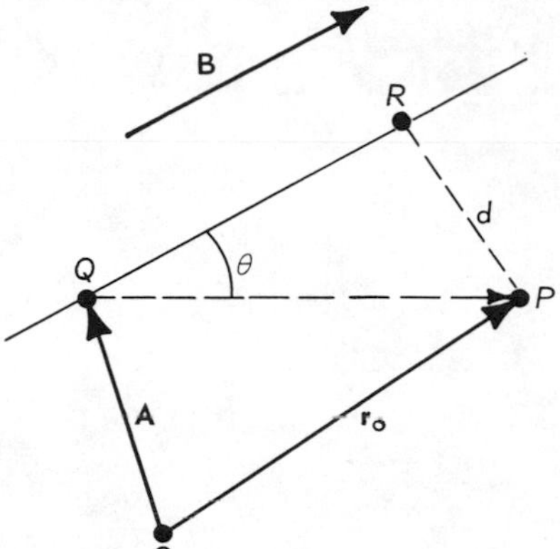


Fig. 6.11 Solution to Prob. 6.12.

**Solution:** In Fig. 6.11, if $\overrightarrow{OQ}=\mathbf{A}$, then $\overrightarrow{QP}=\mathbf{r}_0-\mathbf{A}$. Now if $\theta$ is the angle between $\overrightarrow{QP}$ and $\overrightarrow{QR}$ and hence $\mathbf{B}$,

$$d=|\overrightarrow{PR}|=|\overrightarrow{QP}|\sin\theta.$$

But from the definition of the magnitude of the cross product of two vectors (1.59),

$$|(\mathbf{r}_0-\mathbf{A})\times\mathbf{B}|=|\mathbf{B}|\,|\overrightarrow{QP}|\sin\theta=B\,|\overrightarrow{QP}|\sin\theta=Bd.$$

Hence,

$$d=\frac{|(\mathbf{r}_0-\mathbf{A})\times\mathbf{B}|}{B}.$$

**PROBLEM 6.13** Find the shortest distance $d$ between the two straight lines that pass through the two distinct points $P$ and $Q$, whose position vectors are $\mathbf{A}$ and $\mathbf{C}$ with the directions $\mathbf{B}$ and $\mathbf{D}$, respectively.

**Solution:** In Fig. 6.12, assume that $\mathbf{B}$ and $\mathbf{D}$ are not collinear, i.e., $\mathbf{B}\times\mathbf{D}\neq\mathbf{0}$, and that there exist points $M$ and $N$ on the two lines such that $\overline{MN}$ is perpendicular to both lines. Then the shortest distance $d$ between these two straight lines is $\overline{MN}$. Since $\overline{MN}$ is perpendicular to both vectors $\mathbf{B}$ and $\mathbf{D}$, the vector

$$\frac{\mathbf{B}\times\mathbf{D}}{|\mathbf{B}\times\mathbf{D}|}$$

is a unit vector in the direction of $\overrightarrow{MN}$.

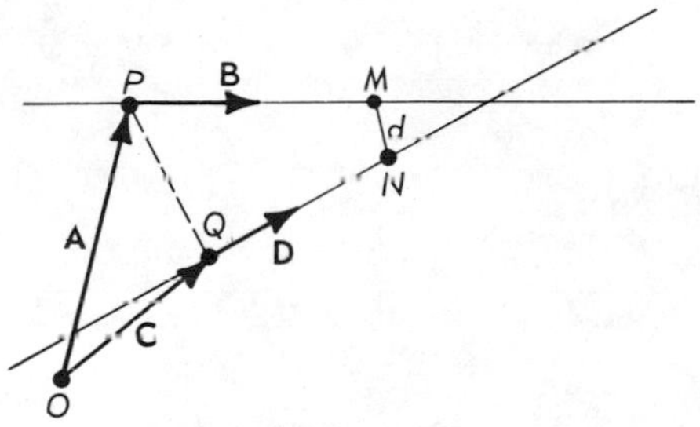


Fig. 6.12 Solution to Prob. 6.13.

But $\overrightarrow{MN}$ is the component of $\overrightarrow{PQ}$ in the direction of $\overrightarrow{MN}$; thus we have $\overrightarrow{PQ}=\mathbf{C}-\mathbf{A}$, and hence,

$$d=|\overrightarrow{MN}|=\left|\overrightarrow{PQ}\cdot\frac{\mathbf{B}\times\mathbf{D}}{|\mathbf{B}\times\mathbf{D}|}\right|=\frac{|(\mathbf{C}-\mathbf{A})\cdot\mathbf{B}\times\mathbf{D}|}{|\mathbf{B}\times\mathbf{D}|}. \tag{6.5}$$

It is noted that if $d=0$, i.e., if $|(\mathbf{C}-\mathbf{A})\cdot\mathbf{B}\times\mathbf{D}|=|(\mathbf{A}-\mathbf{C})\cdot\mathbf{B}\times\mathbf{D}|=0$, the two straight lines intersect. Hence, we can deduce that $(\mathbf{A}-\mathbf{C})\cdot\mathbf{B}\times\mathbf{D}=0$ is the condition that the two lines intersect. This condition agrees with the result (6.3) obtained in Prob. 6.11.

**PROBLEM 6.14** Find the distance $d$ from the point $(1,-2,1)$ to the straight line that joins the points $(1,2,-1)$ and $(-1,-2,1)$.

**Solution:** Let $\mathbf{r}_0=[1,-2,1]$, $\mathbf{A}=[1,2,-1]$, and $\mathbf{B}=[-1,-2,1]$. Then from (6.2) and the position vector $\mathbf{r}=[x,y,z]$, the equation of the straight line that joins the points $(1,2,-1)$ and $(-1,-2,1)$ is

$$(\mathbf{r}-\mathbf{A})\times(\mathbf{B}-\mathbf{A})=\mathbf{0}.$$

Hence, replacing **B** in the distance formula (6.4) by **B** − **A**,

$$d = \frac{|(\mathbf{r}_0 - \mathbf{A}) \times (\mathbf{B} - \mathbf{A})|}{|\mathbf{B} - \mathbf{A}|}.$$

Now clearly $\mathbf{B} - \mathbf{A} = [-2, -4, 2]$, $|\mathbf{B} - \mathbf{A}| = 2\sqrt{6}$, and $\mathbf{r}_0 - \mathbf{A} = [0, -4, 2]$. Hence,

$$(\mathbf{r}_0 - \mathbf{A}) \times (\mathbf{B} - \mathbf{A}) = \begin{vmatrix} \mathbf{i} & \mathbf{j} & \mathbf{k} \\ 0 & -4 & 2 \\ -2 & -4 & 2 \end{vmatrix} = [0, 4, -8],$$

and the magnitude $|(\mathbf{r}_0 - \mathbf{A}) \times (\mathbf{B} - \mathbf{A})| = 4\sqrt{5}$. Thus the distance is

$$d = \frac{4\sqrt{5}}{2\sqrt{6}} = \frac{2\sqrt{5}}{\sqrt{6}}.$$

**PROBLEM 6.15** Find the shortest distance $d$ between the line that joins the points $P(1, 2, -1)$ and $R(1, -1, 1)$ and that which joins the points $Q(2, -2, 1)$ and $S(2, 0, -2)$.

**Solution:** Let the position vectors of $P$ and $Q$ be denoted by **A** and **C**, and $\overrightarrow{PR} = \mathbf{B}$ and $\overrightarrow{QS} = \mathbf{D}$ (see Fig. 6.12). Then the problem is reduced to that of Prob. 6.13, i.e., finding the shortest distance between two lines that pass through two distinct points. Now,

$$\mathbf{A} = [1, 2, -1], \quad \mathbf{B} = \overrightarrow{PR} = [1 - 1, -1 - 2, 1 - (-1)] = [0, -3, 2],$$
$$\mathbf{C} = [2, -2, 1], \quad \mathbf{D} = \overrightarrow{QS} = [2 - 2, 0 - (-2), -2 - 1] = [0, 2, -3],$$
$$\overrightarrow{PQ} = \mathbf{C} - \mathbf{A} = [2 - 1, -2 - 2, 1 - (-1)] = [1, -4, 2].$$

Since

$$\mathbf{B} \times \mathbf{D} = \begin{vmatrix} \mathbf{i} & \mathbf{j} & \mathbf{k} \\ 0 & -3 & 2 \\ 0 & 2 & -3 \end{vmatrix} = [5, 0, 0],$$

the magnitude $|\mathbf{B} \times \mathbf{D}| = 5$. Hence by (6.5), the required distance is

$$d = \frac{|(\mathbf{C} - \mathbf{A}) \cdot (\mathbf{B} \times \mathbf{D})|}{|\mathbf{B} \times \mathbf{D}|} = \frac{5}{5} = 1.$$

The vector equation of a plane that is perpendicular to a nonzero vector **B** and that passes through a point whose position vector is **A** is

$$(\mathbf{r} - \mathbf{A}) \cdot \mathbf{B} = 0. \tag{6.6}$$

**PROBLEM 6.16** Prove (6.6).

**Solution:** In Fig. 6.13, let **r** be the position vector of any point in space. Then the point will lie in the plane if and only if **r** − **A** is perpendicular to **B**, i.e.,

$$(\mathbf{r} - \mathbf{A}) \cdot \mathbf{B} = 0.$$

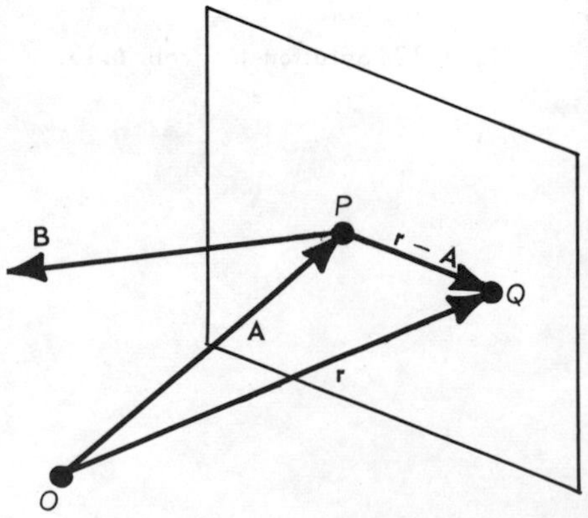

Fig. 6.13 Solution to Prob. 6.16.

**PROBLEM 6.17** In Fig. 6.14 the arbitrary points $P$ and $Q$ are specified by the position vectors $\mathbf{r}_0$ and **A** relative to the point $O$. Show that the distance $d$ from $P$ to the plane that is perpendicular to the nonzero vector **B** and passes through $Q$ is

$$d = \frac{|(\mathbf{r}_0 - \mathbf{A}) \cdot \mathbf{B}|}{B}. \tag{6.7}$$

**Solution:** Let $\mathbf{r}$ be the position vector of the base of the perpendicular from $P$ to the plane. Then from Fig. 6.14 for some scalar $\lambda$,

$$\mathbf{r} = \mathbf{r}_0 + \lambda \mathbf{B}. \tag{6.8}$$

The desired distance $d$ is then,

$$d = |\mathbf{r} - \mathbf{r}_0| = |\lambda \mathbf{B}| = |\lambda| B, \tag{6.9}$$

where $B = |\mathbf{B}|$. Now from (6.8),

$$\mathbf{r} - \mathbf{A} = \mathbf{r}_0 - \mathbf{A} + \lambda \mathbf{B}.$$

Taking the dot product of both sides with $\mathbf{B}$ and then using (6.6),

$$(\mathbf{r} - \mathbf{A}) \cdot \mathbf{B} = (\mathbf{r}_0 - \mathbf{A}) \cdot \mathbf{B} + \lambda \mathbf{B} \cdot \mathbf{B} = (\mathbf{r}_0 - \mathbf{A}) \cdot \mathbf{B} + \lambda B^2 = 0.$$

Hence,

$$\lambda = -\frac{(\mathbf{r}_0 - \mathbf{A}) \cdot \mathbf{B}}{B^2},$$

and substituting into (6.9), the distance is

$$d = |\lambda| B = \frac{|(\mathbf{r}_0 - \mathbf{A}) \cdot \mathbf{B}|}{B}.$$

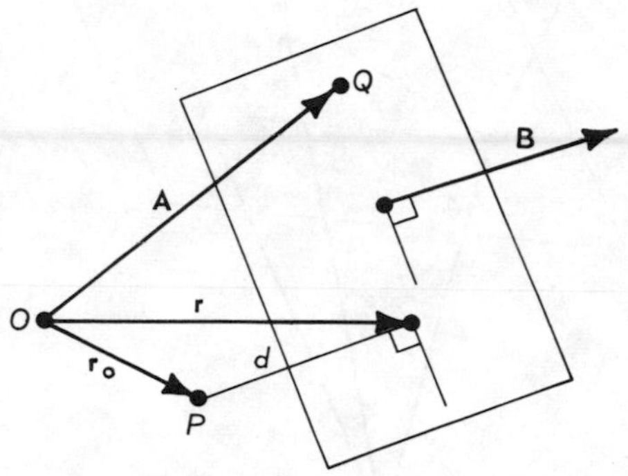


Fig. 6.14 Solution to Prob. 6.17.

**PROBLEM 6.18** Show that the equation of a plane can be expressed as

$$ax + by + cz + k = 0. \tag{6.10}$$

**Solution:** From (6.6), the vector equation of the plane that is perpendicular to a nonzero vector $\mathbf{B}$ and passes through a point whose position vector is $\mathbf{A}$ is expressed as

$$(\mathbf{r} - \mathbf{A}) \cdot \mathbf{B} = 0.$$

In terms of components, i.e., $\mathbf{r} = [x, y, z]$, $\mathbf{A} = [A_1, A_2, A_3]$, and $\mathbf{B} = [B_1, B_2, B_3]$, (6.6) becomes $(x - A_1)B_1 + (y - A_2)B_2 + (z - A_3)B_3 = 0$, or

$$B_1 x + B_2 y + B_3 z - (A_1 B_1 + A_2 B_2 + A_3 B_3) = 0. \tag{6.11}$$

Now if we let $B_1 = a$, $B_2 = b$, $B_3 = c$, and $-(A_1 B_1 + A_2 B_2 + A_3 B_3) = k$, (6.11) reduces to

$$ax + by + cz + k = 0.$$

**PROBLEM 6.19** Show that the distance $d$ between an arbitrary point $(x_0, y_0, z_0)$ and the plane $ax + by + cz + k = 0$ is

$$d = \frac{|ax_0 + by_0 + cz_0 + k|}{(a^2 + b^2 + c^2)^{1/2}}. \tag{6.12}$$

**Solution:** Referring to Prob. 6.18, if we let $\mathbf{B} = [a, b, c]$, $-\mathbf{A} \cdot \mathbf{B} = k$, and $\mathbf{r}_0 = [x_0, y_0, z_0]$,

$$B = |\mathbf{B}| = (a^2 + b^2 + c^2)^{1/2}.$$

Hence on taking the dot product,

$$(\mathbf{r}_0 - \mathbf{A}) \cdot \mathbf{B} = \mathbf{r}_0 \cdot \mathbf{B} - \mathbf{A} \cdot \mathbf{B} = ax_0 + by_0 + cz_0 + k.$$

Hence from (6.7), the required distance is

$$d = \frac{|(\mathbf{r}_0 - \mathbf{A}) \cdot \mathbf{B}|}{B} = \frac{|ax_0 + by_0 + cz_0 + k|}{(a^2 + b^2 + c^2)^{1/2}}.$$

**PROBLEM 6.20** Find a vector equation to represent the plane that passes through three-given points whose position vectors are **A**, **B**, and **C**.

**Solution:** In Fig. 6.15, let $P$, $Q$, and $R$ be the three given points with position vectors $\overrightarrow{OP} = \mathbf{A}$, $\overrightarrow{OQ} = \mathbf{B}$, and $\overrightarrow{OR} = \mathbf{C}$. Then $\overrightarrow{PQ} = \mathbf{B} - \mathbf{A}$ and $\overrightarrow{PR} = \mathbf{C} - \mathbf{A}$. From the definition of the cross product (1.54), the vector

$$\mathbf{G} = \overrightarrow{PQ} \times \overrightarrow{PR} = (\mathbf{B} - \mathbf{A}) \times (\mathbf{C} - \mathbf{A}) = \mathbf{A} \times \mathbf{B} + \mathbf{B} \times \mathbf{C} + \mathbf{C} \times \mathbf{A} \tag{6.13}$$

is perpendicular to the plane. Hence, from Prob. 6.16, the vector equation of the plane is

$$(\mathbf{r} - \mathbf{A}) \cdot \mathbf{G} = 0, \tag{6.14}$$

where **r** is the position vector of any point on the plane.

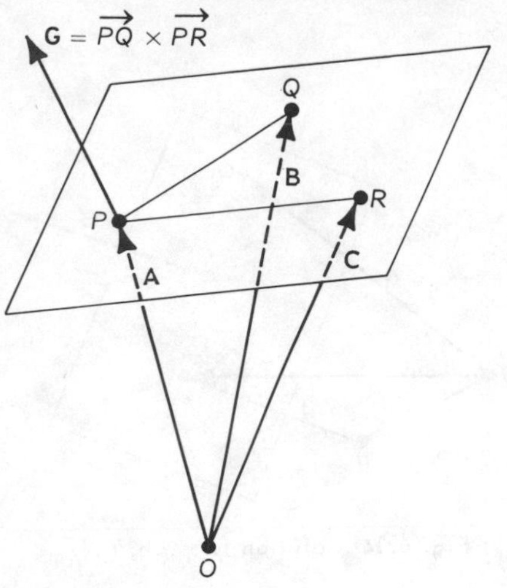


Fig. 6.15 Solution to Prob. 6.20.

Since

$$\mathbf{A} \cdot \mathbf{G} = \mathbf{A} \cdot (\mathbf{A} \times \mathbf{B} + \mathbf{B} \times \mathbf{C} + \mathbf{C} \times \mathbf{A}) = \mathbf{A} \cdot \mathbf{B} \times \mathbf{C} = [\mathbf{A}\,\mathbf{B}\,\mathbf{C}],$$

(6.14) can be rewritten to give the vector equation of the plane as

$$\mathbf{r} \cdot \mathbf{G} = [\mathbf{A}\,\mathbf{B}\,\mathbf{C}]. \tag{6.15}$$

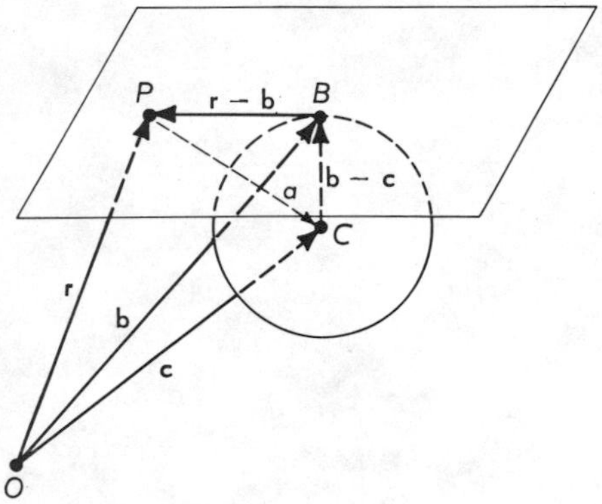


Fig. 6.16 The sphere of Prob. 6.21.

**PROBLEM 6.21** The sphere shown in Fig. 6.16 has a radius $a$, and its center $C$ is specified by the position vector **c**, relative to $O$. An arbitrary point $B$ on the sphere is specified by the position vector **b**. If **r** is the position vector of any point $P$ on the plane that is tangent to the sphere at $B$, then show that the vector equation of the tangent plane is

$$(\mathbf{r} - \mathbf{c}) \cdot (\mathbf{b} - \mathbf{c}) = a^2. \tag{6.16}$$

**Solution:** From Fig. 6.16, the vector $\overrightarrow{BP}$ is in the plane and is specified by $\mathbf{r} - \mathbf{b}$. Since the plane is perpendicular to the sphere at $B$, $\mathbf{r} - \mathbf{b}$ is perpendicular to the radius vector $\mathbf{b} - \mathbf{c}$ of the sphere. Thus,

$$(\mathbf{r} - \mathbf{b}) \cdot (\mathbf{b} - \mathbf{c}) = 0. \tag{6.17}$$

Since $\mathbf{b} = \mathbf{c} + (\mathbf{b} - \mathbf{c})$, (6.17) becomes

$$[(\mathbf{r} - \mathbf{c}) - (\mathbf{b} - \mathbf{c})] \cdot (\mathbf{b} - \mathbf{c}) = 0. \tag{6.18}$$

Simplifying,

$$(\mathbf{r} - \mathbf{c}) \cdot (\mathbf{b} - \mathbf{c}) = (\mathbf{b} - \mathbf{c}) \cdot (\mathbf{b} - \mathbf{c}). \tag{6.19}$$

But $(\mathbf{b} - \mathbf{c}) \cdot (\mathbf{b} - \mathbf{c}) = a^2$. Thus, the required equation is (6.16).

## 6.3 Applications to Differential Geometry

In this section some formulas for space curves are derived by vector methods.

The *space curve* $C$, as seen in Sec. 3.4, can be represented by the vector function $\mathbf{r}(t)$ with a scalar parameter $t$; i.e.,

$$\mathbf{r}(t) = x(t)\,\mathbf{i} + y(t)\,\mathbf{j} + z(t)\,\mathbf{k}.$$

Then the *unit tangent vector* **T** to $C$ at any point on $C$ is expressed by

$$\mathbf{T} = \frac{\mathbf{r}'(t)}{|\mathbf{r}'(t)|},$$

where $\mathbf{r}'(t) = d\mathbf{r}(t)/dt$ and $|\mathbf{r}'(t)| \neq 0$.

If the parameter $t$ is replaced by an arc length $s$ that measures the distance along $C$ from some fixed point on it, then $C$ is represented by

$$\mathbf{r}(s) = x(s)\,\mathbf{i} + y(s)\,\mathbf{j} + z(s)\,\mathbf{k}, \qquad [3.65]$$

and the unit tangent vector to $C$ is

$$\mathbf{T} = \mathbf{r}'(s) = \frac{d\mathbf{r}(s)}{ds} \qquad [3.68]$$

in the direction of increasing $s$.

If $\mathbf{T}$ is the unit tangent vector to a curve $C$ at any point on $C$, then its derivative $\mathbf{T}'(s) = d\mathbf{T}(s)/ds$ is normal to itself. (Cf., Prob. 3.22.)

The *unit principal normal vector* $\mathbf{N}$ is defined by

$$\frac{d\mathbf{T}}{ds} = \kappa\mathbf{N}, \qquad (6.20)$$

where

$$\kappa = \left|\frac{d\mathbf{T}}{ds}\right| \qquad (6.21)$$

is called the *curvature* of $C$ at any point. The *radius of curvature* $\rho$ of $C$ at any point is

$$\rho = \frac{1}{\kappa}, \qquad (6.22)$$

where $\kappa \neq 0$.

The *binormal vector* $\mathbf{B}$ to $C$ at any point is defined by

$$\mathbf{B} = \mathbf{T} \times \mathbf{N}; \qquad (6.23)$$

its magnitude is

$$|\mathbf{B}| = B = 1; \qquad (6.24)$$

it is perpendicular to its derivative with respect to $s$; i.e.,

$$\mathbf{B} \perp \frac{d\mathbf{B}}{ds}. \qquad (6.25)$$

The *torsion* $\tau$ of a curve $C$ at any point is defined by

$$\frac{d\mathbf{B}}{ds} = -\tau\mathbf{N}. \qquad (6.26)$$

The reciprocal of $\tau$, denoted by $\sigma = 1/\tau$, is called the *radius of torsion.*

The unit tangent vector $\mathbf{T}$, the unit principal normal vector $\mathbf{N}$, and the binormal vector $\mathbf{B}$ are said to be *trihedral* at any point on $C$ because they form a right-handed system of unit vectors; i.e.,

$$\mathbf{B} = \mathbf{T} \times \mathbf{N}, \qquad \mathbf{N} = \mathbf{B} \times \mathbf{T}, \qquad \mathbf{T} = \mathbf{N} \times \mathbf{B}. \qquad (6.27)$$

**PROBLEM 6.22** Verify (6.24–7).

**Solution:** From the definition of the binormal vector (6.23) and since $|\mathbf{T}| = |\mathbf{N}| = 1$ and $\mathbf{T} \perp \mathbf{N}$,

$$|\mathbf{B}| = |\mathbf{T} \times \mathbf{N}| = |\mathbf{T}|\,|\mathbf{N}|\,|\sin 90^\circ| = 1.$$

Since $|\mathbf{B}| = 1$,

$$\mathbf{B} \cdot \mathbf{B} = B^2 = 1.$$

Differentiating both sides with respect to $s$ yields $\dfrac{d\mathbf{B}}{ds} \cdot \mathbf{B} = 0$, which implies that

$$\mathbf{B} \perp d\mathbf{B}/ds.$$

From (6.23), $\mathbf{B} \cdot \mathbf{T} = 0$ and $\mathbf{B} \cdot \mathbf{N} = 0$. Differentiating both sides of the first equation with respect to $s$,

$$\frac{d\mathbf{B}}{ds} \cdot \mathbf{T} + \mathbf{B} \cdot \frac{d\mathbf{T}}{ds} = 0.$$

Thus, using (6.20),

$$\frac{d\mathbf{B}}{ds} \cdot \mathbf{T} = -\mathbf{B} \cdot \frac{d\mathbf{T}}{ds} = -\mathbf{B} \cdot (\kappa \mathbf{N}) = -\kappa \mathbf{B} \cdot \mathbf{N} = 0,$$

which implies that $d\mathbf{B}/ds$ is also orthogonal to $\mathbf{T}$. Therefore, $d\mathbf{B}/ds$ must be parallel to $\mathbf{N}$. Hence,

$$\frac{d\mathbf{B}}{ds} = -\tau \mathbf{N}.$$

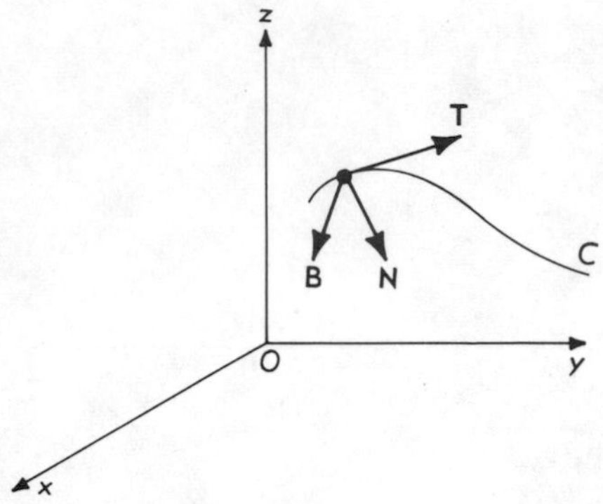

Fig. 6.17 Trihedral.

From these results we conclude that **T**, **N**, and **B** form a right-handed system of unit vectors or trihedral (see Fig. 6.17); i.e.,

$$\mathbf{B} = \mathbf{T} \times \mathbf{N}, \quad \mathbf{N} = \mathbf{B} \times \mathbf{T}, \quad \mathbf{T} = \mathbf{N} \times \mathbf{B}.$$

**PROBLEM 6.23** Show that

$$\frac{d\mathbf{N}}{ds} = \tau \mathbf{B} - \kappa \mathbf{T}. \tag{6.28}$$

**Solution:** From the definition of the trihedral (6.27),

$$\mathbf{N} = \mathbf{B} \times \mathbf{T}.$$

Hence using (6.20), (6.26), and (6.27), its derivative is

$$\frac{d\mathbf{N}}{ds} = \frac{d\mathbf{B}}{ds} \times \mathbf{T} + \mathbf{B} \times \frac{d\mathbf{T}}{ds} = -\tau \mathbf{N} \times \mathbf{T} + \mathbf{B} \times (\kappa \mathbf{N}) = \tau \mathbf{B} - \kappa \mathbf{T}.$$

The formulas (6.20), (6.26), and (6.28) are known as the *Frenet-Serret formulas*, and can also be written as

$$\frac{d\mathbf{T}}{ds} = \omega \times \mathbf{T}, \tag{6.29}$$

$$\frac{d\mathbf{B}}{ds} = \omega \times \mathbf{B}, \tag{6.30}$$

$$\frac{d\mathbf{N}}{ds} = \omega \times \mathbf{N}, \tag{6.31}$$

where

$$\omega = \tau \mathbf{T} + \kappa \mathbf{B} \tag{6.32}$$

is the *Darboux vector* of the curve $C$.

**PROBLEM 6.24** Show that the Frenet-Serret formulas (6.20), (6.26), and (6.28) can be rewritten as (6.29–31).

**Solution:** If $\omega = \tau \mathbf{T} + \kappa \mathbf{B}$, then we have on using (1.58) and (6.27),

$$\omega \times \mathbf{T} = (\tau\mathbf{T} + \kappa\mathbf{B}) \times \mathbf{T} = \tau\mathbf{T} \times \mathbf{T} + \kappa\mathbf{B} \times \mathbf{T} = \kappa\mathbf{N},$$

$$\omega \times \mathbf{B} = (\tau\mathbf{T} + \kappa\mathbf{B}) \times \mathbf{B} = \tau\mathbf{T} \times \mathbf{B} + \kappa\mathbf{B} \times \mathbf{B} = -\tau\mathbf{N},$$

$$\omega \times \mathbf{N} = (\tau\mathbf{T} + \kappa\mathbf{B}) \times \mathbf{N} = \tau\mathbf{T} \times \mathbf{N} + \kappa\mathbf{B} \times \mathbf{N} = \tau\mathbf{B} - \kappa\mathbf{T}.$$

**PROBLEM 6.25** Show that

$$\frac{d\mathbf{T}}{ds} \cdot \frac{d\mathbf{B}}{ds} = -\kappa\tau, \tag{6.33}$$

$$\mathbf{B} \cdot \frac{d\mathbf{N}}{ds} = \tau, \tag{6.34}$$

$$\mathbf{T} \cdot \frac{d\mathbf{N}}{ds} = -\kappa. \tag{6.35}$$

**Solution:** Using the Frenet-Serret formulas (6.20), (6.26), and (6.28) and the fact that $\mathbf{N} \cdot \mathbf{N} = N^2 = 1$,

$$\frac{d\mathbf{T}}{ds} \cdot \frac{d\mathbf{B}}{ds} = \kappa\mathbf{N} \cdot (-\tau\mathbf{N}) = -\kappa\tau(\mathbf{N} \cdot \mathbf{N}) = -\kappa\tau.$$

Since $\mathbf{B} \cdot \mathbf{B} = B^2 = 1$ and $\mathbf{B} \cdot \mathbf{T} = 0$,

$$\mathbf{B} \cdot \frac{d\mathbf{N}}{ds} = \mathbf{B} \cdot (\tau\mathbf{B} - \kappa\mathbf{T}) = \tau(\mathbf{B} \cdot \mathbf{B}) - \kappa(\mathbf{B} \cdot \mathbf{T}) = \tau.$$

Since $\mathbf{T} \cdot \mathbf{T} = T^2 = 1$ and $\mathbf{T} \cdot \mathbf{B} = 0$,

$$\mathbf{T} \cdot \frac{d\mathbf{N}}{ds} = \mathbf{T} \cdot (\tau\mathbf{B} - \kappa\mathbf{T}) = \tau(\mathbf{T} \cdot \mathbf{B}) - \kappa(\mathbf{T} \cdot \mathbf{T}) = -\kappa.$$

**PROBLEM 6.26** Show that the necessary and sufficient condition for a curve $C$ to be a straight line is that its curvature $\kappa$ be zero.

**Solution:** If $C$ is a straight line, then the unit tangent vector $\mathbf{T}$ is a constant vector; i.e.,

$$\frac{d\mathbf{T}}{ds} = \kappa\mathbf{N} = \mathbf{0}.$$

This yields $\kappa = 0$, since $\mathbf{N} \neq \mathbf{0}$.

Conversely, if $\kappa = 0$, then we have $d\mathbf{T}/ds = \mathbf{0}$; consequently, $\mathbf{T}$ is a constant vector and $C$ is a straight line.

A curve that lies in a space plane is called a *plane curve*; otherwise, it is called a *twisted curve*.

**PROBLEM 6.27** Show that the necessary and sufficient condition for a curve $C$ to be a plane curve is that the torsion $\tau$ of $C$ be zero. (It is assumed that $\kappa \neq 0$.)

**Solution:** If $C$ lies in a plane, then by choosing the origin of this plane, both vectors $\mathbf{r}'(s) = d\mathbf{r}(s)/ds$ and $\mathbf{r}''(s) = d^2\mathbf{r}(s)/ds^2$ will also lie in this plane. Hence, $\mathbf{T} = \mathbf{r}'(s)$ and

$$\mathbf{N} = \frac{1}{\kappa}\frac{d\mathbf{T}}{ds} = \frac{1}{\kappa}\mathbf{r}''(s)$$

also lie in the plane; consequently, $\mathbf{B} = \mathbf{T} \times \mathbf{N}$ is a constant vector, normal to the plane. Thus,

$$\frac{d\mathbf{B}}{ds} = -\tau\mathbf{N} = \mathbf{0},$$

which implies that $\tau = 0$.

Conversely, if $\tau = 0$, then $d\mathbf{B}/ds = -\tau\mathbf{N} = \mathbf{0}$; hence, $\mathbf{B}$ is a constant vector. Let the curve $C$ be represented by $\mathbf{r}(s)$. Then, since $\mathbf{T} \perp \mathbf{B}$ and $\tau = 0$,

$$\frac{d}{ds}(\mathbf{r}\cdot\mathbf{B}) = \frac{d\mathbf{r}}{ds}\cdot\mathbf{B} + \mathbf{r}\cdot\frac{d\mathbf{B}}{ds} = \mathbf{T}\cdot\mathbf{B} + -\tau\mathbf{r}\cdot\mathbf{N} = 0.$$

Since $\mathbf{r}\cdot\mathbf{B} = 0$ is the equation of a plane normal to $\mathbf{B}$ (see Prob. 6.16), it follows that the curve is a plane curve.

**PROBLEM 6.28** Show that if the curve $C$ is represented by $\mathbf{r}(t)$, which is twice differentiable, then the curvature $\kappa$ of $C$ at any point is

$$\kappa = \frac{|\mathbf{r}'(t) \times \mathbf{r}''(t)|}{|\mathbf{r}'(t)|^3}. \tag{6.36}$$

**Solution:** Let $\mathbf{r}(t) = \mathbf{r}[s(t)]$, where $s$ is the arc length. Then its derivative is

$$\mathbf{r}'(t) = \frac{d\mathbf{r}(t)}{dt} = \frac{d\mathbf{r}}{ds}\frac{ds}{dt} = \frac{ds}{dt}\mathbf{T}, \tag{6.37}$$

and because $|\mathbf{T}| = 1$, the magnitude is

$$|\mathbf{r}'(t)| = \left|\frac{ds}{dt}\right|. \tag{6.38}$$

Next, using the Frenet-Serret formulas (6.20), (6.26), and (6.28),

$$\frac{d\mathbf{T}}{dt} = \frac{d\mathbf{T}}{ds}\frac{ds}{dt} = \kappa\mathbf{N}\frac{ds}{dt}. \tag{6.39}$$

Now from (6.37),

$$\mathbf{r}''(t) = \frac{d}{dt}\mathbf{r}'(t) = \frac{d^2s}{dt^2}\mathbf{T} + \frac{ds}{dt}\frac{d\mathbf{T}}{dt} = \frac{d^2s}{dt^2}\mathbf{T} + \left(\frac{ds}{dt}\right)^2\kappa\mathbf{N}. \tag{6.40}$$

Thus,

$$\begin{aligned}\mathbf{r}'(t) \times \mathbf{r}''(t) &= \left(\frac{ds}{dt}\mathbf{T}\right) \times \left[\frac{d^2s}{dt^2}\mathbf{T} + \left(\frac{ds}{dt}\right)^2\kappa\mathbf{N}\right]\\ &= \left(\frac{ds}{dt}\right)^3\kappa\mathbf{T}\times\mathbf{N}\\ &= \left(\frac{ds}{dt}\right)^3\kappa\mathbf{B},\end{aligned} \tag{6.41}$$

and because $|\mathbf{B}| = 1$, the magnitude is

$$|\mathbf{r}'(t) \times \mathbf{r}''(t)| = \left|\frac{ds}{dt}\right|^3\kappa = |\mathbf{r}'(t)|^3\kappa. \tag{6.42}$$

Hence, the curvature is

$$\kappa = \frac{|\mathbf{r}'(t) \times \mathbf{r}''(t)|}{|\mathbf{r}'(t)|^3}.$$

**PROBLEM 6.29.** Show that if the curve $C$ is represented by $\mathbf{r}(t)$, which is thrice differentiable, then the torsion $\tau$ of $C$ at any point is

$$\tau = \frac{[\mathbf{r}'(t)\,\mathbf{r}''(t)\,\mathbf{r}'''(t)]}{|\mathbf{r}'(t) \times \mathbf{r}''(t)|^2}. \tag{6.43}$$

**Solution:** Differentiating (6.40) with respect to $t$,

$$\begin{aligned}
\mathbf{r}'''(t) &= \frac{d\mathbf{r}''(t)}{dt} \\
&= \frac{d}{dt}\left[\frac{d^2s}{dt^2}\mathbf{T} + \left(\frac{ds}{dt}\right)^2 \kappa\mathbf{N}\right] \\
&= \frac{d^3s}{dt^3}\mathbf{T} + \frac{d^2s}{dt^2}\frac{d\mathbf{T}}{dt} + 2\left(\frac{ds}{dt}\right)\frac{d^2s}{dt^2}\kappa\mathbf{N} + \left(\frac{ds}{dt}\right)^2 \frac{d\kappa}{dt}\mathbf{N} + \left(\frac{ds}{dt}\right)^2 \kappa\frac{d\mathbf{N}}{dt}.
\end{aligned} \tag{6.44}$$

From (6.39),

$$\frac{d\mathbf{T}}{dt} = \kappa\frac{ds}{dt}\mathbf{N},$$

and from (6.28),

$$\frac{d\mathbf{N}}{dt} = \frac{d\mathbf{N}}{ds}\frac{ds}{dt} = \frac{ds}{dt}(\tau\mathbf{B} - \kappa\mathbf{T}).$$

Substituting these results into (6.44), and rearranging the terms,

$$\mathbf{r}'''(t) = \left[\frac{d^3s}{dt^3} - \left(\frac{ds}{dt}\right)^3\kappa^2\right]\mathbf{T} + \left[3\left(\frac{ds}{dt}\right)\left(\frac{d^2s}{dt^2}\right)\kappa + \left(\frac{ds}{dt}\right)^2\left(\frac{d\kappa}{dt}\right)\right]\mathbf{N} + \left(\frac{ds}{dt}\right)^3\kappa\tau\mathbf{B}. \tag{6.45}$$

Now, from (2.53), (6.41), and (6.45),

$$\begin{aligned}
[\mathbf{r}'(t)\,\mathbf{r}''(t)\,\mathbf{r}'''(t)] &= [\mathbf{r}'''(t)\,\mathbf{r}'(t)\,\mathbf{r}''(t)] \\
&= \mathbf{r}'''(t)\cdot[\mathbf{r}'(t) \times \mathbf{r}''(t)] \\
&= \left(\frac{ds}{dt}\right)^6 \kappa^2\tau.
\end{aligned}$$

Thus because of (6.42), the torsion is

$$\tau = \frac{[\mathbf{r}'(t)\,\mathbf{r}''(t)\,\mathbf{r}'''(t)]}{\left[\left(\frac{ds}{dt}\right)^3\kappa\right]^2} = \frac{[\mathbf{r}'(t)\,\mathbf{r}''(t)\,\mathbf{r}'''(t)]}{|\mathbf{r}'(t) \times \mathbf{r}''(t)|^2}.$$

**PROBLEM 6.30** Show that if a curve $C$ is represented by $\mathbf{r}(t)$, which is twice differentiable, then

$$\mathbf{T} = \frac{\mathbf{r}'(t)}{|\mathbf{r}'(t)|}, \tag{6.46}$$

$$\mathbf{B} = \frac{\mathbf{r}'(t) \times \mathbf{r}''(t)}{|\mathbf{r}'(t) \times \mathbf{r}''(t)|}, \tag{6.47}$$

$$\mathbf{N} = \frac{[\mathbf{r}'(t) \times \mathbf{r}''(t)] \times \mathbf{r}'(t)}{|[\mathbf{r}'(t) \times \mathbf{r}''(t)] \times \mathbf{r}'(t)|}. \tag{6.48}$$

**Solution:** Equation (6.46) is already derived in (3.69). To verify (6.47), we have from (6.41–2),

$$\mathbf{B} = \frac{1}{\left(\frac{ds}{dt}\right)^3\kappa}\mathbf{r}'(t) \times \mathbf{r}''(t) = \frac{\mathbf{r}'(t) \times \mathbf{r}''(t)}{|\mathbf{r}'(t) \times \mathbf{r}''(t)|}.$$

To verify (6.48), substitute (6.46) and (6.47) into the second equation $\mathbf{N} = \mathbf{B} \times \mathbf{T}$ of (6.27); then observing that $\mathbf{N}$ is a unit vector,

$$\mathbf{N} = \mathbf{B} \times \mathbf{T} = \frac{[\mathbf{r}'(t) \times \mathbf{r}''(t)] \times \mathbf{r}'(t)}{|[\mathbf{r}'(t) \times \mathbf{r}''(t)] \times \mathbf{r}'(t)|}.$$

**PROBLEM 6.31** Find $\mathbf{T}$, $\mathbf{N}$, $\mathbf{B}$, $\kappa$, and $\tau$ for the circle of radius $a$ represented by

$$\mathbf{r}(s) = a \cos\left(\frac{s}{a}\right)\mathbf{i} + a \sin\left(\frac{s}{a}\right)\mathbf{j}. \tag{3.67}$$

**Solution:** The tangent vector to the circle (3.67) is

$$\mathbf{T} = \frac{d\mathbf{r}(s)}{ds} = -\sin\left(\frac{s}{a}\right)\mathbf{i} + \cos\left(\frac{s}{a}\right)\mathbf{j}. \tag{3.71}$$

For the unit principal normal $\mathbf{N}$, the derivative of $\mathbf{T}$ yields

$$\frac{d\mathbf{T}}{ds} = -\frac{1}{a}\cos\left(\frac{s}{a}\right)\mathbf{i} - \frac{1}{a}\sin\left(\frac{s}{a}\right)\mathbf{j} = \kappa\mathbf{N}.$$

Thus, the curvature is

$$\begin{aligned}\kappa = \left|\frac{d\mathbf{T}}{ds}\right| &= \left\{\left[\frac{1}{a}\cos\left(\frac{s}{a}\right)\right]^2 + \left[\frac{1}{a}\sin\left(\frac{s}{a}\right)\right]^2\right\}^{1/2} \\ &= \frac{1}{a}\left[\cos^2\left(\frac{s}{a}\right) + \sin^2\left(\frac{s}{a}\right)\right]^{1/2} \\ &= \frac{1}{a}. \end{aligned} \tag{6.49}$$

Hence, the unit principal normal is

$$\mathbf{N} = \frac{1}{\kappa}\frac{d\mathbf{T}}{ds} = -\cos\left(\frac{s}{a}\right)\mathbf{i} - \sin\left(\frac{s}{a}\right)\mathbf{j} = -\frac{1}{a}\mathbf{r}(s). \tag{6.50}$$

The binormal vector $\mathbf{B}$ is

$$\mathbf{B} = \mathbf{T} \times \mathbf{N} = \begin{vmatrix} \mathbf{i} & \mathbf{j} & \mathbf{k} \\ -\sin\frac{s}{a} & \cos\frac{s}{a} & 0 \\ -\cos\frac{s}{a} & -\sin\frac{s}{a} & 0 \end{vmatrix} = \mathbf{k}\left[\sin^2\left(\frac{s}{a}\right) + \cos^2\left(\frac{s}{a}\right)\right] = \mathbf{k}. \tag{6.51}$$

Since $d\mathbf{B}/ds = \mathbf{0} = -\tau\mathbf{N}$, the torsion is

$$\tau = 0. \tag{6.52}$$

Equation (6.49) shows that a circle has a constant curvature that is equal to the reciprocal of its radius, and (6.52) indicates that a circle is a plane curve.

A *helix* is a space curve whose tangent makes a constant angle with a fixed line, called its axis.

**PROBLEM 6.32** Find $\mathbf{T}$, $\mathbf{N}$, $\mathbf{B}$, $\kappa$, and $\tau$ for a circular helix represented by

$$\mathbf{r}(t) = (a\cos t)\,\mathbf{i} + (a \sin t)\,\mathbf{j} + bt\mathbf{k}. \tag{6.53}$$

**Solution:** From (6.53),

$$\mathbf{r}'(t) = -(a \sin t)\mathbf{i} + (a \cos t)\mathbf{j} + b\mathbf{k},$$
$$\mathbf{r}''(t) = -(a \cos t)\mathbf{i} - (a \sin t)\mathbf{j},$$
$$\mathbf{r}'''(t) = (a \sin t)\mathbf{i} - (a \cos t)\mathbf{k}.$$

Accordingly,

$$\mathbf{r}'(t) \times \mathbf{r}''(t) = \begin{vmatrix} \mathbf{i} & \mathbf{j} & \mathbf{k} \\ -a \sin t & a \cos t & b \\ -a \cos t & -a \sin t & 0 \end{vmatrix} = (ab \sin t)\mathbf{i} - (ab \cos t)\mathbf{j} + a^2\mathbf{k},$$

$$[\mathbf{r}'(t) \times \mathbf{r}''(t)] \times \mathbf{r}'(t) = \begin{vmatrix} \mathbf{i} & \mathbf{j} & \mathbf{k} \\ ab \sin t & -ab \cos t & a^2 \\ -a \sin t & a \cos t & b \end{vmatrix}$$
$$= (-ab^2 - a^3) \cos t\,\mathbf{i} - (ab^2 - a^3) \sin t\,\mathbf{j}$$
$$= -a(a^2 + b^2) \cos t\,\mathbf{i} - a(a^2 + b^2) \sin t\,\mathbf{j},$$

$$[\mathbf{r}'(t)\,\mathbf{r}''(t)\,\mathbf{r}'''(t)] = \begin{vmatrix} -a \sin t & a \cos t & b \\ -a \cos t & -a \sin t & 0 \\ a \sin t & -a \cos t & 0 \end{vmatrix}$$
$$= b \begin{vmatrix} -a \cos t & -a \sin t \\ a \sin t & -a \cos t \end{vmatrix}$$
$$= ba^2(\cos^2 t + \sin^2 t)$$
$$= a^2 b.$$

Hence the magnitudes are

$$|\mathbf{r}'(t)| = (a^2 \sin^2 t + a^2 \cos^2 t + b^2)^{1/2} = (a^2 + b^2)^{1/2},$$
$$|\mathbf{r}'(t) \times \mathbf{r}''(t)| = (a^2 b^2 \sin^2 t + a^2 b^2 \cos^2 t + a^4)^{1/2} = [a^2(a^2 + b^2)]^{1/2} = a(a^2 + b^2)^{1/2},$$
$$|[\mathbf{r}'(t) \times \mathbf{r}''(t)] \times \mathbf{r}'(t)| = [a^2(a^2 + b^2)^2(\cos^2 t + \sin^2 t)]^{1/2} = a(a^2 + b^2).$$

Hence, from (6.46-8), (6.36), and (6.43),

$$\mathbf{T} = \frac{\mathbf{r}'(t)}{|\mathbf{r}'(t)|} = -\left[\frac{a}{(a^2 + b^2)^{1/2}} \sin t\right]\mathbf{i} + \left[\frac{a}{(a^2 + b^2)^{1/2}} \cos t\right]\mathbf{j} + \left[\frac{b}{(a^2 + b^2)^{1/2}}\right]\mathbf{k}, \tag{6.54}$$

$$\mathbf{B} = \frac{\mathbf{r}'(t) \times \mathbf{r}''(t)}{|\mathbf{r}'(t) \times \mathbf{r}''(t)|} = \left[\frac{b}{(a^2 + b^2)^{1/2}} \sin t\right]\mathbf{i} - \left[\frac{b}{(a^2 + b^2)^{1/2}} \cos t\right]\mathbf{j} + \left[\frac{a}{(a^2 + b^2)^{1/2}}\right]\mathbf{k}, \tag{6.55}$$

$$\mathbf{N} = \frac{[\mathbf{r}'(t) \times \mathbf{r}''(t)] \times \mathbf{r}'(t)}{|[\mathbf{r}'(t) \times \mathbf{r}''(t)] \times \mathbf{r}'(t)|} = -(\cos t)\mathbf{i} - (\sin t)\mathbf{j}, \tag{6.56}$$

$$\kappa = \frac{|\mathbf{r}'(t) \times \mathbf{r}''(t)|}{|\mathbf{r}'(t)|^3} = \frac{a(a^2 + b^2)^{1/2}}{(a^2 + b^2)^{3/2}} = \frac{a}{a^2 + b^2}, \tag{6.57}$$

$$\tau = \frac{[\mathbf{r}'(t)\,\mathbf{r}''(t)\,\mathbf{r}'''(t)]}{|\mathbf{r}'(t) \times \mathbf{r}''(t)|^2} = \frac{a^2 b}{a^2(a^2 + b^2)} = \frac{b}{a^2 + b^2}. \tag{6.58}$$

## 6.4 Supplementary Problems

**PROBLEM 6.33** Prove that the sum of the squares of the diagonals of a parallelogram equals the sum of the squares of its sides.

**PROBLEM 6.34** Prove that the midpoint of the hypotenuse of a right triangle is equidistant from the three vertices.

**PROBLEM 6.35** Prove that the line that joins one vertex of a parallelogram to the midpoint of its opposite side divides the diagonal in the ratio 2 : 1.

**PROBLEM 6.36** If $ABCD$ is a quadrilateral with $M$ and $N$ the midpoints of the diagonals $AC$ and $BD$, respectively, prove that

$$AB^2 + BC^2 + CD^2 + DA^2 = AC^2 + BD^2 + 4MN^2.$$

**PROBLEM 6.37** If the diagonals of a parallelogram are orthogonal, then show that the parallelogram is a rhombus.

**PROBLEM 6.38** Show that if two circles intersect, the line that joins their centers is the perpendicular bisector of the line segment that joins their points of intersection.

**PROBLEM 6.39** Find the distance from the point (−2, 1, 5) to the straight line that joins the points (1, 2, −5) and (7, 5, −9).
*Answer*: $7/\sqrt{61}$.

**PROBLEM 6.40** Find the shortest distance between the line that joins the points $P$ (1, 2, 3) and $R$ (−1, 0, 2) and that which joins the points $Q$ (0, 1, 7) and $S$ (2, 0, 5).
*Answer*: 3.

**PROBLEM 6.41** Find the shortest distance from the point (1, −2, 1) to the plane determined by the three points (2, 4, 1), (−1, 0, 1), and (−1, 4, 2).
*Answer*: 14/13.

**PROBLEM 6.42** Show that the equation of the plane that encompasses three given points, whose position vectors are **A**, **B**, and **C**, can be written in the symmetrical form

$$(3\mathbf{r} - \mathbf{A} - \mathbf{B} - \mathbf{C}) \cdot (\mathbf{A} \times \mathbf{B} + \mathbf{B} \times \mathbf{C} + \mathbf{C} \times \mathbf{A}) = 0,$$

where **r** is the position vector of any point on the plane.

**PROBLEM 6.43** Show that the point of intersection of the straight line represented by $(\mathbf{r} - \mathbf{A}) \times \mathbf{B} = \mathbf{0}$ and the plane represented by $(\mathbf{r} - \mathbf{C}) \cdot \mathbf{D} = 0$ is the point whose position vector is

$$\mathbf{A} + \left[(\mathbf{C} - \mathbf{A}) \cdot \frac{\mathbf{D}}{(\mathbf{B} \cdot \mathbf{D})}\right] \mathbf{B}.$$

**PROBLEM 6.44** Show that the only plane curves of constant nonzero curvature are circles.

**PROBLEM 6.45** If the curve $C$ is represented by $y = y(x)$ in the $xy$-plane, show that the radius of curvature is

$$\kappa = \frac{|y''|}{(1 + y'^2)^{3/2}},$$

where the primes denote derivatives.

**PROBLEM 6.46** Find **T**, **B**, **N**, $\kappa$, and $\tau$ at $t = 0$ for the curve $C$ represented by

$$\mathbf{r}(t) = (3t \cos t)\mathbf{i} + (3t \sin t)\mathbf{j} + 4t\mathbf{k}.$$

*Answer*: $\mathbf{T} = [\frac{3}{5}, \frac{4}{5}, 0]$, $\mathbf{B} = [-\frac{4}{5}, 0, \frac{3}{5}]$, $\mathbf{N} = [0, 1, 0]$, $\kappa = \tau = \frac{6}{25}$.

**PROBLEM 6.47** Find $\kappa$ and $\tau$ for the curve $C$ represented by

$$\mathbf{r}(t) = a(3t - t^3)\mathbf{i} + 3at^2\mathbf{j} + a(3t + t^3)\mathbf{k}.$$

*Answer*: $\kappa = \tau = 1/[3a(1 + t^2)^2]$.

**PROBLEM 6.48** If the curve $C$ is represented by $\mathbf{r}(s)$, where $s$ is the arc length, then show that

$$\kappa = [\mathbf{r}''(s) \cdot \mathbf{r}''(s)]^{1/2}, \quad \tau = \frac{[\mathbf{r}'(s)\mathbf{r}''(s)\mathbf{r}'''(s)]}{\mathbf{r}''(s) \cdot \mathbf{r}''(s)}$$

**PROBLEM 6.49** For a helix, prove that (a) $\mathbf{T} \cdot \mathbf{e} = \cos \alpha$, where $\mathbf{e}$ is the unit vector in the direction of the axis, and $\alpha$ is a constant angle such that $0 < \alpha < \pi/2$; (b) $\mathbf{N} \cdot \mathbf{e} = 0$; (c) $\omega \times \mathbf{e} = \mathbf{0}$, where $\omega = \tau\mathbf{T} + \kappa\mathbf{B}$ is the Darboux vector; (d) $\kappa/\tau = \tan \alpha$.

**PROBLEM 6.50** Find $\kappa$ and $\tau$ for the curve $C$ represented by

$$\mathbf{r}(t) = e^t\mathbf{i} - e^t\mathbf{j} + \sqrt{2}t\,\mathbf{k}.$$

*Answer:* $\kappa = -\tau = \sqrt{2}/(e^t + e^{-t})^2$.

**PROBLEM 6.51** Show that $\mathbf{r}'(t) \times \mathbf{r}''(t) = \mathbf{0}$ at every point on a curve is a necessary and sufficient condition that the curve be a straight line.

**PROBLEM 6.52** Show that all the vectors $\mathbf{r} = \mathbf{r}(s)$ are parallel if and only if $[\mathbf{r}(s)\mathbf{r}'(s)\,\mathbf{r}''(s)] = 0$.

**PROBLEM 6.53** Show that $\mathbf{T}'(s) \times \mathbf{T}''(s) = \kappa^2\omega$, where $\omega$ is the Darboux vector.

**PROBLEM 6.54** Prove that $\mathbf{r}'''(s) = \kappa'\mathbf{N} - \kappa^2\mathbf{T} + \kappa\tau\mathbf{B}$.

# 7 CHAPTER APPLICATIONS TO MECHANICS

## 7.1 Displacement, Velocity, and Acceleration Vectors

Let the position vector $\mathbf{r}(t)$ of a moving particle in space be dependent on time $t$. If the initial point of the particle has a position vector $\mathbf{r}(t_0)$ at time $t_0$, then the *displacement vector* of the particle for any arbitrary time $t$ is

$$\mathbf{r}(t) - \mathbf{r}(t_0). \tag{7.1}$$

The *velocity vector* $\mathbf{v}(t)$ and the *acceleration vector* $\mathbf{a}(t)$ of the particle are defined by the equations

$$\mathbf{v}(t) = \frac{d\mathbf{r}}{dt} = \mathbf{r}'(t), \tag{7.2}$$

$$\mathbf{a}(t) = \frac{d\mathbf{v}(t)}{dt} = \frac{d^2\mathbf{r}}{dt^2} = \mathbf{r}''(t). \tag{7.3}$$

The position vector $\mathbf{r}$, velocity vector $\mathbf{v}$, and acceleration vector $\mathbf{a}$ in rectangular coordinates are

$$\mathbf{r}(t) = x(t)\,\mathbf{i} + y(t)\,\mathbf{j} + z(t)\,\mathbf{k}, \tag{7.4}$$

$$\mathbf{v}(t) = \mathbf{r}'(t) = x'(t)\,\mathbf{i} + y'(t)\,\mathbf{j} + z'(t)\,\mathbf{k}, \tag{7.5}$$

$$\mathbf{a}(t) = \mathbf{v}'(t) = \mathbf{r}''(t) = x''(t)\,\mathbf{i} + y''(t)\,\mathbf{j} + z''(t)\,\mathbf{k}. \tag{7.6}$$

**PROBLEM 7.1** Verify (7.4–6).

**Solution:** In rectangular coordinates, the position vector is

$$\mathbf{r}(t) = x(t)\,\mathbf{i} + y(t)\,\mathbf{j} + z(t)\,\mathbf{k}.$$

Since the unit vectors $\mathbf{i}$, $\mathbf{j}$, and $\mathbf{k}$ are constant in time,

$$\mathbf{v} = \mathbf{r}'(t) = x'(t)\,\mathbf{i} + y'(t)\,\mathbf{j} + z'(t)\,\mathbf{k},$$

$$\mathbf{a} = \mathbf{v}'(t) = \mathbf{r}''(t) = x''(t)\,\mathbf{i} + y''(t)\,\mathbf{j} + z''(t)\,\mathbf{k}.$$

The position, velocity, and acceleration vectors in cylindrical coordinates are

$$\mathbf{r}(t) = \rho\,\mathbf{e}_\rho + z\mathbf{k}, \tag{7.7}$$

$$\mathbf{v}(t) = \frac{d\rho}{dt}\,\mathbf{e}_\rho + \rho\,\frac{d\phi}{dt}\,\mathbf{e}_\phi + \frac{dz}{dt}\,\mathbf{k}, \tag{7.8}$$

$$\mathbf{a}(t) = \left[\frac{d^2\rho}{dt^2} - \rho\left(\frac{d\phi}{dt}\right)^2\right]\mathbf{e}_\rho + \left(\rho\,\frac{d^2\phi}{dt^2} + 2\,\frac{d\rho}{dt}\,\frac{d\phi}{dt}\right)\mathbf{e}_\phi + \frac{d^2z}{dt^2}\,\mathbf{k}. \tag{7.9}$$

**PROBLEM 7.2** Verify (7.7–9).

**Solution:** Referring to Fig. 7.1 and Sec. 5.4, the position vector in cylindrical coordinates is

$$\mathbf{r}(t) = \rho\,\mathbf{e}_\rho + z\,\mathbf{k}. \qquad [7.7]$$

Since $\mathbf{k}$ is constant in time and the unit vector $\mathbf{e}_\rho$ changes direction in time, the velocity vector is

$$\mathbf{v}(t) = \frac{d\mathbf{r}(t)}{dt} = \frac{d\rho}{dt}\,\mathbf{e}_\rho + \rho\,\frac{d\mathbf{e}_\rho}{dt} + \frac{dz}{dt}\,\mathbf{k}. \qquad (7.10)$$

Now, from (5.81a), the relationship between $\mathbf{e}_\rho$ in cylindrical coordinates and $\mathbf{i}$ and $\mathbf{j}$ in rectangular coordinates is

$$\mathbf{e}_\rho = \cos\phi\,\mathbf{i} + \sin\phi\,\mathbf{j}, \qquad [5.81a]$$

and hence, because of (5.81b), its derivative is

$$\frac{d\mathbf{e}_\rho}{dt} = -\sin\phi\,\frac{d\phi}{dt}\,\mathbf{i} + \cos\phi\,\frac{d\phi}{dt}\,\mathbf{j}$$

$$= \frac{d\phi}{dt}(-\sin\phi\,\mathbf{i} + \cos\phi\,\mathbf{j})$$

$$= \frac{d\phi}{dt}\,\mathbf{e}_\phi. \qquad (7.11)$$

Hence, the velocity vector in cylindrical coordinates is

$$\mathbf{v}(t) = \frac{d\rho}{dt}\,\mathbf{e}_\rho + \rho\,\frac{d\phi}{dt}\,\mathbf{e}_\phi + \frac{dz}{dt}\,\mathbf{k}. \qquad [7.8]$$

Similarly, $\mathbf{e}_\phi$ also changes direction in time, and thus,

$$\mathbf{a}(t) = \frac{d\mathbf{v}(t)}{dt} = \frac{d^2\rho}{dt^2}\,\mathbf{e}_\rho + \frac{d\rho}{dt}\,\frac{d\mathbf{e}_\rho}{dt} + \frac{d}{dt}\left(\rho\,\frac{d\phi}{dt}\right)\mathbf{e}_\phi + \rho\,\frac{d\phi}{dt}\,\frac{d\mathbf{e}_\phi}{dt} + \frac{d^2z}{dt^2}\,\mathbf{k}. \qquad (7.12)$$

From (5.81b), $\mathbf{e}_\phi$ in terms of $\mathbf{i}$ and $\mathbf{j}$ is

$$\mathbf{e}_\phi = -\sin\phi\,\mathbf{i} + \cos\phi\,\mathbf{j}, \qquad [5.81b]$$

and hence, because of (5.81a), its derivative is

$$\frac{d\mathbf{e}_\phi}{dt} = -\cos\phi\,\frac{d\phi}{dt}\,\mathbf{i} - \sin\phi\,\frac{d\phi}{dt}\,\mathbf{j}$$

$$= -\frac{d\phi}{dt}(\cos\phi\,\mathbf{i} + \sin\phi\,\mathbf{j})$$

$$= -\frac{d\phi}{dt}\,\mathbf{e}_\rho. \qquad (7.13)$$

Substituting (7.11) and (7.13) into (7.12) and rearranging the terms,

$$\mathbf{a}(t) = \left[\frac{d^2\rho}{dt^2} - \rho\left(\frac{d\phi}{dt}\right)^2\right]\mathbf{e}_\rho + \left(\rho\,\frac{d^2\phi}{dt^2} + 2\,\frac{d\rho}{dt}\,\frac{d\phi}{dt}\right)\mathbf{e}_\phi + \frac{d^2z}{dt^2}\,\mathbf{k}. \qquad [7.9]$$

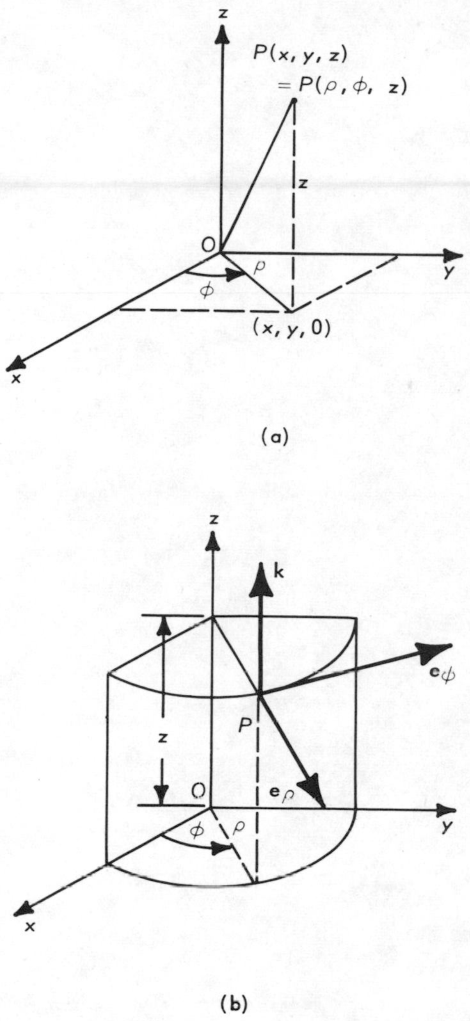


Fig. 7.1 Cylindrical coordinates.

*Kepler's Second Law of Planetary Motion* states that if the acceleration of a particle moving in a plane is directed towards the origin, then

$$\rho^2\,\frac{d\phi}{dt} = \text{constant}. \qquad (7.14)$$

Equivalently, the radius vector from the origin to the particle sweeps out equal areas in equal intervals of time.

**PROBLEM 7.3** Prove Kepler's second law of planetary motion (7.14).

**Solution:** Since the polar coordinates of a plane are merely cylindrical coordinates with $z = 0$, from (7.9), the acceleration vector $\mathbf{a}$ in plane polar coordinates can be expressed as

$$\mathbf{a} = \left[\frac{d^2\rho}{dt^2} - \rho\left(\frac{d\phi}{dt}\right)^2\right]\mathbf{e}_\rho + \left(\rho\frac{d^2\phi}{dt^2} + 2\frac{d\rho}{dt}\frac{d\phi}{dt}\right)\mathbf{e}_\phi$$

$$= \left[\frac{d^2\rho}{dt^2} - \rho\left(\frac{d\phi}{dt}\right)^2\right]\mathbf{e}_\rho + \frac{1}{\rho}\frac{d}{dt}\left(\rho^2\frac{d\phi}{dt}\right)\mathbf{e}_\phi. \tag{7.15}$$

Now, since the acceleration vector is directed towards the origin, the component of the acceleration in the $\mathbf{e}_\phi$ direction is zero; i.e.,

$$\frac{1}{\rho}\frac{d}{dt}\left(\rho^2\frac{d\phi}{dt}\right) = 0. \tag{7.16}$$

Hence,

$$\rho^2\frac{d\phi}{dt} = \text{constant}. \qquad [7.14]$$

Also, from (7.7), the radius vector in plane polar coordinates is

$$\mathbf{r} = \rho\,\mathbf{e}_\rho, \tag{7.17}$$

and from (7.11), its differential is

$$d\mathbf{r} = d\rho\,\mathbf{e}_\rho + \rho\,d\mathbf{e}_\rho = d\rho\,\mathbf{e}_\rho + \rho\,d\phi\,\mathbf{e}_\phi. \tag{7.18}$$

Now if $A$ is the area swept out by $\mathbf{r}$ at any time $t$, then from

$$\oint_C \mathbf{r}\times d\mathbf{r} = 2\iint_S d\mathbf{S}, \qquad [4.127]$$

we have

$$|\mathbf{r}\times d\mathbf{r}| = 2\,dA. \tag{7.19}$$

From (7.17–8),

$$\mathbf{r}\times d\mathbf{r} = \rho\mathbf{e}_\rho\times(d\rho\,\mathbf{e}_\rho + \rho\,d\phi\,\mathbf{e}_\phi) = \rho^2\,d\phi\,\mathbf{k} \tag{7.20}$$

since $\mathbf{e}_\rho\times\mathbf{e}_\rho = 0$ and $\mathbf{e}_\rho\times\mathbf{e}_\phi = \mathbf{k}$. Hence, the radial area $dA$ swept over during the time $dt$ is

$$dA = \frac{1}{2}\rho^2\,d\phi,$$

and consequently, from (7.14),

$$\frac{dA}{dt} = \frac{1}{2}\rho^2\frac{d\phi}{dt} = \text{constant}. \tag{7.21}$$

Equation (7.21) shows that equal areas are swept out in equal intervals of time.

The *speed* $v(t)$ of a particle at time $t$ is the magnitude of the velocity vector $\mathbf{v}(t)$. If $s$ is the arc length that measures the distance of the particle from its starting point on a path C along a curve, then from (3.54),

$$v(t) = |\mathbf{v}(t)| = |\mathbf{r}'(t)| = \frac{ds}{dt}. \tag{7.22}$$

**PROBLEM 7.4** Show that the acceleration vector

$$\mathbf{a}(t) = \frac{dv}{at}\mathbf{T} + \kappa v^2\mathbf{N} = \frac{dv}{dt}\mathbf{T} + \frac{v^2}{\rho}\mathbf{N}, \tag{7.23}$$

where $\kappa$ and $\rho = 1/\kappa$ are the curvature and radius of curvature of the path $C$, $\mathbf{T}$ is the unit tangent vector to $C$ at $\mathbf{r}(t)$, and $\mathbf{N}$, the unit principal normal vector. (See Sec. 6.3.)

**Solution:** From Sec. 3.4, we know that the velocity vector $\mathbf{v}(t) = \mathbf{r}'(t)$ is tangent to $C$ at the terminal point of $\mathbf{r}(t)$. Then, if $v(t)$ is the speed of the particle, the velocity vector is

$$\mathbf{v}(t) - v(t)\frac{\mathbf{r}'(t)}{|\mathbf{r}'(t)|} = v(t)\,\mathbf{T}. \tag{7.24}$$

Differentiating (7.24) with respect to time $t$ and then using the Frenet-Serret formulas (6.20), (6.26), and (6.28), as well as (7.22), the acceleration vector is

$$\begin{aligned}\mathbf{a}(t) = \mathbf{v}'(t) &= \frac{d}{dt}[v(t)\,\mathbf{T}]\\ &= \frac{dv}{dt}\mathbf{T} + v(t)\frac{d\mathbf{T}}{dt}\\ &= \frac{dv}{dt}\mathbf{T} + v\frac{d\mathbf{T}}{ds}\frac{ds}{dt}\\ &= \frac{dv}{dt}\mathbf{T} + v^2\kappa\,\mathbf{N}\\ &= \frac{dv}{dt}\mathbf{T} + \frac{v^2}{\rho}\mathbf{N}.\end{aligned}$$

Equation (7.23) shows that the acceleration of the particle can be resolved into two components: a *tangential component* of magnitude $dv/dt$ and a *normal component* of magnitude $v^2\kappa = v^2/\rho$. The normal component, called the *centripetal acceleration*, is caused by the fact that the velocity vector changes direction. (See Fig. 7.2)

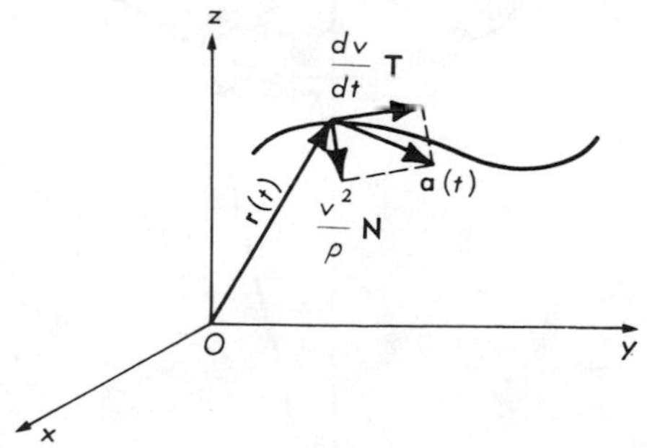


Fig. 7.2 Centripetal acceleration.

**PROBLEM 7.5** Find the tangential component $a_t$ and normal component $a_n$ of the acceleration vector if the velocity and acceleration vectors of a particle are known.

**Solution:** Let the velocity and acceleration vectors be

$$\mathbf{v} = v(t)\,\mathbf{T}, \tag*{[7.24]}$$

$$\mathbf{a} = a_t\,\mathbf{T} + a_n\,\mathbf{N}. \tag{7.25}$$

Since $\mathbf{v}\cdot\mathbf{T} = v$ and $\mathbf{v}\cdot\mathbf{N} = 0$, we take the dot product of both sides of (7.25) with $\mathbf{v}$ and obtain

$$a_t = \frac{\mathbf{a}\cdot\mathbf{v}}{v}. \tag{7.26}$$

Since $\mathbf{v}\times\mathbf{T} = \mathbf{0}$ and $|\mathbf{v}\times\mathbf{N}| = v$, by taking the cross product of both sides of (7.25) with $\mathbf{v}$ and then taking the absolute value of both sides yields

$$a_n = \frac{|\mathbf{a} \times \mathbf{v}|}{v}. \tag{7.27}$$

Hence, the acceleration vector in (7.25) becomes

$$\mathbf{a} = \frac{\mathbf{a} \cdot \mathbf{v}}{v} \mathbf{T} + \frac{|\mathbf{a} \times \mathbf{v}|}{v} \mathbf{N}. \tag{7.28}$$

Comparing (7.25) and (7.23),

$$a_t = \frac{dv}{dt} = \frac{\mathbf{a} \cdot \mathbf{v}}{v},$$

$$a_n = \frac{v^2}{\rho} = \frac{|\mathbf{a} \times \mathbf{v}|}{v}.$$

**PROBLEM 7.6** The position vector of a particle, moving in a plane, at any time $t$ is

$$\mathbf{r} = (a \cos \omega t)\, \mathbf{i} + (b \sin \omega t)\, \mathbf{j}. \tag{7.29}$$

Show that its acceleration is always directed toward the origin.

**Solution:** Taking the derivative of (7.29), the velocity vector is

$$\mathbf{v} = \mathbf{r}'(t) = -\omega a \sin \omega t\, \mathbf{i} + \omega b \cos \omega t\, \mathbf{j}.$$

Then the acceleration vector is

$$\begin{aligned} \mathbf{a} = \mathbf{v}'(t) = \mathbf{r}''(t) &= -\omega^2 a \cos \omega t\, \mathbf{i} - \omega^2 b \sin \omega t\, \mathbf{j} \\ &= -\omega^2 (a \cos \omega t\, \mathbf{i} + b \sin \omega t\, \mathbf{j}) \\ &= -\omega^2 \mathbf{r}. \end{aligned} \tag{7.30}$$

Hence, its acceleration is always directed toward the origin; i.e., this is the centripetal acceleration caused by rotation.

## 7.2 Angular Velocity and Angular Acceleration

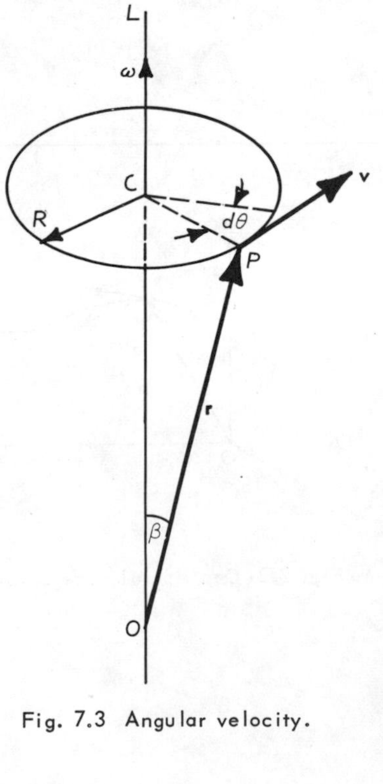

Fig. 7.3 Angular velocity.

Let a particle $P$ rotate about a fixed line $L$ at a fixed distance $R$ from it. As the particle moves in the circular path, the rate of change of the angular position $\theta(t)$ is called the *angular speed* $\omega$; i.e.,

$$\omega = \frac{d\theta(t)}{dt}. \tag{7.31}$$

The *angular velocity* $\boldsymbol{\omega}$ of the particle is a vector of magnitude $\omega$; its direction along $L$ is that of a right-hand screw advance when the screw is turned in the same sense as the rotation of the particle. (See Fig. 7.3.)

The *angular acceleration* of the particle $\alpha(t)$ is

$$\alpha(t) = \frac{d\omega}{dt}. \tag{7.32}$$

**PROBLEM 7.7** Show that the velocity vector $\mathbf{v}$ of a particle rotating about a fixed axis $L$ can be written as

$$\mathbf{v} = \boldsymbol{\omega} \times \mathbf{r}, \tag{7.33}$$

where $\mathbf{r}$ specifies the position of the particle from $L$. Note that the origin $O$ can be any point on $L$.

**Solution:** For motion in a circle of radius $R$, the speed $v$ of the particle is

$$v = R\frac{d\theta}{dt} = R\omega, \tag{7.34}$$

where $\theta$ is the angular position and $\omega$, the angular speed of the particle. Now, referring to Fig. 7.3, if $\beta$ is the angle between $\boldsymbol{\omega}$ and $\mathbf{r}$, then

$$|\omega \times \mathbf{r}| = \omega r \sin\beta = \omega R = v.$$

The velocity vector $\mathbf{v}$ lies in the plane of the circle and is perpendicular to $\mathbf{r}$. Since $\omega \times \mathbf{r}$ is perpendicular to the plane spanned by $\mathbf{r}$ and $\omega$, it is perpendicular to the radius $CP$; i.e., $\mathbf{v}$ and $\omega \times \mathbf{r}$ are parallel. Thus,

$$\mathbf{v} = \omega \times \mathbf{r}.$$

**PROBLEM 7.8** If $\boldsymbol{\alpha} = d\omega/dt$ is the angular acceleration of the particle rotating about a fixed axis $L$, show that its acceleration vector $\mathbf{a}$ can be expressed as

(a)
$$\mathbf{a} = \omega \times \mathbf{v} + \boldsymbol{\alpha} \times \mathbf{r}, \tag{7.35}$$

or

(b)
$$\mathbf{a} = -\omega^2\mathbf{r} + \boldsymbol{\alpha} \times \mathbf{r}. \tag{7.36}$$

**Solution:** (a) Differentiating (7.33),

$$\mathbf{a} = \frac{d\mathbf{v}}{dt} = \frac{d}{dt}(\omega \times \mathbf{r})$$

$$= \omega \times \frac{d\mathbf{r}}{dt} + \frac{d\omega}{dt} \times \mathbf{r}$$

$$= \omega \times \mathbf{v} + \boldsymbol{\alpha} \times \mathbf{r}.$$

(b) Next, since $\mathbf{v} = \omega \times \mathbf{r}$, and using the definition of the vector triple product (1.83),

$$\mathbf{a} = \omega \times (\omega \times \mathbf{r}) + \boldsymbol{\alpha} \times \mathbf{r}$$

$$= (\boldsymbol{\omega} \cdot \mathbf{r})\boldsymbol{\omega} - \omega^2\mathbf{r} + \boldsymbol{\alpha} \times \mathbf{r}. \tag{7.37}$$

If, in addition to choosing the origin $O$ on the axis $L$, we let $O$ be in the plane of motion, then $\omega \perp \mathbf{r}$, or $\omega \cdot \mathbf{r} = 0$; consequently,

$$\mathbf{a} = -\omega^2\mathbf{r} + \boldsymbol{\alpha} \times \mathbf{r}.$$

Note that $\boldsymbol{\alpha} \times \mathbf{r}$ is the tangential acceleration and $\boldsymbol{\omega} \times (\boldsymbol{\omega} \times \mathbf{r})$, the centripetal acceleration.

**PROBLEM 7.9** Show that when a particle rotates with a constant angular velocity, the curl of the velocity field is twice the angular velocity of the particle.

**Solution:** Since $\mathbf{v} = \omega \times \mathbf{r}$, and by applying (3.158) and the definition of $\nabla$, the curl of the velocity field is

$$\nabla \times \mathbf{v} = \nabla \times (\omega \times \mathbf{r})$$

$$= \omega(\nabla \cdot \mathbf{r}) - \mathbf{r}(\nabla \cdot \omega) + (\mathbf{r} \cdot \nabla)\omega - (\omega \cdot \nabla)\mathbf{r}.$$

Now, since $\omega$ is a constant vector, $\nabla \cdot \omega = 0$ and $(\mathbf{r} \cdot \nabla)\omega = 0$. From

$$\nabla \cdot \mathbf{r} = \frac{\partial x}{\partial x} + \frac{\partial y}{\partial y} + \frac{\partial z}{\partial z} = 3, \qquad [3.129]$$

$\nabla \cdot \mathbf{r} = 3$, and from

$$(\mathbf{f} \cdot \nabla)\mathbf{r} = \mathbf{f}, \tag{3.149}$$

$(\omega \cdot \nabla)\mathbf{r} = \omega$. Hence, the curl is

$$\nabla \times \mathbf{v} = \omega(\nabla \cdot \mathbf{r}) - (\omega \cdot \nabla)\mathbf{r} = 3\omega - \omega = 2\omega. \tag{7.38}$$

## 7.3 Forces and Moments

The motion of a particle is governed by Newton's *laws of motion*:

(1) A particle remains in its state of rest or uniform rectilinear motion unless acted upon by a force.

(2) The time rate of change of the product of the mass and velocity of a particle is proportional to the force acting upon the particle.

The product of mass $m$ and velocity $\mathbf{v}$ is called the *linear momentum* $\mathbf{p}$ of the particle and is represented by

$$\mathbf{p} = m\mathbf{v}. \tag{7.39}$$

Thus Newton's second law of motion can be written as

$$\mathbf{f} = \frac{d\mathbf{p}}{dt} = \frac{d}{dt}(m\mathbf{v}). \tag{7.40}$$

If the mass $m$ is a constant and $\mathbf{a}$ is the acceleration vector, then (7.40) can be rewritten as

$$\mathbf{f} = m\frac{d\mathbf{v}}{dt} = m\frac{d^2\mathbf{r}}{dt^2} = m\mathbf{a}. \tag{7.41}$$

(3) To every action or force, there is always an equal and opposite reaction or force.

This law applies only to *central forces*, which are those exerted by two particles on each other and directed along the line connecting them.

**PROBLEM 7.10** The force exerted by the sun on a planet is

$$\mathbf{f} = -\left(Gm\frac{M}{r^3}\right)\mathbf{r}, \tag{7.42}$$

where $G$ is the gravitational constant, $m$ and $M$, the masses of the planet and sun, and $r$, the position vector from the sun at the origin to any point on the planet.

(a) Using Newton's second law (7.41), show that

$$\frac{d}{dt}(\mathbf{r} \times \mathbf{v}) = \mathbf{r} \times \left(-\frac{Gm}{r^3}\mathbf{r}\right) = \mathbf{0}; \tag{7.43}$$

and hence, for some constant vector $\mathbf{h}$,

$$\mathbf{r} \times \mathbf{v} = \mathbf{r} \times \frac{d\mathbf{r}}{dt} = \mathbf{h}. \tag{7.44}$$

(b) Show that $dA/dt = \frac{1}{2}h$, where $A$ is the area swept out by $\mathbf{r}$, and thus prove Kepler's second law of planetary motion (7.14).

**Solution:** (a) From Newton's second law of motion (7.41), the force vector is $\mathbf{f} = -(GmM/r^3)\,\mathbf{r} = m(d\mathbf{v}/dt)$, and, consequently,

$$\frac{d\mathbf{v}}{dt} = -\frac{GM}{r^3}\mathbf{r}. \tag{7.45}$$

Now since $d\mathbf{r}/dt = \mathbf{v}$ and $\mathbf{v} \times \mathbf{v} = \mathbf{0}$,

$$\frac{d}{dt}(\mathbf{r} \times \mathbf{v}) = \mathbf{r} \times \frac{d\mathbf{v}}{dt} + \frac{d\mathbf{r}}{dt} \times \mathbf{v} = \mathbf{r} \times \frac{d\mathbf{v}}{dt}. \tag{7.46}$$

Hence, substituting the value of $d\mathbf{v}/dt$ from (7.45) into (7.46) and because $\mathbf{r} \times \mathbf{r} = \mathbf{0}$,

$$\frac{d}{dt}(\mathbf{r} \times \mathbf{v}) = \mathbf{r} \times \frac{d\mathbf{v}}{dt} = \mathbf{r} \times \left(-\frac{GM}{r^3}\mathbf{r}\right) = \mathbf{0}. \tag{7.47}$$

Thus (7.47) implies that

$$\mathbf{r} \times \mathbf{v} = \mathbf{r} \times \frac{d\mathbf{r}}{dt} = \mathbf{h}.$$

(b) Now, if $A$ is the area swept out by $\mathbf{r}$ at any time $t$, then from

$$\oint_C \mathbf{r} \times d\mathbf{r} = 2 \iint_S d\mathbf{S}, \qquad [4.127]$$

we have $|\mathbf{r} \times d\mathbf{r}| = 2\, dA$, where $dA$ is the sectoral area. (See Fig. 7.4.) Hence, if $h$ is a constant, then

$$2\frac{dA}{dt} = h \qquad \text{or} \qquad \frac{dA}{dt} = \frac{1}{2}h;$$

i.e., equal areas are swept out by $\mathbf{r}$ in equal intervals of time.

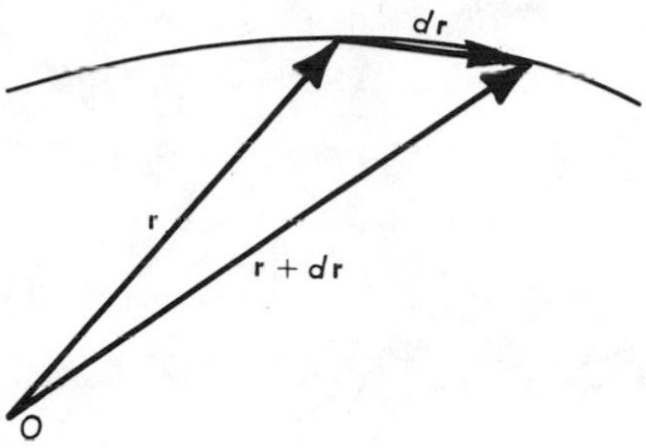

Fig. 7.4 Verification of Kepler's second law of planetary motion.

The *angular momentum* $\mathbf{L}$ of a particle with respect to an origin is

$$\mathbf{L} = \mathbf{r} \times \mathbf{p}, \tag{7.48}$$

where $\mathbf{r}$ is the position vector of the particle, relative to the origin, and $\mathbf{p}$ is the linear momentum.

The *moment* or *torque* $\boldsymbol{\tau}$ of a force $\mathbf{f}$ acting on a particle, relative to the origin, is

$$\boldsymbol{\tau} = \mathbf{r} \times \mathbf{f}. \tag{7.49}$$

**PROBLEM 7.11** Show that

$$\boldsymbol{\tau} = \frac{d\mathbf{L}}{dt}. \tag{7.50}$$

**Solution:** From the definition of a torque (7.49) and Newton's second law of motion (7.40),

$$\boldsymbol{\tau} = \mathbf{r} \times \frac{d\mathbf{p}}{dt}. \tag{7.51}$$

Now differentiating (7.48),

$$\frac{d\mathbf{L}}{dt} = \frac{d}{dt}(\mathbf{r} \times \mathbf{p}) = \frac{d\mathbf{r}}{dt} \times \mathbf{p} + \mathbf{r} \times \frac{d\mathbf{p}}{dt}.$$

Since $d\mathbf{p}/dt - \mathbf{f}$ and

$$\frac{d\mathbf{r}}{dt} \times \mathbf{p} = \mathbf{v} \times (m\mathbf{v}) = m(\mathbf{v} \times \mathbf{v}) = \mathbf{0},$$

$$\frac{d\mathbf{L}}{dt} = \mathbf{r} \times \mathbf{f} = \boldsymbol{\tau};$$

i.e., the torque is equal to the time rate of change of angular momentum. Note that the derivation did not assume a constant mass.

A particle is said to be *free* if it experiences no force.

**PROBLEM 7.12** Show that the linear momentum of a free particle is conserved.

**Solution:** If the force $\mathbf{f}$ acting on a particle is zero, then Newton's second law of motion (7.40) becomes

$$\frac{d\mathbf{p}}{dt} = \mathbf{0}, \tag{7.52}$$

which implies that $\mathbf{p}$ is a constant vector in time. Therefore, the linear momentum of a free particle is conserved.

**PROBLEM 7.13** Show that the angular momentum of a particle is conserved if there is no torque acting on it.

**Solution:** If the torque $\boldsymbol{\tau}$ acting on a particle is zero, then (7.50) reduces to

$$\frac{d\mathbf{L}}{dt} = \mathbf{0}, \tag{7.53}$$

which implies that $\mathbf{L}$ is a constant vector in time. Hence the angular momentum of a particle is conserved if there is no torque.

## 7.4 Work and Energy

The *work* $W$ done by a force $\mathbf{f}$ to move a particle along a curve C from point 1 to point 2 is defined by the line integral

$$W_{12} = \int_{\mathbf{r}_1}^{\mathbf{r}_2} \mathbf{f} \cdot d\mathbf{r}, \tag{7.54}$$

where $\mathbf{r}_1$ and $\mathbf{r}_2$ are the position vectors of points 1 and 2, respectively.

The work done by $\mathbf{f}$ is generally dependent on the path C. If $\mathbf{f}$ is perpendicular to the direction of motion, $W = 0$; i.e., no work is done.

**PROBLEM 7.14** Show that, for a constant mass, the work done in going from point 1 to point 2 is

$$W_{12} = \frac{1}{2} m\mathbf{v}_2 \cdot \mathbf{v}_2 - \frac{1}{2} m\mathbf{v}_1 \cdot \mathbf{v}_1 = \frac{1}{2} m\,(v_2^2 - v_1^2), \tag{7.55}$$

where $\mathbf{v}_1$ and $\mathbf{v}_2$ are the velocities of the particle at points 1 and 2, respectively.

**Solution:** Now, $\mathbf{f} = m(d\mathbf{v}/dt)$, and $d\mathbf{r} = \dfrac{d\mathbf{r}}{dt}\,dt = \mathbf{v}\,dt$. Thus, the work done is

$$W_{12} = \int_{\mathbf{r}_1}^{\mathbf{r}_2} \mathbf{f} \cdot d\mathbf{r} = \int_{t_1}^{t_2} m \frac{d\mathbf{v}}{dt} \cdot \mathbf{v}\, dt = \int_{\mathbf{v}_1}^{\mathbf{v}_2} m\mathbf{v} \cdot d\mathbf{v}$$

$$= \frac{m}{2} \int_{\mathbf{v}=\mathbf{v}_1}^{\mathbf{v}=\mathbf{v}_2} d(\mathbf{v} \cdot \mathbf{v})$$

$$= \frac{m}{2} (\mathbf{v} \cdot \mathbf{v}) \Big|_{\mathbf{v}_1}^{\mathbf{v}_2}$$

$$= \frac{m}{2} (\mathbf{v}_2 \cdot \mathbf{v}_2) - \frac{m}{2} (\mathbf{v}_1 \cdot \mathbf{v}_1)$$

$$= \frac{m}{2} (v_2^2 - v_1^2).$$

Since the *kinetic energy* $T$ of a particle is the scalar quantity defined as

$$T = \frac{1}{2} m\mathbf{v} \cdot \mathbf{v} = \frac{1}{2} mv^2, \tag{7.56}$$

(7.55) can be rewritten as

$$W_{12} = T_2 - T_1, \tag{7.57}$$

which shows that the work done is equal to the change in the kinetic energy of the particle.

A force $\mathbf{f}$ is said to be *conservative* if the work $W$ done by it around any closed path is zero; i.e.,

$$\oint \mathbf{f} \cdot d\mathbf{r} = 0. \tag{7.58}$$

If $\mathbf{f}$ is a conservative force, then

$$\nabla \times \mathbf{f} = \mathbf{0}, \tag{7.59}$$

and $\mathbf{f}$ can be expressed as the gradient of a scalar function $-V$, i.e.,

$$\mathbf{f} = -\nabla V, \tag{7.60}$$

where $V$ is called the *potential* or *potential energy*. The region is simply connected if $V$ is single-valued. Since any constant can be added to $V$ in (7.60) without affecting the result, the zero level of potential energy is arbitrary. Hence, potential energy has no absolute meaning, and only differences of potential energy have physical meaning.

Specifically, potential energy $V$ is the work done by a conservative force $\mathbf{f}$ in moving a particle from point 1 to point 2. That is, the work done by a conservative force in moving a particle is the difference in potential energies of the particle at the two points. Symbolically, if $\mathbf{f}$ is a conservative force, then the work done in moving the particle from point 1 to point 2 is

$$W_{12} = \int_{\mathbf{r}_1}^{\mathbf{r}_2} \mathbf{f} \cdot d\mathbf{r} = V_1 - V_2, \tag{7.61}$$

where $V_1$ and $V_2$ are the potential energies at points 1 and 2, respectively.

**PROBLEM 7.15** Verify (7.59–60).

**Solution:** The condition (7.59) is established in Prob. 4.58. For convenience, the solution is repeated here. Since f is conservative, we have from (7.58),

$$\oint_C \mathbf{f} \cdot d\mathbf{r} = 0 \qquad [7.58]$$

for any closed curve $C$. Now assume that $\nabla \times \mathbf{f} \neq \mathbf{0}$ at some point $P$ on $C$. If we assume that $\nabla \times \mathbf{f}$ is continuous, there will be some region about $P$ where $\nabla \times \mathbf{f} \neq \mathbf{0}$. Choose a small plane surface $S$ in this region and a unit normal vector $\mathbf{n}$ to $S$, parallel to $\nabla \times \mathbf{f}$, i.e., $\nabla \times \mathbf{f} \cong a\mathbf{n}$, where $a > 0$. Let $C$ be the boundary of $S$. Then by Stokes' theorem (4.104),

$$\oint_C \mathbf{f} \cdot d\mathbf{r} = \iint_S \nabla \times \mathbf{f} \cdot d\mathbf{S} = \iint_S a\mathbf{n} \cdot \mathbf{n}\, dS = a \iint_S dS = aS > 0,$$

which contradicts the fact that f is conservative. Hence, $\nabla \times \mathbf{f} = \mathbf{0}$.

Equation (7.60) is established in Probs. 4.57 and 4.58. The solution to Prob. 4.57 is repeated here. If $\mathbf{f} = -\nabla V$ for a scalar function $V$, then, by Stokes' theorem (4.104),

$$\oint_C \mathbf{f} \cdot d\mathbf{r} = \oint_C (-\nabla V) \cdot d\mathbf{r}$$

$$= \iint_S \nabla \times (-\nabla V)\, d\mathbf{S},$$

where $S$ is the surface enclosed by $C$. But from (3.134), $\nabla \times (-\nabla V) = \mathbf{0}$; hence,

$$\oint_C \mathbf{f} \cdot d\mathbf{r} = 0;$$

i.e., f is conservative.

**PROBLEM 7.16** Verify (7.61).

**Solution:** Since f is conservative, we have from (7.60),

$$W_{12} = \int_{r_1}^{r_2} \mathbf{f} \cdot d\mathbf{r} = -\int_{r_1}^{r_2} \nabla V \cdot d\mathbf{r}.$$

Now from (3.120),

$$\nabla V \cdot d\mathbf{r} = dV.$$

Hence, the work done in moving the particle from point 1 to point 2 is

$$W_{12} = \int_{r_1}^{r_2} \mathbf{f} \cdot d\mathbf{r} = -\int_{V=V_1}^{V=V_2} dV = -(V_2 - V_1) = V_1 - V_2.$$

**PROBLEM 7.17** (a) Show that a force, such as the gravitational force in Prob. 7.10, that obeys the *inverse square law*,

$$\mathbf{f} = -\frac{k}{r^3}\mathbf{r} = -\frac{k}{r^2}\mathbf{e}_r, \qquad (7.62)$$

where $k$ is a constant, is a conservative force. (b) Find the potential energy of the particle acted upon by this force.

**Solution:** (a) From (3.169), i.e., $\nabla \times [f(r)\mathbf{r}] = [f'(r)/r]\, \mathbf{r} \times \mathbf{r} = \mathbf{0}$,

$$\nabla \times \mathbf{f} = \nabla \times \left(-\frac{k}{r^3}\mathbf{r}\right) = \mathbf{0}.$$

Hence the force f is conservative.

(b) The work done is

$$W_{12} = \int_{r_1}^{r_2} \mathbf{f} \cdot d\mathbf{r} = \int_{r_1}^{r_2} \left( -\frac{k}{r^3} \mathbf{r} \right) \cdot d\mathbf{r}$$

$$= -\int_{r_1}^{r_2} \frac{k}{r^2} dr$$

$$= \frac{k}{r} \Big|_{r_1}^{r_2}$$

$$= k \left( \frac{1}{r_2} - \frac{1}{r_1} \right)$$

$$= V_1 - V_2.$$

When $r_2 = \infty$, it is usually understood that $V_2 = 0$; then with this datum, the gravitational potential becomes

$$V = -\frac{k}{r}. \tag{7.63}$$

*Hooke's law* states that an elastic force $\mathbf{f}$ is directly proportional to the displacement vector $\mathbf{r}$ of the particle upon which it acts. Thus,

$$\mathbf{f} = -k\mathbf{r}, \tag{7.64}$$

where $k$ is a constant.

**PROBLEM 7.18** (a) Verify that (7.64) is a conservative force, and (b) find the potential energy of a particle acted upon by this $\mathbf{f}$.

**Solution:** (a) From (3.141), the curl of $\mathbf{f}$ is

$$\nabla \times \mathbf{f} = \nabla \times (-k\mathbf{r}) = -k\nabla \times \mathbf{r} = \mathbf{0}.$$

Hence, the elastic force $\mathbf{f}$ is conservative.

(b) The work done in moving the particle from point 1 to point 2 is

$$W_{12} = \int_{r_1}^{r_2} \mathbf{f} \cdot d\mathbf{r} = \int_{r_1}^{r_2} (-k\mathbf{r}) \cdot d\mathbf{r}$$

$$= -k \int_{r_1}^{r_2} r\, dr$$

$$= -\frac{k}{2} r^2 \Big|_{r_1}^{r_2}$$

$$= \frac{k}{2} r_1^2 - \frac{k}{2} r_2^2$$

$$= V_1 - V_2.$$

We take $V = 0$ when $r = 0$. Thus the potential energy of a particle becomes

$$V = \frac{k}{2} r^2. \tag{7.65}$$

The *principle of conservation of energy* states that if a force $\mathbf{f}$ acting on a particle is conservative, the sum of the kinetic energy $T$ and potential energy $V$ of the particle is a constant; i.e.,

$$T + V = E. \tag{7.66}$$

$E$ is called the *total mechanical energy* of the particle.

**PROBLEM 7.19** Prove the principle of conservation of energy (7.66).

**Solution:** From (7.61), the work done by a conservative force to move a particle from point 1 to point 2 is

$$W_{12} = V_1 - V_2, \qquad [7.61]$$

where $V_1$ and $V_2$ are the potential energies of the particle at points 1 and 2. Now, from (7.57), if $T_1$ and $T_2$ are the kinetic energies of the particle at points 1 and 2, the work done is

$$W_{12} = T_2 - T_1. \qquad [7.57]$$

Hence, combining (7.57) and (7.61),

$$T_1 + V_1 = T_2 + V_2.$$

Thus the total mechanical energy $T + V$ is the same at points 1 and 2; hence, it is a constant. Thus, if $E$ is a constant,

$$T_1 + V_1 = T_2 + V_2 = E.$$

## 7.5 Systems of Particles

In this section, we extend the ideas of Sec. 7.4 to a system consisting of a finite number of particles.

*External forces* are those that act upon a particle due to sources outside the system.

*Internal forces* are those that act upon a particle due to all other particles within the system.

Let the mass of a $i$th particle be $m_i$ and its position vector be $\mathbf{r}_i$; then we define a vector $\overline{\mathbf{r}}$ that specifies the *center of mass* (c.m.) of the system as

$$\overline{\mathbf{r}} = \frac{\Sigma m_i \mathbf{r}_i}{\Sigma m_i} = \frac{\Sigma m_i \mathbf{r}_i}{M}, \tag{7.67}$$

where the total mass of the system is $M = \Sigma m_i$. The summation is over all particles.

**PROBLEM 7.20** Show that the center of mass of a system moves as if it were a particle of mass equal to the total mass of the system acted on by the external forces.

**Solution:** From Newton's second law of motion (7.41), the equation of motion for the $i$th particle is

$$m_i \frac{d^2\mathbf{r}_i}{dt^2} = \mathbf{f}_i^{(e)} + \sum_j \mathbf{f}_{ji}, \tag{7.68}$$

where $\mathbf{f}_i^{(e)}$ is the external force acting upon the $i$th particle and $\mathbf{f}_{ji}$, the internal force acting upon the $i$th particle because of the $j$th particle. (Note that $\mathbf{f}_{ii} = \mathbf{0}$.) Summed over all particles, (7.68) becomes

$$\sum_i m_i \frac{d^2\mathbf{r}_i}{dt^2} = \sum_i \mathbf{f}_i^{(e)} + \sum_i \sum_j \mathbf{f}_{ji}. \tag{7.69}$$

Now, from Newton's third law of action and reaction, each pair of the internal forces $\mathbf{f}_{ij} = -\mathbf{f}_{ji}$. Hence, the double sum in (7.69) vanishes, and the internal forces of the system cancel out in the summation. Using (7.67), (7.69) reduces to

$$M \frac{d^2\bar{\mathbf{r}}}{dt^2} = \sum_i \mathbf{f}_i^{(e)}, \tag{7.70}$$

indicating that the center of mass moves as if the sum of the external forces $\sum_i \mathbf{f}_i^{(e)}$, acted upon the entire mass of the system, is concentrated at the center of mass.

**PROBLEM 7.21** Show that the total linear momentum of a system,

$$\mathbf{P} = \sum m_i \frac{d\mathbf{r}_i}{dt}, \tag{7.71}$$

is equal to the product of the total mass of the system and the velocity of the center of mass.

**Solution:** Since $\Sigma m_i \mathbf{r}_i = M\bar{\mathbf{r}}$, from (7.67) the total linear momentum is

$$\mathbf{P} = \sum m_i \frac{d\mathbf{r}_i}{dt} = M \frac{d\bar{\mathbf{r}}}{dt}. \tag{7.72}$$

The *principle of conservation of linear momentum* for a system of particles states that if the total external force of a system is zero, then the total linear momentum is conserved.

**PROBLEM 7.22** Prove the principle of conservation of linear momentum for a system of particles.

**Solution:** Using (7.72), (7.70) reduces to

$$\frac{d\mathbf{P}}{dt} = \sum \mathbf{f}_i^{(e)}. \tag{7.73}$$

Now, if $\Sigma \mathbf{f}_i^{(e)} = \mathbf{0}$,

$$\frac{d\mathbf{P}}{dt} = \mathbf{0}, \tag{7.74}$$

which implies that $\mathbf{P}$ is a constant in time. Therefore, the total linear momentum is conserved.

With the origin $O$ as the reference point, the *total angular momentum* of a system of particles is

$$\mathbf{L} = \sum_i \mathbf{r}_i \times \mathbf{p}_i. \tag{7.75}$$

**PROBLEM 7.23** Show that the total angular momentum of a system of particles about a point $O$ is the sum of the angular momentum at the center of mass about $O$ and the angular momentum about the center of mass.

**Solution:** Let $\bar{\mathbf{r}}$ be the position vector from $O$ to the center of mass c.m., and $\bar{\mathbf{r}}_i$, the position vector of the $i$th particle with respect to c.m. (See Fig. 7.5.) Then

$$\mathbf{r}_i = \bar{\mathbf{r}} + \bar{\mathbf{r}}_i, \tag{7.76}$$

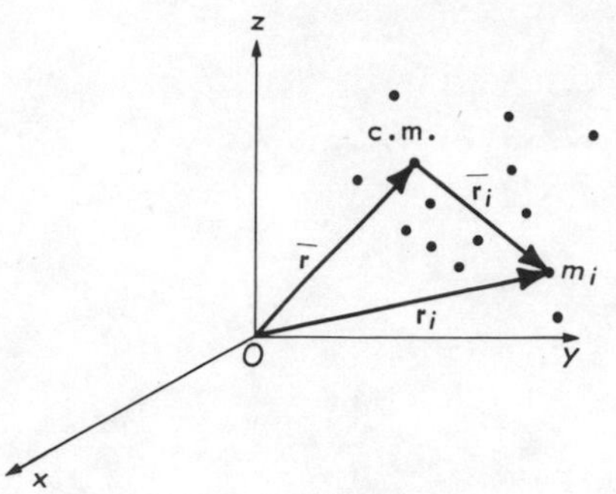


Fig. 7.5 The center of mass of a system of particles and the position vector of the $i$th particle.

$$\mathbf{v}_i = \overline{\mathbf{v}} + \overline{\mathbf{v}}_i, \tag{7.77}$$

where $\overline{\mathbf{v}} = d\overline{\mathbf{r}}/dt$ is the velocity of the center of mass relative to $O$ and $\overline{\mathbf{v}}_i = d\overline{\mathbf{r}}_i/dt$, the velocity of the $i$th particle relative to the center of mass of the system. Now, using (7.75),

$$\mathbf{L} = \sum_i \mathbf{r}_i \times \mathbf{p}_i = \sum_i \mathbf{r}_i \times m_i \mathbf{v}_i$$

$$= \sum_i (\overline{\mathbf{r}} + \overline{\mathbf{r}}_i) \times m_i (\overline{\mathbf{v}} + \overline{\mathbf{v}}_i)$$

$$= \sum_i m_i \left[(\overline{\mathbf{r}} \times \overline{\mathbf{v}}) + (\overline{\mathbf{r}}_i \times \overline{\mathbf{v}}) + (\overline{\mathbf{r}} \times \overline{\mathbf{v}}_i) + (\overline{\mathbf{r}}_i \times \overline{\mathbf{v}}_i)\right]. \tag{7.78}$$

The two middle terms can be written as

$$\left(\sum_i m_i \overline{\mathbf{r}}_i\right) \times \overline{\mathbf{v}} + \overline{\mathbf{r}} \times \frac{d}{dt}\left(\sum_i m_i \overline{\mathbf{r}}_i\right), \tag{7.79}$$

which vanishes since from (7.67),

$$\sum_i m_i \overline{\mathbf{r}}_i = \sum_i m_i (\mathbf{r}_i - \overline{\mathbf{r}})$$

$$= \sum_i m_i \mathbf{r}_i - \overline{\mathbf{r}} \sum_i m_i$$

$$= M\overline{\mathbf{r}} - \overline{\mathbf{r}}M$$

$$= \mathbf{0}. \tag{7.80}$$

Thus, rewriting the remaining terms,

$$\mathbf{L} = M\overline{\mathbf{r}} \times \overline{\mathbf{v}} + \sum_i m_i \overline{\mathbf{r}}_i \times \overline{\mathbf{v}}_i = \overline{\mathbf{r}} \times (M\overline{\mathbf{v}}) + \sum_i \overline{\mathbf{r}}_i \times (m_i \overline{\mathbf{v}}_i)$$

$$= \overline{\mathbf{r}} \times \mathbf{P} + \sum_i \overline{\mathbf{r}}_i \times \overline{\mathbf{p}}_i. \tag{7.81}$$

From (7.81), it is noted that $\mathbf{L}$ is dependent on the origin $O$ except when the center of mass is at rest with respect to $O$ ($\mathbf{P} = \mathbf{0}$). In this case,

$$\mathbf{L} = \sum_i \overline{\mathbf{r}}_i \times \overline{\mathbf{p}}_i. \tag{7.82}$$

**PROBLEM 7.24** Show that the time derivative of the total angular momentum is equal to the sum of all the external torques about the origin.

**Solution:** The equation of motion for the $i$th particle (7.68) can be written as

$$\frac{d\mathbf{p}_i}{dt} = \mathbf{f}_i^{(e)} + \sum_j \mathbf{f}_{ji}. \tag{7.83}$$

Hence, referring to Prob. 7.11,

$$\sum_i \left(\mathbf{r}_i \times \frac{d\mathbf{p}_i}{dt}\right) = \sum_i \frac{d}{dt}(\mathbf{r}_i \times \mathbf{p}_i) = \frac{d}{dt}\mathbf{L} = \sum_i \mathbf{r}_i \times \mathbf{f}_i^{(e)} = \sum_i \sum_{\substack{j \\ i \neq j}} \mathbf{r}_i \times \mathbf{f}_{ji}. \tag{7.84}$$

The last term on the right in (7.84) can be written as

$$\sum_i \sum_{\substack{j \\ i \neq j}} (\mathbf{r}_i \times \mathbf{f}_{ji}) = \sum_{i<j} [(\mathbf{r}_i \times \mathbf{f}_{ji}) + (\mathbf{r}_j \times \mathbf{f}_{ij})]. \tag{7.85}$$

Now, since $\mathbf{f}_{ji} = -\mathbf{f}_{ij}$,

$$(\mathbf{r}_i \times \mathbf{f}_{ji}) + (\mathbf{r}_j \times \mathbf{f}_{ij}) = (\mathbf{r}_i - \mathbf{r}_j) \times \mathbf{f}_{ji}. \tag{7.86}$$

But, if $\mathbf{r}_{ij}$ is the vector that connects the $i$th and $j$th particles,

$$\mathbf{r}_i - \mathbf{r}_j = \mathbf{r}_{ij}. \tag{7.87}$$

(See Fig. 7.6.) Since $\mathbf{f}_{ji}$ is directed along $\mathbf{r}_{ij}$,

$$(\mathbf{r}_i - \mathbf{r}_j) \times \mathbf{f}_{ji} = \mathbf{r}_{ij} \times \mathbf{f}_{ji} = \mathbf{0}, \tag{7.88}$$

$$\frac{d}{dt}\mathbf{L} = \sum_i \mathbf{r}_i \times \mathbf{f}_i^{(e)} = \sum_i \tau_i^{(e)}. \tag{7.89}$$

The right-hand side of (7.89) is merely the sum of all the external torques about the origin $O$.

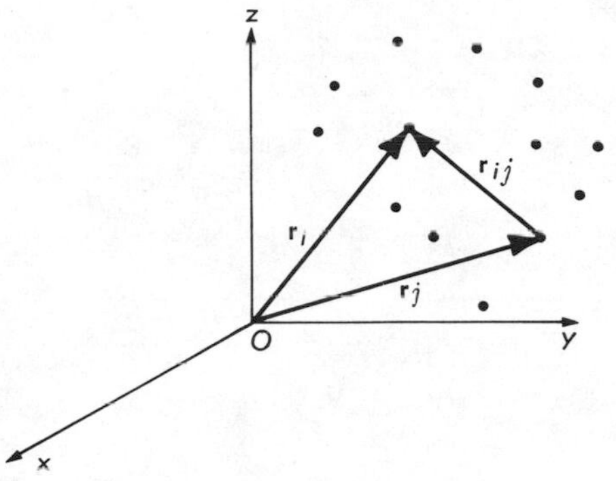


Fig. 7.6 The vector $r_{ij}$ between the $i$th and $j$th particles.

The *principle of conservation of total angular momentum* states that if the external torque is zero, then the total angular momentum of the system remains constant in time.

**PROBLEM 7.25** Prove the principle of conservation of total angular momentum.

**Solution:** If $\sum_i \tau_i^{(e)} = \mathbf{0}$, then (7.89) reduces to

$$\frac{d\mathbf{L}}{dt} = \mathbf{0}, \tag{7.90}$$

which implies that $\mathbf{L}$ is constant in time.

Note that in the absence of an external torque, the principle of conservation of angular momentum for a system holds only if the internal forces are central in character; i.e., $\mathbf{f}_{ij} = -\mathbf{f}_{ji}$.

As in the case of a single particle, the *work* done by all forces to move a system from a configuration 1, in which all $\mathbf{r}_i$ are specified, to a configuration 2, in which all $\mathbf{r}_i$ have some different specification, can be written as

$$W_{12} = \sum_i \int_1^2 \mathbf{f}_i \cdot d\mathbf{r}_i. \tag{7.91}$$

Thus if $\mathbf{f}_i^{(e)}$ and $\mathbf{f}_{ji}$ are the external and internal forces, then the work done is

$$\begin{aligned} W_{12} &= \sum_i \int_1^2 \left[\mathbf{f}_i^{(e)} + \sum_j \mathbf{f}_{ji}\right] \cdot d\mathbf{r}_i \\ &= \sum_i \int_1^2 \mathbf{f}_i^{(e)} \cdot d\mathbf{r}_i + \sum_i \sum_{\substack{j \\ i\neq j}} \int_1^2 \mathbf{f}_{ji} \cdot d\mathbf{r}_i. \end{aligned} \tag{7.92}$$

Note that the work done by the internal forces, i.e., the second term on the right-hand side of (7.92), does not cancel out.

The *total kinetic energy* of the system is defined as

$$T = \sum_i T_i = \sum_i \frac{1}{2} m\,\mathbf{v}_i \cdot \mathbf{v}_i = \frac{1}{2} \sum_i m v_i^2. \tag{7.93}$$

**PROBLEM 7.26** Show that the work done on a system can be written as the difference of the final and initial kinetic energies; i.e.,

$$W_{12} = T_2 - T_1. \tag{7.94}$$

**Solution:** If $m_i$, $\mathbf{v}_i$, $\mathbf{r}_i$, and $\mathbf{f}_i$ are the mass, velocity, position vector, and the force acting on the $i$th particle of the system, then

$$\mathbf{f}_i = m_i \frac{d\,\mathbf{v}_i}{dt}, \qquad d\,\mathbf{r}_i = \frac{d\,\mathbf{r}_i}{dt}\,dt = \mathbf{v}_i\,dt.$$

Thus the work done in moving a system of particles from configuration 1 to configuration 2 is

$$\begin{aligned} W_{12} &= \sum_i \int_1^2 \mathbf{f}_i \cdot d\,\mathbf{r}_i = \sum_i \int_1^2 m_i \frac{d\mathbf{v}_i}{dt} \cdot \mathbf{v}_i\,dt \\ &= \sum_i \int_1^2 d\left(\frac{1}{2} m_i v_i^2\right) \\ &= T_2 - T_1. \end{aligned} \tag{7.95}$$

**PROBLEM 7.27** Show that the total kinetic energy of the system is equal to the sum of the kinetic energy obtained if all the mass were concentrated at the center of mass, moving with the velocity of the center of mass, and the kinetic energy of motion of the individual particles relative to the center of mass.

**Solution:** If $\overline{\mathbf{v}}$ is the velocity of the center of mass relative to the origin $O$ and $\overline{\mathbf{v}}_i$ is the velocity of the $i$th particle relative to the center of mass, then the velocity of the $i$th particle relative to $O$ is $\mathbf{v}_i = \overline{\mathbf{v}} + \overline{\mathbf{v}}_i$. Then the total kinetic energy is

$$\begin{aligned} T &= \frac{1}{2} \sum_i m_i \mathbf{v}_i \cdot \mathbf{v}_i \\ &= \frac{1}{2} \sum_i m_i (\overline{\mathbf{v}} + \overline{\mathbf{v}}_i) \cdot (\overline{\mathbf{v}} + \overline{\mathbf{v}}_i) \\ &= \frac{1}{2} \sum_i m_i \overline{\mathbf{v}} \cdot \overline{\mathbf{v}} + \frac{1}{2} \sum_i m_i \overline{\mathbf{v}}_i \cdot \overline{\mathbf{v}}_i + \overline{\mathbf{v}} \cdot \frac{d}{dt}\left(\sum_i m_i \overline{\mathbf{r}}_i\right). \end{aligned} \tag{7.96}$$

But by (7.80), $\sum_i m_i \overline{\mathbf{r}}_i = \mathbf{0}$, and the last term vanishes. Thus, the total kinetic energy is

$$T = \frac{1}{2} M \overline{v}^2 + \frac{1}{2} \sum_i m_i \overline{v}_i^2, \tag{7.97}$$

## 7.6 Rigid Bodies

A *rigid body* is a system of particles in which the distances between pairs of particles are fixed and cannot vary with time.

Before discussing the motion of rigid bodies, consider the concept of an infinitesimal rotation.

A particle $P$ that is moving arbitrarily in space may always be considered at a given instant to be moving in a plane along a circular path about a given fixed axis. The line which passes through the center of the circular path and is perpendicular to the instantaneous plane of motion is called the *instantaneous axis of rotation.* Thus, an arbitrary *infinitesimal displacement* may always be represented by a *pure infinitesimal rotation* about the instantaneous axis of rotation. For example, the instantaneous motion of a disk rolling down an inclined plane can be described as a rotation about the point of contact between the disk and the plane. In this case, the instantaneous axis of rotation is the line passing through this point of contact and perpendicular to the disk.

Therefore, referring to Fig. 7.7, if the position vector of a point $P$ changes from $\mathbf{r}$ to $\mathbf{r} + d\mathbf{r}$, the infinitesimal displacement of $P$ is

$$d\mathbf{r} = d\mathbf{\Omega} \times \mathbf{r}, \tag{7.98}$$

where $d\mathbf{\Omega}$ is a quantity whose magnitude is equal to the infinitesimal rotation angle and that has a direction along the instantaneous axis of rotation. Note that in this case the origin is located on the instantaneous axis of rotation.

The concept of an infinitesimal rotation provides a powerful tool for describing the motion of a rigid body in time, since any finite displacement of the rigid body with one point fixed can be built up as a succession of infinitesimal displacements. Thus, to describe the *motion* of a rigid body, two coordinate systems are needed, that is, a *coordinate system fixed in space* and a *coordinate system fixed with respect to the body.* Hence, six quantities must be specified in order to denote the position of the body. (See Fig. 7.8.)

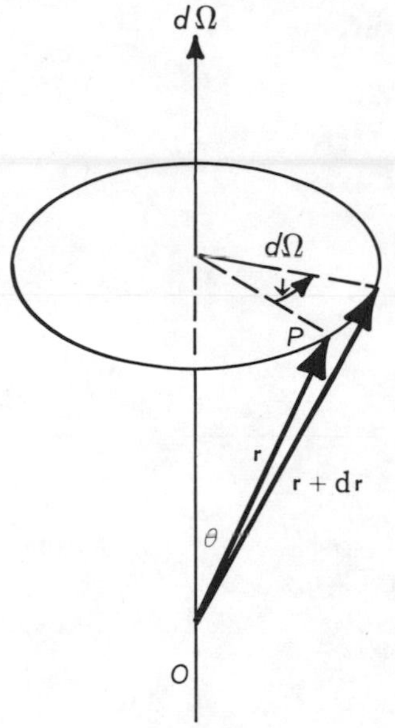


Fig. 7.7 Change in a vector produced by an infinitesimal rotation.

**PROBLEM 7.28** Consider two sets of coordinate systems: one set $\xi$, $\eta$, $\zeta$ is the fixed coordinate system in space designated as the *space* coordinates, and the other, an arbitrary set $x$, $y$, $z$ designated as the *body* coordinates which may be in motion with respect to the space coordinate system. Show that the time rate of change of the position vector $\mathbf{r}$ as observed in the space coordinate system can be expressed as

$$\left(\frac{d\mathbf{r}}{dt}\right)_{\text{space}} = \left(\frac{d\mathbf{r}}{dt}\right)_{\text{body}} + \boldsymbol{\omega} \times \mathbf{r}, \tag{7.99}$$

where $(d\mathbf{r}/dt)_{\text{body}}$ is the time rate of change of $\mathbf{r}$ with respect to the body coordinate system and $\boldsymbol{\omega}$, the angular velocity of the body coordinate system with respect to the space coordinate system.

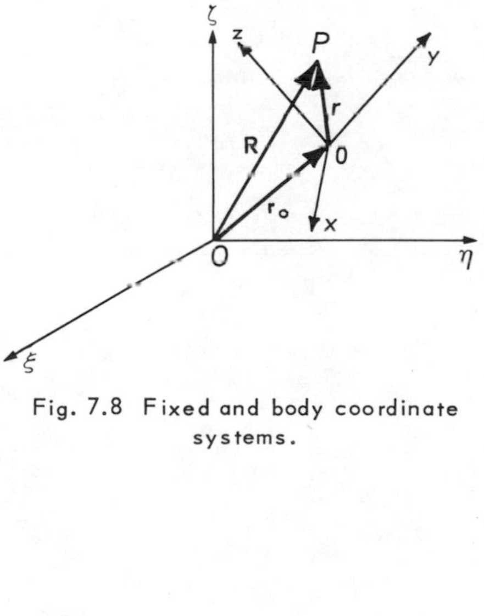


Fig. 7.8 Fixed and body coordinate systems.

**Solution:** If the body coordinate system undergoes an infinitesimal rotation $d\mathbf{\Omega}$, corresponding to some arbitrary infinitesimal displacement, the motion of a point $P$, at rest in the body coordinate system, can be represented by

$$(d\mathbf{r})_{\text{space}} = d\mathbf{\Omega} \times \mathbf{r}, \tag{7.100}$$

where the quantity $(d\mathbf{r})_{\text{space}}$ is measured in the fixed space coordinate system.

Dividing (7.100) by the time interval $dt$ in which the infinitesimal rotation takes place,

$$\left(\frac{d\mathbf{r}}{dt}\right)_{\text{space}} = \frac{d\mathbf{\Omega}}{dt} \times \mathbf{r} = \boldsymbol{\omega} \times \mathbf{r} \tag{7.101}$$

for the fixed point $P$ in the body coordinate system, where

$$\boldsymbol{\omega} = \frac{d\mathbf{\Omega}}{dt} \tag{7.102}$$

is the angular velocity of the body coordinate system: the instantaneous angular rate of rotation of the body coordinate system with respect to the fixed space coordinate system. The vector $\omega$ lies along the instantaneous axis of rotation, the axis of the infinitesimal rotation occurring at the time $t$.

Now, if the time rate of change of $\mathbf{r}$ with respect to the body coordinate system is $(d\mathbf{r}/dt)_{\text{body}}$, then this time rate of change must be added to (7.101) to obtain the time rate of change of $\mathbf{r}$ in the space coordinate system and we obtain

$$\left(\frac{d\mathbf{r}}{dt}\right)_{\text{space}} = \left(\frac{d\mathbf{r}}{dt}\right)_{\text{body}} + \omega \times \mathbf{r}.$$

Note that though (7.99) is established with the position vector $\mathbf{r}$, it is valid for any arbitrary vector. This is illustrated in the following problem.

**PROBLEM 7.29** Show that for any arbitrary vector $\mathbf{F}$,

$$\left(\frac{d\mathbf{F}}{dt}\right)_{\text{space}} = \left(\frac{d\mathbf{F}}{dt}\right)_{\text{body}} + \omega \times \mathbf{F}, \tag{7.103}$$

where $\omega$ is the angular velocity of the body coordinate system with respect to the space coordinate system.

**Solution:** If $\mathbf{F}$ is expressed in the body coordinate system as

$$\mathbf{F} = F_1\mathbf{i} + F_2\mathbf{j} + F_3\mathbf{k}, \tag{7.104}$$

then its derivative with respect to $t$ is

$$\left(\frac{d\mathbf{F}}{dt}\right)_{\text{space}} = \left(\frac{dF_1}{dt}\right)\mathbf{i} + \left(\frac{dF_2}{dt}\right)\mathbf{j} + \left(\frac{dF_3}{dt}\right)\mathbf{k} + F_1\frac{d\mathbf{i}}{dt} + F_2\frac{d\mathbf{j}}{dt} + F_3\frac{d\mathbf{k}}{dt} \tag{7.105}$$

since $\mathbf{i}$, $\mathbf{j}$, $\mathbf{k}$ are no longer constant because of the motion of the body coordinate system. On comparing with (7.101),

$$\frac{d\mathbf{i}}{dt} = \omega \times \mathbf{i}, \quad \frac{d\mathbf{j}}{dt} = \omega \times \mathbf{j}, \quad \frac{d\mathbf{k}}{dt} = \omega \times \mathbf{k} \tag{7.106}$$

since $F_1$, $F_2$, and $F_3$ are measured in the body coordinate system; consequently, $dF_1/dt$, $dF_2/dt$, and $dF_3/dt$ are the time rate of change of $F_1$, $F_2$, and $F_3$ as measured in the body coordinate system. Hence, (7.105) becomes

$$\left(\frac{d\mathbf{F}}{dt}\right)_{\text{space}} = \left(\frac{d\mathbf{F}}{dt}\right)_{\text{body}} + \omega \times (F_1\mathbf{i} + F_2\mathbf{j} + F_3\mathbf{k})$$

$$= \left(\frac{d\mathbf{F}}{dt}\right)_{\text{body}} + \omega \times \mathbf{F}.$$

Note that (7.103) can be rewritten as an operator equation acting on some given vector; i.e.,

$$\left(\frac{d}{dt}\right)_{\text{space}} = \left(\frac{d}{dt}\right)_{\text{body}} + \omega \times. \tag{7.107}$$

Equation (7.107) can be used as the basic *kinematical law* upon which the dynamical equations of motion for a rigid body are founded. It can also be used to discuss the motion of a particle or system of particles, relative to a rotating coordinate system.

**PROBLEM 7.30** Show that the angular acceleration $\alpha = d\omega/dt$ is the same in both the body and space coordinate systems.

**Solution:** Using (7.103) or (7.107), and since $\omega \times \omega = \mathbf{0}$ from (1.58),

$$\left(\frac{d\omega}{dt}\right)_{\text{space}} = \left(\frac{d\omega}{dt}\right)_{\text{body}} + \omega \times \omega = \alpha. \tag{7.108}$$

**PROBLEM 7.31** Show that the velocity $\mathbf{v}_s$ of a particle $P$ relative to the space coordinate system can be expressed as

$$\mathbf{v}_s = \mathbf{v}_0 + \mathbf{v}_b + \omega \times \mathbf{r}, \tag{7.109}$$

where $\mathbf{v}_0$ is the linear velocity of the origin of the moving body coordinate system, $\mathbf{v}_b$, the velocity of $P$ relative to the moving system, $\boldsymbol{\omega}$, the angular velocity of the moving system, and $\omega \times \mathbf{r}$, the velocity caused by the rotation of the moving system. (See Fig. 7.8.)

**Solution:** As shown in Fig. 7.8, the position vectors $\mathbf{R}$ and $\mathbf{r}$ specify the particle $P$ in the space and moving body systems, respectively. Thus,

$$\mathbf{R} = \mathbf{r}_0 + \mathbf{r}, \tag{7.110}$$

where $\mathbf{r}_0$ is the position vector of the origin of the moving body system in the space system. Then,

$$\left(\frac{d\mathbf{R}}{dt}\right)_{\text{space}} = \left(\frac{d\mathbf{r}_0}{dt}\right)_{\text{space}} + \left(\frac{d\mathbf{r}}{dt}\right)_{\text{space}} \tag{7.111}$$

Using (7.99), (7.111) reduces to

$$\left(\frac{d\mathbf{R}}{dt}\right)_{\text{space}} = \left(\frac{d\mathbf{r}_0}{dt}\right)_{\text{space}} + \left(\frac{d\mathbf{r}}{dt}\right)_{\text{body}} + \omega \times \mathbf{r}. \tag{7.112}$$

Then, if we let

$$\mathbf{v}_s = \left(\frac{d\mathbf{R}}{dt}\right)_{\text{space}}, \quad \mathbf{v}_0 = \left(\frac{d\mathbf{r}_0}{dt}\right)_{\text{space}}, \quad \mathbf{v}_b = \left(\frac{d\mathbf{r}}{dt}\right)_{\text{body}},$$

(7.111) becomes

$$\mathbf{v}_s = \mathbf{v}_0 + \mathbf{v}_b + \omega \times \mathbf{r}.$$

If the moving system experiences only rotation, (7.108) becomes

$$\mathbf{v}_s - \mathbf{v}_b + \omega \times \mathbf{r}. \tag{7.113}$$

**PROBLEM 7.32** Show that if the moving system has only rotation to an observer in the rotating coordinate system ($\omega$ = constant), the effective force on a particle $P$ of mass $m$ is

$$\mathbf{f}_{\text{eff}} = m\,\mathbf{a}_s - 2m\,(\omega \times \mathbf{v}_b) - m\,\omega \times (\omega \times \mathbf{r}), \tag{7.114}$$

where $\mathbf{a}_s$ is the acceleration of $P$ in the space coordinate system.

**Solution:** The equation of motion in the fixed space coordinate system is

$$\mathbf{f} = m\mathbf{a}_s = m\left(\frac{d\mathbf{v}_s}{dt}\right)_{\text{space}}. \tag{7.115}$$

Differentiating (7.113),

$$\mathbf{f} = m\left(\frac{d\mathbf{v}_b}{dt}\right)_{\text{space}} + m\,\omega \times \left(\frac{d\mathbf{r}}{dt}\right)_{\text{space}} \tag{7.116}$$

since $\boldsymbol{\omega}$ = constant, and hence, $d\omega/dt = \mathbf{0}$.

Now, using (7.107), or substituting $\mathbf{v}_b$ for $\mathbf{F}$ in (7.103),

$$\left(\frac{d\mathbf{v}_b}{dt}\right)_{\text{space}} = \left(\frac{d\mathbf{v}_b}{dt}\right)_{\text{body}} + \boldsymbol{\omega} \times \mathbf{v}_b$$

$$= \mathbf{a}_b + \boldsymbol{\omega} \times \mathbf{v}_b, \tag{7.117}$$

where $\mathbf{a}_b$ is the acceleration in the rotating body coordinate system.

From (7.99),

$$\boldsymbol{\omega} \times \left(\frac{d\mathbf{r}}{dt}\right)_{\text{space}} = \boldsymbol{\omega} \times \left(\frac{d\mathbf{r}}{dt}\right)_{\text{body}} + \boldsymbol{\omega} \times (\boldsymbol{\omega} \times \mathbf{r})$$

$$= \boldsymbol{\omega} \times \mathbf{v}_b + \boldsymbol{\omega} \times (\boldsymbol{\omega} \times \mathbf{r}). \tag{7.118}$$

Substituting (7.117) and (7.118) into (7.116),

$$\mathbf{f} = m\mathbf{a}_s = m\mathbf{a}_b + 2m\boldsymbol{\omega} \times \mathbf{v}_b + m\boldsymbol{\omega} \times (\boldsymbol{\omega} \times \mathbf{r}), \tag{7.119}$$

which can be rewritten as

$$m\mathbf{a}_s - 2m(\boldsymbol{\omega} \times \mathbf{v}_b) - m\boldsymbol{\omega} \times (\boldsymbol{\omega} \times \mathbf{r}) = m\mathbf{a}_b. \tag{7.120}$$

Hence to an observer in the rotating body system, it appears as if the particle is moving under the influence of an effective force $\mathbf{f}_{\text{eff}}$ given by

$$\mathbf{f}_{\text{eff}} = m\mathbf{a}_s - 2m(\boldsymbol{\omega} \times \mathbf{v}_b) - m\boldsymbol{\omega} \times (\boldsymbol{\omega} \times \mathbf{r}).$$

**PROBLEM 7.33** Identify the nature of the forces occurring in (7.114).

**Solution:** The first term $m\mathbf{a}_s$ in (7.114) is the usual force from Newton's second law of motion.

The last term $-m\boldsymbol{\omega} \times (\boldsymbol{\omega} \times \mathbf{r})$ is a vector normal to $\boldsymbol{\omega}$ and pointing outward; its magnitude is $m\omega^2 r \sin\theta$. (See Fig. 7.7.) Hence, this term is identified as the usual *centrifugal force*.

The middle term $-2m(\boldsymbol{\omega} \times \mathbf{v}_b)$ is a totally new quantity that results from the motion of the particle in the rotating coordinate system; since this force is proportional to $\mathbf{v}_b$, it vanishes if there is no motion. This term is often called *Coriolis' force*.

Any general displacement of a rigid body can be represented by a translation plus a rotation, i.e., a linear translation of some point of the body plus a rotation about that point.

*Charles' theorem:* Consider a rigid body that is composed of $n$ particles of masses $m_i$, $i = 1, 2, \cdots, n$. If the origin of the body system is chosen to be the center of mass, then the total kinetic energy of the body can be expressed as

$$T = T_{\text{transl}} + T_{\text{rot}}, \tag{7.121}$$

where $T_{\text{transl}}$ and $T_{\text{rot}}$ represent the translational and rotational kinetic energies

$$T_{\text{transl}} = \frac{1}{2}\sum_i m_i \bar{v}^2 = \frac{1}{2}M\bar{v}^2, \tag{7.122a}$$

$$T_{\text{rot}} = \frac{1}{2}\sum_i m_i (\boldsymbol{\omega} \times \mathbf{r}_i)^2, \tag{7.122b}$$

where $\bar{v}$ is the instantaneous linear velocity of the center of mass and $\boldsymbol{\omega}$, the instantaneous angular velocity of the body about the center of mass.

**PROBLEM 7.34** Prove Charles' theorem.

**Solution:** Since we are considering a rigid body so that

$$\mathbf{v}_b = \left(\frac{d\mathbf{r}}{dt}\right)_{\text{body}} = \mathbf{0},$$

the instantaneous velocity of the $i$th particle in the fixed coordinate system is, from (7.109),

$$\mathbf{v}_i = \bar{\mathbf{v}} + \omega \times \mathbf{r}_i. \tag{7.123}$$

It is understood that all velocities are measured in the fixed space coordinate system.

For the total kinetic energy, from (7.93),

$$T = \frac{1}{2}\sum_i m_i(\bar{\mathbf{v}} + \omega \times \mathbf{r}_i)^2$$

$$= \frac{1}{2}\sum_i m_i \bar{\mathbf{v}}^2 + \sum_i m_i \bar{\mathbf{v}} \cdot \omega \times \mathbf{r}_i + \frac{1}{2}\sum_i m_i(\omega \times \mathbf{r}_i)^2. \tag{7.124}$$

By noting that $\bar{\mathbf{v}}$ and $\omega$ are not the characteristics of the $i$th particle, because of (7.67),

$$\sum_i m_i \bar{\mathbf{v}} \cdot \omega \times \mathbf{r}_i = \bar{\mathbf{v}} \cdot \omega \times \sum_i m_i \mathbf{r}_i = \bar{\mathbf{v}} \cdot \omega \times (M\bar{\mathbf{r}}) = 0 \tag{7.125}$$

since the center of mass is chosen as the origin of the body system, so that $\bar{\mathbf{r}} = \mathbf{0}$. Thus (7.124) reduces to

$$T = \frac{1}{2}\sum_i m_i \bar{\mathbf{v}}^2 + \frac{1}{2}\sum_i m_i(\omega \times \mathbf{r}_i)^2$$

$$= T_{\text{transl}} + T_{\text{rot}}.$$

**PROBLEM 7.35** Show that the total angular momentum of the rigid body in Prob. 7.34 can be expressed as

$$\mathbf{L} = \sum_i m_i \mathbf{r}_i \times (\omega \times \mathbf{r}_i). \tag{7.126}$$

**Solution:** If the origin of the body coordinate system is taken to be at the center of mass of the body, then from (7.75) or (7.81), the total angular momentum is

$$\mathbf{L} = \sum_i \mathbf{r}_i \times \mathbf{p}_i. \tag{7.127}$$

Now $\mathbf{p}_i = m_i \mathbf{v}_i$, and using (7.123) for $\mathbf{v}_i$,

$$\mathbf{L} = \sum_i m_i \mathbf{r}_i \times \mathbf{v}_i$$

$$= \sum_i m_i \mathbf{r}_i \times (\bar{\mathbf{v}} + \omega \times \mathbf{r}_i)$$

$$= -\bar{\mathbf{v}} \times \sum_i m_i \mathbf{r}_i + \sum_i m_i \mathbf{r}_i \times (\omega \times \mathbf{r}_i). \tag{7.128}$$

As before, $\sum_i m_i \mathbf{r}_i = M\bar{\mathbf{r}} = \mathbf{0}$ since $\bar{\mathbf{r}} = \mathbf{0}$. Thus, the total angular momentum is

$$\mathbf{L} = \sum_i m_i \mathbf{r}_i \times (\omega \times \mathbf{r}_i).$$

**PROBLEM 7.36** Show that

$$T_{\text{rot}} = \frac{1}{2}\boldsymbol{\omega}\cdot\mathbf{L}. \tag{7.129}$$

**Solution:** From (7.122b),

$$T_{\text{rot}} = \frac{1}{2}\sum_i m_i\,(\boldsymbol{\omega}\times\mathbf{r}_i)^2.$$

Now, from (1.61),

$$(\boldsymbol{\omega}\times\mathbf{r}_i)^2 = (\boldsymbol{\omega}\times\mathbf{r}_i)\cdot(\boldsymbol{\omega}\times\mathbf{r}_i) = \omega^2 r_i^2 - (\boldsymbol{\omega}\cdot\mathbf{r}_i)^2.$$

Therefore,

$$T_{\text{rot}} = \frac{1}{2}\sum_i m_i\,[\omega^2 r_i^2 - (\boldsymbol{\omega}\cdot\mathbf{r}_i)^2]. \tag{7.130}$$

Next, from (7.126),

$$\mathbf{L} = \sum_i m_i\,\mathbf{r}_i\times(\boldsymbol{\omega}\times\mathbf{r}_i).$$

Using the vector identity (1.83),

$$\mathbf{r}_i\times(\boldsymbol{\omega}\times\mathbf{r}_i) = r_i^2\,\boldsymbol{\omega} - (\boldsymbol{\omega}\cdot\mathbf{r}_i)\,\mathbf{r}_i.$$

Hence,

$$\begin{aligned}\frac{1}{2}\boldsymbol{\omega}\cdot\mathbf{L} &= \frac{1}{2}\sum_i m_i\;\boldsymbol{\omega}\cdot[r_i^2\,\boldsymbol{\omega} - (\boldsymbol{\omega}\cdot\mathbf{r}_i)\,\mathbf{r}_i] \\ &= \frac{1}{2}\sum_i m_i\,[r_i^2\omega^2 - (\boldsymbol{\omega}\cdot\mathbf{r}_i)^2] \\ &= T_{\text{rot}}.\end{aligned}$$

## 7.7 Supplementary Problems

**PROBLEM 7.37** Express **r**, **v**, and **a** in spherical coordinates.

*Answer*: $\mathbf{r} = r\,\mathbf{e}_r$, $\mathbf{v} = (dr/dt)\,\mathbf{e}_r + r(d\theta/dt)\,\mathbf{e}_\theta + r\sin\theta\,(\partial\phi/\partial t)\,\mathbf{e}_\phi$,

$$\mathbf{a} = \left[\frac{d^2r}{dt^2} - r\left(\frac{d\theta}{dt}\right)^2 - r\sin^2\theta\left(\frac{d\phi}{dt}\right)^2\right]\mathbf{e}_r + \left[2\frac{dr}{dt}\frac{d\theta}{dt} + r\frac{d^2\theta}{dt^2} - r\sin\theta\cos\theta\left(\frac{d\phi}{dt}\right)^2\right]\mathbf{e}_\phi$$

$$+\left(2\sin\theta\frac{dr}{dt}\frac{d\phi}{dt} + 2\,r\cos\theta\frac{d\theta}{dt}\frac{d\phi}{dt} + r\sin\theta\frac{d^2\phi}{dt^2}\right)\mathbf{e}_\phi.$$

**PROBLEM 7.38** A particle moves in the *xy*-plane with velocity **v** and acceleration **a**. Show that $|\mathbf{v}\times\mathbf{a}| = v^3/\rho$ and the radius of curvature $\rho$ can be evaluated by the formula

$$\rho = \frac{\left[\left(\dfrac{dx}{dt}\right)^2 + \left(\dfrac{dy}{dt}\right)^2\right]^{3/2}}{\left(\dfrac{dx}{dt}\dfrac{d^2y}{dt^2} - \dfrac{dy}{dt}\dfrac{d^2x}{dt^2}\right)}.$$

[*Hint*: Write $\mathbf{v} = v\,\mathbf{T}$ and use (7.22).]

**PROBLEM 7.39** A particle $P$ moves on a straight line from the center of a disk toward the edge. The disk rotates counterclockwise with constant angular speed $\omega$. Assuming that the disk is in the $xy$-plane, find the acceleration $\mathbf{a}$ of $P$. [*Hint:* Write $\mathbf{r} = t\,\mathbf{u}$, where $\mathbf{u}$ is a unit vector rotating with the disk.]

*Answer*: $2\dfrac{d\mathbf{u}}{dt} - \omega^2 t\,\mathbf{u}$.

**PROBLEM 7.40** Let $P$ and $Q$ be two particles moving along the curves $C_1$ and $C_2$. Let $\mathbf{r} = \mathbf{r}_Q - \mathbf{r}_P$, where $\mathbf{r}_P$ and $\mathbf{r}_Q$ are the position vectors of $P$ and $Q$. Then $d\mathbf{r}/dt$ is the relative velocity of $Q$ with respect to $P$. If one of the particles describes a circle of radius $a$ while the other moves along the diameter, then show that the relative velocity of these particles, moving with the same speed $v$, is $v(1 - \sin\theta)\,\mathbf{i} + v(\cos\theta)\,\mathbf{j}$. (See Fig. 7.9.)

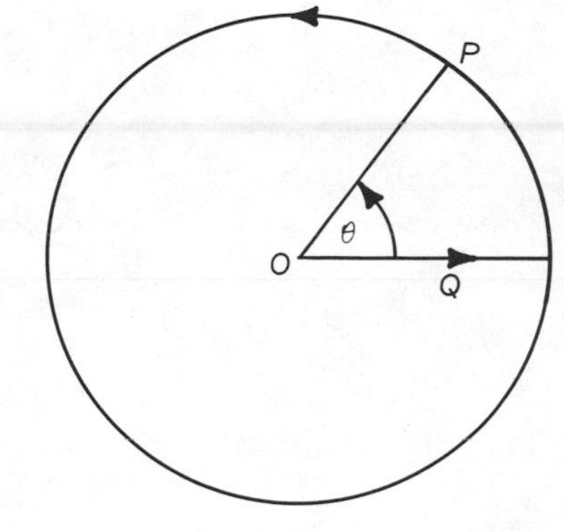


Fig. 7.9 Relative velocity.

**PROBLEM 7.41** A particle is attracted toward the origin with a force $\mathbf{f} = f(r)\,\mathbf{e}_r$; that is, the force is a central force. Show that the angular momentum of the particle is constant.

**PROBLEM 7.42** The force acting upon a moving particle of mass $m$, which carries a charge $q$ moving through an electromagnetic field is

$$\mathbf{f} = q(\mathbf{E} + \mathbf{v} \times \mathbf{B}),$$

where $\mathbf{E}$ is the electric field vector, $\mathbf{B}$, the magnetic induction vector, and $\mathbf{v}$, the velocity of the charged particle. This equation is known as the *Lorentz force equation.* If there is no electric field, that is, $\mathbf{E} = \mathbf{0}$, and if the particle enters the magnetic field in a direction perpendicular to that of $\mathbf{B}$, show that the particle moves in a circular path, and find the radius of the circle.

*Answer*: $mv/qB$.

**PROBLEM 7.43** Show that the moment of a force $\mathbf{f}$ applied at $P$ relative to the origin $O$ is unchanged if $\mathbf{f}$ slides along its line of action.

**PROBLEM 7.44** Let $\mathbf{f} = -(k/r^2)\,\mathbf{r}$ be the central force that moves a particle $P$ along the helix $C$, which is defined by

$$\mathbf{r}(\phi) = (a\cos\phi)\,\mathbf{i} + (a\sin\phi)\,\mathbf{j} + b\phi\,\mathbf{k}.$$

Find the work done by $\mathbf{f}$ in moving $P$ from the point $\phi = 0$ to the point $\phi = \pi$.

*Answer*: $k\left(\dfrac{1}{\sqrt{a^2 + b^2\pi^2}} - \dfrac{1}{a}\right)$.

**PROBLEM 7.45** The force of gravity near a point on the earth's surface (with the $z$-axis pointing up) can be expressed as $\mathbf{f} = -mg\mathbf{k}$, where $m$ is the mass of the particle and $\mathbf{g} = -g\mathbf{k}$, the acceleration of gravity. Find the potential energy of the particle at height $z$.

*Answer*: $mgz$.

**PROBLEM 7.46** Show that the definition of the center of mass (7.67) is independent of the choice of the origin.

**PROBLEM 7.47** If the external and internal forces of a system of particles are both conservative, show that it is possible to define a total potential energy $V$ of the system such that the total energy $T + V$ is conserved.

**PROBLEM 7.48** Show that in a rigid body the internal forces do not do work, and the internal potential must remain constant.
[*Hint:* Show that in a rigid body, $\mathbf{f}_{ij}$ is orthogonal to $d\mathbf{r}_{ij}$.]

**PROBLEM 7.49** Using the components $\omega_j$ and $r_{i,j}$ of the vectors $\omega$ and $\mathbf{r}_i$, that is, $\omega = [\omega_1, \omega_2, \omega_3]$ and $\mathbf{r}_i = [r_{i,1}, r_{i,2}, r_{i,3}]$, show that (7.130) can be expressed as

$$T_{\text{rot}} = \frac{1}{2} \sum_{j,k} I_{jk}\omega_j\omega_k,$$

where

$$I_{jk} = \sum_i m_i \left( \delta_{jk} \sum_q r_{i,q}^2 - r_{i,j} r_{i,k} \right),$$

$$\delta_{jk} = \begin{cases} 1 & \text{for } j = k \\ 0 & \text{for } j \neq k; \end{cases}$$

$I_{11}$, $I_{22}$, $I_{33}$ are called the *moments of inertia* about the x-, y-, and z-axes, respectively, and $-I_{12}$, $-I_{13}$, etc., are called the *products of inertia.*

**PROBLEM 7.50** For central forces acting on a particle, show that

$$\mathbf{r} \times (d\mathbf{r}/dt) = 2\mathbf{a},$$

where $\mathbf{a}$ is a constant vector. Interpret this result geometrically.
[*Hint:* For central force $\mathbf{f}$, $\mathbf{r} \times \mathbf{f} = \mathbf{0}$.]

**PROBLEM 7.51** A projectile moving under the force of gravity near the surface of the earth moves, neglecting air resistance, according to the equation $md^2\mathbf{r}/dt = -mg\mathbf{k}$, where the z-axis is taken in the vertical direction. Show that the solution to this equation is

$$\mathbf{r} = \mathbf{r}_0 + \mathbf{v}_0 t - \frac{1}{2} gt^2\mathbf{k},$$

where $\mathbf{r}_0$ and $\mathbf{v}_0$ are the initial position vector and the initial velocity vector, respectively, of the projectile.

**PROBLEM 7.52** A moving particle of mass $m$ is located by spherical coordinates $r(t)$, $\theta(t)$, $\phi(t)$. The force acting on it has spherical components $f_r$, $f_\theta$, $f_\phi$. Calculate the spherical components of the angular momentum vector and of the torque vector about the origin, and verify, by direct calculation, that

$$d\mathbf{L}/dt = \tau. \qquad [7.50]$$

**PROBLEM 7.53** Consider a system of particles with position vector $\mathbf{r}_i$ and applied forces $\mathbf{f}_i$. Show that

$$\frac{d}{dt} \sum_i \mathbf{p}_i \cdot \mathbf{r}_i = 2T + \sum_i \mathbf{f}_i \cdot \mathbf{r}_i,$$

where $\mathbf{p}_i$ are the linear momentums of the particles, and $T$ is the total kinetic energy of the system.

# 8 CHAPTER

# APPLICATIONS TO FLUID MECHANICS

## 8.1 Equation of Continuity

A *fluid* is a substance which deforms continuously under an applied shear stress.

*Pressure* is the intensity of distributed force due to the action of fluids and is measured as force per unit area.

*Density* is defined as mass per unit volume.

The state of a moving fluid is completely determined if the distribution of the fluid velocity $\mathbf{v}$, the pressure $p$, and the density $\rho$ are given. All these quantities are, in general, functions of the space coordinates $x$, $y$, $z$, and of time $t$; i.e.,

$$\mathbf{v}(\mathbf{r}, t) = \mathbf{v}(x, y, z, t) = \text{velocity of the fluid at position } \mathbf{r} \text{ and time } t,$$

$$p(\mathbf{r}, t) = p(x, y, z, t) = \text{pressure of the fluid at position } \mathbf{r} \text{ and time } t,$$

$$\rho(\mathbf{r}, t) = \rho(x, y, z, t) = \text{density of the fluid at position } \mathbf{r} \text{ and time } t.$$

The mass in any region $R$ enclosed by $S$ is

$$\iiint_R \rho \, dV. \tag{8.1}$$

Since $\mathbf{v} \cdot d\mathbf{S}$ measures the volume of fluid crossing a surface element per unit time and $\rho \mathbf{v} \cdot d\mathbf{S}$ measures its mass,

$$\oiint_S \rho \mathbf{v} \cdot d\mathbf{S} \tag{8.2}$$

is a measure of the rate at which the fluid mass flux is leaving $R$ through $S$.

Next, the decrease per unit time in the mass of fluid in $R$ can be written as

$$-\frac{\partial}{\partial t} \iiint_R \rho \, dV. \tag{8.3}$$

If $\rho$ and $\mathbf{v}$ are the density and velocity of a moving fluid, then the *equation of continuity of fluid dynamics* is

$$\nabla \cdot (\rho \mathbf{v}) + \frac{\partial \rho}{\partial t} = 0. \tag{8.4}$$

**PROBLEM 8.1** Derive (8.4).

**Solution:** Equating (8.2) and (8.3),

$$\oint\!\!\oint_S \rho\,\mathbf{v}\cdot d\mathbf{S} = -\frac{\partial}{\partial t}\iiint_R \rho\, dV. \tag{8.5}$$

By the divergence theorem (4.58), the surface integral can be transformed as

$$\oint\!\!\oint_S \rho\,\mathbf{v}\cdot d\mathbf{S} = \iiint_R \nabla\cdot(\rho\,\mathbf{v})\, dV. \tag{8.6}$$

Thus, (8.5) can be rewritten as

$$\iiint_R \left[\nabla\cdot(\rho\,\mathbf{v}) + \frac{\partial\rho}{\partial t}\right] dV = 0. \tag{8.7}$$

Since (8.7) must hold for any volume, the integrand must vanish; i.e.,

$$\nabla\cdot(\rho\,\mathbf{v}) + \frac{\partial\rho}{\partial t} = 0. \qquad [8.4]$$

The *mass flux density* of a fluid is given by the vector

$$\mathbf{J} = \rho\,\mathbf{v}. \tag{8.8}$$

It has the same direction as the motion of the fluid, and its magnitude equals the mass of fluid flowing in unit time through unit area perpendicular to the velocity. Its units are "mass per square length per unit of time." Using **J**, the equation of continuity (8.4) can be written as

$$\nabla\cdot\mathbf{J} + \frac{\partial\rho}{\partial t} = 0. \tag{8.9}$$

**PROBLEM 8.2** Show that the equation of continuity (8.4) can be rewritten as

$$\rho\nabla\cdot\mathbf{v} + \mathbf{v}\cdot\nabla\rho + \frac{\partial\rho}{\partial t} = 0. \tag{8.10}$$

**Solution:** By (3.155),

$$\nabla\cdot(\rho\,\mathbf{v}) = \rho\nabla\cdot\mathbf{v} + \mathbf{v}\cdot\nabla\rho.$$

Thus (8.4) reduces to (8.10).

A fluid is *incompressible* if its density $\rho$ is constant.

**PROBLEM 8.3** Show that the velocity vector of an incompressible fluid is solenoidal.

**Solution:** If the fluid is incompressible, then $\partial\rho/\partial t = 0$ and $\nabla\rho = \mathbf{0}$. Thus the equation of continuity (8.10) reduces to

$$\rho\nabla\cdot\mathbf{v} = 0$$

or

$$\nabla\cdot\mathbf{v} = 0; \tag{8.11}$$

i.e., **v** is solenoidal.

## 8.2 Equation of Motion

*Thermal conductivity* of a fluid is a measure of the heat exchanged between its different parts per unit area per unit time per unit temperature gradient.

The *viscosity* of a fluid is a measure of its resistance to deformation.

A *perfect*, or *ideal*, fluid has zero viscosity. Thus, a shear stress cannot be imposed, nor can internal friction be induced.

*Euler's equation of motion* of a fluid is

$$\frac{d\mathbf{v}}{dt} = \mathbf{f} - \frac{1}{\rho}\nabla p, \tag{8.12a}$$

or, in general,

$$\frac{\partial \mathbf{v}}{\partial t} + (\mathbf{v}\cdot\nabla)\mathbf{v} = \mathbf{f} - \frac{1}{\rho}\nabla p, \tag{8.12b}$$

where $\mathbf{f}(\mathbf{r})$ is the external force per unit mass acting on the fluid.

**PROBLEM 8.4** From Newton's second law of motion (7.41), establish Euler's equation (8.12).

**Solution:** Consider some region $R$ enclosed by $S$ in the fluid. If $\mathbf{f}(\mathbf{r})$ is the external force per unit mass acting on the fluid, the resultant external force acting on $R$ is

$$\mathbf{f}_e = \iiint_R \rho \mathbf{f}\, dV. \tag{8.13}$$

If $p(\mathbf{r}, t)$ is the fluid pressure, then the resultant force due to fluid pressure is

$$\mathbf{f}_p = -\oint\!\!\oint_S p\, d\mathbf{S}.$$

By the gradient theorem (4.94), this surface integral can be converted into a volume integral; i.e.,

$$\mathbf{f}_p = -\oint\!\!\oint_S p\, d\mathbf{S} = -\iiint_R \nabla p\, dV. \tag{8.14}$$

By Newton's second law of motion (7.41),

$$\frac{d}{dt}\iiint_R \rho\mathbf{v}\, dV = \mathbf{f}_e + \mathbf{f}_p. \tag{8.15}$$

The left-hand side term of (8.15) is the rate of change of the total amount of momentum associated with the fluid which is inside a surface $S$ at any instant. If this integral is changed from volume to mass by writing $\rho\, dV = dm$, then $dm$ is invariable as $S$ moves with the fluid. Hence, the total force acting on $R$ is

$$\frac{d}{dt}\iiint_R \rho\mathbf{v}\, dV = \iiint_R \frac{d\mathbf{v}}{dt}\, dm = \iiint_R \rho\frac{d\mathbf{v}}{dt}\, dV \tag{8.16}$$

by resubstituting $dm = \rho\, dV$.

Combining (8.13), (8.14), and (8.16),

$$\iiint_R \rho \frac{d\mathbf{v}}{dt}\, dV = \iiint_R \rho \mathbf{f}\, dV - \iiint_R \nabla p\, dV,$$

or, on simplification,

$$\iiint_R \left(\rho \frac{d\mathbf{v}}{dt} - \rho \mathbf{f} + \nabla p\right) dV = \mathbf{0}. \tag{8.17}$$

Since $R$ is an arbitrary region in the fluid,

$$\rho \frac{d\mathbf{v}}{dt} - \rho \mathbf{f} + \nabla p = \mathbf{0};$$

hence, we obtain Euler's equation (8.12a); i.e.,

$$\frac{d\mathbf{v}}{dt} = \mathbf{f} - \frac{1}{\rho} \nabla p. \tag{8.18}$$

Since $\mathbf{v}(\mathbf{r}, t)$ depends on the time as well as on the spatial coordinates, from the result of Prob. 3.55 and (3.151),

$$d\mathbf{v} = \frac{\partial \mathbf{v}}{\partial t}\, dt + (d\mathbf{r} \cdot \nabla)\mathbf{v},$$

or, dividing both sides by $dt$,

$$\frac{d\mathbf{v}}{dt} = \frac{\partial \mathbf{v}}{\partial t} + (\mathbf{v} \cdot \nabla)\mathbf{v}. \tag{8.19}$$

Substituting (8.19) into (8.18) gives

$$\frac{\partial \mathbf{v}}{\partial t} + (\mathbf{v} \cdot \nabla)\mathbf{v} = \mathbf{f} - \frac{1}{\rho} \nabla p.$$

**PROBLEM 8.5** Show that Euler's equation (8.12b) can be rewritten as

$$\frac{\partial \mathbf{v}}{\partial t} + \frac{1}{2} \nabla(v^2) - \mathbf{v} \times (\nabla \times \mathbf{v}) = \mathbf{f} - \frac{1}{\rho} \nabla p. \tag{8.20}$$

**Solution:** From Prob. 3.62, we have the vector identity

$$\nabla(\mathbf{f} \cdot \mathbf{g}) = \mathbf{f} \times (\nabla \times \mathbf{g}) + \mathbf{g} \times (\nabla \times \mathbf{f}) + (\mathbf{f} \cdot \nabla)\mathbf{v} + (\mathbf{g} \cdot \nabla)\mathbf{f}. \qquad [3.159]$$

If $\mathbf{f} = \mathbf{g} = \mathbf{v}$ in (3.159), then

$$\nabla(\mathbf{v} \cdot \mathbf{v}) = \nabla(v^2) = 2\mathbf{v} \times (\nabla \times \mathbf{v}) + 2(\mathbf{v} \cdot \nabla)\mathbf{v}$$

or, on simplification,

$$(\mathbf{v} \cdot \nabla)\mathbf{v} = \frac{1}{2} \nabla(v^2) - \mathbf{v} \times (\nabla \times \mathbf{v}). \tag{8.21}$$

Substituting (8.21) into Euler's equation (8.12b),

$$\frac{\partial \mathbf{v}}{\partial t} + \frac{1}{2} \nabla(v^2) - \mathbf{v} \times (\nabla \times \mathbf{v}) = \mathbf{f} - \frac{1}{\rho} \nabla p.$$

**PROBLEM 8.6** Derive the equation of motion for an incompressible fluid if the external force acting on the fluid is conservative.

**Solution:** If the external force field $\mathbf{f}$ is conservative, then from Prob. 7.15, $\mathbf{f} = -\nabla V$, where $V$ is a scalar potential function.

If the fluid is incompressible, then $\rho$ is a constant, and

$$\frac{1}{\rho}\nabla p = \nabla\left(\frac{p}{\rho}\right).$$

Hence, on substitution in (8.20),

$$\frac{\partial \mathbf{v}}{\partial t} - \mathbf{v}\times(\nabla\times\mathbf{v}) = -\nabla\left(V + \frac{p}{\rho} + \frac{1}{2}v^2\right), \tag{8.22}$$

which is the desired equation.

The equations of motion can be supplemented by boundary conditions that must be satisfied at the surfaces bounding the fluid. For an ideal fluid and a solid surface, the necessary boundary condition is simply that the fluid cannot penetrate the solid surface. Hence, if the surface is at rest,

$$v_n = 0,$$

where $v_n$ is the normal component of the fluid velocity at the surface.

For a moving surface, $v_n$ must be equal to the normal component of the velocity of the surface.

## 8.3 Fluid Statics

We now consider the case where a fluid is at rest and the pressure is in equilibrium with the applied external force field.

**PROBLEM 8.7** Derive the equation of equilibrium of the fluid at rest.

**Solution:** The velocity of the fluid at rest is zero, and (8.18) becomes

$$\frac{1}{\rho}\nabla p = \mathbf{f}, \tag{8.23}$$

which is the desired equilibrium equation.

Equation (8.23) shows that surfaces of constant pressure are everywhere perpendicular to the external force field.

**PROBLEM 8.8** Show that if there is no external force, the pressure of the fluid is the same at every point in the fluid.

**Solution:** If $\mathbf{f} = \mathbf{0}$, then (8.23) becomes

$$\nabla p = \mathbf{0}; \tag{8.24}$$

i.e., $p$ is constant.

**PROBLEM 8.9** Consider a fluid at rest in a uniform gravitational field. If the field is incompressible, show that

$$p = -\rho g z + c, \tag{8.25}$$

where c is a constant, $g$, the local gravitational constant, and $z$ is measured positively upward from the surface of the earth.

**Solution:** Taking the $z$-axis positively upward from the surface of the earth,

$$\mathbf{f} = -g\mathbf{k}, \tag{8.26}$$

and from (8.23),

$$\frac{\partial p}{\partial x} = \frac{\partial p}{\partial y} = 0, \qquad \frac{\partial p}{\partial z} = -\rho g.$$

Hence, on integration,

$$p = -\rho g z + c.$$

Equation (8.25) indicates that the pressure decreases linearly with increasing height.

## 8.4 Steady Flow and Streamlines

*Steady flow* is one in which the velocity is constant in time at any point in the fluid; i.e., $\partial \mathbf{v}/\partial t = \mathbf{0}$.

The *equation of motion for steady flow* is

$$\frac{1}{2}\nabla(v^2) - \mathbf{v} \times (\nabla \times \mathbf{v}) = \mathbf{f} - \frac{1}{\rho}\nabla p, \tag{8.27}$$

where $v$ is the constant velocity in time at any point in the fluid, $p$ is the fluid pressure, $\mathbf{f}$ is the external force per unit mass acting on the fluid, and $\rho$ is the density of the fluid.

**PROBLEM 8.10** Derive the equation of motion for steady flow.

**Solution:** Since $\partial \mathbf{v}/\partial t = \mathbf{0}$ for steady flow, Euler's equation of motion (8.20) reduces to (8.27).

A *pathline* is the trajectory of a single particle of fluid.

A *streamline* is the curve such that the tangent to it at any point gives the direction of the velocity at that point and is found at an instant of time. In steady flow, the streamlines do not vary with time, and they coincide with the pathlines.

The streamlines are determined by the equations

$$\frac{dx}{v_1} = \frac{dy}{v_2} = \frac{dz}{v_3}, \tag{8.28}$$

where $d\mathbf{r} = [dx, dy, dz]$ and $\mathbf{v} = [v_1, v_2, v_3]$.

The general form of *Bernoulli's equation* states that for an incompressible ideal fluid that moves under the action of conservative forces $\mathbf{f}$ and whose flow is steady,

$$V + \frac{p}{\rho} + \frac{1}{2}v^2 = c \tag{8.29}$$

along a streamline, where c is a constant and $\mathbf{f} = -\nabla V$.

**PROBLEM 8.11** Verify (8.29).

**Solution:** Since $\partial \mathbf{v}/\partial t = \mathbf{0}$ for steady flow, (8.22) becomes

$$\mathbf{v} \times (\nabla \times \mathbf{v}) = \nabla\left(V + \frac{p}{\rho} + \frac{1}{2}v^2\right). \tag{8.30}$$

The vector $\mathbf{v} \times (\nabla \times \mathbf{v})$ is perpendicular to $\mathbf{v}$; therefore, if we dot product both sides of (8.30) with **v**,

$$\mathbf{v}\cdot\left[\nabla\left(V+\frac{p}{\rho}+\frac{1}{2}\,v^2\right)\right]=0. \tag{8.31}$$

Hence, $\nabla(V + p/\rho + 1/2\,v^2)$ is everywhere normal to the velocity field **v**. Thus, **v** is parallel to the surface; i.e.,

$$V+\frac{p}{\rho}+\frac{1}{2}\,v^2=c, \qquad [8.29]$$

and therefore, $V + p/\rho + 1/2v^2$ is constant along a streamline. The values of the constant are, in general, different for each streamline.

If $v$ remains essentially constant, (8.29) shows that the velocity is *inversely proportional* to the pressure.

**PROBLEM 8.12** Show that for steady flow of an incompressible fluid under the action of conservative forces if $\boldsymbol{\Omega} = \nabla \times \mathbf{v}$, then

$$(\boldsymbol{\Omega}\cdot\nabla)\mathbf{v}-(\mathbf{v}\cdot\nabla)\boldsymbol{\Omega}=\mathbf{0}. \tag{8.32}$$

**Solution:** If we take the curl of both sides of (8.30),

$$\nabla\times[\mathbf{v}\times(\nabla\times\mathbf{v})]=\mathbf{0} \tag{8.33}$$

since $\nabla \times \nabla(V + p/\rho + 1/2\,v^2) = \mathbf{0}$ because of (3.142).

Substituting $\nabla \times \mathbf{v} = \boldsymbol{\Omega}$ in the above, and from (3.158),

$$\nabla\times[\mathbf{v}\times\boldsymbol{\Omega}]=\mathbf{v}[\nabla\cdot\boldsymbol{\Omega}]-\boldsymbol{\Omega}(\nabla\cdot\mathbf{v})+(\boldsymbol{\Omega}\cdot\nabla)\mathbf{v}-(\mathbf{v}\cdot\nabla)\boldsymbol{\Omega}=\mathbf{0}. \tag{8.34}$$

Since the fluid is incompressible,

$$\nabla\cdot\mathbf{v}=0. \qquad [8.11]$$

Also, from (3.143), $\nabla\cdot\boldsymbol{\Omega} = \nabla\cdot(\nabla\times\mathbf{v}) = 0$. Hence, (8.34) becomes

$$(\boldsymbol{\Omega}\cdot\nabla)\mathbf{v}-(\mathbf{v}\cdot\nabla)\boldsymbol{\Omega}=\mathbf{0}.$$

## 8.5 Irrotational Flow — Velocity Potential

The *vorticity* or *vortex vector* is

$$\boldsymbol{\Omega}=\nabla\times\mathbf{v}. \tag{8.35}$$

An *irrotational*, or *potential*, *flow* is one for which $\boldsymbol{\Omega} = \mathbf{0}$ everywhere.

A *rotational*, or *vortex*, *flow* is one in which $\boldsymbol{\Omega}$ is not everywhere zero.

As we know from Prob. 4.73, any vector field having zero curl can be expressed as the gradient of some scalar function. If we apply this result to the velocity vector **v** in an irrotational flow, this scalar function is called the *velocity potential* $\phi$; i.e.,

$$\mathbf{v}=\nabla\phi. \tag{8.36}$$

**PROBLEM 8.13** If a fluid rotates like a rigid body with constant angular velocity $\omega$ with respect to some axis, show that the vorticity $\boldsymbol{\Omega}$ is twice the angular velocity $\omega$.

**Solution:** From Prob. 7.9,

$$\nabla\times\mathbf{v}=2\omega. \qquad [7.38]$$

Hence, by (8.35),

$$\mathbf{\Omega} = \nabla \times \mathbf{v} = 2\omega. \tag{8.37}$$

For irrotational flow of an incompressible ideal fluid, the velocity potential $\phi$ satisfies *Laplace's equation*; i.e.,

$$\nabla^2 \phi = 0. \tag{8.38}$$

**PROBLEM 8.14** Verify Laplace's equation (8.38).

**Solution:** The result of Prob. 8.3 shows that if the fluid is incompressible,

$$\nabla \cdot \mathbf{v} = 0. \qquad [8.11]$$

Since $\mathbf{v} = \nabla\phi$ for an irrotational flow,

$$\nabla \cdot \mathbf{v} = \nabla \cdot \nabla\phi = \nabla^2\phi = 0.$$

**PROBLEM 8.15** For an incompressible ideal fluid, which moves under the action of a conservative force field and whose flow is irrotational, show that

$$\frac{\partial \phi}{\partial t} + V + \frac{p}{\rho} + \frac{1}{2} v^2 = c(t), \tag{8.39}$$

where $c(t)$ is a function of time.

**Solution:** Substituting $\mathbf{v} = \nabla\phi$ and $\nabla \times \mathbf{v} = \mathbf{0}$ in

$$\frac{\partial \mathbf{v}}{\partial t} - \mathbf{v} \times (\nabla \times \mathbf{v}) = -\nabla\left(V + \frac{p}{\rho} + \frac{1}{2} v^2\right), \qquad [8.22]$$

we have

$$\frac{\partial}{\partial t}(\nabla\phi) = -\nabla\left(V + \frac{p}{\rho} + \frac{1}{2} v^2\right), \tag{8.40}$$

or, on simplification,

$$\nabla\left(\frac{\partial \phi}{\partial t} + V + \frac{p}{\rho} + \frac{1}{2} v^2\right) = 0. \tag{8.41}$$

Therefore, if $c(t)$ is a function of time, then

$$\frac{\partial \phi}{\partial t} + V + \frac{p}{\rho} + \frac{1}{2} v^2 = c(t).$$

*Bernoulli's equation* for irrotational flow states that if the flow of an ideal incompressible fluid is both steady and irrotational, then

$$V + \frac{p}{\rho} + \frac{1}{2} v^2 = c, \tag{8.42}$$

where $V$ is the potential function, $p$, the pressure, $v$, the velocity, $\rho$, the density, and $c$, a constant

**PROBLEM 8.16** Prove Bernoulli's equation (8.42).

**Solution:** For steady flow, $c(t)$ is a constant, and

$$\frac{\partial \phi}{\partial t} = 0.$$

Hence, (8.39) reduces to Bernoulli's equation (8.42).

**PROBLEM 8.17** Discuss the difference between Bernoulli's equation for irrotational flow (8.42) and that for other flows (8.29).

**Solution:** In the general case, the "constant" $c$ in (8.29) is a constant along any given streamline, but is different for different streamlines.

In irrotational flow, $c$ in (8.42) is constant throughout the fluid.

A *stagnation point* is a point at which the velocity is zero.

**PROBLEM 8.18** If there is no action of conservative forces, show that in steady flow of an incompressible fluid, the greatest pressure occurs at a stagnation point.

**Solution:** If there is no action of external conservative forces, Bernoulli's equation (8.42) reduces to

$$\frac{p}{\rho} + \frac{1}{2} v^2 = c, \tag{8.43}$$

where $c$ is a constant. Solving (8.43) for $p$,

$$p = c\rho - \frac{1}{2} \rho v^2. \tag{8.44}$$

Thus, the pressure $p$ is maximum at points where the velocity $\mathbf{v}$ is zero.

## 8.6 Vortex Flow and Circulation

A *vortex line* is a line that is everywhere parallel to the vorticity.

A *vortex tube* is a surface $A$, generated by the vortex lines through a closed curve $C$. It is characterized by the property

$$\mathbf{n} \cdot \Omega = \mathbf{n} \cdot \nabla \times \mathbf{v} = 0 \text{ on } A,$$

where $\mathbf{n}$ is the unit normal vector to the vortex tube $A$.

The vortex lines or vortex tubes may change as time changes, since, in general, $\Omega$ depends on time.

The *strength of a vortex tube* is defined as

$$\iint_S \Omega \cdot d\mathbf{S}, \tag{8.45}$$

where $S$ is the cross section of the vortex tube bounded by a simple closed curve $C$ encircling the vortex tube. (See Fig. 8.1.)

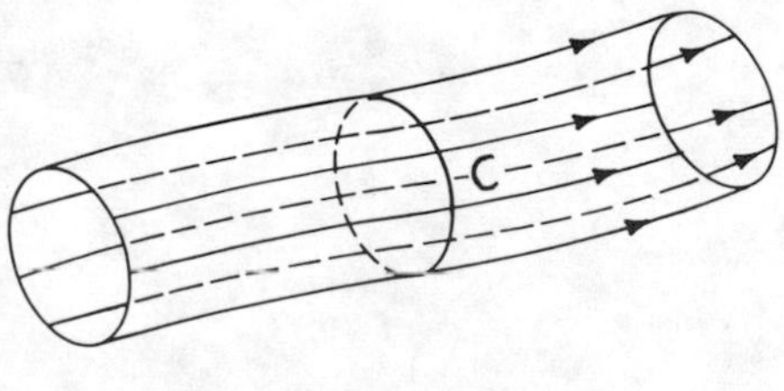

Fig. 8.1 Vortex tube.

The *circulation* of $\mathbf{v}$ (or, simply, *circulation*) along a closed curve $C$ is given by the line integral (cf., Sec. 4.1),

$$\oint_C \mathbf{v} \cdot d\mathbf{r}. \tag{8.46}$$

**PROBLEM 8.19** If a fluid is incompressible and the external force field is conservative, show that

$$\frac{d\Omega}{dt} = (\Omega \cdot \nabla)\, \mathbf{v}. \tag{8.47}$$

**Solution:** Euler's equation of motion for this case is

$$\frac{\partial \mathbf{v}}{\partial t} - \mathbf{v} \times (\nabla \times \mathbf{v}) = -\nabla \left( V + \frac{p}{\rho} + \frac{1}{2} v^2 \right). \qquad [8.22]$$

Taking the curl of both sides of (8.22) and using $\nabla \times \mathbf{v} = \mathbf{\Omega}$,

$$\frac{\partial \mathbf{\Omega}}{\partial t} - \nabla \times (\mathbf{v} \times \mathbf{\Omega}) = \mathbf{0}, \qquad (8.48)$$

since $\nabla \times \nabla \psi = \mathbf{0}$ because of (3.142).

Now, in a manner similar to that of Prob. 8.12, by making use of the vector identity (3.158),

$$\nabla \times (\mathbf{v} \times \mathbf{\Omega}) = \mathbf{v}(\nabla \cdot \mathbf{\Omega}) - \mathbf{\Omega}(\nabla \cdot \mathbf{v}) + (\mathbf{\Omega} \cdot \nabla)\mathbf{v} - (\mathbf{v} \cdot \nabla)\mathbf{\Omega}. \qquad (8.49)$$

Again, since $\nabla \cdot \mathbf{\Omega} = \nabla \cdot (\nabla \times \mathbf{v}) = 0$ and

$$\nabla \cdot \mathbf{v} = 0, \qquad [8.11]$$

we have

$$\nabla \times (\mathbf{v} \times \mathbf{\Omega}) = (\mathbf{\Omega} \cdot \nabla)\mathbf{v} - (\mathbf{v} \cdot \nabla)\mathbf{\Omega}. \qquad (8.50)$$

Substituting (8.50) in (8.48),

$$\frac{\partial \mathbf{\Omega}}{\partial t} + (\mathbf{v} \cdot \nabla)\mathbf{\Omega} = (\mathbf{\Omega} \cdot \nabla)\mathbf{v}. \qquad (8.51)$$

From the result of Prob. 3.36,

$$\frac{\partial}{\partial t} + (\mathbf{v} \cdot \nabla) = \frac{d}{dt}.$$

Hence, substituting this in the left-hand side of (8.51),

$$\frac{d\mathbf{\Omega}}{dt} = (\mathbf{\Omega} \cdot \nabla)\mathbf{v}.$$

**PROBLEM 8.20** Show that the strength of a vortex tube is equal to the circulation, i.e.,

$$\iint_S \mathbf{\Omega} \cdot d\mathbf{S} = \oint_C \mathbf{v} \cdot d\mathbf{r}, \qquad (8.52)$$

where $S$ is the cross section bounded by $C$.

**Solution:** In view of Stokes' theorem (4.104),

$$\oint_C \mathbf{v} \cdot d\mathbf{r} = \iint_S \nabla \times \mathbf{v} \cdot d\mathbf{S} = \iint_S \mathbf{\Omega} \cdot d\mathbf{S}.$$

Note that the circulation may, in certain cases, differ from zero even when the flow is irrotational; i.e., $\mathbf{\Omega} = \mathbf{0}$. (Cf., Prob. 4.72.)

A *barotropid fluid* is one whose density is a function of pressure alone.

*Kelvin's theorem, or the law of conservation of circulation,* states that the velocity of circulation is constant with respect to time for a closed curve C moving with the fluid particle if (a) the external force field acting on the fluid is conservative and (b) it is a barotropid fluid.

**PROBLEM 8.21** Prove Kelvin's theorem or the law of conservation of circulation.

**Solution:** Let

$$K = \oint_C \mathbf{v} \cdot d\mathbf{r}. \tag{8.53}$$

The particles comprising $C$ change position with time, and in uniform flow, the curve remains closed. At any time $t$ the circulation around $C$ is

$$K(t) = \oint_C \mathbf{v} \cdot \frac{d\mathbf{r}}{ds}\, ds = \oint_C \mathbf{v} \cdot \mathbf{T}\, ds, \tag{8.54}$$

where $\mathbf{T}$ is the unit vector tangent to $C$ and $s$ is the arc length.

Since both $\mathbf{v}$ and $\mathbf{T}$ vary with time,

$$\frac{dK}{dt} = \oint_C \frac{d}{dt}(\mathbf{v} \cdot \mathbf{T})\, ds = \oint_C \left(\frac{d\mathbf{v}}{dt} \cdot \mathbf{T} + \mathbf{v} \cdot \frac{d\mathbf{T}}{dt}\right) ds. \tag{8.55}$$

The variable $s$ is the variable of integration along $C$ at any instant of time and is, therefore, independent of the motion of the curve with time. Hence,

$$\frac{d\mathbf{T}}{dt} = \frac{d}{dt}\left(\frac{d\mathbf{r}}{ds}\right) = \frac{d}{ds}\left(\frac{d\mathbf{r}}{dt}\right) = \frac{d\mathbf{v}}{ds}, \tag{8.56}$$

and (8.55) becomes

$$\frac{dK}{dt} = \oint_C \left(\frac{d\mathbf{v}}{dt} \cdot \mathbf{T} + \mathbf{v} \cdot \frac{d\mathbf{v}}{ds}\right) ds. \tag{8.57}$$

If the external force field $\mathbf{f}$ is conservative, it can be expressed as $\mathbf{f} = -\nabla V$, and Euler's equation (8.18) becomes

$$\frac{d\mathbf{v}}{dt} = -\nabla V - \frac{1}{\rho} \nabla p. \tag{8.58}$$

If $\rho$ is a function of $p$ alone, and

$$\psi = V + \int \frac{dp}{\rho}, \tag{8.59}$$

then

$$\nabla \psi - \nabla V + \nabla \left(\int \frac{dp}{\rho}\right). \tag{8.60}$$

Now, from the result of Prob. 3.38,

$$\nabla \left(\int \frac{dp}{\rho}\right) = \left(\frac{d}{dp} \int \frac{dp}{\rho}\right) \nabla p = \frac{1}{\rho} \nabla p. \tag{8.61}$$

Hence, because of (8.58),

$$\nabla \psi = \nabla V + \frac{1}{\rho} \nabla p = -\frac{d\mathbf{v}}{dt}. \tag{8.62}$$

Thus, (8.57) reduces to

$$\frac{dK}{dt} = \oint_C \left(-\nabla \psi \cdot \mathbf{T} + \mathbf{v} \cdot \frac{d\mathbf{v}}{ds}\right) ds. \tag{8.63}$$

Since, from (3.106), $\nabla \psi \cdot \mathbf{T} = \partial \psi / \partial s$,

$$\frac{dK}{dt} = -\oint_C \left[\frac{\partial}{\partial s}\left(\psi - \frac{1}{2}\, \mathbf{v} \cdot \mathbf{v}\right)\right] ds = -\oint_C \left[\frac{\partial}{\partial s}\left(\psi - \frac{1}{2}\, v^2\right)\right] ds. \tag{8.64}$$

Since the quantity $\psi - \frac{1}{2}v^2$ has the same value at the common initial-terminal point of $C$, this integral vanishes, and

$$\frac{dK}{dt} = 0,$$

or, if c is a constant, we obtain Kelvin's theorem:

$$K = \oint \mathbf{v} \cdot d\mathbf{r} = c. \tag{8.65}$$

*Helmholtz's first theorem on vorticity* states that vortex tubes move with the fluid.

**PROBLEM 8.22** Prove Helmholtz's first theorem on vorticity.

**Solution:** If $\mathbf{n}$ is a unit vector perpendicular to the vortex tube $A$, then on $A$ the vortex tube is characterized by the property

$$\mathbf{n} \cdot \boldsymbol{\Omega} = \mathbf{n} \cdot \nabla \times \mathbf{v} = 0.$$

If $\Gamma$ is a simple closed curve lying on a vortex tube but not encircling the tube (see Fig. 8.2), then

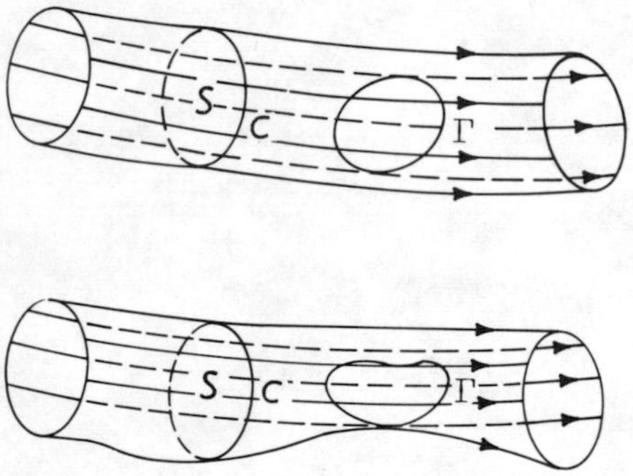

Fig. 8.2 Proof of Helmholtz's first theorem on vorticity.

$$K = \oint_{\Gamma} \mathbf{v} \cdot d\mathbf{r} = \iint_{A_\Gamma} \boldsymbol{\Omega} \cdot d\mathbf{S} = \iint_{A_\Gamma} \boldsymbol{\Omega} \cdot \mathbf{n}\, dS = 0, \tag{8.66}$$

where $A_\Gamma$ is the part of the vortex tube $A$ enclosed by $\Gamma$. Assume that $\Gamma$ is carried by the fluid motion into the simple closed curve $\Gamma'$, and $A'$ is the surface passing through $\Gamma'$ and generated by the original vortex tube $A$. Then from Kelvin's theorem (8.65), the circulation remains zero for all time, i.e.,

$$K = \oint_{\Gamma'} \mathbf{v} \cdot d\mathbf{r} = \iint_{A_{\Gamma'}} \nabla \times \mathbf{v} \cdot d\mathbf{S} = \iint_{A_{\Gamma'}} \boldsymbol{\Omega} \cdot \mathbf{n}\, dS = 0, \tag{8.67}$$

where $A_{\Gamma'}$ is the part of $A'$ enclosed by $\Gamma'$. Since $A_{\Gamma'}$ is arbitrary, it follows that on $A'$,

$$\boldsymbol{\Omega} \cdot \mathbf{n} = 0.$$

Hence, $A'$ is a vortex tube. In other words, as time varies, the vortex tube continues to maintain itself as a vortex tube. Hence, we conclude that vortex tubes move with the fluid.

*Helmholtz's second theorem on vorticity* states that the strength of a vortex tube remains constant.

**PROBLEM 8.23** Prove Helmholtz's second theorem on vorticity.

**Solution:** The strength of a vortex tube is

$$\iint_S \boldsymbol{\Omega} \cdot d\mathbf{S} = \iint_S \nabla \times \mathbf{v} \cdot d\mathbf{S} = \oint_C \mathbf{v} \cdot d\mathbf{r}, \tag{8.52}$$

where $S$ is any surface cutting the vortex tube bounded by a closed curve $C$ encircling the vortex tube. (See Fig. 8.2.)

If $C'$ is the curve into which $C$ is transformed by the fluid motion, then by Kelvin's Theorem (8.65), the circulation remains constant in time and

$$K = \oint_C \mathbf{v}\cdot d\mathbf{r} = \oint_{C'} \mathbf{v}\cdot d\mathbf{r} = \iint_{S'} \boldsymbol{\Omega}\cdot d\mathbf{S}, \tag{8.68}$$

where $S'$ is the cross section of the displaced vortex tube bounded by $C'$. Hence, the strength of a vortex tube is constant with respect to time.

Next, consider a closed surface $S$ consisting of a vortex tube $A$ with cross sections $S_1$ and $S_2$ bounded by closed curves $C_1$ and $C_2$, respectively (Fig. 8.3). Since $\boldsymbol{\Omega} = \nabla \times \mathbf{v}$ is solenoidal, i.e., $\nabla\cdot\boldsymbol{\Omega} = 0$, by the divergence theorem (4.58),

$$\oint\!\!\oint_S \boldsymbol{\Omega}\cdot d\mathbf{S} = \iint_A \boldsymbol{\Omega}\cdot d\mathbf{S} + \iint_{S_1} \boldsymbol{\Omega}\cdot d\mathbf{S} + \iint_{S_2} \boldsymbol{\Omega}\cdot d\mathbf{S} = \iiint_R \nabla\cdot\boldsymbol{\Omega}\, dV = 0. \tag{8.69}$$

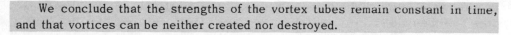

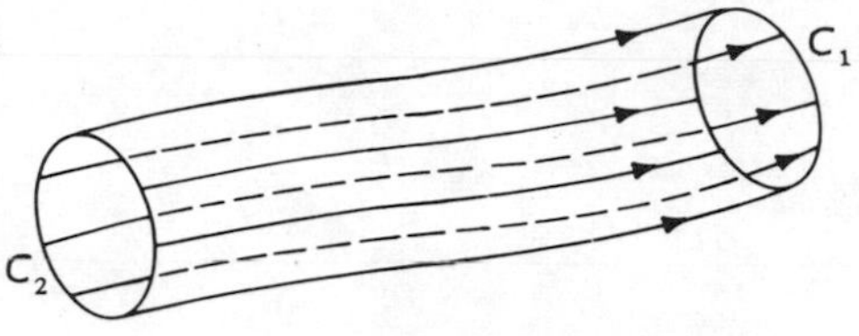

Fig. 8.3 Proof of Helmholtz's second theorem on vorticity.

Now, since $\boldsymbol{\Omega}\cdot\mathbf{n} = 0$ on $A$,

$$\iint_A \boldsymbol{\Omega}\cdot d\mathbf{S} = \iint_A \boldsymbol{\Omega}\cdot\mathbf{n}\, dS = 0.$$

Thus,

$$\iint_{S_1} \boldsymbol{\Omega}\cdot d\mathbf{S} = -\iint_{S_2} \boldsymbol{\Omega}\cdot d\mathbf{S},$$

or,

$$\iint_{S_1} \boldsymbol{\Omega}\cdot\mathbf{n}\, dS = -\iint_{S_2} \boldsymbol{\Omega}\cdot\mathbf{n}\, dS = \iint_{S_2} \boldsymbol{\Omega}\cdot(-\mathbf{n})\, dS. \tag{8.70}$$

If $\mathbf{n}$ is the outward normal, it is the positive normal for $S_1$ and the negative normal for $S_2$, and conversely. Thus, (8.70) shows that the strength of a vortex tube at any cross section is constant.

We conclude that the strengths of the vortex tubes remain constant in time, and that vortices can be neither created nor destroyed.

**PROBLEM 8.24** Determine the shape of the surface of an incompressible fluid subject to a gravitational field, contained in a cylindrical vessel that rotates about its vertical axis with a constant angular velocity $\omega$.

**Solution:** If the axis of the cylinder is the $z$-axis, then $\boldsymbol{\omega} = \omega\mathbf{k}$. Euler's equation (8.18) can be written as

$$\frac{d\mathbf{v}}{dt} = -\nabla V - \frac{1}{\rho}\nabla p = -\nabla\psi, \tag{8.71}$$

where $\mathbf{f} = -\nabla V = -\nabla(gz)$ and $\psi = (gz + p/\rho)$. (See Prob. 7.45.)

Now, from (7.33), $\mathbf{v} = \boldsymbol{\omega}\times\mathbf{r}$. Since $\boldsymbol{\omega}$ is a constant vector,

$$\begin{aligned}\frac{d\mathbf{v}}{dt} &= \boldsymbol{\omega}\times\mathbf{v}\\ &= \boldsymbol{\omega}\times(\boldsymbol{\omega}\times\mathbf{r})\\ &= \boldsymbol{\omega}(\boldsymbol{\omega}\cdot\mathbf{r}) - \omega^2\mathbf{r}\\ &= \omega^2 z\mathbf{k} - \omega^2(x\mathbf{i} + y\mathbf{j} + z\mathbf{k})\\ &= -\omega^2(x\mathbf{i} + y\mathbf{j})\\ &= -\frac{1}{2}\omega^2\nabla(x^2 + y^2).\end{aligned} \tag{8.72}$$

Substituting (8.72) into (8.71),

$$\nabla\left[\psi - \frac{1}{2}\,\omega^2(x^2 + y^2)\right] = 0$$

or, if c is a constant,

$$\psi - \frac{1}{2}\,\omega^2(x^2 + y^2) = c.$$

Hence, substituting the value of $\psi$, and simplifying,

$$\frac{p}{\rho} = \frac{1}{2}\,\omega^2(x^2 + y^2) - gz + c.$$

At the free surface, $p = \text{const}$. Thus the surface is a paraboloid of revolution and is given by

$$z = \frac{1}{2}\,\frac{\omega^2(x^2 + y^2)}{g}, \tag{8.73}$$

where the origin is taken at the lowest point of the surface.

## 8.7 Equation of Energy

The *kinetic energy* $T$ of a fluid in a simply connected region $R$ with boundary $S$ is

$$T = \frac{1}{2}\iiint_R \rho v^2\,dV = \frac{1}{2}\iiint_R \rho\,\mathbf{v}\cdot\mathbf{v}\,dV. \tag{8.74}$$

**PROBLEM 8.25** Show that for the irrotational flow of an incompressible fluid in a region $R$ in which the velocity potential $\phi$ is single-valued, the kinetic energy $T$ of the fluid is

$$T = \frac{1}{2}\,\rho \oiint_S \phi\,\frac{\partial\phi}{\partial n}\,dS, \tag{8.75}$$

where $S$ is the surface enclosing $R$ and $\partial\phi/\partial n$ is the normal derivative of $\phi$.

**Solution:** For irrotational flow, $\mathbf{v} = \nabla\phi$. Hence, from (8.74), the kinetic energy $T$ is

$$T = \frac{1}{2}\,\rho\iiint_R |\nabla\phi|^2\,dV. \tag{8.76}$$

Now, if we set $\psi = \phi$ in Green's first theorem (4.80),

$$\iiint_R (\phi\nabla^2\phi + |\nabla\phi|^2)\,dV = \oiint_S \phi\,\frac{\partial\phi}{\partial n}\,dS. \tag{8.77}$$

Thus (8.76) can be rewritten as

$$T = \frac{1}{2}\,\rho\oiint_S \phi\,\frac{\partial\phi}{\partial n}\,ds - \frac{1}{2}\,\rho\iiint_R \phi\nabla^2\phi\,dV. \tag{8.78}$$

From (8.38), $\nabla^2\phi = 0$; hence, the kinetic energy is

$$T = \frac{1}{2} \rho \oiint_S \phi \frac{\partial \phi}{\partial n} dS.$$

*Kelvin's minimum energy theorem* states that the irrotational flow of an incompressible fluid in a simply connected region $R$ has less kinetic energy than any other flow having the same normal component of velocity on the boundary $S$.

**PROBLEM 8.26** Prove Kelvin's minimum energy theorem.

**Solution:** Let $T_0$ represent the kinetic energy of the irrotational flow associated with the velocity potential $\phi$. Let $T$ be the kinetic energy of any other flow in which

$$\mathbf{v} = \nabla\phi + \mathbf{v}_1. \tag{8.79}$$

Then, by the boundary condition on $S$,

$$\mathbf{v}_1 \cdot \mathbf{n} = 0, \tag{8.80}$$

and the equations of continuity yield

$$\nabla \cdot \mathbf{v} = \nabla^2\phi + \nabla \cdot \mathbf{v}_1 = 0, \quad \nabla^2\phi = 0.$$

Hence,

$$\nabla \cdot \mathbf{v}_1 = 0. \tag{8.81}$$

Now from (8.74), the kinetic energy is

$$T = \frac{1}{2} \rho \iiint_R \mathbf{v} \cdot \mathbf{v}\, dV = \frac{1}{2} \rho \iiint_R (\nabla\phi + \mathbf{v}_1) \cdot (\nabla\phi + \mathbf{v}_1) dV$$

$$= \frac{1}{2} \rho \iiint_R |\nabla\phi|^2 dV + \frac{1}{2} \rho \iiint_R v_1^2\, dV + \rho \iiint_R \nabla\phi \cdot \mathbf{v}_1\, dV$$

$$= T_0 + \frac{1}{2} \rho \iiint_R v_1^2\, dV + \rho \iiint_R \nabla\phi \cdot \mathbf{v}_1\, dV. \tag{8.82}$$

Using (3.155),

$$\nabla\phi \cdot \mathbf{v}_1 = \nabla \cdot (\phi \mathbf{v}_1) - \phi \nabla \cdot \mathbf{v}_1 = \nabla \cdot (\phi \mathbf{v}_1)$$

since, from (8.81), $\nabla \cdot \mathbf{v}_1 = 0$. Thus, using the divergence theorem (4.58),

$$\iiint_R \nabla\phi \cdot \mathbf{v}_1\, dV = \iiint_R \nabla \cdot (\phi \mathbf{v}_1)\, dV$$

$$= \oiint_S \phi \mathbf{v}_1 \cdot \mathbf{n}\, dS$$

$$= 0$$

since, from (8.80), $\mathbf{v}_1 \cdot \mathbf{n} = 0$ on $S$. Therefore, it follows that

$$T = T_0 + \frac{1}{2} \rho \iiint_R v_1^2\, dV. \tag{8.83}$$

Clearly, from (8.83), $T \geq T_0$, and $T = T_0$ only when $\mathbf{v}_1 \equiv \mathbf{0}$, or $\mathbf{v} = \nabla\phi$. This is the required result.

**PROBLEM 8.27** For the irrotational flow of an incompressible fluid in region $R$ bounded by $S$, if $d(\rho\, dV)/dt = 0$, where $dV$ = differential volume, show that

$$\frac{dT}{dt} = \iiint_R \rho \mathbf{v} \cdot \mathbf{f}\, dV - \oiint_S p\mathbf{v} \cdot d\mathbf{S}, \tag{8.84}$$

and give the physical meaning of (8.84).

**Solution:** From (8.74),

$$\frac{dT}{dt} = \frac{1}{2} \rho \iiint_R \frac{d}{dt} (\mathbf{v} \cdot \mathbf{v})\, dV$$

$$= \rho \iiint_R \left(\mathbf{v} \cdot \frac{d\mathbf{v}}{dt}\right) dV. \tag{8.85}$$

By Euler's equation,

$$\frac{d\mathbf{v}}{dt} = \mathbf{f} - \frac{1}{\rho} \nabla p. \tag{8.18}$$

Substituting (8.18) into (8.85) and simplifying,

$$\frac{dT}{dt} = \rho \iiint_R \mathbf{v} \cdot \left(\mathbf{f} - \frac{1}{\rho} \nabla p\right) dV$$

$$= \iiint_R \rho \mathbf{v} \cdot \mathbf{f}\, dV - \iiint_R \mathbf{v} \cdot \nabla p\, dV. \tag{8.86}$$

Proceeding in a manner similar to that of Prob. 8.26,

$$\mathbf{v} \cdot \nabla p = \nabla \cdot (p\mathbf{v}) - p \nabla \cdot \mathbf{v} = \nabla \cdot (p\mathbf{v})$$

since $\nabla \cdot \mathbf{v} = 0$ for incompressible fluid. Thus, by applying the divergence theorem (4.58),

$$\frac{dT}{dt} = \iiint_R \rho \mathbf{v} \cdot \mathbf{f}\, dV - \iiint_R \nabla \cdot (p\mathbf{v})\, dV$$

$$= \iiint_R \rho \mathbf{v} \cdot \mathbf{f}\, dV - \oiint_S p\mathbf{v} \cdot d\mathbf{S}.$$

The left-hand side of (8.84) is the rate of increase of the kinetic energy of a fluid. The first term of the right-hand side of (8.84) is the work of the external forces on the fluid, and the second term is the work of the bounding-surface pressure on the fluid.

## 8.8 Supplementary Problems

**PROBLEM 8.28** If the fluid is at rest, show that

$$\nabla \times (\rho \mathbf{f}) = \mathbf{0}, \qquad \mathbf{f} \cdot \nabla \times \mathbf{f} = 0,$$

where $\mathbf{f}$ is the external force field acting on the fluid.

**PROBLEM 8.29** Derive Bernoulli's equation for the steady flow of ideal incompressible fluid under the gravitational field.

*Answer*: $gz + \dfrac{p}{\rho} + \dfrac{1}{2}v^2 = c$, where c is a constant.

**PROBLEM 8.30** Show that the function $c(t)$ in (8.39) can be put equal to zero without loss of generality.

[*Hint:* Since $\mathbf{v} = \nabla\phi$, we can add to $\phi$ any function of time. Replace $\phi$ by $\phi + \int c(t)\,dt$.]

**PROBLEM 8.31** If the fluid is incompressible and the fluid motion is 2-dimensional, show that a *stream function* $\psi(x, y)$ exists such that

$$v_1 = \frac{\partial\psi}{\partial y}, \quad v_2 = -\frac{\partial\psi}{\partial x},$$

where $\mathbf{v} = v_1\,\mathbf{i} + v_2\,\mathbf{j}$ is the velocity of the fluid.

**PROBLEM 8.32** If the fluid motion is 2-dimensional, incompressible, and irrotational, show that the stream function $\psi(x, y)$ of Prob. 8.31 satisfies the Laplace equation

$$\frac{\partial^2\psi}{\partial x^2} + \frac{\partial^2\psi}{\partial y^2} = 0.$$

**PROBLEM 8.33** If a fluid is incompressible and has a constant vorticity $\mathbf{\Omega}$, show that

$$\nabla^2\mathbf{v} = \mathbf{0},$$

where $\mathbf{v}$ is the velocity of the fluid.

[*Hint:* $\nabla \times (\nabla \times \mathbf{v}) = \nabla \times \mathbf{\Omega} = \mathbf{0}$.]

**PROBLEM 8.34** If the external force field acting on a fluid is conservative and the density of the fluid depends only on the pressure of the fluid, then prove the Helmholtz equation

$$\frac{d}{dt}\left(\frac{\mathbf{\Omega}}{\rho}\right) = \left(\frac{\mathbf{\Omega}}{\rho}\cdot\nabla\right)\mathbf{v}.$$

[*Hint:* See Prob. 8.19 and use the general continuity equation (8.4).]

**PROBLEM 8.35** Show that the vortex lines or vortex tubes can neither begin or terminate within the fluid; thus, they are either closed or reach the boundary.

**PROBLEM 8.36** For the irrotational flow of an incompressible fluid in region $R$ bounded by $S$ and a conservative external force field, i.e., $\mathbf{f} = -\nabla V$, show that

$$\frac{dT}{dt} = \oiint \rho V\mathbf{v}\cdot d\mathbf{S} + \oiint p\mathbf{v}\cdot d\mathbf{S}.$$

In other words, the rate of increase of the kinetic energy of a fluid body is equal to the sum of the work of the external forces and the pressures on its surface.

# 9 CHAPTER APPLICATIONS TO ELECTROMAGNETIC THEORY

## 9.1 Equation of Continuity

The *charge density* $\rho$ is the density of the charge per unit volume.

A *current* $I$ is produced by the motion of the charge and is determined by the density $\rho$ and velocity $\mathbf{v}$ of the charge.

The *current density* $\mathbf{J}$ is the product of the charge density $\rho$ and the velocity $\mathbf{v}$ of the charge; i.e.,

$$\mathbf{J} = \rho \mathbf{v}. \tag{9.1}$$

Thus the current $I$ through a surface $S$ is the rate at which the charge passes through $S$, i.e.,

$$I = \iint_S \rho \mathbf{v} \cdot d\mathbf{S} = \iint_S \mathbf{J} \cdot d\mathbf{S} = \iint_S \mathbf{J} \cdot \mathbf{n}\, dS, \tag{9.2}$$

where $\mathbf{n}$ is a unit vector normal to $S$. Note that the sign of $I$ depends on the choice of $\mathbf{n}$. If $S$ is a closed surface, $\mathbf{n}$ is taken to be the outward normal vector.

An *electromagnetic field* is produced by a distribution of electric current and charge.

The *principle of conservation of charge* states that, in a region $R$ bounded by a surface $S$, the rate at which the charge decreases is equal to the rate at which the charge leaves $R$ through $S$.

The *equation of continuity* states that for any region $R$ bounded by a surface $S$,

$$\nabla \cdot \mathbf{J} + \frac{\partial \rho}{\partial t} = 0, \tag{9.3}$$

or, equivalently, on substituting (9.1),

$$\nabla \cdot (\rho \mathbf{v}) + \frac{\partial \rho}{\partial t} = 0. \tag{9.4}$$

**PROBLEM 9.1** Using the principle of conservation of charge, derive the equation of continuity.

**Solution:** If $\rho(\mathbf{r}, t)$ is the charge density, then the total charge $Q$ within a region $R$ enclosed by $S$ is

$$Q = \iiint_R \rho\, dV. \tag{9.5}$$

Now, from (9.2),

$$\oiint_S \mathbf{J} \cdot d\mathbf{S} = \oiint_S \mathbf{J} \cdot \mathbf{n}\, dS \tag{9.6}$$

is a measure of the rate at which the charge leaves $R$ through $S$, since $\mathbf{n}$ is the outward normal to $S$.

However, the rate at which the charge decreases in $R$ is

$$-\frac{dQ}{dt} = -\frac{d}{dt}\iiint_R \rho\, dV = -\iiint_R \frac{\partial \rho}{\partial t}\, dV. \tag{9.7}$$

In (9.7), we must use $\partial\rho/\partial t$ inside the integral, since $\rho(\mathbf{r}, t)$ is a function of $\mathbf{r}$ and $t$.

Equating (9.6) and (9.7),

$$\oiint_S \mathbf{J} \cdot d\mathbf{S} = -\iiint_R \frac{\partial \rho}{\partial t}\, dV. \tag{9.8}$$

From the divergence theorem (4.58),

$$\oiint_S \mathbf{J} \cdot d\mathbf{S} = \iiint_R \nabla \cdot \mathbf{J}\, dV; \tag{9.9}$$

thus, (9.8) can be rewritten as

$$\iiint_R \left(\nabla \cdot \mathbf{J} + \frac{\partial \rho}{\partial t}\right) dV = 0. \tag{9.10}$$

Since (9.10) holds for any region $R$, the integrand must be zero; i.e.,

$$\nabla \cdot \mathbf{J} + \frac{\partial \rho}{\partial t} = 0. \qquad [9.3]$$

Using (9.1), (9.3) can be expressed as

$$\nabla \cdot (\rho \mathbf{v}) + \frac{\partial \rho}{\partial t} = 0. \qquad [9.4]$$

By analogy with the corresponding equation of continuity of fluid dynamics (8.4), (9.3) or (9.4) is usually termed the equation of continuity.

## 9.2 The Electromagnetic Field

The electromagnetic field produced by charge distributions and their motion (current distribution) is described by the vectors $\mathbf{E}(\mathbf{r}, t)$ and $\mathbf{B}(\mathbf{r}, t)$.

A *Lorentz force* is the force $\mathbf{f}$ experienced by a charge $q$ moving with a velocity $\mathbf{v}(\mathbf{r}, t)$ in the electromagnetic field and is

$$\mathbf{f} = q(\mathbf{E} + \mathbf{v} \times \mathbf{B}). \tag{9.11}$$

Equation (9.11) is the defining equation of the vectors $\mathbf{E}$ and $\mathbf{B}$, where $\mathbf{E}$ is the *electric field intensity* and $\mathbf{B}$ is the *magnetic induction* or *magnetic flux density*. An important implication of (9.11) is the assumption that the properties of field or space described by $\mathbf{E}$ and $\mathbf{B}$ exist whether or not we place $q$ in the field to observe the force. Thus, when a test charge is introduced into an actual electric field for measuring purposes, it must be so small that it does not affect the original fields. In this case, (9.11) can be expressed as

$$\lim_{q \to 0} \frac{\mathbf{f}}{q} = \mathbf{E} + \mathbf{v} \times \mathbf{B}. \tag{9.12}$$

The electromagnetic field is also specified by the vectors **D**, the *electric flux density* or *electric displacement*, and **H**, the *magnetic field intensity*. In a given medium, **D** and **H** are related to **E** and **B** by functional relationships characteristic of the medium. For linear, homogeneous, and isotropic media, the appropriate relations are

$$\mathbf{D} = \varepsilon \mathbf{E}, \tag{9.13}$$

$$\mathbf{B} = \mu \mathbf{H}, \tag{9.14}$$

where $\varepsilon$ and $\mu$ are constants called the *permittivity* and *permeability* of the medium, respectively.

The current density **J** and the electric field intensity **E** are related by

$$\mathbf{J} = \sigma \mathbf{E}, \tag{9.15}$$

where $\sigma$ is the *conductivity* of the medium.

Equations (9.13–5) are often referred to as the *constituent relations.*

The values of $\varepsilon$, $\mu$, and $\sigma$ depend on the system of units. In the mks rationalized system of units used throughout in this chapter, the force is measured in newtons, the velocity in m/sec, and the charge in coulombs (*C*). The coulomb is the basic electric unit which, with the meter, the kilogram, and the second, permits the definition of all other electromagnetic units.

## 9.3 Maxwell's Equations

*Maxwell's equations* can be written as

$$\nabla \times \mathbf{E} + \frac{\partial \mathbf{B}}{\partial t} = \mathbf{0}, \tag{9.16}$$

$$\nabla \times \mathbf{H} - \frac{\partial \mathbf{D}}{\partial t} = \mathbf{J}, \tag{9.17}$$

$$\nabla \cdot \mathbf{B} = 0, \tag{9.18}$$

$$\nabla \cdot \mathbf{D} = \rho. \tag{9.19}$$

**PROBLEM 9.2** Show that (9.18) can be derived from (9.16).

**Solution:** Taking the divergence of (9.16),

$$\nabla \cdot (\nabla \times \mathbf{E}) + \nabla \cdot \left(\frac{\partial \mathbf{B}}{\partial t}\right) = 0$$

or, since $\nabla \cdot (\nabla \times \mathbf{E}) = 0$ because of (3.143),

$$\nabla \cdot (\nabla \times \mathbf{E}) = -\nabla \cdot \left(\frac{\partial \mathbf{B}}{\partial t}\right) = 0. \tag{9.20}$$

If all derivatives of **B** are assumed continuous, interchanging the differentiation with respect to space and time yields

$$\nabla \cdot \left(\frac{\partial \mathbf{B}}{\partial t}\right) = \frac{\partial}{\partial t}(\nabla \cdot \mathbf{B}) = 0,$$

or, hence, in time,

$$\nabla \cdot \mathbf{B} = c,$$

where c is a constant. If at any instance in time in its past history $\mathbf{B} = \mathbf{0}$, this constant must be zero. Since it can be assumed that the field originated at some past time,

$$\nabla \cdot \mathbf{B} = 0.$$

**PROBLEM 9.3** Show that (9.19) can be derived from (9.17) with the continuity equation (9.3).

**Solution:** Taking the divergence of (9.17),

$$\nabla \cdot (\nabla \times \mathbf{H}) - \nabla \cdot \left(\frac{\partial \mathbf{D}}{\partial t}\right) = \nabla \cdot \mathbf{J},$$

or hence, since $\nabla \cdot (\nabla \times \mathbf{H}) = 0$ because of (3.143) and

$$\nabla \cdot \left(\frac{\partial \mathbf{D}}{\partial t}\right) = \frac{\partial}{\partial t}(\nabla \cdot \mathbf{D}) \tag{9.21}$$

if we assume that all derivatives of $\mathbf{D}$ are continuous,

$$\nabla \cdot \mathbf{J} + \frac{\partial}{\partial t}(\nabla \cdot \mathbf{D}) = 0. \tag{9.22}$$

Now using the continuity equation (9.3),

$$\frac{\partial}{\partial t}(\nabla \cdot \mathbf{D} - \rho) = 0,$$

or hence, in time, if c is a constant, then

$$\nabla \cdot \mathbf{D} - \rho - c.$$

Again, if the field originated at some time in the past and since all the charges can be removed from any finite region of space, this constant must be zero; then

$$\nabla \cdot \mathbf{D} = \rho.$$

Note that, by the argument of the vanishing of the fields and the charge density at some time within any finite region of space, the two divergence equations (9.18–9) are not independent relations if one assumes the conservation of charge. This argument is not necessary, of course, since Maxwell's equations (9.16–9) are subject to independent experimental verification.

*Faraday's induction law* states that the electromotive force around any closed contour is equal to the negative of the time rate of change of the magnetic flux linking the contour; i.e.,

$$\oint_C \mathbf{E} \cdot d\mathbf{r} = -\frac{\partial}{\partial t} \iint_S \mathbf{B} \cdot d\mathbf{S}. \tag{9.23}$$

**PROBLEM 9.4** Using Maxwell's equation (9.16), prove Faraday's induction law.

**Solution:** Integrating (9.16) over a surface $S$ bounded by a closed curve $C$ yields

$$\iint_S \nabla \times \mathbf{E} \cdot d\mathbf{S} + \iint_S \frac{\partial \mathbf{B}}{\partial t} \cdot d\mathbf{S} = 0. \tag{9.24}$$

Applying Stokes' theorem (4.104) to the first term of (9.24),

$$\oint_C \mathbf{E} \cdot d\mathbf{r} + \iint_S \frac{\partial \mathbf{B}}{\partial t} \cdot d\mathbf{S} = 0.$$

If C is fixed, $\partial/\partial t$ may be brought out from under the sign of integration; i.e.,

$$\oint_C \mathbf{E} \cdot d\mathbf{r} = -\frac{\partial}{\partial t} \iint_S \mathbf{B} \cdot d\mathbf{S}. \qquad [9.23]$$

The magnetic flux, i.e., the flux of **B** through **S**, is

$$\Phi = \iint_S \mathbf{B} \cdot d\mathbf{S}. \qquad (9.25)$$

Thus, the circulation of **E** around C or the electromotive force around C is

$$\text{emf} = \oint_C \mathbf{E} \cdot d\mathbf{r}. \qquad (9.26)$$

Note that (9.16) or (9.23) verifies the experimental fact that a *varying magnetic field induces an electric field.*

Faraday's experiments showed that the time rate of change of $\Phi$ can result from the movement of C in which the electromotive force (emf) is induced by, or from a time variation of, **B**. Hence, Faraday's law is generally written as

$$\oint_C \mathbf{E} \cdot d\mathbf{r} = -\frac{d}{dt} \iint_S \mathbf{B} \cdot d\mathbf{S} \qquad (9.27)$$

or, the electromotive force is

$$\text{emf} = -\frac{d}{dt}\Phi. \qquad (9.28)$$

**PROBLEM 9.5** Express Maxwell's equation (9.17) in an equivalent integral form and give a physical interpretation.

**Solution:** Integrating (9.17) over a surface S bounded by a closed curve C yields

$$\iint_S \nabla \times \mathbf{H} \cdot d\mathbf{S} - \iint_S \frac{\partial \mathbf{D}}{\partial t} \cdot d\mathbf{S} = \iint_S \mathbf{J} \cdot d\mathbf{S}. \qquad (9.29)$$

Applying Stokes' theorem (4.104) to the first term of the left-hand side of (9.29),

$$\oint_C \mathbf{H} \cdot d\mathbf{r} = I + \iint_S \frac{\partial \mathbf{D}}{\partial t} \cdot d\mathbf{S}, \qquad (9.30)$$

where $I$ is the total current linking the curve C, as defined in (9.2). Equation (9.30) is the equivalent integral form of (9.17) and indicates that the magnetomotive force (mmf) is equal to the sum of the current $I$ linking the curve C and the rate of change of the electric flux linking C. Equation (9.17) or (9.30) verifies the experimental fact that a *magnetic field can be produced, not only by a current, but also by a time-varying electric field.*

Maxwell called the term $\partial\mathbf{D}/\partial t$ *displacement current*, although actually nothing is displaced in the field. **D** is therefore called *electric displacement* and should be thought of as being parallel to the corresponding term in (9.16); i.e., the mmf is associated with a time-varying flux of **D**, just as the emf is associated with a time-varying flux of **B**.

The *electric flux* $\Phi_e$ through a surface $S$ is

$$\Phi_e = \iint_S \mathbf{D} \cdot d\mathbf{S}. \tag{9.31}$$

Because of (9.31), **D** is also called *electric flux density*.

*Gauss' law for the electric field* states that the net outward electric flux through a closed surface $S$ is proportional to the electric charge enclosed by the surface; i.e.,

$$\oiint_S \mathbf{D} \cdot d\mathbf{S} = Q. \tag{9.32}$$

**PROBLEM 9.6** Using (9.19), derive Gauss' law for the electric field.

**Solution:** Since $\nabla \cdot \mathbf{D} = \rho$, applying Gauss' divergence theorem (4.58) yields

$$\oiint_S \mathbf{D} \cdot d\mathbf{S} = \iiint_R \nabla \cdot \mathbf{D}\, dV = \iiint_R \rho\, dV = Q,$$

where $Q$ is the total charge enclosed by $S$. Thus,

$$\oiint_S \mathbf{D} \cdot d\mathbf{S} = Q.$$

*Gauss' law for the magnetic field* states that the net outward magnetic flux through a closed surface $S$ is identically zero; i.e.,

$$\oiint_S \mathbf{B} \cdot d\mathbf{S} = 0. \tag{9.33}$$

**PROBLEM 9.7** Derive Gauss' law for the magnetic field.

**Solution:** Since $\nabla \cdot \mathbf{B} = 0$ from (9.18), applying Gauss' divergence theorem yields

$$\oiint_S \mathbf{B} \cdot d\mathbf{S} = \iiint_R \nabla \cdot \mathbf{B}\, dV = 0.$$

**PROBLEM 9.8** Show that there can be no permanent distribution of free charge in a homogeneous medium having nonzero conductivity.

**Solution:** In a medium having nonzero conductivity $\sigma$, (9.19) and (9.13) show that

$$\nabla \cdot \mathbf{D} = \nabla \cdot (\varepsilon \mathbf{E}) = \rho, \tag{9.34}$$

while the equations of continuity (9.3) and (9.15) yield

$$\nabla \cdot \mathbf{J} + \frac{\partial \rho}{\partial t} = \nabla \cdot (\sigma \mathbf{E}) + \frac{\partial \rho}{\partial t} = 0. \tag{9.35}$$

Now, using (3.155),

$$\nabla\cdot(\varepsilon\mathbf{E}) = \varepsilon\nabla\cdot\mathbf{E} + \mathbf{E}\cdot\nabla\varepsilon = \rho, \tag{9.36}$$

$$\nabla\cdot(\sigma\mathbf{E}) = \sigma\nabla\cdot\mathbf{E} + \mathbf{E}\cdot\nabla\sigma = -\frac{\partial\rho}{\partial t}. \tag{9.37}$$

Eliminating $\nabla\cdot\mathbf{E}$ between (9.36) and (9.37),

$$\rho + \frac{\varepsilon}{\sigma}\frac{\partial\rho}{\partial t} = \sigma\mathbf{E}\cdot\left(\frac{\sigma\nabla\varepsilon - \varepsilon\nabla\sigma}{\sigma^2}\right) = \mathbf{J}\cdot\nabla\left(\frac{\varepsilon}{\sigma}\right). \tag{9.38}$$

This result was obtained using the vector identity of Prob. 3.89(b). If the medium is homogeneous, $\nabla(\varepsilon/\sigma) = \mathbf{0}$, and (9.38) reduces to

$$\rho + \tau\frac{\partial\rho}{\partial t} = 0, \tag{9.39}$$

where

$$\tau = \frac{\varepsilon}{\sigma} \tag{9.40}$$

is the so-called *relaxation time*. The solution of (9.39) is

$$\rho(t) = \rho_0 e^{-t/\tau} = \rho_0 e^{-\sigma t/\varepsilon}, \tag{9.41}$$

where $\rho_0$ is the value of $\rho$ at $t = 0$. Thus, the charge density decays exponentially and is independent of the $\mathbf{E}$ applied. Hence, we conclude that there can be no permanent distribution of free charge in a homogeneous medium with nonzero conductivity. The relaxation time $\tau$ is equal to the time required for $\rho$ to decay to $1/e$ of its original value and varies inversely with the conductivity. Thus, the charge will almost instantaneously disappear from the interior of a good conductor such as copper, but will remain for a long time within a good insulator, such as fused quartz.

## 9.4 Potential Functions of the Electromagnetic Field

The *vector potential* $\mathbf{A}(\mathbf{r}, t)$ is a vector function for which the electromagnetic fields $\mathbf{E}$ and $\mathbf{B}$ are related by

$$\mathbf{B} = \nabla\times\mathbf{A}, \tag{9.42}$$

and the *scalar potential* $\phi(\mathbf{r}, t)$ is a scalar function for which

$$\mathbf{E} = -\frac{\partial\mathbf{A}}{\partial t} - \nabla\phi. \tag{9.43}$$

The existence of $\mathbf{A}$ completely determines $\mathbf{B}$ by (9.42), but the converse is *not* true since the curl of the gradient of any scalar vanishes identically. Note that the gradient of any scalar function $\psi$ can be added to $\mathbf{A}$ without affecting $\mathbf{B}$. (Cf., Prob. 3.47.)

**PROBLEM 9.9** Verify (9.42–3).

**Solution:** Since $\mathbf{B}$ satisfies (9.18), that is, $\nabla\cdot\mathbf{B} = 0$, then from Prob. 4.78, a vector function $\mathbf{A}$ exists such that

$$\mathbf{B} = \nabla\times\mathbf{A}. \qquad [9.42]$$

Hence, Maxwell's first equation (9.16) becomes

$$\nabla \times \left(\mathbf{E} + \frac{\partial \mathbf{A}}{\partial t}\right) = \mathbf{0}. \tag{9.44}$$

Thus, from the result of Prob. 4.73, if $\phi$ is some scalar function, $\mathbf{E} + \dfrac{\partial \mathbf{A}}{\partial t} = -\nabla\phi$, or, consequently,

$$\mathbf{E} = -\frac{\partial \mathbf{A}}{\partial t} - \nabla\phi. \qquad [9.43]$$

**PROBLEM 9.10** If **A** is replaced by

$$\mathbf{A}' = \mathbf{A} + \nabla\psi, \tag{9.45}$$

show that $\phi$ should be replaced by

$$\phi' = \phi - \frac{\partial \psi}{\partial t} \tag{9.46}$$

for (9.43) to remain unchanged.

**Solution:** If **A** is replaced by $\mathbf{A}' = \mathbf{A} + \nabla\psi$, (9.43) becomes

$$\mathbf{E} = -\frac{\partial}{\partial t}(\mathbf{A}' - \nabla\psi) - \nabla\phi = -\frac{\partial \mathbf{A}'}{\partial t} - \nabla\left(\phi - \frac{\partial \psi}{\partial t}\right). \tag{9.47}$$

Hence, if we set $\phi' = \phi - \partial\psi/\partial t$, (9.47) becomes

$$\mathbf{E} = -\frac{\partial \mathbf{A}'}{\partial t} - \nabla\psi', \tag{9.48}$$

which is identical to (9.43).

The transformations (9.45-6) are called *gauge transformations.* Thus (9.42-3) are unaltered by (9.45-6). We therefore say that the field vectors are *invariant to gauge transformations.*

**PROBLEM 9.11** Show that in a linear homogeneous isotropic medium in which $\varepsilon$, $\mu$ are constants and $\sigma = 0$, the scalar potential $\phi$ and the vector potential **A** satisfy

$$\nabla^2\mathbf{A} - \mu\varepsilon \frac{\partial^2 \mathbf{A}}{\partial t^2} - \nabla\left(\nabla\cdot\mathbf{A} + \mu\varepsilon\frac{\partial \phi}{\partial t}\right) = -\mu\mathbf{J}, \tag{9.49}$$

$$\nabla^2\phi + \frac{\partial}{\partial t}\nabla\cdot\mathbf{A} = -\frac{\rho}{\varepsilon}. \tag{9.50}$$

**Solution:** Using (9.13) and (9.14), Maxwell's second equation (9.17) can be written as

$$\nabla \times \mathbf{B} - \mu\varepsilon\frac{\partial \mathbf{E}}{\partial t} = \mu\mathbf{J}. \tag{9.51}$$

Substituting for **B** and **E** from (9.42-3),

$$\nabla \times (\nabla \times \mathbf{A}) + \mu\varepsilon\frac{\partial^2 \mathbf{A}}{\partial t^2} + \mu\varepsilon\,\nabla\left(\frac{\partial \phi}{\partial t}\right) = \mu\mathbf{J}. \tag{9.52}$$

Substituting the vector identity,

$$\nabla \times (\nabla \times \mathbf{A}) = \nabla(\nabla\cdot\mathbf{A}) - \nabla^2\mathbf{A}, \qquad [3.163]$$

in (9.52),

$$\nabla^2\mathbf{A} - \mu\varepsilon\,\frac{\partial^2\mathbf{A}}{\partial t^2} - \nabla\left(\nabla\cdot\mathbf{A} + \mu\varepsilon\,\frac{\partial\phi}{\partial t}\right) = -\mu\mathbf{J}. \qquad [9.49]$$

Next, using (9.13), (9.19) can be written as

$$\nabla\cdot\mathbf{E} = \frac{\rho}{\varepsilon}. \qquad (9.53)$$

Substituting for **E** from (9.43),

$$\nabla\cdot\left[-\frac{\partial\mathbf{A}}{\partial t} - \nabla\phi\right] = \frac{\rho}{\varepsilon}, \qquad (9.54)$$

or, consequently,

$$\nabla^2\phi + \frac{\partial}{\partial t}\nabla\cdot\mathbf{A} = -\frac{\rho}{\varepsilon}. \qquad [9.50]$$

The *Lorentz condition for potentials* **A** and $\phi$ is

$$\nabla\cdot\mathbf{A} + \mu\varepsilon\,\frac{\partial\phi}{\partial t} = 0. \qquad (9.55)$$

**PROBLEM 9.12** If potentials **A** and $\phi$ satisfy (9.55) then show that **A** and $\phi$ satisfy the *inhomogeneous wave equations*

$$\nabla^2\mathbf{A} - \mu\varepsilon\,\frac{\partial^2\mathbf{A}}{\partial t^2} = -\mu\mathbf{J}, \qquad (9.56)$$

$$\nabla^2\phi - \mu\varepsilon\,\frac{\partial^2\phi}{\partial t^2} = -\frac{\rho}{\varepsilon}. \qquad (9.57)$$

**Solution:** If the potentials **A** and $\phi$ satisfy (9.55), then

$$\nabla\cdot\mathbf{A} = -\mu\varepsilon\,\frac{\partial\phi}{\partial t}. \qquad (9.58)$$

Hence, (9.49) reduces to (9.56). Substituting (9.58) into (9.50), we obtain (9.57).

**PROBLEM 9.13** Show that there exist vector and scalar potentials that satisfy the Lorentz condition (9.55).

**Solution:** Suppose that the potentials **A** and $\phi$ do not satisfy (9.55); i.e.,

$$\nabla\cdot\mathbf{A} + \mu\varepsilon\,\frac{\partial\phi}{\partial t} \neq 0. \qquad (9.59)$$

By making a gauge transformation to $\mathbf{A}'$ and $\phi'$, i.e.,

$$\mathbf{A}' = \mathbf{A} + \nabla\psi, \qquad \phi' = \phi - \frac{\partial\psi}{\partial t},$$

we obtain

$$\nabla\cdot\mathbf{A}' + \mu\varepsilon\,\frac{\partial\phi'}{\partial t} = \nabla\cdot\mathbf{A} + \mu\varepsilon\,\frac{\partial\phi}{\partial t} + \nabla^2\psi - \mu\varepsilon\,\frac{\partial^2\psi}{\partial t^2}. \qquad (9.60)$$

Thus, it suffices to find a gauge function $\psi$ that satisfies

$$\nabla^2\psi - \mu\varepsilon\,\frac{\partial^2\psi}{\partial t^2} = -\left(\nabla\cdot\mathbf{A} + \mu\varepsilon\,\frac{\partial\phi}{\partial t}\right). \qquad (9.61)$$

Then new potentials $\mathbf{A}'$ and $\phi'$ will satisfy the Lorentz condition (9.55).

Since the potentials $\mathbf{A}$ and $\phi$ may be related by the Lorentz condition (9.55), the electromagnetic field can be represented in terms of a single vector function. This is shown in the Prob. 9.14.

The *Hertz vector* $\mathbf{\Pi}$ is a single-valued vector function, whose time rate of change is proportional to the potential $\mathbf{A}$. Thus, in a medium with constants $\mu$ and $\varepsilon$, the Hertz vector satisfies

$$\mathbf{A} = \mu\varepsilon \frac{\partial \mathbf{\Pi}}{\partial t}. \tag{9.62}$$

**PROBLEM 9.14** Show that in a medium with constants $\mu$ and $\varepsilon$, the field vectors $\mathbf{E}$ and $\mathbf{B}$ can be represented in terms of the Hertz vector $\mathbf{\Pi}$ as

$$\mathbf{E} = -\mu\varepsilon \frac{\partial^2 \mathbf{\Pi}}{\partial t^2} + \nabla(\nabla \cdot \mathbf{\Pi}), \tag{9.63}$$

$$\mathbf{B} = \mu\varepsilon\, \nabla \times \frac{\partial \mathbf{\Pi}}{\partial t}. \tag{9.64}$$

Also find the equation that $\mathbf{\Pi}$ must satisfy.

**Solution:** Substituting (9.62) in (9.42-3) yields

$$\mathbf{B} = \nabla \times \mathbf{A} = \nabla \times \left(\mu\varepsilon \frac{\partial \mathbf{\Pi}}{\partial t}\right) = \mu\varepsilon\, \nabla \times \frac{\partial \mathbf{\Pi}}{\partial t}, \qquad [9.64]$$

$$\mathbf{E} = -\frac{\partial \mathbf{A}}{\partial t} - \nabla\phi = -\mu\varepsilon \frac{\partial^2 \mathbf{\Pi}}{\partial t^2} - \nabla\phi. \tag{9.65}$$

Now Maxwell's second equation (9.17) can be written as

$$\nabla \times \mathbf{B} = \mu \mathbf{J} + \mu\varepsilon \frac{\partial \mathbf{E}}{\partial t}. \tag{9.66}$$

Substituting (9.64-5) into (9.66),

$$\mu\varepsilon \frac{\partial}{\partial t} \nabla \times \nabla \times \mathbf{\Pi} = \mu \mathbf{J} + \mu\varepsilon \frac{\partial}{\partial t}\left(-\mu\varepsilon \frac{\partial^2 \mathbf{\Pi}}{\partial t^2} - \nabla\phi\right),$$

or, on simplification,

$$\frac{\partial}{\partial t}\left[\nabla \times (\nabla \times \mathbf{\Pi}) + \mu\varepsilon \frac{\partial^2 \mathbf{\Pi}}{\partial t^2} + \nabla\phi\right] = \frac{\mathbf{J}}{\varepsilon}. \tag{9.67}$$

Integrating (9.67) with respect to time $t$,

$$\nabla \times (\nabla \times \mathbf{\Pi}) + \mu\varepsilon \frac{\partial^2 \mathbf{\Pi}}{\partial t^2} + \nabla\phi = \int \frac{\mathbf{J}}{\varepsilon}\, dt, \tag{9.68}$$

where the arbitrary constant is set equal to zero since it does not affect the determination of the field.

Using the vector identity (3.163), (9.68) can be rewritten as

$$\nabla^2 \mathbf{\Pi} - \mu\varepsilon \frac{\partial^2 \mathbf{\Pi}}{\partial t^2} - [\nabla(\nabla \cdot \mathbf{\Pi}) + \nabla\phi] = -\int \frac{\mathbf{J}}{\varepsilon}\, dt. \tag{9.69}$$

Hence, if the condition

$$\nabla(\nabla \cdot \mathbf{\Pi}) + \nabla\phi = \mathbf{0}, \tag{9.70}$$

or

$$\nabla\phi = -\nabla(\nabla \cdot \mathbf{\Pi}) \tag{9.71}$$

is imposed on $\phi$ and $\mathbf{\Pi}$, then $\mathbf{\Pi}$ satisfies the inhomogeneous wave equation

$$\nabla^2\mathbf{\Pi} - \mu\varepsilon \frac{\partial^2 \mathbf{\Pi}}{\partial t^2} = -\int \frac{\mathbf{J}}{\varepsilon}\, dt. \tag{9.72}$$

Substituting (9.71) into (9.65) yields

$$\mathbf{E} = -\mu\varepsilon \frac{\partial^2 \mathbf{\Pi}}{\partial t^2} + \nabla(\nabla \cdot \mathbf{\Pi}). \qquad [9.63]$$

Note that (9.70) is equivalent to the Lorentz condition (9.55).

## 9.5 Energy in the Electromagnetic Field, and the Poynting Vector

The *Poynting vector* $\mathbf{P}$ is

$$\mathbf{P} = \mathbf{E} \times \mathbf{H}. \tag{9.73}$$

The *energy density W of the electromagnetic field* is

$$W = \frac{1}{2}(\mathbf{E} \cdot \mathbf{D} + \mathbf{H} \cdot \mathbf{B}). \tag{9.74}$$

**PROBLEM 9.15** In a homogeneous isotropic medium with constants $\varepsilon$ and $\mu$, show that

$$\nabla \cdot \mathbf{P} + \frac{\partial W}{\partial t} = -\mathbf{J} \cdot \mathbf{E}. \tag{9.75}$$

**Solution:** Using the vector identity (3.157),

$$\nabla \cdot \mathbf{P} = \nabla \cdot (\mathbf{E} \times \mathbf{H}) = \mathbf{H} \cdot \nabla \times \mathbf{E} - \mathbf{E} \cdot \nabla \times \mathbf{H}. \tag{9.76}$$

Substituting Maxwell's equations (9.16–7) into (9.76),

$$\nabla \cdot \mathbf{P} = \mathbf{H} \cdot \left(-\frac{\partial \mathbf{B}}{\partial t}\right) - \mathbf{E} \cdot \left(\mathbf{J} + \frac{\partial \mathbf{D}}{\partial t}\right),$$

or, consequently,

$$\nabla \cdot \mathbf{P} + \mathbf{E} \cdot \frac{\partial \mathbf{D}}{\partial t} + \mathbf{H} \cdot \frac{\partial \mathbf{B}}{\partial t} = -\mathbf{E} \cdot \mathbf{J}. \tag{9.77}$$

Now, from (9.13–4),

$$\mathbf{E} \cdot \frac{\partial \mathbf{D}}{\partial t} = \varepsilon \mathbf{E} \cdot \frac{\partial \mathbf{E}}{\partial t} = \frac{1}{2}\varepsilon \frac{\partial}{\partial t}(\mathbf{E} \cdot \mathbf{E}) = \frac{1}{2}\frac{\partial}{\partial t}(\mathbf{E} \cdot \varepsilon \mathbf{E}) = \frac{\partial}{\partial t}\left(\frac{1}{2}\mathbf{E} \cdot \mathbf{D}\right), \tag{9.78}$$

$$\mathbf{H} \cdot \frac{\partial \mathbf{B}}{\partial t} = \mu \mathbf{H} \cdot \frac{\partial \mathbf{H}}{\partial t} = \frac{1}{2}\mu \frac{\partial}{\partial t}(\mathbf{H} \cdot \mathbf{H}) = \frac{1}{2}\frac{\partial}{\partial t}(\mathbf{H} \cdot \mu \mathbf{H}) = \frac{\partial}{\partial t}\left(\frac{1}{2}\mathbf{H} \cdot \mathbf{B}\right). \tag{9.79}$$

Thus, (9.77) reduces to

$$\nabla \cdot \mathbf{P} + \frac{\partial}{\partial t}\left[\frac{1}{2}(\mathbf{E} \cdot \mathbf{D} + \mathbf{H} \cdot \mathbf{B})\right] = -\mathbf{E} \cdot \mathbf{J}, \tag{9.80}$$

or hence,

$$\nabla \cdot \mathbf{P} + \frac{\partial W}{\partial t} = -\mathbf{E} \cdot \mathbf{J}. \qquad [9.75]$$

Note that if the conductivity $\sigma$ of the medium is zero, $\mathbf{J} = \sigma\mathbf{E} = \mathbf{0}$, and (9.75) reduces to

$$\nabla \cdot \mathbf{P} + \frac{\partial W}{\partial t} = 0, \qquad (9.81)$$

which is exactly the same form as the continuity equation (9.3). The "current density $\mathbf{J}$" is now $\mathbf{P}$ and the "charge density $\rho$" is now $W$. Thus we can associate the Poynting vector $\mathbf{P}$ with the flow of energy density.

*Poynting's theorem* states that in a homogeneous isotropic space, if $R$ is the region bounded by a closed surface $S$, then

$$-\frac{\partial}{\partial t}\iiint_R W\, dV = \oiint_S \mathbf{P} \cdot d\mathbf{S} + \iiint_R \mathbf{J} \cdot \mathbf{E}\, dV, \qquad (9.82)$$

where $\mathbf{P}$ is the Poynting vector and $W$ is the energy density of the electromagnetic field.

**PROBLEM 9.16** Prove Poynting's theorem, and interpret it physically.

**Solution:** Since (9.75) can be rewritten as

$$-\frac{\partial W}{\partial t} = \nabla \cdot \mathbf{P} + \mathbf{J} \cdot \mathbf{E}, \qquad (9.83)$$

integrating (9.83) over $R$ and using the divergence theorem (4.58),

$$-\frac{\partial}{\partial t}\iiint_R W\, dV = \iiint_R \nabla \cdot \mathbf{P}\, dV + \iiint_R \mathbf{J} \cdot \mathbf{E}\, dV$$

$$= \oiint_S \mathbf{P} \cdot d\mathbf{S} + \iiint_R \mathbf{J} \cdot \mathbf{E}\, dV. \qquad [9.82]$$

If $W$ is the energy density of the electromagnetic field,

$$\iiint_R W\, dV \qquad (9.84)$$

is the total energy of the electromagnetic field stored in the region $R$. Hence, the left-hand side of (9.82) represents the rate of decrease of the total energy of the electromagnetic field stored in $R$. The loss of available stored energy must be accounted for by the terms on the right-hand side of (9.82). If the conductivity of the medium is $\sigma$, then, from (9.15), the second term on the right-hand side of (9.82) becomes

$$\iiint_R \mathbf{J} \cdot \mathbf{E}\, dV = \iiint_R \sigma E^2\, dV = \iiint_R \frac{J^2}{\sigma}\, dV, \qquad (9.85)$$

which is the ohmic loss or joule heat loss.

The first term on the right-hand side of (9.82) is the energy flux flowing out of the region $R$ through the surface $S$. Thus, the decrease of the energy of the electromagnetic field stored in $R$ is partly accounted for by the joule heat loss and the rest flows out of $R$ across the bounding surface $S$.

From the above interpretation, the Poynting vector $\mathbf{P}$, defined by

$$\mathbf{P} = \mathbf{E} \times \mathbf{H}, \qquad [9.73]$$

may be interpreted as the flux of energy of the electromagnetic field, and it gives the amount of field energy passing through unit area of the surface per unit time.

## 9.6 Boundary Conditions

Although Maxwell's equations (9.16–7) are of the utmost importance, they do not, in themselves, define a unique field. There are an infinite number of solutions to these equations. By stating boundary conditions, a unique solution is obtained. In the following, the boundary conditions, which must be satisfied by the field vectors, are derived.

**PROBLEM 9.17** Show that the normal components of $\mathbf{B}$ across a surface separating two media are continuous.

**Solution:** For two media bounded by a common surface $\mathbf{S}$, as shown in Fig. 9.1, construct an infinitesimal right cylinder with end faces of area $\Delta S$ in adjacent media. The end surfaces are parallel to the common boundary surface and are separated by a distance $\Delta h$.

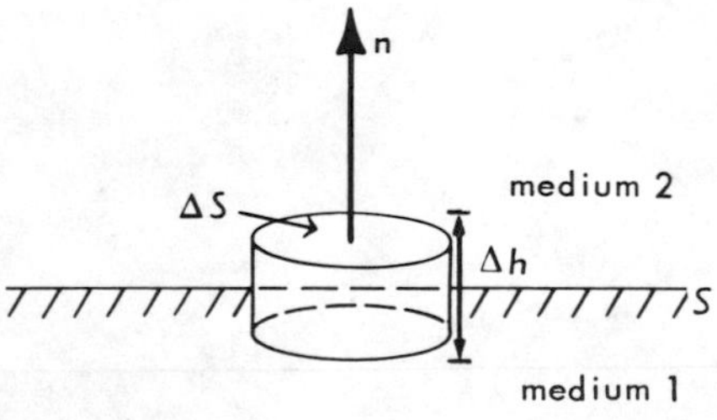


Fig. 9.1 Media bounded by a common surface.

Applying Gauss' law for the magnetic field (9.33) to the region enclosed by the cylinder,

$$\oiint \mathbf{B} \cdot \mathbf{n}\, dS = 0 \qquad (9.86)$$

when integrated over the walls and end surfaces of the cylinder. The unit vector $\mathbf{n}$ normal to $S$ is drawn from medium 1 to medium 2. If $\mathbf{B}_1$ and $\mathbf{B}_2$ denote the value of $\mathbf{B}$ at a point on $S$ in mediums 1 and 2, respectively, then

$$\lim_{\Delta h \to 0} \oiint \mathbf{B} \cdot \mathbf{n}\, dS = (\mathbf{B}_2 \cdot \mathbf{n} - \mathbf{B}_1 \cdot \mathbf{n})\,\Delta S = 0. \qquad (9.87)$$

The limit $\Delta h \longrightarrow 0$ is taken to ensure that there is no contribution from the walls of the cylinder. Thus,

$$(\mathbf{B}_2 - \mathbf{B}_1) \cdot \mathbf{n} = 0 \qquad (9.88)$$

or, consequently,

$$\mathbf{B}_2 \cdot \mathbf{n} = \mathbf{B}_1 \cdot \mathbf{n}, \qquad (9.89)$$

which states that normal components of $\mathbf{B}$ across a surface separating two media are continuous.

**PROBLEM 9.18** Show that the normal components of $\mathbf{D}$ across a surface separating two media satisfy

$$(\mathbf{D}_2 - \mathbf{D}_1) \cdot \mathbf{n} = \rho_s, \qquad (9.90)$$

where $\rho_s$ is the surface charge density.

**Solution:** This case can be treated similarly to Prob. 9.17, but in this case, Gauss' law for the electric field (9.32) is

$$\oiint \mathbf{D}\cdot\mathbf{n}\,dS = Q, \tag{9.91}$$

where $Q$ is the total charge enclosed in the cylinder; i.e.,

$$Q = \rho\,\Delta h \Delta S.$$

In the limit, as $\Delta h \longrightarrow 0$, the volume charge density $\rho$ becomes infinite since the total charge $Q$ remains constant. Since a surface charge density $\rho_s$ is the charge per unit area,

$$Q = \rho\,\Delta h \Delta S = \rho_s\,\Delta S. \tag{9.92}$$

Then from (9.91),

$$(\mathbf{D}_2 - \mathbf{D}_1)\cdot\mathbf{n} = \rho_s.$$

We conclude that normal components of $\mathbf{D}$ are continuous unless there is a surface charge on the boundary surface of the two media.

**PROBLEM 9.19** Show that the tangential components of $\mathbf{E}$ through a surface separating two media are continuous.

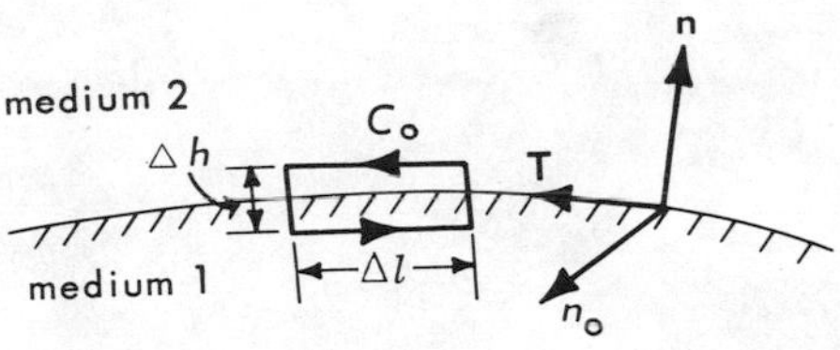


Fig. 9.2 Rectangular path across a surface separating two media.

**Solution:** For a rectangular path $C_0$, as shown in Fig. 9.2, integrating Maxwell's first equation

$$\nabla\times\mathbf{E} + \frac{\partial\mathbf{B}}{\partial t} = \mathbf{0} \tag{9.16}$$

over the surface $S_0$ bounded by a rectangular loop $C_0$ yields

$$\iint_{S_0} \nabla\times\mathbf{E}\cdot\mathbf{n}_0\,dS = -\iint_{S_0} \frac{\partial\mathbf{B}}{\partial t}\cdot\mathbf{n}_0\,dS, \tag{9.93}$$

where $\mathbf{n}_0$ is the positive normal to $S_0$, as shown in Fig. 9.2. Applying Stokes' theorem (4.104) to the left-hand side of (9.93) gives

$$\oint_{C_0} \mathbf{E}\cdot d\mathbf{r} = -\iint_{S_0} \frac{\partial\mathbf{B}}{\partial t}\cdot\mathbf{n}_0\,dS. \tag{9.94}$$

As shown in Fig. 9.2, if the unit tangent vector $\mathbf{T}$ is

$$\mathbf{T} - \mathbf{n}_0\times\mathbf{n}, \tag{9.95}$$

then, in the limit as $\Delta h \longrightarrow 0$, (9.94) can be approximated by

$$\mathbf{T}\cdot(\mathbf{E}_2 - \mathbf{E}_1)\,\Delta l = -\frac{\partial\mathbf{B}}{\partial t}\cdot\mathbf{n}_0\,\Delta h\Delta l,$$

or, consequently,

$$\mathbf{n}_0\times\mathbf{n}\cdot(\mathbf{E}_2 - \mathbf{E}_1) + \mathbf{n}_0\cdot\frac{\partial\mathbf{B}}{\partial t}\,\Delta h = 0. \tag{9.96}$$

Since $\mathbf{n}_0\times\mathbf{n}\cdot\mathbf{E} = \mathbf{n}_0\cdot\mathbf{n}\times\mathbf{E}$ from (1.72) and in the limit as $\Delta h \longrightarrow 0$, $\Delta l \longrightarrow 0$,

$$\mathbf{n}_0\cdot\left[\mathbf{n}\times(\mathbf{E}_2 - \mathbf{E}_1) + \lim_{\Delta h\to 0}\left(\frac{\partial\mathbf{B}}{\partial t}\,\Delta h\right)\right] = 0. \tag{9.97}$$

Since the orientation of the rectangle, and hence also of $\mathbf{n}_0$, is arbitrary,

$$\mathbf{n}\times(\mathbf{E}_2 - \mathbf{E}_1) = -\lim_{\Delta h\to 0}\left(\frac{\partial\mathbf{B}}{\partial t}\,\Delta h\right) = 0, \tag{9.98}$$

provided $\partial\mathbf{B}/\partial t$ is bounded. Thus,

$$\mathbf{n} \times \mathbf{E}_2 = \mathbf{n} \times \mathbf{E}_1, \tag{9.99}$$

which states that the tangential components of **E** through a surface separating two media are continuous.

**PROBLEM 9.20** Show that the tangential components of **H** through a surface separating two media satisfy

$$\mathbf{n} \times (\mathbf{H}_2 - \mathbf{H}_1) = \mathbf{J}_s, \tag{9.100}$$

where $\mathbf{J}_s$ is the surface current density.

**Solution:** This case can be treated similarly to Prob. 9.19. Integrating Maxwell's second equation (9.17),

$$\oint_{C_0} \mathbf{H} \cdot d\mathbf{r} = \iint_{S_0} \mathbf{J} \cdot \mathbf{n}_0 \, dS + \iint_{S_0} \frac{\partial \mathbf{D}}{\partial t} \cdot \mathbf{n}_0 \, dS. \tag{9.101}$$

Hence, on proceeding in a manner similar to that used to obtain (9.98),

$$\mathbf{n} \times (\mathbf{H}_2 - \mathbf{H}_1) = \lim_{\Delta h \to 0} \left( \mathbf{J} + \frac{\partial \mathbf{D}}{\partial t} \right) \Delta h. \tag{9.102}$$

The second term on the right of (9.102) vanishes as $\Delta h \longrightarrow 0$ since $\partial \mathbf{D}/\partial t$ is bounded. If the current density **J** is finite, i.e., $\sigma$ is finite, the first term also vanishes. But if the current $I = \mathbf{J} \cdot \mathbf{n}_0 \, \Delta h \Delta l$ through the rectangle remains finite even in the limit $\Delta h \longrightarrow 0$, we define a surface current density $\mathbf{J}_s$ as the current per unit length,

$$I = \mathbf{J} \cdot \mathbf{n}_0 \, \Delta h \Delta l = \mathbf{J}_s \cdot \mathbf{n}_0 \, \Delta l. \tag{9.103}$$

Then (9.102) reduces to

$$\mathbf{n} \times (\mathbf{H}_2 - \mathbf{H}_1) = \mathbf{J}_s.$$

## 9.7 Static Fields

*Static fields* are those for which the time derivatives are zero; i.e., there is no time variation of the fields.

**PROBLEM 9.21** Derive Maxwell's equations for static fields.

**Solution:** With the restriction $\partial/\partial t = 0$, (9.16–7) become

$$\nabla \times \mathbf{E}(\mathbf{r}) = \mathbf{0}, \tag{9.104}$$

$$\nabla \times \mathbf{H}(\mathbf{r}) = \mathbf{J}(\mathbf{r}). \tag{9.105}$$

Equations (9.18) and (9.19) remain the same; i.e.,

$$\nabla \cdot \mathbf{B}(\mathbf{r}) = 0, \tag{9.106}$$

$$\nabla \cdot \mathbf{D}(\mathbf{r}) = \rho(\mathbf{r}). \tag{9.107}$$

For static fields, the electric and magnetic fields are completely decoupled from one another. The examination of the relations

$$\nabla \times \mathbf{E} = \mathbf{0}, \qquad \nabla \cdot \mathbf{D} = \rho,$$

and the consequences thereof, constitute the study of *electrostatic fields*.

Similarly, the examination of the relation

$$\nabla \times \mathbf{H} = \mathbf{J}, \qquad \nabla \cdot \mathbf{B} = 0,$$

and the consequences thereof, form the study of *magnetostatic fields.*

**PROBLEM 9.22** Show that the electrostatic field $\mathbf{E}$ is irrotational and, therefore, conservative; that is, it can be represented as the gradient of scalar potential function $\phi$; i.e.,

$$\mathbf{E} = -\nabla\phi. \tag{9.108}$$

**Solution:** Since for an electrostatic field,

$$\nabla \times \mathbf{E} = \mathbf{0}, \qquad [9.104]$$

$\mathbf{E}$ is irrotational and, from Prob. 4.73, can be expressed as

$$\mathbf{E} = -\nabla\phi.$$

With (9.104) or (9.108) and from Probs. 4.71 and 7.15, the line integral of $\mathbf{E}$ around any closed path is zero and the field is conservative.

Note that (9.108) is also the special case of (9.43) with $\partial\mathbf{A}/\partial t = 0$.

*Poisson's equation* for a scalar potential function $\phi$ of the electrostatic field is

$$\nabla^2\phi = -\frac{\rho}{\varepsilon}, \tag{9.109}$$

where $\rho$ is the charge density and $\varepsilon$ is a constant.

*Laplace's equation* for electrostatic fields is obtained from Poisson's equation by setting $\rho = 0$; i.e.,

$$\nabla^2\phi = 0. \tag{9.110}$$

**PROBLEM 9.23** Derive Poisson's equation for the scalar potential function $\phi$ of the electrostatic field.

**Solution:** Since

$$\mathbf{E} = -\nabla\phi, \qquad [9.108]$$

from (9.107) and (9.13),

$$\nabla \cdot \mathbf{D} = \nabla \cdot (\varepsilon\mathbf{E}) = \rho. \tag{9.111}$$

If $\varepsilon$ is constant, $\nabla \cdot (\varepsilon\mathbf{E}) = \varepsilon\nabla \cdot \mathbf{E}$, and (9.111) becomes

$$\nabla \cdot \mathbf{E} = \frac{\rho}{\varepsilon}. \tag{9.112}$$

Substituting (9.108) for $\mathbf{E}$ into (9.112), we obtain $\nabla^2\phi = -\rho/\varepsilon$.

**PROBLEM 9.24** Show that for a static field, the scalar potential $\phi(\mathbf{r})$ is the negative of the work done by the field on a unit positive charge to bring the charge from infinity to the point $\mathbf{r}$.

**Solution:** With $q = 1$, the work done by the Lorentz force (9.11) on a unit positive charge is

$$W = \int_\infty^{\mathbf{r}} \mathbf{f} \cdot d\mathbf{r} = \int_\infty^{\mathbf{r}} (\mathbf{E} + \mathbf{v} \times \mathbf{B}) \cdot d\mathbf{r}$$

$$= \int_\infty^{\mathbf{r}} \mathbf{E} \cdot d\mathbf{r} - \int_\infty^{\mathbf{r}} \mathbf{B} \cdot \mathbf{v} \times d\mathbf{r}, \tag{9.113}$$

where the last expression is obtained with the use of (1.77).

Since the motion produced by $\mathbf{v}$ is along $d\mathbf{r}$, $\mathbf{v} \times d\mathbf{r} = \mathbf{0}$ and the magnetic field does not contribute to the work done on the charge. Thus, because $\phi(\infty) \equiv 0$, using (3.120),

$$W = \int_{\infty}^{\mathbf{r}} \mathbf{E} \cdot d\mathbf{r} = \int_{\infty}^{\mathbf{r}} (-\nabla\phi) \cdot d\mathbf{r} = -\int_{\infty}^{\mathbf{r}} d\phi = \phi(\infty) - \phi(\mathbf{r}) = -\phi(\mathbf{r}). \quad (9.114)$$

From (9.114), the scalar potential of an electrostatic field can also be interpreted as the work required to bring a unit positive charge from infinity to a point within the field; i.e.,

$$\phi(\mathbf{r}) = -\int_{\infty}^{\mathbf{r}} \mathbf{E} \cdot d\mathbf{r}. \quad (9.115)$$

**PROBLEM 9.25** Find the electric field $\mathbf{E}$ and the potential $\phi$ of a point charge of magnitude $q$.

**Solution:** If a point charge $q$ is located at the origin, Gauss' law for the electric field (9.32) becomes

$$\oint\!\!\oint_S \mathbf{D} \cdot d\mathbf{S} = \oint\!\!\oint_S \mathbf{D} \cdot \mathbf{n}\, dS = q. \quad (9.116)$$

If $S$ is a spherical surface of radius $r$ with center at the origin, then $\mathbf{n} = \mathbf{e}_r$ and $\mathbf{D} \cdot \mathbf{n} = \mathbf{D} \cdot \mathbf{e}_r = D_r$, where $D_r$ is the radial component of $\mathbf{D}$. Thus, (9.116) becomes

$$\oint\!\!\oint_S D_r\, dS = q. \quad (9.117)$$

From the symmetry of the configuration, $\mathbf{D} = D_r \mathbf{e}_r$, and on the surface of constant radius $D_r$ is a constant. Since the surface area of a sphere of radius $r$ is $4\pi r^2$,

$$\oint\!\!\oint_S D_r\, dS = D_r(r) 4\pi r^2 = q.$$

Hence, $D_r(r) = q/(4\pi r^2)$ and

$$\mathbf{D} = D_r \mathbf{e}_r = \frac{q}{4\pi r^2} \mathbf{e}_r. \quad (9.118)$$

Since $\mathbf{D} = \varepsilon \mathbf{E}$,

$$\mathbf{E} = \frac{q}{4\pi \varepsilon r^2} \mathbf{e}_r. \quad (9.119)$$

Now, since $\mathbf{E}$ has only a radial component, using the spherical coordinates expression (5.96) of $\nabla\phi$, $\mathbf{E} = -\nabla\phi$ reduces to $E_r = -d\phi(\mathbf{r})/dr$, or, consequently, $d\phi(\mathbf{r})/dr = -q/4\pi\varepsilon r^2$. Integrating both sides,

$$\int_a^b \frac{d\phi(\mathbf{r})}{dr}\, dr = -\int_a^b \frac{q\, dr}{4\pi\varepsilon r^2} = -\frac{q}{4\pi\varepsilon} \int_a^b \frac{dr}{r^2},$$

and hence,

$$\phi(b) - \phi(a) = \frac{q}{4\pi\varepsilon}\left(\frac{1}{b} - \frac{1}{a}\right). \quad (9.120)$$

If $a = \infty$, $b = r$, and $\phi(\infty) \equiv 0$,

$$\phi(\mathbf{r}) = \frac{q}{4\pi \varepsilon r}. \tag{9.121}$$

*Coulomb's law for electrostatic fields* states that the force $\mathbf{f}$ between two charges $q_1$ and $q_2$ is inversely proportional to the square of the distance $r_{12}$ between them; i.e., if $\mathbf{e}_r$ is the unit vector directed from $q_1$ to $q_2$, then

$$\mathbf{f} = \frac{q_1 q_2}{4\pi \varepsilon r_{12}^2} \mathbf{e}_r. \tag{9.122}$$

**PROBLEM 9.26** Prove Coloumb's law for electrostatic fields.

**Solution:** From the definition of a Lorentz force (9.11), the force $\mathbf{f}$ experienced by a point charge $q_2$ in the electrostatic field is

$$\mathbf{f} = q_2 \mathbf{E}. \tag{9.123}$$

If the field $\mathbf{E}$ is produced by a point charge $q_1$, then substituting (9.119) for $\mathbf{E}$ into (9.123), we obtain Coulomb's law for electrostatic fields (9.122).

An *electric dipole* is formed by two equal and opposite charges separated by an arbitrarily small distance $\mathbf{l}$, where the vector $\mathbf{l}$ initiates on the negative charge and terminates on the positive charge.

The *electric dipole moment* $\mathbf{p}$ is the product of the charge $q$ and the distance vector $\mathbf{l}$; i.e.,

$$\mathbf{p} = q\mathbf{l}. \tag{9.124}$$

A *point dipole* is formed when $\mathbf{l} \longrightarrow 0$ and $q \longrightarrow \infty$ such that the electric dipole moment $\mathbf{p}$ remains constant.

**PROBLEM 9.27** If the electric dipole is located at the origin and the electric dipole moment is in the positive $z$-direction, show that the potential and the electric field of the dipole in a vacuum, whose permittivity is $\varepsilon_0$, are

$$\phi(\mathbf{r}) = \frac{\mathbf{p} \cdot \mathbf{r}}{4\pi\varepsilon_0 r^3} = -\frac{1}{4\pi\varepsilon_0} \mathbf{p} \cdot \nabla\left(\frac{1}{r}\right), \tag{9.125}$$

$$\mathbf{E}(\mathbf{r}) = \frac{3(\mathbf{p}\cdot\mathbf{r})\mathbf{r} - r^2\mathbf{p}}{4\pi\varepsilon_0 r^5}, \tag{9.126}$$

where $\mathbf{r} = r\mathbf{e}_r$ is the vector from the origin to the point of observation, and $r >> |\mathbf{l}|$.

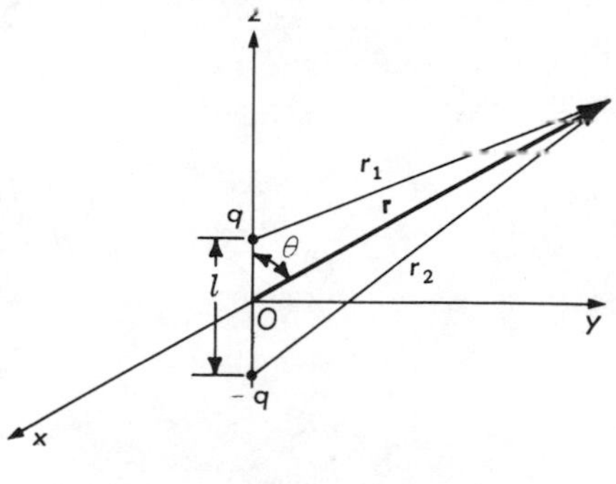


Fig. 9.3 A dipole at the origin, and the point of observation at $r$.

**Solution:** In Fig. 9.3, the potential at a point $P$ due to $\mathbf{p}$ is, from (9.121),

$$\phi(\mathbf{r}) = \frac{q}{4\pi\varepsilon_0 r_1} + \frac{-q}{4\pi\varepsilon_0 r_2} = \frac{q}{4\pi\varepsilon_0}\left(\frac{1}{r_1} - \frac{1}{r_2}\right).$$

If $l << r$, then

$$\begin{aligned}\frac{1}{r_1} - \frac{1}{r_2} &\simeq \frac{1}{r - (l/2)\cos\theta} - \frac{1}{r + (l/2)\cos\theta} \\ &= \frac{l\cos\theta}{r^2}\,\frac{1}{1 - (l\cos\theta/2r)^2} \\ &\simeq \frac{l\cos\theta}{r^2}.\end{aligned}$$

Substituting this in the value of $\phi(\mathbf{r})$,

$$\phi(\mathbf{r}) = \frac{ql \cos\theta}{4\pi\varepsilon_0 r^2}. \qquad (9.127)$$

Since the direction of the electric dipole moment **p** is along the $z$-axis, it is seen from Fig. 9.3 that

$$\mathbf{p}\cdot\mathbf{r} = ql\mathbf{k}\cdot\mathbf{r} = qlr\cos\theta.$$

Therefore, from (9.127),

$$\phi(\mathbf{r}) = \frac{\mathbf{p}\cdot\mathbf{r}}{4\pi\varepsilon_0 r^3}. \qquad (9.128)$$

Also,

$$\nabla\left(\frac{1}{r}\right) = -\frac{1}{r^3}\mathbf{r} = -\frac{1}{r^2}\mathbf{e}_r. \qquad [3.126]$$

Hence,

$$\phi(\mathbf{r}) = \frac{\mathbf{p}\cdot\mathbf{r}}{4\pi\varepsilon_0 r^3} = -\frac{1}{4\pi\varepsilon_0}\mathbf{p}\cdot\nabla\left(\frac{1}{r}\right).$$

Using (3.113), the electric field **E** is

$$\mathbf{E} = -\nabla\phi = -\frac{1}{4\pi\varepsilon_0}\nabla\left(\frac{\mathbf{p}\cdot\mathbf{r}}{r^3}\right)$$

$$= -\frac{1}{4\pi\varepsilon_0 r^3}\nabla(\mathbf{p}\cdot\mathbf{r}) - \frac{(\mathbf{p}\cdot\mathbf{r})}{4\pi\varepsilon_0}\nabla\left(\frac{1}{r^3}\right). \qquad (9.129)$$

Now, from (3.119),

$$\nabla(\mathbf{p}\cdot\mathbf{r}) = \mathbf{p}, \qquad (9.130)$$

and from (3.125),

$$\nabla\left(\frac{1}{r^3}\right) = -3\frac{\mathbf{r}}{r^5}. \qquad (9.131)$$

Substituting (9.130–1) into (9.129),

$$\mathbf{E} = \frac{3(\mathbf{p}\cdot\mathbf{r})\mathbf{r} - r^2\mathbf{p}}{4\pi\varepsilon_0 r^5}.$$

**PROBLEM 9.28** Show that, in a static field produced by steady current,

$$\nabla\cdot\mathbf{J} = 0. \qquad (9.132)$$

**Solution:** The basic equations for the magnetostatic fields are

$$\nabla\times\mathbf{H} = \mathbf{J}, \qquad [9.105]$$

$$\nabla\cdot\mathbf{B} = 0. \qquad [9.106]$$

Since $\nabla\cdot(\nabla\times\mathbf{H}) = 0$ from (3.143), taking the divergence of both sides of (9.105),

$$\nabla\cdot(\nabla\times\mathbf{H}) = \nabla\cdot\mathbf{J} = 0.$$

Note that (9.132) can also be obtained from the continuity equation (9.3) by setting $\partial\rho/\partial t = 0$.

*Ampere's circuital law in magnetostatics* states that in a magnetostatic field, if $I$ is the total steady current through a surface $S$ bounded by a closed curve $C$, then

$$\oint_C \mathbf{H} \cdot d\mathbf{r} = I. \tag{9.133}$$

This law corresponds to Gauss' law in electrostatics.

**PROBLEM 9.29** Prove Ampere's circuital law in magnetostatics.

**Solution:** Integrating (9.105) over a surface $S$ bounded by a closed curve $C$, we have, from (9.2), for the total steady current $I$ through $S$,

$$\iint_S \nabla \times \mathbf{H} \cdot d\mathbf{S} = \iint_S \mathbf{J} \cdot d\mathbf{S} = I. \tag{9.134}$$

Applying Stokes' theorem (4.104) to (9.134) yields

$$\oint_C \mathbf{H} \cdot d\mathbf{r} = I.$$

Note that (9.133) can also be readily obtained from (9.30) by setting $\partial \mathbf{D}/\partial t = 0$.

Ampere's circuital law (9.133) can be used to compute the magnetic field vectors for cases where a high degree of symmetry exists.

**PROBLEM 9.30** Find the magnetic field $\mathbf{H}$ of an infinite straight wire carrying a steady current $I$.

**Solution:** Let a straight wire extend along the $z$-axis from $-\infty$ to $\infty$. Since there is cylindrical symmetry, choose a circular path with a point on the $z$-axis as center with radius $a$, as shown in Fig. 9.4. Because of symmetry, the vector $\mathbf{H}$ is not only azimuthal but is also in the same direction as $d\mathbf{r}$, and its magnitude is constant around the contour. Hence, by (9.133),

$$\oint_C \mathbf{H} \cdot d\mathbf{r} - H_\phi (2\pi a) = I.$$

Thus,

$$\mathbf{H} = H_\phi \, \mathbf{e}_\phi = \frac{I}{2\pi a} \mathbf{e}_\phi. \tag{9.135}$$

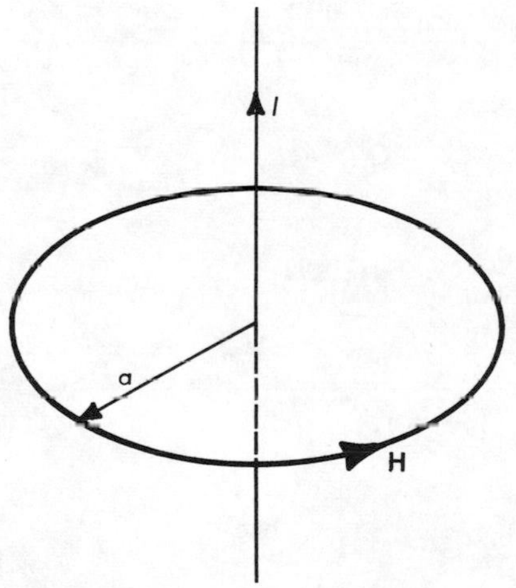


Fig. 9.4 An infinite wire carrying current $I$ and its magnetic field $\mathbf{H}$.

**PROBLEM 9.31** Show that in the magnetostatic field, the vector potential $\mathbf{A}(\mathbf{r})$ satisfies

$$\nabla^2 \mathbf{A} = -\mu_0 \mathbf{J}, \tag{9.136}$$

with the condition $\nabla \cdot \mathbf{A} = 0$, where $\mu_0$ is the permeability of vacuum.

**Solution:** Since $\mathbf{B} = \nabla \times \mathbf{A}$ and $\mathbf{B} = \mu_0 \mathbf{H}$, from (9.105),

$$\nabla \times (\nabla \times \mathbf{A}) = \mu_0 \mathbf{J}, \tag{9.137}$$

which reduces to

$$\nabla(\nabla \cdot \mathbf{A}) - \nabla^2 \mathbf{A} = \mu_0 \mathbf{J}.$$

Thus, if we impose the Lorentz condition (9.55) under steady state, i.e.,

$$\nabla \cdot \mathbf{A} = 0, \tag{9.138}$$

we obtain

$$\nabla^2 \mathbf{A} = -\mu_0 \mathbf{J}.$$

Note that (9.136) also can be obtained from the inhomogeneous wave equation (9.56) with $\partial^2 \mathbf{A}/\partial t^2 = 0$.

## 9.8 Harmonic, or Sinusoidal, Time-Varying Fields

Fields produced by charges and currents whose variation with time is simply harmonic, or sinusoidal, are called *harmonic* or *monochromatic fields*.

Suppose that the source varies in time as

$$\mathbf{J}(\mathbf{r}, t) = \mathbf{J}(\mathbf{r}) \cos(\omega t + \alpha). \tag{9.139}$$

Then $\mathbf{J}(\mathbf{r}, t)$ is represented by

$$\begin{aligned} \mathbf{J}(\mathbf{r}, t) &= Re[\mathbf{J}(\mathbf{r})\, e^{j(\omega t + \alpha)}] \\ &= Re[\mathbf{J}(\mathbf{r})\, e^{j\alpha} e^{j\omega t}] \\ &= Re[\overline{\mathbf{J}}(\mathbf{r})\, e^{j\omega t}], \end{aligned} \tag{9.140}$$

where $j = \sqrt{-1}$, $Re(z) =$ real part of $z$, and $\overline{\mathbf{J}}(\mathbf{r}) = \mathbf{J}(\mathbf{r})e^{j\alpha}$ is a complex space vector and a function of space coordinates only.

The *phase* of the complex vector $\overline{\mathbf{J}}(\mathbf{r})$ is $\alpha$.

Since the time factor $e^{j\omega t}$ is a common multiplier, all time derivatives $\partial/\partial t$ can be replaced by $j\omega$. Thus, Maxwell's equations (9.16–7) reduce to

$$\nabla \times \overline{\mathbf{E}} + j\omega \overline{\mathbf{B}} = \mathbf{0}, \tag{9.141}$$

$$\nabla \times \overline{\mathbf{H}} - j\omega \overline{\mathbf{D}} = \overline{\mathbf{J}}. \tag{9.142}$$

The equation of continuity (9.3) now becomes

$$\nabla \cdot \overline{\mathbf{J}} + j\omega \overline{\rho} = 0. \tag{9.143}$$

For harmonic fields in homogeneous, isotropic, and linear media, the harmonic form of Maxwell's equations (9.141–2) reduces to

$$\nabla \times \overline{\mathbf{E}} + j\omega\, \mu \overline{\mathbf{H}} = \mathbf{0}, \tag{9.144}$$

$$\nabla \times \overline{\mathbf{H}} - j\omega\, \varepsilon \overline{\mathbf{E}} = \overline{\mathbf{J}}. \tag{9.145}$$

**PROBLEM 9.32** Show that Maxwell's equations (9.144–5) in current-free regions are invariant to the transformation

$$\overline{\mathbf{E}}' = \pm \sqrt{\frac{\mu}{\varepsilon}}\, \overline{\mathbf{H}}, \qquad \overline{\mathbf{H}}' = \mp \sqrt{\frac{\varepsilon}{\mu}}\, \overline{\mathbf{E}}. \tag{9.146}$$

**Solution:** If $\overline{\mathbf{J}} = \mathbf{0}$, then (9.144–5) become

$$\nabla \times \overline{\mathbf{E}} + j\omega\mu \overline{\mathbf{H}} = \mathbf{0}, \tag{9.147}$$

$$\nabla \times \overline{\mathbf{H}} - j\omega\varepsilon \overline{\mathbf{E}} = \mathbf{0}. \tag{9.148}$$

From (9.146),

$$\overline{\mathbf{E}} = \mp \sqrt{\frac{\mu}{\varepsilon}}\, \overline{\mathbf{H}}', \quad \overline{\mathbf{H}} = \pm \sqrt{\frac{\varepsilon}{\mu}}\, \overline{\mathbf{E}}'. \tag{9.149}$$

Substituting (9.149) into (9.147–8),

$$\nabla \times \overline{\mathbf{H}}' - j\omega\varepsilon \overline{\mathbf{E}}' = \mathbf{0}, \tag{9.150}$$

$$\nabla \times \overline{\mathbf{E}}' + j\omega\mu \overline{\mathbf{H}}' = \mathbf{0}, \tag{9.151}$$

which state that the new vectors $\overline{\mathbf{E}}'$ and $\overline{\mathbf{H}}'$ also satisfy Maxwell's equations.

Note that transformation (9.146) is, in essence, an interchange of $\overline{\mathbf{E}}$ and $\overline{\mathbf{H}}$, except for scale factors.

*Lorentz' lemma* states that if $\overline{\mathbf{E}}_a$, $\overline{\mathbf{H}}_a$, and $\overline{\mathbf{E}}_b$, $\overline{\mathbf{H}}_b$ represent solutions to Maxwell's equations (9.147-8) in a source-free region, arising from different sources operating at the same frequency outside the region under consideration, then

$$\nabla\cdot(\overline{\mathbf{E}}_a\times\overline{\mathbf{H}}_b-\overline{\mathbf{E}}_b\times\overline{\mathbf{H}}_a)=0. \tag{9.152}$$

**PROBLEM 9.33** Prove Lorentz's lemma.

**Solution:** Using vector identity (3.157),

$$\nabla\cdot(\overline{\mathbf{E}}_a\times\overline{\mathbf{H}}_b)=\overline{\mathbf{H}}_b\cdot\nabla\times\overline{\mathbf{E}}_a-\overline{\mathbf{E}}_a\cdot\nabla\times\overline{\mathbf{H}}_b. \tag{9.153}$$

Since $\overline{\mathbf{E}}_a$, $\overline{\mathbf{H}}_b$ satisfy (9.147-8),

$$\nabla\times\overline{\mathbf{E}}_a=-j\omega\mu\overline{\mathbf{H}}_a,\quad \nabla\times\overline{\mathbf{H}}_b=j\omega\varepsilon\overline{\mathbf{E}}_b.$$

Substituting these into (9.153),

$$\nabla\cdot(\overline{\mathbf{E}}_a\times\overline{\mathbf{H}}_b)=-j\omega\mu\,\overline{\mathbf{H}}_a\cdot\overline{\mathbf{H}}_b-j\omega\varepsilon\,\overline{\mathbf{E}}_a\cdot\overline{\mathbf{E}}_b. \tag{9.154}$$

Interchanging subscripts $a$ and $b$,

$$\nabla\cdot(\overline{\mathbf{E}}_b\times\overline{\mathbf{H}}_a)=-j\omega\mu\,\overline{\mathbf{H}}_a\cdot\overline{\mathbf{H}}_b-j\omega\varepsilon\overline{\mathbf{E}}_a\cdot\overline{\mathbf{E}}_b \tag{9.155}$$

since the dot product is commutative. Hence, subtracting (9.155) from (9.154),

$$\nabla\cdot(\overline{\mathbf{E}}_a\times\overline{\mathbf{H}}_b-\overline{\mathbf{E}}_b\times\overline{\mathbf{H}}_a)=0. \qquad [9.152]$$

*Lorentz' reciprocity theorem* states that if $\overline{\mathbf{E}}_a$, $\overline{\mathbf{H}}_a$, and $\overline{\mathbf{E}}_b$, $\overline{\mathbf{H}}_b$ are solutions to Maxwell's equations (9.147-8) in a source-free region, then

$$\oint\!\!\oint_S(\overline{\mathbf{E}}_a\times\overline{\mathbf{H}}_b-\overline{\mathbf{E}}_b\times\overline{\mathbf{H}}_a)\cdot d\mathbf{S}=0. \tag{9.156}$$

This result is obtained by applying Gauss' divergence theorem to Lorentz' lemma (9.152).

**PROBLEM 9.34** Show that in the harmonic field, the Lorentz condition reduces to

$$\nabla\cdot\overline{\mathbf{A}}+j\omega\mu\varepsilon\overline{\phi}=0, \tag{9.157}$$

and the complex field vectors $\overline{\mathbf{E}}(\mathbf{r})$ and $\overline{\mathbf{B}}(\mathbf{r})$ can be expressed as

$$\overline{\mathbf{B}}=\nabla\times\overline{\mathbf{A}}, \tag{9.158}$$

$$\overline{\mathbf{E}}=-j\omega\overline{\mathbf{A}}+\frac{1}{j\omega\mu\varepsilon}\nabla(\nabla\cdot\overline{\mathbf{A}}). \tag{9.159}$$

**Solution:** Since, in the harmonic field, all time derivatives $\partial/\partial t$ may be replaced by $j\omega$, (9.157) is derived from the Lorentz condition (9.55). Similarly, (9.158) and (9.159) are, respectively, obtained from (9.42) and (9.43) by substituting

$$\overline{\phi}=-\frac{1}{j\omega\mu\varepsilon}\nabla\cdot\overline{\mathbf{A}}, \tag{9.160}$$

which is obtained from (9.157).

**PROBLEM 9.35** Show that, in a source-free region, all the harmonic field vectors, as well as the harmonic potentials, satisfy the Helmholtz equations

$$\nabla^2 \overline{\mathbf{E}} + K^2 \overline{\mathbf{E}} = \mathbf{0}, \tag{9.161}$$

$$\nabla^2 \overline{\mathbf{H}} + K^2 \overline{\mathbf{H}} = \mathbf{0}, \tag{9.162}$$

$$\nabla^2 \overline{\mathbf{A}} + K^2 \overline{\mathbf{A}} = \mathbf{0}, \tag{9.163}$$

$$\nabla^2 \overline{\phi} + K^2 \overline{\phi} = 0, \tag{9.164}$$

where

$$K = \omega\sqrt{\mu\varepsilon}. \tag{9.165}$$

**Solution:** The curl of (9.147) is

$$\nabla \times (\nabla \times \overline{\mathbf{E}}) = -j\omega\mu\nabla \times \overline{\mathbf{H}}. \tag{9.166}$$

From (9.148), $\nabla \times \overline{\mathbf{H}} = j\omega\varepsilon\overline{\mathbf{E}}$; hence, substituting for $\nabla \times \overline{\mathbf{H}}$ in (9.166),

$$\nabla \times (\nabla \times \overline{\mathbf{E}}) = -j\omega\mu(j\omega\varepsilon)\overline{\mathbf{E}} = \omega^2\mu\varepsilon\overline{\mathbf{E}} = K^2\overline{\mathbf{E}}. \tag{9.167}$$

From (3.163),

$$\nabla \times (\nabla \times \overline{\mathbf{E}}) = \nabla(\nabla \cdot \overline{\mathbf{E}}) - \nabla^2\overline{\mathbf{E}} = -\nabla^2\overline{\mathbf{E}}$$

since $\nabla \cdot \overline{\mathbf{E}} = 0$ in a source-free region. Hence, (9.167) can be rewritten as

$$\nabla^2 \overline{\mathbf{E}} + K^2 \overline{\mathbf{E}} = \mathbf{0}.$$

Similarly from (9.147) and (9.148),

$$\nabla^2 \overline{\mathbf{H}} + K^2 \overline{\mathbf{E}} = \mathbf{0}.$$

Note that (9.163–4) can also be derived from (9.56–7) by setting $\overline{\mathbf{J}} = \mathbf{0}$, $\overline{\rho} = 0$, and replacing $\partial^2/\partial t^2$ by $(j\omega)(j\omega) = -\omega^2$

## 9.9 Plane Waves

The *wave or propagation vector* is a vector whose magnitude is equal to $\omega\sqrt{\mu\varepsilon}$; i.e.,

$$\mathbf{K} = K_x\mathbf{i} + K_y\mathbf{j} + K_z\mathbf{k}, \tag{9.168}$$

where $|\mathbf{K}| = K = (K_x^2 + K_y^2 + K_z^2)^{1/2} = \omega\sqrt{\mu\varepsilon}$. The magnitude $K$ is called a *wave number*.

**PROBLEM 9.36** If $\mathbf{r}$ is the position vector, $\overline{\mathbf{E}}_0$ is a constant complex vector, and

$$\overline{\mathbf{E}}(\mathbf{r}) = \overline{\mathbf{E}}_0 e^{\pm j\mathbf{K}\cdot\mathbf{r}}, \tag{9.169}$$

show that

$$\nabla \cdot \overline{\mathbf{E}}(\mathbf{r}) = \pm j\mathbf{K} \cdot \overline{\mathbf{E}}(\mathbf{r}), \tag{9.170}$$

$$\nabla \times \overline{\mathbf{E}}(\mathbf{r}) = \pm j\mathbf{K} \times \overline{\mathbf{E}}(\mathbf{r}). \tag{9.171}$$

**Solution:** If $\overline{\mathbf{E}}(\mathbf{r}) = \overline{\mathbf{E}}_0^{\pm j\mathbf{K}\cdot\mathbf{r}}$, then from (3.155–6),

$$\nabla \cdot \overline{\mathbf{E}}(\mathbf{r}) = \nabla \cdot (\overline{\mathbf{E}}_0 e^{\pm j\mathbf{K}\cdot\mathbf{r}}) = e^{\pm j\mathbf{K}\cdot\mathbf{r}}\nabla \cdot \overline{\mathbf{E}}_0 + \nabla(e^{\pm j\mathbf{K}\cdot\mathbf{r}}) \cdot \overline{\mathbf{E}}_0, \tag{9.172}$$

$$\nabla \times \overline{\mathbf{E}}(\mathbf{r}) = \nabla \times (\overline{\mathbf{E}}_0 e^{\pm j\mathbf{K}\cdot\mathbf{r}}) = e^{\pm j\mathbf{K}\cdot\mathbf{r}}\nabla \times \overline{\mathbf{E}}_0 + \nabla(e^{\pm j\mathbf{K}\cdot\mathbf{r}}) \times \overline{\mathbf{E}}_0. \tag{9.173}$$

Since $\overline{\mathbf{E}}_0$ is a constant complex vector, $\nabla \cdot \overline{\mathbf{E}}_0 = 0$, $\nabla \times \overline{\mathbf{E}}_0 = \mathbf{0}$. Hence, (9.172–3) reduce to

$$\nabla \cdot \overline{\mathbf{E}}(\mathbf{r}) = \nabla(e^{\pm j\mathbf{K}\cdot\mathbf{r}}) \cdot \overline{\mathbf{E}}_0, \tag{9.174}$$

$$\nabla \times \overline{\mathbf{E}}(\mathbf{r}) = \nabla(e^{\pm j\mathbf{K}\cdot\mathbf{r}}) \times \overline{\mathbf{E}}_0. \tag{9.175}$$

Since $\mathbf{K}\cdot\mathbf{r} = K_x x + K_y y + K_z z$,

$$\frac{\partial}{\partial x}(e^{\pm j\mathbf{K}\cdot\mathbf{r}}) = \pm jK_x e^{\pm j\mathbf{K}\cdot\mathbf{r}}$$

and similar expressions with respect to $y$ and $z$. Hence, by (3.102),

$$\nabla(e^{\pm j\mathbf{K}\cdot\mathbf{r}}) = \pm je^{\pm j\mathbf{K}\cdot\mathbf{r}}(K_x\mathbf{i} + K_y\mathbf{j} + K_z\mathbf{k}) = \pm j\mathbf{K}(e^{\pm j\mathbf{K}\cdot\mathbf{r}}). \tag{9.176}$$

Substituting (9.176) into (9.174–5),

$$\nabla \cdot \overline{\mathbf{E}}(\mathbf{r}) = \pm je^{\pm j\mathbf{K}\cdot\mathbf{r}}\mathbf{K}\cdot\overline{\mathbf{E}}_0 = \pm j\mathbf{K}\cdot(\overline{\mathbf{E}}_0 e^{\pm j\mathbf{K}\cdot\mathbf{r}}) = \pm j\mathbf{K}\cdot\overline{\mathbf{E}}(\mathbf{r}),$$

$$\nabla \times \overline{\mathbf{E}}(\mathbf{r}) = \pm je^{\pm j\mathbf{K}\cdot\mathbf{r}}\mathbf{K}\times\overline{\mathbf{E}}_0 = \pm j\mathbf{K}\times(\overline{\mathbf{E}}_0 e^{\pm j\mathbf{K}\cdot\mathbf{r}}) = \pm j\mathbf{K}\times\overline{\mathbf{E}}(\mathbf{r}).$$

Observing (9.176) and (9.170-1), note that assuming (9.169), i.e., if the spatial variation is of the form $e^{\pm j\mathbf{K}\cdot\mathbf{r}}$, then the $\nabla$ operator can be replaced by the vector $\pm j\mathbf{K}$.

**PROBLEM 9.37** Show that the field vector (9.169) satisfies the Helmholtz equation (9.161).

**Solution:** From the vector identity (3.163),

$$\nabla^2\overline{\mathbf{E}} = \nabla(\nabla\cdot\overline{\mathbf{E}}) - \nabla\times(\nabla\times\overline{\mathbf{E}}). \tag{9.177}$$

If $\overline{\mathbf{E}} = \overline{\mathbf{E}}_0 e^{\pm j\mathbf{K}\cdot\mathbf{r}}$, where $\overline{\mathbf{E}}_0$ is a constant complex vector, we can replace $\nabla$ by the vector $\pm j\mathbf{K}$. Thus from (9.177), with the use of vector identity (1.83) and $j^2 = -1$,

$$\begin{aligned}\nabla^2\overline{\mathbf{E}} &= \pm j\mathbf{K}(\pm j\mathbf{K}\cdot\overline{\mathbf{E}}) - (\pm j\mathbf{K})\times(\pm j\mathbf{K}\times\overline{\mathbf{E}})\\ &= -(\mathbf{K}\cdot\overline{\mathbf{E}})\mathbf{K} + \mathbf{K}\times(\mathbf{K}\times\overline{\mathbf{E}})\\ &= -(\mathbf{K}\cdot\overline{\mathbf{E}})\mathbf{K} + (\mathbf{K}\cdot\overline{\mathbf{E}})\mathbf{K} - (\mathbf{K}\cdot\mathbf{K})\overline{\mathbf{E}}\\ &= -K^2\overline{\mathbf{E}}.\end{aligned} \tag{9.178}$$

Hence,

$$\nabla^2\overline{\mathbf{E}} + K^2\overline{\mathbf{E}} = (-K^2 + K^2)\overline{\mathbf{E}} = \mathbf{0}. \qquad [9.161]$$

A *plane* (*monochromatic*) *wave* propagating in the direction of the wave vector $\mathbf{K}$ is a harmonic field represented by

$$\mathbf{E}(\mathbf{r}, t) = \mathrm{Re}[\overline{\mathbf{E}}(\mathbf{r})e^{j\omega t}] = \mathrm{Re}[\overline{\mathbf{E}}_0 e^{j(\omega t - \mathbf{K}\cdot\mathbf{r})}]. \tag{9.179}$$

The *surface of constant phase* is defined by

$$\omega t - \mathbf{K}\cdot\mathbf{r} = \text{const.} \tag{9.180}$$

The *velocity of propagation* $\mathbf{v}_p$ is defined as the velocity at which planes of constant phase move.

A *transverse wave* is a wave for which both the electric and magnetic field vectors $\overline{\mathbf{E}}$ and $\overline{\mathbf{H}}$ are perpendicular to the direction of propagation $\mathbf{K}$.

The *characteristic impedance* $\eta$ of a medium with constants $\varepsilon$ and $\mu$ is the ratio of the magnitude of the electric field vector $\mathbf{E}$ to that of the magnetic field vector $\mathbf{H}$; i.e.,

$$\eta = \frac{|\mathbf{E}|}{|\mathbf{H}|}.$$

**PROBLEM 9.38** Show that (a) a surface of constant phase is a plane normal to $\mathbf{K}$, (b) the velocity of propagation of a plane wave $\mathbf{v}_p$ is

$$v_p = \frac{1}{\sqrt{\mu\varepsilon}}, \tag{9.181}$$

(c) the electric field vector $\overline{\mathbf{E}}$ is normal to the direction of propagation $\mathbf{K}$, (d) the magnetic field vector $\overline{\mathbf{H}}$ is perpendicular to both $\mathbf{K}$ and $\overline{\mathbf{E}}$ and is

$$\overline{\mathbf{H}} = \frac{\mathbf{K}\times\overline{\mathbf{E}}}{\omega\mu}, \tag{9.182}$$

and (e) the characteristic impedance $\eta$ is

$$\eta = \frac{|\overline{\mathbf{E}}|}{|\overline{\mathbf{H}}|} = \sqrt{\frac{\mu}{\varepsilon}}. \tag{9.183}$$

**Solution:** (a) If a surface of constant phase is found by setting $t = \text{const}$ in (9.180), we obtain the constant-phase condition

$$\mathbf{K}\cdot\mathbf{r} = \text{const}, \tag{9.184}$$

which is the equation of a plane normal to $\mathbf{K}$. (Cf., Prob. 6.16.)

(b) If $\xi$ is the component of $\mathbf{r}$ in the $\mathbf{K}$-direction (see Fig. 9.5), then from (1.30) we can write $\mathbf{K}\cdot\mathbf{r} = K\xi$, and (9.180) becomes $\omega t - K\xi = \text{const}$. Differentiating with respect to time $t$ yields

$$v_p = \frac{d\xi}{dt} = \frac{\omega}{K} = \frac{\omega}{\omega\sqrt{\mu\varepsilon}} = \frac{1}{\sqrt{\mu\varepsilon}}.$$

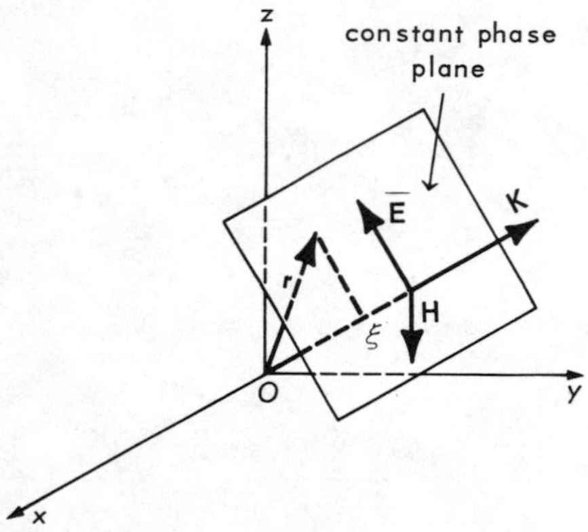

Fig. 9.5 A plane wave propagating along K.

(c) In a source-free region, from (9.148),

$$\overline{\mathbf{E}} = \frac{1}{j\omega\varepsilon}\nabla\times\overline{\mathbf{H}}. \tag{9.185}$$

Thus,

$$\nabla\cdot\overline{\mathbf{E}} = \frac{1}{j\omega\varepsilon}\nabla\cdot(\nabla\times\overline{\mathbf{H}}) = 0. \tag{9.186}$$

Replacing $\nabla$ by $-j\mathbf{K}$,

$$-j\mathbf{K}\cdot\overline{\mathbf{E}} = 0, \tag{9.187}$$

which implies that $\overline{\mathbf{E}}(\mathbf{r})$ is normal to the direction of propagation $\mathbf{K}$.

(d) In a source-free region, from (9.147),

$$\overline{\mathbf{H}} = -\frac{1}{j\omega\mu}\nabla\times\overline{\mathbf{E}}. \tag{9.188}$$

Replacing $\nabla$ by $-j\mathbf{K}$,

$$\overline{\mathbf{H}} = -\frac{1}{j\omega\mu}(-j\mathbf{K}\times\overline{\mathbf{E}}) = \frac{\mathbf{K}\times\overline{\mathbf{E}}}{\omega\mu}, \qquad [9.182]$$

which shows that $\overline{\mathbf{H}}$ is perpendicular to both $\mathbf{K}$ and $\overline{\mathbf{E}}$.

From the requirement $\nabla\cdot\overline{\mathbf{H}} = 0$ we can also obtain the relation

$$-j\mathbf{K}\cdot\overline{\mathbf{H}} = 0, \tag{9.189}$$

which shows that $\overline{\mathbf{H}}$ is also normal to $\mathbf{K}$.

Replacing $\nabla$ by $-j\mathbf{K}$ in (9.185),

$$\overline{\mathbf{E}} = -\frac{\mathbf{K}\times\overline{\mathbf{H}}}{\omega\varepsilon} = \frac{\overline{\mathbf{H}}\times\mathbf{K}}{\omega\varepsilon}. \tag{9.190}$$

Thus (9.182) and (9.190) show that $(\overline{\mathbf{E}}, \overline{\mathbf{H}}, \mathbf{K})$ form a set of right-handed orthogonal vectors. (See Fig. 9.5.)

(e) From (9.182), and since $\overline{\mathbf{E}}$ and $\mathbf{K}$ are orthogonal,

$$|\overline{\mathbf{H}}| = \frac{1}{\omega\mu} |\mathbf{K} \times \overline{\mathbf{E}}| = \frac{K}{\omega\mu} |\overline{\mathbf{E}}|.$$

Thus, the impedance is

$$\eta = \frac{|\overline{\mathbf{E}}|}{|\overline{\mathbf{H}}|} = \frac{\omega\mu}{K} = \frac{\omega\mu}{\omega\sqrt{\mu\varepsilon}} = \sqrt{\frac{\mu}{\varepsilon}}.$$

## 9.10 Supplementary Problems

**PROBLEM 9.39** Show that in a homogeneous isotropic media, **E** and **H** satisfy the inhomogeneous wave equations,

$$\nabla^2 \mathbf{E} - \mu\varepsilon \frac{\partial^2 \mathbf{E}}{\partial t^2} = \mu \frac{\partial \mathbf{J}}{\partial t} + \frac{1}{\varepsilon} \nabla \rho,$$

$$\nabla^2 \mathbf{H} - \mu\varepsilon \frac{\partial^2 \mathbf{H}}{\partial t^2} = -\nabla \times \mathbf{J}.$$

**PROBLEM 9.40** Show that in a homogeneous isotropic media and source-free region, **E** and **H** satisfy

$$\nabla^2 \mathbf{E} - \mu\varepsilon \frac{\partial^2 \mathbf{E}}{\partial t^2} - \mu\sigma \frac{\partial \mathbf{E}}{\partial t} = \mathbf{0},$$

$$\nabla^2 \mathbf{H} - \mu\varepsilon \frac{\partial^2 \mathbf{H}}{\partial t^2} - \mu\sigma \frac{\partial \mathbf{H}}{\partial t} = \mathbf{0}.$$

**PROBLEM 9.41** A useful gauge for the electromagnetic field in the case where there are no charges is the *Coulomb gauge*, where $\nabla \cdot \mathbf{A} = 0$. Show that in this case the potentials **A** and $\phi$ satisfy

$$\nabla^2 \mathbf{A} - \mu\varepsilon \frac{\partial^2 \mathbf{A}}{\partial t^2} = -\mu \mathbf{J} + \mu\varepsilon \nabla \frac{\partial \phi}{\partial t},$$

$$\nabla^2 \phi = -\frac{\rho}{\varepsilon}.$$

Also, show that for the new potentials to satisfy the Coulomb-gauge condition, the gauge function $\psi$ must satisfy Laplace's equation $\nabla^2 \psi = 0$.

**PROBLEM 9.42** Show that the potentials at the point defined by the position vector **r** in uniform electric and magnetic fields are

$$\phi = -\mathbf{E} \cdot \mathbf{r}, \qquad \mathbf{A} = \frac{1}{2} (\mathbf{B} \times \mathbf{r}).$$

**PROBLEM 9.43** Show that the magnetic flux $\Phi$ and the vector potential **A** are related by

$$\Phi = \oint_C \mathbf{A} \cdot d\mathbf{r},$$

and hence, that the emf in a fixed circuit C is

$$\text{emf} = \frac{d}{dt} \oint_C \mathbf{A} \cdot d\mathbf{r}.$$

**PROBLEM 9.44** Show that the force per unit volume $\mathbf{f}_V$, sometimes referred to as the *Lorentz force density*, on a region of free space (vacuum) containing charges and currents due to an electromagnetic field can be expressed as

$$\mathbf{f}_V = \rho \mathbf{E} + \mathbf{J} \times \mathbf{B}.$$

**PROBLEM 9.45** Using Maxwell's equations, show that

$$\mathbf{f}_V = -\varepsilon_0 \frac{\partial}{\partial t}(\mathbf{E} \times \mathbf{B}) + \varepsilon_0 \mathbf{E}(\nabla \cdot \mathbf{E}) - \frac{1}{2}\varepsilon_0 \nabla (E^2) + \varepsilon_0 (\mathbf{E} \cdot \nabla)\mathbf{E}$$
$$+ \frac{1}{\mu_0}\mathbf{B}(\nabla \cdot \mathbf{B}) - \frac{1}{2\mu_0}\nabla (B^2) + \frac{1}{\mu_0}(\mathbf{B} \cdot \nabla)\mathbf{B}.$$

The quantity $\varepsilon_0 \mathbf{E} \times \mathbf{B} = \mathbf{D} \times \mathbf{B}$ is sometimes referred to as the *momentum density* of the electromagnetic field.
[*Hint:* Use the vector identity $\mathbf{g} \times (\nabla \times \mathbf{g}) = \frac{1}{2}\nabla(g^2) - (\mathbf{g} \cdot \nabla)\mathbf{g}$, which can be derived from (3.159) by letting $\mathbf{f} = \mathbf{g}$.]

**PROBLEM 9.46** Find the electric field $\mathbf{E}$ and the potential $\phi$ due to an infinite line charge with charge density per unit length $\rho_l$.

*Answer*: $\mathbf{E} = \dfrac{\rho_l}{2\pi\varepsilon\rho}\mathbf{e}_\rho, \quad \phi(\rho_1) - \phi(\rho_2) = \dfrac{\rho_l}{2\pi\varepsilon}\ln\left(\dfrac{\rho_2}{\rho_1}\right).$

**PROBLEM 9.47** A spherical volume of radius $a$ centered at the origin contains an electric charge of uniform density $\rho_0$. Find the electric field $\mathbf{E}(\mathbf{r})$ and the potential $\phi(\mathbf{r})$ due to this charge distribution.

*Answer*: For $0 \le r \le a$, $\quad \mathbf{E}(\mathbf{r}) = \dfrac{\rho_0}{3\varepsilon_0} r\,\mathbf{e}_r, \quad \phi(\mathbf{r}) = \dfrac{\rho_0}{3\varepsilon_0}a^2 + \dfrac{\rho_0}{6\varepsilon}(r^2 - a^2).$

For $r > a$, $\quad \mathbf{E}(\mathbf{r}) = \dfrac{a^3\rho_0}{3\varepsilon_0 r^2}\mathbf{e}_r, \quad \phi(\mathbf{r}) = \dfrac{a^3\rho_0}{3\varepsilon_0 r}.$

**PROBLEM 9.48** A coaxial cable consists of a solid inner conductor of circular cross section of radius $a$ surrounded by a hollow conducting cylinder of inner and outer radii $b$ and $c$, respectively. A total current $I$ flows in the inner conductor and returns through the outer conductor with uniform distribution. Assuming that the axis of the cable is coincident with the $z$-axis and its length is infinite, find the magnetic field $\mathbf{H}$ inside and between the two conductors.

*Answer*: For $\rho \le a$, $\quad \mathbf{H} = \dfrac{I}{2\pi a^2}\rho\,\mathbf{e}_\phi; \quad a \le \rho \le b, \quad \mathbf{H} = \dfrac{I}{2\pi\rho}\mathbf{e}_\phi.$

For $b \le \rho \le c$, $\quad \mathbf{H} = \dfrac{I}{2\pi\rho}\dfrac{c^2 - \rho^2}{c^2 - b^2}\mathbf{e}_\phi.$

**PROBLEM 9.49** Show that the force on an electric dipole in an electric field $\mathbf{E}$ is

$$\mathbf{f} = (\mathbf{p} \cdot \nabla)\mathbf{E}.$$

**PROBLEM 9.50** Show that the torque on an electric dipole placed in a uniform electric field $\mathbf{E}$ is

$$\tau_e = \mathbf{p} \times \mathbf{E}.$$

**PROBLEM 9.51** Find the expression for the force exerted on a wire carrying a current $I$ when the wire is immersed in a magnetic field $\mathbf{B}$.

*Answer*: $\mathbf{f} = I \oint_C d\mathbf{r} \times \mathbf{B}$.

**PROBLEM 9.52** In a harmonic field, if the complex Poynting vector is defined as

$$\overline{\mathbf{P}} = \frac{1}{2}\,(\overline{\mathbf{E}} \times \overline{\mathbf{H}}^*),$$

show that

$$\nabla \cdot \mathbf{P} + 2j\omega \left(\frac{1}{4}\,\mu\,|\overline{\mathbf{H}}|^2 - \frac{1}{4}\,\varepsilon\,|\overline{\mathbf{E}}|^2\right) = -\frac{1}{2}\,(\overline{\mathbf{E}} \cdot \overline{\mathbf{J}}^*),$$

where $\overline{\mathbf{H}}^*$ and $\overline{\mathbf{J}}^*$ are complex conjugate vectors of $\overline{\mathbf{H}}$ and $\overline{\mathbf{J}}$, respectively, and

$$|\overline{\mathbf{H}}|^2 = \overline{\mathbf{H}} \cdot \overline{\mathbf{H}}^*, \quad |\overline{\mathbf{E}}|^2 = \overline{\mathbf{E}} \cdot \overline{\mathbf{E}}^*;$$

give a physical interpretation of this equation.

**PROBLEM 9.53** Find the electric field at a distance $a$ from an infinitely long line charge of strength $\rho_l$ coulombs/m.

[*Hint:* Use Gauss' law (9.32).]

*Answer:* $\mathbf{E} = E_\rho \mathbf{e}_\rho = \rho_l / 2\pi\varepsilon_0 a \mathbf{e}_\rho$.

**PROBLEM 9.54** Show that the electric field of the electric dipole of Fig. 9.3 can be expressed as

$$\mathbf{E} = \frac{p}{4\pi\varepsilon_0 r^3}\,(2\cos\theta\,\mathbf{e}_r + \sin\theta\,\mathbf{e}_\theta).$$

**PROBLEM 9.55** Show that the energy stored in an electrostatic field can be expressed as

$$\frac{1}{2}\iiint \mathbf{E} \cdot \mathbf{D}\,dV = \frac{1}{2}\iiint \rho\phi\,dV,$$

where $\rho$ is the charge density and $\phi$ is the scalar potential of the electrostatic field.

**PROBLEM 9.56** Show that the energy stored in a magnetostatic field can be expressed as

$$\frac{1}{2}\iiint \mathbf{B} \cdot \mathbf{H}\,dV = \frac{1}{2}\iiint \mathbf{J} \cdot \mathbf{A}\,dV,$$

where $\mathbf{J}$ is the current density and $\mathbf{A}$ is the vector potential of the magnetostatic field.

# CHAPTER 10 DIFFERENTIAL FORMS

## 10.1 Differential Forms

An *exterior differential form* on 3-dimensional space with coordinates $x, y, z$ is an expression obtained by adding and multiplying real-valued functions and the differentials $dx$, $dy$, $dz$ of the coordinates. These operations of addition and multiplication obey the usual *associative* and *distributive laws*; however, the multiplication is *not commutative*, but instead obeys the *anticommutative law*: if we replace $x$, $y$, $z$ by $x_1$, $x_2$, $x_3$, respectively, then

$$dx_i\,dx_j = -dx_j\,dx_i \quad \text{for} \quad 1 \le i, j \le 3. \tag{10.1}$$

Because of this anticommutative rule, we denote this multiplication of forms by a *wedge* $\wedge$.

If each summand of a differential form contains $p$ $dx_i$'s, where $p = 0, 1, 2, 3$, the form is called a *differential form* of $p$th *degree* or simply a *p-form*. Thus,

a *0-form* is just a differentiable function $f(x, y, z)$;
a *1-form* is an expression $f\,dx + g\,dy + h\,dz$;
a *2-form* is an expression $f\,dx \wedge dy + g\,dy \wedge dz + h\,dz \wedge dx$;
a *3-form* is an expression $f\,dx \wedge dy \wedge dz$.

The coefficients $f$, $g$, $h$ are assumed to be infinitely differentiable scalar functions of the coordinates.

An exterior differential form is identically zero if and only if all the coefficients in its definition are identically zero.

As a natural extension of the above definitions, on $n$-dimensional space with coordinates $x_1, \ldots, x_n$, a differential form of $p$th degree (or $p$-form) is an expression of the form

$$\sum a_{i_1 \ldots i_p}(x_1, \ldots, x_n)\,dx_{i_1} \wedge \ldots \wedge dx_{i_p},$$

where the sum is taken over all possible combinations of the $p$ indices, and the coefficients $a_{i_1 \ldots i_p}(x_1, \ldots, x_n)$ are assumed to be infinitely differentiable functions of the coordinates (or $n$ variables).

## 10.2 Sum and Exterior Product of Forms

Differential forms of the same class are *added* by combining coefficients of like terms. Thus, in index notation for 1-forms,

$$\sum f_i\,dx_i + \sum g_i\,dx_i = \sum (f_i + g_i)\,dx_i. \tag{10.2}$$

The corresponding rule holds for 2- or 3-forms. However, when two terms contain the same differentials, but in different orders, they must be brought into agreement before adding their coefficients, using the anticommutative law (10.1).

*Multiplication*, sometimes referred to as *exterior product* or *wedge product* of differential forms of the same class, besides obeying the *associative* and *distributive laws*, also obeys the *anticommutative law* (10.1), which, in index notation, is

$$dx_i \wedge dx_j = -dx_j \wedge dx_i. \tag{10.3}$$

Because of this anticommutative rule, the order of factors must be preserved when forms are multiplied.

In general, the exterior product of a $p$-form and a $q$-form is a $(p+q)$-form. Since a 0-form is merely a function, exterior multiplication by a 0-form does not affect the degree of a form.

**PROBLEM 10.1** Show that in a differential form "repetitions of differentials are zero"; i. e.,

$$dx_i \wedge dx_i = 0. \tag{10.4}$$

**Solution:** This result is a natural consequence of the anticommutative law (10.3). Thus, setting $i = j$ in (10.3),

$$dx_i \wedge dx_i = -dx_i \wedge dx_i.$$

Thus,

$$dx_i \wedge dx_i = 0.$$

**PROBLEM 10.2** Show that on 3-dimensional space, all $p$-forms with $p > 3$ are zero.

**Solution:** This is again a consequence of the anticommutative law (10.3). A product of more than three $dx_i$'s must contain $dx_i$ twice. But, according to (10.4), repeats are zero. Thus all $p$-forms with $p > 3$ are zero. For example, since $dx \wedge dx = 0$,

$$dx \wedge dy \wedge dx \wedge dz = -dx \wedge dx \wedge dy \wedge dz = 0.$$

Thus, in general, the exterior product of a $p$-form and a $q$-form is zero in an $n$-dimensional space if $p + q$ is larger than $n$, since there will be repeats.

In this chapter, differential forms are, in general, represented by lower case Greek letters.

**PROBLEM 10.3** For the differential forms

$$\alpha = x\,dx - y\,dy, \quad \beta = x\,dx - z\,dy + y^2\,dz, \quad \gamma = z\,dy,$$

$$\omega = y\,dx \wedge dz + x\,dy \wedge dz, \text{ and } \theta = xyz\,dx \wedge dy \wedge dz,$$

compute the exterior products: (a) $\alpha \wedge \beta$, (b) $\alpha \wedge \beta \wedge \gamma$, (c) $\alpha \wedge \omega$, and (d) $\alpha \wedge \theta$.

**Solution:** (a) Since $dx \wedge dx = dy \wedge dy = 0$, $dy \wedge dx = -dx \wedge dy$, and $dx \wedge dz = -dz \wedge dx$,

$$\begin{aligned} \alpha \wedge \beta &= (x\,dx - y\,dy) \wedge (x\,dx - z\,dy + y^2\,dz) \\ &= x^2\,dx \wedge dx - xy\,dy \wedge dx - xz\,dx \wedge dy + yz\,dy \wedge dy + xy^2\,dx \wedge dz \\ &\quad - y^3\,dy \wedge dz \\ &= x(y - z)\,dx \wedge dy - y^3\,dy \wedge dz - xy^2\,dz \wedge dx. \end{aligned}$$

(b) Since $dx \wedge dy \wedge dy$ and $dy \wedge dz \wedge dy$ each contain repeats, both are zero and $dz \wedge dx \wedge dy = -dx \wedge dz \wedge dy = dx \wedge dy \wedge dz$. Hence,

$$\begin{aligned}\alpha \wedge \beta \wedge \gamma &= [x(y-z)\,dx \wedge dy - y^2dy \wedge dz - xy^2dz \wedge dx] \wedge z dy \\ &= xz(y-z)\,dx \wedge dy \wedge dy - y^2dy \wedge dz \wedge dy - xy^2z\,dz \wedge dx \wedge dy \\ &= -xy^2z\,dx \wedge dy \wedge dz.\end{aligned}$$

(c) Since $dx \wedge dx \wedge dz = dy \wedge dy \wedge dz = 0$ and $dy \wedge dx \wedge dz = -dx \wedge dy \wedge dz$,

$$\begin{aligned}\alpha \wedge \omega &= (x\,dx - y\,dy) \wedge (y\,dx \wedge dz + x\,dy \wedge dz) \\ &= xy\,dx \wedge dx \wedge dz - y^2dy \wedge dx \wedge dz + x^2\,dx \wedge dy \wedge dz - xy\,dy \wedge dy \wedge dz \\ &= (x^2 + y^2)dx \wedge dy \wedge dz.\end{aligned}$$

(d) Since $dx \wedge dx \wedge dy \wedge dz$ and $dy \wedge dx \wedge dy \wedge dz$ each contain repeats, both are zero. Hence,

$$\begin{aligned}\alpha \wedge \theta &= (x\,dx - y\,dy) \wedge (xyz\,dx \wedge dy \wedge dz) \\ &= x^2yz\,dx \wedge dx \wedge dy \wedge dz - xy^2z\,dy \wedge dx \wedge dy \wedge dz \\ &= 0.\end{aligned}$$

**PROBLEM 10.4** Establish the anticommutative law for the 1-forms $\alpha$ and $\beta$; i.e., show that

$$\alpha \wedge \beta = -\beta \wedge \alpha. \tag{10.5}$$

**Solution:** In the index notation, if the differential forms are

$$\alpha = \sum_i f_i\,dx_i, \quad \beta = \sum_j g_j\,dx_j,$$

then by the anticommutative law (10.3),

$$\begin{aligned}\alpha \wedge \beta &= \left(\sum_i f_i\,dx_i\right) \wedge \left(\sum_j g_j\,dx_j\right) \\ &= \sum_i \sum_j f_i g_j\,dx_i \wedge dx_j \\ &= -\sum_i \sum_j f_i g_j\,dx_j \wedge dx_i \\ &= -\left(\sum_j g_j\,dx_j\right) \wedge \left(\sum_i f_i\,dx_i\right) \\ &= -\beta \wedge \alpha.\end{aligned}$$

**PROBLEM 10.5** For the 1-forms

$$\alpha = f_1\,dx + f_2\,dy + f_3\,dz, \tag{10.6}$$

$$\beta = g_1\,dx + g_2\,dy + g_3\,dz, \tag{10.7}$$

$$\gamma = h_1\,dy \wedge dz + h_2\,dz \wedge dx + h_3\,dx \wedge dy, \tag{10.8}$$

compute the exterior products $\alpha \wedge \beta$ and $\alpha \wedge \gamma$, and show that these results correspond to vector- and scalar- products of two ordinary vectors.

**Solution:** Using (10.3–4),

$$\begin{aligned}
\alpha \wedge \beta &= (f_1\,dx + f_2\,dy + f_3\,dz) \wedge (g_1\,dx + g_2\,dy + g_3\,dz) \\
&= f_1 g_1\,dx \wedge dx + f_2 g_1\,dy \wedge dx + f_3 g_1\,dz \wedge dx \\
&\quad + f_1 g_2\,dx \wedge dy + f_2 g_2\,dy \wedge dy + f_3 g_2\,dz \wedge dy \\
&\quad + f_1 g_3\,dx \wedge dz + f_2 g_3\,dy \wedge dz + f_3 g_3\,dz \wedge dz \\
&= (f_2 g_3 - f_3 g_2)\,dy \wedge dz + (f_3 g_1 - f_1 g_3)\,dz \wedge dx \\
&\quad + (f_1 g_2 - f_2 g_1)\,dx \wedge dy,
\end{aligned} \tag{10.9}$$

$$\begin{aligned}
\alpha \wedge \gamma &= (f_1\,dx + f_2\,dy + f_3\,dz) \wedge (h_1\,dy \wedge dz + h_2\,dz \wedge dx + h_3\,dx \wedge dy) \\
&= f_1 h_1\,dx \wedge dy \wedge dz + f_2 h_1\,dy \wedge dy \wedge dz + f_3 h_1\,dz \wedge dy \wedge dz \\
&\quad + f_1 h_2\,dx \wedge dz \wedge dx + f_2 h_2\,dy \wedge dz \wedge dx + f_3 h_2\,dz \wedge dz \wedge dx \\
&\quad + f_1 h_3\,dx \wedge dx \wedge dy + f_2 h_3\,dy \wedge dx \wedge dy + f_3 h_3\,dz \wedge dx \wedge dy \\
&= (f_1 h_1 + f_2 h_2 + f_3 h_3)\,dx \wedge dy \wedge dz.
\end{aligned} \tag{10.10}$$

Now, make the following correspondences between differential forms and vector functions:

$$\text{1-form } \alpha = f_1\,dx + f_2\,dy + f_3\,dz \longleftrightarrow \text{vector } \mathbf{f} = [f_1, f_2, f_3], \tag{10.11}$$

$$\text{1-form } \beta = g_1\,dx + g_2\,dy + g_3\,dz \longleftrightarrow \text{vector } \mathbf{g} = [g_1, g_2, g_3], \tag{10.12}$$

$$\text{2-form } \gamma = h_1\,dy \wedge dz + h_2\,dz \wedge dx + h_3\,dx \wedge dy \longleftrightarrow \text{vector } \mathbf{h} = [h_1, h_2, h_3]. \tag{10.13}$$

Then, comparing definitions of exterior and vector products (10.9) and (2.25), we see that the exterior product $\alpha \wedge \beta$ of two 1-forms (2-form) corresponds to the vector product of $\mathbf{f} \times \mathbf{g}$. Also, comparing definitions of exterior and scalar products (10.10) and (2.24), we see that the exterior product $\alpha \wedge \gamma$ of a 1-form and a 2-form (3-form) corresponds to the scalar product of $\mathbf{f} \cdot \mathbf{h}$.

Thus, in general, to any 1- or 2-form there will correspond a vector-function, and to any 0- or 3-form there will correspond a scalar function. Correspondences between the operations of differential forms and the operations involving vector- and scalar-functions are further illustrated in the later sections.

## 10.3 Change of Variables and the Jacobian of a Transformation

**PROBLEM 10.6** If a transformation is described by $x = x(u, v)$ and $y = y(u, v)$, show that

$$dx \wedge dy = \frac{\partial(x, y)}{\partial(u, v)}\,du \wedge dv, \tag{10.14}$$

where

$$\frac{\partial(x, y)}{\partial(u, v)} = \begin{vmatrix} \dfrac{\partial x}{\partial u} & \dfrac{\partial x}{\partial v} \\ \dfrac{\partial y}{\partial u} & \dfrac{\partial y}{\partial v} \end{vmatrix} = \begin{vmatrix} x_u & x_v \\ y_u & y_v \end{vmatrix} \tag{10.15}$$

is the Jacobian of the transformation.

**Solution:** Since the differentials are

$$dx = \frac{\partial x}{\partial u}\,du + \frac{\partial x}{\partial v}\,dv = x_u\,du + x_v\,dv, \qquad dy = \frac{\partial y}{\partial u}\,du + \frac{\partial y}{\partial v}\,dv = y_u\,du + y_v\,dv,$$

the exterior product is

$$\begin{aligned} dx \wedge dy &= (x_u\, du + x_v\, dv) \wedge (y_u\, du + y_v\, dv) \\ &= x_u y_u\, du \wedge du + x_u y_v\, du \wedge dv + x_v y_u\, dv \wedge du + x_v y_v\, dv \wedge dv \\ &= (x_u y_v - x_v y_u)\, du \wedge dv \\ &= \begin{vmatrix} x_u & x_v \\ y_u & y_v \end{vmatrix} du \wedge dv \\ &= \frac{\partial(x, y)}{\partial(u, v)}\, du \wedge dv. \end{aligned}$$

**PROBLEM 10.7** If $x = x(u, v, w)$, $y = y(u, v, w)$, and $z = z(u, v, w)$ describes a transformation show that

$$dx \wedge dy \wedge dz = \frac{\partial(x, y, z)}{\partial(u, v, w)}\, du \wedge dv \wedge dw, \tag{10.16}$$

where

$$\frac{\partial(x, y, z)}{\partial(u, v, w)} = \begin{vmatrix} \frac{\partial x}{\partial u} & \frac{\partial x}{\partial v} & \frac{\partial x}{\partial w} \\ \frac{\partial y}{\partial u} & \frac{\partial y}{\partial v} & \frac{\partial y}{\partial w} \\ \frac{\partial z}{\partial u} & \frac{\partial z}{\partial v} & \frac{\partial z}{\partial w} \end{vmatrix} = \begin{vmatrix} x_u & x_v & x_w \\ y_u & y_v & y_w \\ z_u & z_v & z_w \end{vmatrix} \tag{10.17}$$

is the Jacobian of the transformation.

**Solution:** The differentials are

$$dx = \frac{\partial x}{\partial u} du + \frac{\partial x}{\partial v} dv + \frac{\partial x}{\partial w} dw = x_u\, du + x_v\, dv + x_w\, dw,$$

$$dy = \frac{\partial y}{\partial u} du + \frac{\partial y}{\partial v} dv + \frac{\partial y}{\partial w} dw = y_u\, du + y_v\, dv + y_w\, dw,$$

$$dz = \frac{\partial z}{\partial u} du + \frac{\partial z}{\partial v} dv + \frac{\partial z}{\partial w} dw = z_u\, du + z_v\, dv + z_w\, dw.$$

Then, proceeding in a manner similar to that of Prob. 10.6, the exterior product is

$$\begin{aligned} dx \wedge dy \wedge dz &= (x_u\, du + x_v\, dv + x_w\, dw) \wedge (y_u\, du + y_v\, dv + y_w\, dw) \\ &\quad \wedge (z_u\, du + z_v\, dv + z_w\, dw) \\ &= [x_u(y_v z_w - y_w z_u) - y_u(x_v z_w - x_w z_v) \\ &\quad + z_u(x_v y_w - x_w y_v)]\, du \wedge dv \wedge dw \\ &= \begin{vmatrix} x_u & x_v & x_w \\ y_u & y_v & y_w \\ z_u & z_v & z_w \end{vmatrix} du \wedge dv \wedge dw \\ &= \frac{\partial(x, y, z)}{\partial(u, v, w)}\, du \wedge dv \wedge dw. \end{aligned}$$

**PROBLEM 10.8** Show that (10.14) is equivalent to the anticommutative law (10.3) of exterior products.

**Solution:** Interchanging $x$ and $y$ in (10.14), and from the property of the determinant, that is, if two rows of a determinant are interchanged the value of the determinant changes sign,

$$dy \wedge dx = \frac{\partial(y,x)}{\partial(u,v)}\, du \wedge dv$$

$$= -\frac{\partial(x,y)}{\partial(u,v)}\, du \wedge dv$$

$$= -dx \wedge dy. \qquad (10.18)$$

It is also seen that (10.14) and (10.16) appear in elementary calculus, i.e., the theorem on transformation of multiple integral requires that $dxdy$ be replaced by $\partial(x,y)/\partial(u,v)\, dudv$ when making the substitution $x = x(u,v)$, $y = y(u,v)$. Thus, differential forms can be used in calculating the Jacobian of a transformation.

**PROBLEM 10.9** The cylindrical coordinate system is defined by the transformation $x = u \cos v$, $y = u \sin v$, $z = w$. [See (5.36).] Using differential forms, find the Jacobian $\partial(x,y,z)/\partial(u,v,w)$.

**Solution:** The differentials are

$$dx = \cos v\, du - u \sin v\, dv,$$

$$dy = \sin v\, du + u \cos v\, dv,$$

$$dz = dw.$$

Then from (10.16), the exterior product is

$$dx \wedge dy \wedge dz = [(\cos v)\, du - (u \sin v)\, dv] \wedge [(\sin v)\, du + (u \cos v)\, dv] \wedge dw$$

$$= (u \cos^2 v\, du \wedge dv - u \sin^2 v\, dv \wedge du) \wedge dw$$

$$= u(\cos^2 v + \sin^2 v)\, du \wedge dv \wedge dw$$

$$= u\, du \wedge dv \wedge dw$$

$$= \frac{\partial(x,y,z)}{\partial(u,v,w)}\, du \wedge dv \wedge dw.$$

Thus, the Jacobian is

$$\frac{\partial(x,y,z)}{\partial(u,v,w)} = u,$$

which agrees with the result obtained in (5.37).

## 10.4 Exterior Differentiation

The *exterior derivative* of a p-form $\omega$ is a $(p+1)$-form $d\omega$ obtained by applying an operator $d$ to transform $\omega$ to $d\omega$. The definitions of $d\omega$ for forms in 3-space are as follows.

If the differentiable function $f$ is a 0-form, then $df$ is the 1-form

$$df = \frac{\partial f}{\partial x} dx + \frac{\partial f}{\partial y} dy + \frac{\partial f}{\partial z} dz. \qquad (10.19)$$

If $\omega$ is a 1-form $f_1\, dx + f_2\, dy + f_3\, dz$ whose coefficients $f_i$ are differentiable functions, then $d\omega$ is the 2-form

$$d\omega = df_1 \wedge dx + df_2 \wedge dy + df_3 \wedge dz. \qquad (10.20)$$

If $\omega$ is a 2-form $f_1\, dy \wedge dz + f_2\, dz \wedge dx + f_3\, dx \wedge dy$ whose coefficients $f_i$ are differentiable functions, then $d\omega$ is the 3-form

$$d\omega = df_1 \wedge dy \wedge dz + df_2 \wedge dz \wedge dx + df_3 \wedge dx \wedge dy. \tag{10.21}$$

In summary,

$$d(\text{0-form}) = \text{1-form}, \tag{10.22}$$

$$d(\text{1-form}) = \text{2-form}, \tag{10.23}$$

$$d(\text{2-form}) = \text{3-form}. \tag{10.24}$$

**PROBLEM 10.10** Show that if $f$ is a differentiable function of the coordinates, then the differential $df$ of $f$ is a 1-form.

**Solution:** If $f$ is a differentiable function on 3-dimensional space, then from elementary calculus, the differential $df$ of $f$ can be written as in (10.19); i.e.,

$$df = \frac{\partial f}{\partial x} dx + \frac{\partial f}{\partial y} dy + \frac{\partial f}{\partial z} dz, \qquad [10.19]$$

which is exactly the expression of a 1-form.

**PROBLEM 10.11** Using (10.20), find $d\omega$ for $\omega = yz\, dx + x^2\, dz$.

**Solution:** By the definition of the derivative (10.20),

$$\begin{aligned} d\omega &= d(yz) \wedge dx + d(x^2) \wedge dz \\ &= (y\, dz + z\, dy) \wedge dx + (2x\, dx) \wedge dz \\ &= y\, dz \wedge dx + z\, dy \wedge dx + 2x\, dx \wedge dz \\ &= (y - 2x)\, dz \wedge dx - z\, dx \wedge dy. \end{aligned}$$

**PROBLEM 10.12** Find $d\omega$ when

$$\omega = f_1\, dx + f_2\, dy + f_3\, dz, \tag{10.25}$$

where $f_i (i = 1, 2, 3)$ are differentiable functions.

**Solution:** By (10.20), and using (10.19), the exterior derivative is

$$\begin{aligned} d\omega &= df_1 \wedge dx + df_2 \wedge dy + df_3 \wedge dz \\ &= \left(\frac{\partial f_1}{\partial x} dx + \frac{\partial f_1}{\partial y} dy + \frac{\partial f_1}{\partial z} dz\right) \wedge dx \\ &\quad + \left(\frac{\partial f_2}{\partial x} dx + \frac{\partial f_2}{\partial y} dy + \frac{\partial f_2}{\partial z} dz\right) \wedge dy \\ &\quad + \left(\frac{\partial f_3}{\partial x} dx + \frac{\partial f_3}{\partial y} dy + \frac{\partial f_3}{\partial z} dz\right) \wedge dz \\ &= \left(\frac{\partial f_3}{\partial y} - \frac{\partial f_2}{\partial z}\right) dy \wedge dz + \left(\frac{\partial f_1}{\partial z} - \frac{\partial f_3}{\partial x}\right) dz \wedge dx \\ &\quad + \left(\frac{\partial f_2}{\partial x} - \frac{\partial f_1}{\partial y}\right) dx \wedge dy. \end{aligned} \tag{10.26}$$

**PROBLEM 10.13** Find $d\omega$ for $\omega$ given by

$$\omega = f_1\, dy \wedge dz + f_2\, dz \wedge dx + f_3\, dx \wedge dy, \tag{10.27}$$

where $f_i (i = 1, 2, 3)$ are differentiable functions of $x$, $y$, $z$.

**Solution:** Using the definition of the exterior derivative (10.21) and (10.19),

$$
\begin{aligned}
d\omega &= df_1 \wedge dy \wedge dz + df_2 \wedge dz \wedge dx + df_3 \wedge dx \wedge dy \\
&= \left(\frac{\partial f_1}{\partial x} dx + \frac{\partial f_1}{\partial y} dy + \frac{\partial f_1}{\partial z} dz\right) \wedge dy \wedge dz \\
&+ \left(\frac{\partial f_2}{\partial x} dx + \frac{\partial f_2}{\partial y} dy + \frac{\partial f_2}{\partial z} dz\right) \wedge dz \wedge dx \\
&+ \left(\frac{\partial f_3}{\partial x} dx + \frac{\partial f_3}{\partial y} dy + \frac{\partial f_3}{\partial z} dz\right) \wedge dx \wedge dy \\
&= \left(\frac{\partial f_1}{\partial x} + \frac{\partial f_2}{\partial y} + \frac{\partial f_3}{\partial z}\right) dx \wedge dy \wedge dz. \qquad (10.28)
\end{aligned}
$$

**PROBLEM 10.14** If $\omega = xy\, dy \wedge dz + x\, dz \wedge dx + 3zx\, dx \wedge dy$, find $d\omega$.

**Solution:** The exterior derivative is

$$
\begin{aligned}
d\omega &= d(xy) \wedge dy \wedge dz + dx \wedge dz \wedge dx + d(3zx) \wedge dx \wedge dy \\
&= (x\, dy + y\, dx) \wedge dy \wedge dz + (3z\, dx + 3x\, dz) \wedge dx \wedge dy \\
&= (y + 3x)\, dx \wedge dy \wedge dz.
\end{aligned}
$$

The single operation of differentiation in the system of differential forms corresponds in turn to the operations of taking the gradient of a scalar function and taking the curl and the divergence of a vector function. This is illustrated schematically in Fig. 10.1.

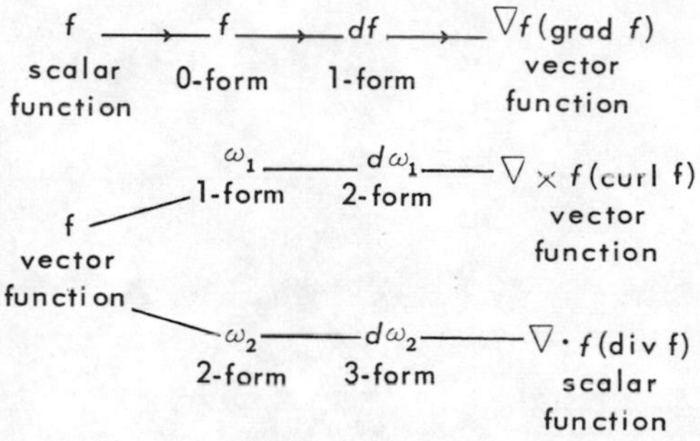

Fig. 10.1

**PROBLEM 10.15** Obtain a relation between the exterior derivatives of a 0-form and gradient, a 1-form and curl, and a 2-form and divergence.

**Solution:** Applying an operator $d$ to the 0-form $f(x, y, z)$ which corresponds to a scalar function, we obtain the 1-form

$$df = \frac{\partial f}{\partial x} dx + \frac{\partial f}{\partial y} dy + \frac{\partial f}{\partial z} dz \qquad [10.19]$$

which, in turn, corresponds to the vector function $\nabla f = [\partial f/\partial x, \partial f/\partial y, \partial f/\partial z]$, the gradient of $f$ as defined by (3.110).

Next, applying the operator $d$ to the 1-form

$$\omega = f_1\, dx + f_2\, dy + f_3\, dz \qquad [10.25]$$

which corresponds to a vector function $\mathbf{f} = [f_1, f_2, f_3]$, we obtain the 2-form

$$d\omega = \left(\frac{\partial f_3}{\partial y} - \frac{\partial f_2}{\partial z}\right) dy \wedge dz + \left(\frac{\partial f_1}{\partial z} - \frac{\partial f_3}{\partial x}\right) dz \wedge dx + \left(\frac{\partial f_2}{\partial x} - \frac{\partial f_1}{\partial y}\right) dx \wedge dy. \qquad [10.26]$$

Thus (10.26) corresponds to the vector function $\nabla \times \mathbf{f}$, the curl of $\mathbf{f}$, as defined in (3.138).

Finally, if we correspond the 2-form

$$\omega = f_1\, dy \wedge dz + f_2\, dz \wedge dx + f_3\, dx \wedge dy \qquad [10.27]$$

to the vector function $\mathbf{f} = [f_1, f_2, f_3]$, then, applying the operator $d$, we obtain the 3-form

$$d\omega = \left(\frac{\partial f_1}{\partial x} + \frac{\partial f_2}{\partial y} + \frac{\partial f_3}{\partial z}\right) dx \wedge dy \wedge dz, \qquad [10.28]$$

which corresponds in turn to the scalar function $\nabla \cdot \mathbf{f}$, the divergence of $\mathbf{f}$. [Cf., (10.28) and (3.127).]

From the above definitions and examples of the exterior derivatives of forms, we see that the general exterior derivatives of forms satisfy the *linearity property*, i.e.,

$$d(a\alpha + b\beta) = a\, d\alpha + b\, d\beta, \tag{10.29}$$

where $\alpha$, $\beta$ are arbitrary forms and $a$, $b$ are numbers.

**PROBLEM 10.16** If $\alpha$ and $\beta$ are 1-forms, show that

$$d(\alpha \wedge \beta) = d\alpha \wedge \beta - \alpha \wedge d\beta. \tag{10.30}$$

**Solution:** In the index notation, let

$$\alpha = \sum_i f_i\, dx_i, \quad \beta = \sum_j g_j\, dx_j, \tag{10.31}$$

where $f_i, g_j (1 \leq i, j \leq 3)$ are differentiable functions of the coordinates. Then from the definition of an exterior derivative,

$$d\alpha = \sum_i df_i \wedge dx_i, \quad d\beta = \sum_j dg_j \wedge dx_j. \tag{10.32}$$

Now,

$$\alpha \wedge \beta = \left(\sum_i f_i\, dx_i\right) \wedge \left(\sum_j g_j\, dx_j\right) = \sum_i \sum_j f_i g_j\, dx_i \wedge dx_j.$$

Using anticommutative law (10.3) and (10.31–2), the exterior derivative is

$$\begin{aligned}
d(\alpha \wedge \beta) &= \sum_i \sum_j d(f_i g_j) \wedge dx_i \wedge dx_j \\
&= \sum_i \sum_j \left[\sum_k \frac{\partial (f_i g_j)}{\partial x_k} dx_k\right] \wedge dx_i \wedge dx_j \\
&= \sum_i \sum_j \left(\sum_k \frac{\partial f_i}{\partial x_k} g_j\, dx_k\right) \wedge dx_i \wedge dx_j \\
&\quad + \sum_i \sum_j \left(\sum_k f_i \frac{\partial g_j}{\partial x_k} dx_k\right) \wedge dx_i \wedge dx_j \\
&= \sum_i \sum_j \left(\sum_k \frac{\partial f_i}{\partial x_k} dx_k\right) \wedge dx_i \wedge g_j dx_j \\
&\quad + \sum_i \sum_j \left(\sum_k \frac{\partial g_j}{\partial x_k} dx_k\right) \wedge f_i\, dx_i \wedge dx_j \\
&= \sum_i \sum_j (df_i \wedge dx_i) \wedge g_j\, dx_j - \sum_i \sum_j f_i\, dx_i \wedge (dg_j \wedge dx_j) \\
&= \sum_i (df_i \wedge dx_i) \wedge \sum_j g_j\, dx_j - \sum_i f_i\, dx_i \wedge \sum_j (dg_j \wedge dx_j) \\
&= d\alpha \wedge \beta - \alpha \wedge d\beta.
\end{aligned}$$

**PROBLEM 10.17** Verify (10.30) with $\alpha = f\, dx$ and $\beta = g\, dy$, where $f$ and $g$ are differentiable functions of the coordinates $x$, $y$, $z$.

**Solution:** Since $\alpha \wedge \beta = f\,dx \wedge g\,dy = fg\,dx \wedge dy$, the exterior derivative is

$$\begin{aligned} d(\alpha \wedge \beta) &= d(fg) \wedge dx \wedge dy \\ &= \left[\frac{\partial(fg)}{\partial x} dx + \frac{\partial(fg)}{\partial y} dy + \frac{\partial(fg)}{\partial z} dz\right] \wedge dx \wedge dy \\ &= \frac{\partial(fg)}{\partial z} dx \wedge dx \wedge dy \\ &= \left(\frac{\partial f}{\partial z} g + f \frac{\partial g}{\partial z}\right) dx \wedge dy \wedge dz. \end{aligned}$$

Now,

$$\begin{aligned} d\alpha = df \wedge dx &= \left(\frac{\partial f}{\partial x} dx + \frac{\partial f}{\partial y} dy + \frac{\partial f}{\partial z} dz\right) \wedge dx \\ &= \frac{\partial f}{\partial y} dy \wedge dx + \frac{\partial f}{\partial z} dz \wedge dx, \end{aligned}$$

and, hence,

$$\begin{aligned} d\alpha \wedge \beta &= \left(\frac{\partial f}{\partial y} dy \wedge dx + \frac{\partial f}{\partial z} dz \wedge dx\right) \wedge g\,dy \\ &= \frac{\partial f}{\partial z} g\,dz \wedge dx \wedge dy \\ &= \frac{\partial f}{\partial z} g\,dx \wedge dy \wedge dz. \end{aligned}$$

Similarly,

$$\begin{aligned} d\beta = dg \wedge dy &= \left(\frac{\partial g}{\partial x} dx + \frac{\partial g}{\partial y} dy + \frac{\partial g}{\partial z} dz\right) \wedge dy \\ &= \frac{\partial g}{\partial x} dx \wedge dy + \frac{\partial g}{\partial z} dz \wedge dy, \end{aligned}$$

and hence,

$$\alpha \wedge d\beta = f\,dx \wedge \left(\frac{\partial g}{\partial x} dx \wedge dy + \frac{\partial g}{\partial z} dz \wedge dy\right) = -f \frac{\partial g}{\partial z} dx \wedge dy \wedge dz.$$

Thus,

$$d\alpha \wedge \beta - \alpha \wedge d\beta = \left(\frac{\partial f}{\partial z} g + f \frac{\partial g}{\partial z}\right) dx \wedge dy \wedge dz = d(\alpha \wedge \beta). \qquad [10.30]$$

If $\alpha$ is a $p$-form and $\beta$ is a $q$-form on $n$-dimensional space, the *generalization* of (10.30) is

$$d(\alpha \wedge \beta) = d\alpha \wedge \beta + (-1)^p\, \alpha \wedge d\beta. \qquad (10.33)$$

**PROBLEM 10.18** Prove (10.33).

**Solution:** If $\alpha$ and $\beta$ are monomials given by

$$\alpha = f\,dx_{i_1} \wedge \ldots \wedge dx_{i_p}, \qquad (10.34)$$

$$\beta = g\,dx_{j_1} \wedge \ldots \wedge dx_{j_q}, \qquad (10.35)$$

then their exterior derivatives are

$$d\alpha = df \wedge dx_{i_1} \wedge \ldots \wedge dx_{i_p}, \tag{10.36}$$

$$d\beta = dg \wedge dx_{j_1} \wedge \ldots \wedge dx_{j_q}, \tag{10.37}$$

Now, with repeated use of the anticommutative law (10.5),

$$\begin{aligned} d(\alpha \wedge \beta) &= d(fg) \wedge dx_{i_1} \wedge \ldots \wedge dx_{i_p} \wedge dx_{j_1} \wedge \ldots \wedge dx_{j_q} \\ &= (f\, dg + g\, df) \wedge dx_{i_1} \wedge \ldots \wedge dx_{i_p} \wedge dx_{j_1} \wedge \ldots \wedge dx_{j_q} \\ &= (df \wedge dx_{i_1} \wedge \ldots \wedge dx_{i_p}) \wedge (g\, dx_{j_1} \wedge \ldots \wedge dx_{j_q}) \\ &\quad + (-1)^p (f\, dx_{i_1} \wedge \ldots \wedge dx_{i_p}) \wedge (dg \wedge dx_{j_1} \wedge \ldots \wedge dx_{j_q}) \\ &= d\alpha \wedge \beta + (-1)^p \alpha \wedge d\beta. \end{aligned} \tag*{[10.33]}$$

Hence, (10.33) is proved for monomials $\alpha$ and $\beta$. The general case follows by linearity.

## 10.5 Poincaré Lemma

*The Poincaré lemma* states that if $\omega$ is any differential form of continuously differentiable functions, then

$$d(d\omega) = 0. \tag{10.38}$$

**PROBLEM 10.19** Prove that for any 0-form $\omega$,

$$d(d\omega) = 0. \tag{10.39}$$

**Solution:** Since a 0-form is a scalar function, let

$$\omega = f(x, y, z),$$

where $f(x, y, z)$ is any twice continuously differentiable function. If we denote partial differentiation by subscript notation (e.g., $\partial f/\partial x = f_x$, $\partial^2 f/\partial x \partial y = f_{xy}$, etc.), then from (10.19),

$$d\omega = df = f_x\, dx + f_y\, dy + f_z\, dz. \tag{10.40}$$

Thus,

$$\begin{aligned} d(d\omega) &= d(df) = df_x \wedge dx + df_y \wedge dy + df_z \wedge dz \\ &= (f_{xx}\, dx + f_{yx}\, dy + f_{zx}\, dz) \wedge dx + (f_{xy}\, dx + f_{yy}\, dy + f_{zx}\, dz) \wedge dy \\ &\quad + (f_{xz}\, dx + f_{yz}\, dy + f_{zz}\, dz) \wedge dz \\ &= (f_{yz} - f_{zy})\, dy \wedge dz + (f_{zx} - f_{xz})\, dz \wedge dx + (f_{xy} - f_{yx})\, dx \wedge dy \\ &= 0, \end{aligned} \tag{10.41}$$

since all the coefficients are zero because $f_{xy} = f_{yx}$, etc.

Similarly, it can be shown that (10.38) also holds for any continuously differentiable function of $n$ variables.

**PROBLEM 10.20** Prove that for any 1-form $\omega$,

$$d(d\omega) = 0. \tag{10.42}$$

**Solution:** Using index notation, a 1-form $\omega$ can be expressed as

$$\omega = \sum f_i\, dx_i, \tag{10.43}$$

where $f_i$ $(i = 1, 2, 3)$ are differentiable functions of $x_i$ $(i = 1, 2, 3)$.

Now, from the definition of the exterior derivative,

$$d\omega = \sum df_i \wedge dx_i. \tag{10.44}$$

Thus, using (10.30),

$$d(d\omega) = \sum d(df_i \wedge dx_i)$$
$$= \sum [d(df_i) \wedge dx_i - df_i \wedge d(dx_i)]. \tag{10.45}$$

But from (10.39),

$$d(df_i) = 0 \quad \text{and} \quad d(dx_i) = 0. \tag{10.46}$$

Hence, $d(d\omega) = 0$.

**PROBLEM 10.21** If $\omega$ is a 2-form, show that

$$d(d\omega) = 0. \tag{10.47}$$

**Solution:** If $\omega$ is a 2-form, then the degree of $d(d\omega)$ is 4, which exceeds 3; hence, from the result of Prob. 10.2,

$$d(d\omega) = 0.$$

**PROBLEM 10.22** Prove (10.38); i.e., show that for any differential form $\omega$,

$$d(d\omega) = 0. \qquad [10.38]$$

**Solution:** Suppose that a $p$-form $\omega$ on $n$-dimensional space is a monomial given by

$$\omega = f\, dx_{i_1} \wedge \ldots \wedge dx_{i_p}, \tag{10.48}$$

where $f$ is a twice continuously differentiable function of $n$ variables. Now, using (10.33),

$$\begin{aligned} d(d\omega) &= d(df \wedge dx_{i_1} \wedge \ldots \wedge dx_{i_p}) \\ &= d(df) \wedge dx_{i_1} \wedge \ldots \wedge dx_{i_p} - df \wedge d(dx_{i_1} \wedge \ldots \wedge dx_{i_p}) \\ &= -df \wedge d(dx_{i_1} \wedge \ldots \wedge dx_{i_p}) \end{aligned} \tag{10.49}$$

since $d(df) = 0$ by (10.39). Thus, it suffices to show that

$$d(dx_{i_1} \wedge \ldots \wedge dx_{i_p}) = 0. \tag{10.50}$$

We prove (10.50) by induction on $p$. Assume that

$$d(dx_{j_1} \wedge \ldots \wedge dx_{j_{p-1}}) = 0. \tag{10.51}$$

Then, again using (10.33),

$$d(dx_{i_1} \wedge \ldots \wedge dx_{i_p}) = d(dx_{i_1}) \wedge dx_{i_2} \wedge \ldots \wedge dx_{i_p} - dx_{i_1} \wedge d(dx_{i_2} \wedge \ldots \wedge dx_{i_p}) = 0$$

since $d(dx_{i_1}) = 0$ by (10.40) and $d(dx_{i_2} \wedge \ldots \wedge dx_{i_p}) = 0$ by the assumption (10.51).

This completes the proof of (10.47) when $\omega$ is a monomial. The general case follows by linearity.

**PROBLEM 10.23** Show that the Poincaré lemma (10.39) for a 0-form $\omega$ corresponds to the vector formula

$$\text{curl (grad } f) = \nabla \times (\nabla f) = \mathbf{0}.$$

**Solution:** Comparing the results of Prob. 10.19 and Prob. 10.15, or using Fig. 10.1, we see that the relation

$$d(d\omega) = 0 \qquad [10.39]$$

holds for a 0-form $\omega$ and hence, corresponds to the vector identity $\nabla \times (\nabla f) = \mathbf{0}$. [See (3.142).]

**PROBLEM 10.24** Show that the Poincaré lemma (10.42) for a 1-form $\omega$ corresponds to the vector formula

$$\text{div}\,(\text{curl}\,\mathbf{f}) = \nabla \cdot (\nabla \times \mathbf{f}) = 0.$$

**Solution:** Figure 10.1 shows that if $\omega$ is a 1-form, $d\omega$ corresponds to the curl of a vector function and $d(d\omega)$ to its divergence. Thus, the relation

$$d(d\omega) = 0 \qquad [10.42]$$

holds for a 1-form $\omega$ and hence, corresponds to the vector identity $\nabla \cdot (\nabla \times \mathbf{f}) = 0$. [See (3.143).]

## 10.6 Invariance of Exterior Derivatives under Transformations

A *transformation*, or *mapping*, $T$ is a rule that assigns to each point $(u_1, \ldots, u_m)$ in an $m$-dimensional space $V_m$, a point $(x_1, \ldots, x_n)$ in an $n$-dimensional space $V_n$; i.e.,

$$T\colon V_m \longrightarrow V_n.$$

A transformation $T$ can be expressed by coordinate functions as

$$x_i = x_i(u_1, \ldots, u_m), \quad i = 1, 2, \ldots, n. \qquad (10.52)$$

A transformation $T$ is *differentiable* if the coordinate functions (10.52) are continuously differentiable.

A transformation $T$ is said to be *one-to-one* if one and only one point in $V_m$ corresponds to one and only one point in $V_n$. The *inverse transformation* $T^{-1}$ of $T$ exists if $T$ is one-to-one, and is denoted by

$$T^{-1}\colon V_n \longrightarrow V_m.$$

If $\omega$ is any $p$-form on $V_n$, then $T\colon V_m \longrightarrow V_n$ on $\omega$ transforms $\omega$ into a $p$-form $\omega^*$ on $V_m$ which is obtained by replacing $x_1, \ldots, x_n$ and $dx_1, \ldots, dx_n$ wherever they occur by the coordinate functions (10.52) and then simplifying the result using the algebra of forms.

The essential operations on differential forms, i.e., sum, wedge product, and exterior derivative, are all preserved by transformations:

$$(\alpha + \beta)^* = \alpha^* + \beta^*, \qquad (10.53)$$

$$(\alpha \wedge \beta)^* = \alpha^* \wedge \beta^*, \qquad (10.54)$$

$$(d\omega)^* = d(\omega^*). \qquad (10.55)$$

Note that in (10.53) differential forms $\alpha$ and $\beta$ must have the same degrees, but in (10.54) $\alpha$ and $\beta$ may have different degrees. Equation (10.55) shows that the operator $d$ is *invariant* under a differentiable transformation.

**PROBLEM 10.25** If the transformation $T$ is

$$x = u + v, \quad y = u - v,$$

and $\alpha = xy\,dx$ and $\beta = y\,dy$, show that

$$(\alpha + \beta)^* = \alpha^* + \beta^*, \quad (\alpha \wedge \beta)^* = \alpha^* \wedge \beta^*, \quad (d\alpha)^* = d(\alpha^*).$$

**Solution:** For given $\alpha$, $\beta$, and $T$,

$$\alpha^* = (u+v)(u-v)\,d(u+v) = (u^2 - v^2)(du + dv) = (u^2 - v^2)\,du + (u^2 - v^2)\,dv,$$

$$\beta^* = (u-v)\,d(u-v) = (u-v)(du - dv) = (u-v)\,du - (u-v)\,dv.$$

Then,

$$\begin{aligned}(\alpha + \beta)^* &= (xy\,dx + y\,dy)^* \\ &= (u+v)(u-v)\,d(u+v) + (u-v)\,d(u-v) \\ &= \alpha^* + \beta^*,\end{aligned}$$

$$\begin{aligned}(\alpha \wedge \beta)^* &= (xy\,dx \wedge y\,dy)^* \\ &= (u+v)(u-v)\,d(u+v) \wedge (u-v)\,d(u-v) \\ &= \alpha^* \wedge \beta^*.\end{aligned}$$

Since

$$\begin{aligned}d\alpha = d(xy\,dx) &= d(xy) \wedge dx \\ &= (x\,dy + y\,dx) \wedge dx \\ &= -x\,dx \wedge dy,\end{aligned}$$

we have

$$\begin{aligned}d(\alpha^*) &= d[(u^2 - v^2)\,du + (u^2 - v^2)\,dv] \\ &= d(u^2 - v^2) \wedge du + d(u^2 - v^2) \wedge dv \\ &= (2u\,du - 2v\,dv) \wedge du + (2u\,du - 2v\,dv) \wedge dv \\ &= -2v\,dv \wedge du + 2u\,du \wedge dv \\ &= 2(u+v)\,du \wedge dv,\end{aligned}$$

and hence,

$$\begin{aligned}(d\alpha)^* &= (-x\,dx \wedge dy)^* \\ &= -(u+v)\,d(u+v) \wedge d(u-v) \\ &= -(u+v)(du + dv) \wedge (du - dv) \\ &= -(u+v)(-du \wedge dv + dv \wedge du) \\ &= 2(u+v)\,du \wedge dv \\ &= d(\alpha^*).\end{aligned}$$

**PROBLEM 10.26** Verify the invariance relation (10.55), that is, $(d\omega)^* = d(\omega^*)$, when $\omega = x\,dy \wedge dz$ and $T$ is the transformation $x = u + v - w$, $y = u^2 - v$, $z = v + w^2$.

**Solution:** Since $d\omega = d(x\,dy \wedge dz) = dx \wedge dy \wedge dz$,

$$\begin{aligned}(d\omega)^* &= d(u+v-w) \wedge d(u^2 - v) \wedge d(v + w^2) \\ &= (du + dv - dw) \wedge (2u\,du - dv) \wedge (dv + 2w\,dw) \\ &= (2u\,dv \wedge du - 2u\,dw \wedge du - du \wedge dv + dw \wedge dv) \wedge (dv + 2w\,dw) \\ &= -2u\,dw \wedge du \wedge dv + 4uw\,dv \wedge du \wedge dw - 2w\,du \wedge dv \wedge dw \\ &= -2(u + w + 2uw)\,du \wedge dv \wedge dw.\end{aligned}$$

Now,

$$\begin{aligned}\omega^* &= (x\,dy \wedge dz)^* \\ &= (u+v-w)\,d(u^2 - v) \wedge d(v + w^2) \\ &= (u+v-w)(2u\,du - dv) \wedge (dv + 2w\,dw) \\ &= (u+v-w)(2u\,du \wedge dv - 4uw\,dw \wedge du - 2w\,dv \wedge dw) \\ &= (2u^2 + 2uv - 2uw)\,du \wedge dv + (-4u^2w - 4uvw + 4uw^2)\,dw \wedge du \\ &\quad + (-2uw - 2vw + 2w^2)\,dv \wedge dw,\end{aligned}$$

and hence, the exterior derivative is

$$\begin{aligned}
d(\omega^*) &= d(2u^2 + 2uv - 2uw) \wedge du \wedge dv \\
&\quad + d(-4u^2w - 4uvw + 4uw^2) \wedge dw \wedge du \\
&\quad + d(-2uw - 2vw + 2w^2) \wedge dv \wedge dw \\
&= (4u\, du + 2u\, dv + 2v du - 2u\, dw - 2w\, du) \wedge du \wedge dv \\
&\quad + (-8uw\, du - 4u^2\, dw - 4vw\, du - 4uw\, dv - 4uv\, dw + 4w^2\, du \\
&\quad + 8uw\, dw) \wedge dw \wedge du \\
&\quad + (-2w\, du - 2u\, dw - 2w\, dv - 2v\, dw + 4w\, dw) \wedge dv \wedge dw \\
&= -2u\, dw \wedge du \wedge dv - 4uw\, dv \wedge dw \wedge du - 2w\, du \wedge dv \wedge dw \\
&= -2(u + w + 2uw)\, du \wedge dv \wedge dw.
\end{aligned}$$

Thus, we have verified that $(d\omega)^* = d(\omega^*)$.

**PROBLEM 10.27** If $T\colon V_m \longrightarrow V_n$ is a differentiable transformation and the function $f(x_1, \cdots, x_n)$ is a 0-form on $V_n$, show that

$$(df)^* = d(f^*). \tag{10.56}$$

**Solution:** If $T\colon V_m \longrightarrow V_n$ is described by (10.52), i.e.,

$$x_i = x_i(u_1, \cdots, u_m), \quad i = 1, 2, \cdots, n,$$

then

$$f^*(u_1, \cdots, u_m) = f[x_1(u_1, \cdots, u_m), \cdots, x_n(u_1, \cdots, u_m)].$$

Since $f$ is differentiable, the derivative is

$$df = \sum \frac{\partial f(x_1, \cdots, x_n)}{\partial x_i} dx_i.$$

Hence,

$$\begin{aligned}
(df)^* &= \sum \frac{\partial f[x_1(u_1, \cdots, u_m), \cdots, x_n(u_1, \cdots, u_m)]}{\partial x_i} \frac{\partial x_i}{\partial u_j} du_j \\
&= \sum \frac{\partial f^*(u_1, \cdots, u_m)}{\partial u_j} du_j \\
&= d(f^*).
\end{aligned}$$

**PROBLEM 10.28** If $\omega$ is a $p$-form on $V_n$ and $T\colon V_m \longrightarrow V_n$ is differentiable, show that

$$(d\omega)^* = d(\omega^*). \tag{10.55}$$

**Solution:** We prove (10.55) by induction. It has been shown in Prob. 10.27 that (10.55) is true when $\omega$ is a 0-form. Now assume that (10.55) is true when $\omega$ is a $(p-1)$-form. Then it suffices to prove (10.55) for a $p$-form of the type

$$\omega \wedge dx_i.$$

By (10.33), the exterior derivative is

$$\begin{aligned}
d(\omega \wedge dx_i) &= d\omega \wedge dx_i + (-1)^{p-1}\, \omega \wedge d(dx_i) \\
&= d\omega \wedge dx_i
\end{aligned}$$

since $d(dx_i) = 0$ by (10.38). Thus,

$$
\begin{aligned}
[d(\omega \wedge dx_i)]^* &= (d\omega \wedge dx_i)^* \\
&= (d\omega)^* \wedge (dx_i)^* \\
&= d(\omega^*) \wedge d(x_i^*) \\
&= d[\omega^* \wedge (dx_i)^*] \\
&= d[(\omega \wedge dx_i)^*].
\end{aligned}
$$

Relation (10.55) also shows that the exterior derivative of a differential form is *independent* of the coordinate system in which it is evaluated.

## 10.7 Integration of Forms

A *smooth space curve* C in 3-dimensional space $V_3$ with coordinates x, y, z is represented by the parametric equations

$$x = x(t), \quad y = y(t), \quad z = z(t), \tag{10.57}$$

with $a \leq t \leq b$. Using the concept of mapping (or transformation) discussed in Sec. 10.6, (10.57) can be described by a differentiable transformation $T$ as

$$T: V_1 \longrightarrow V_3.$$

Thus curve C in $V_3$ is a mapping of a *closed interval* $[a, b]$ on the real line $V_1$ *into* $V_3$. (See Fig. 10.2.)

If $\omega$ is a 1-form on $V_3$, the *integral* of $\omega$ over a curve C is defined by

$$\int_C \omega = \int_{[a,b]} \omega^*, \tag{10.58}$$

where $\omega^*$ is the 1-form transformed from $\omega$ by $T$. Thus, if $\omega$ is expressed as

$$\omega = f_1\,dx + f_2\,dy + f_3\,dz,$$

where the $f_i$ $(i = 1, 2, 3)$ are differentiable functions of x, y, z, then (10.58) is expressed as

$$
\begin{aligned}
\int_C \omega = \int_C f_1\,dx + f_2\,dy + f_3\,dz &= \int_{[a,b]} \omega^* \\
&= \int_a^b [f_1^*(t)x'(t) + f_2^*(t)y'(t) + f_3^*(t)z'(t)]\,dt, \qquad (10.59)
\end{aligned}
$$

where $f_i^*(t) = f_i[x(t), y(t), z(t)]$, $x'(t) = dx(t)/dt$, etc. The right-hand side of (10.59) is just an ordinary integral.

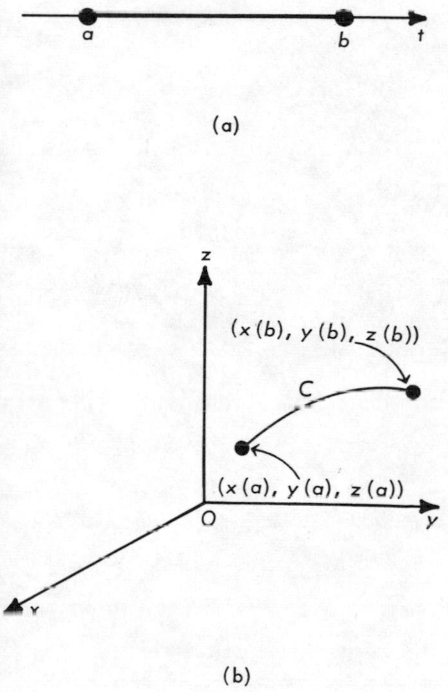


Fig. 10.2 Mapping of the interval $[a, b]$ on $V_1$ into $V_3$.

**PROBLEM 10.29** If $\omega = x^2\,dx + y\,dy + xyz\,dz$ and C is a curve represented by the transformation $x = t$, $y = t$, $z = t$ with $0 \leq t \leq 1$, evaluate $\int_C \omega$.

**Solution:** Since $\omega^* = t^2\,dt + t\,dt + t^3\,dt = (t^2 + t + t^3)\,dt$, then by (10.59),

$$\int_C \omega = \int_{[0,1]} \omega^* = \int_0^1 (t^2 + t + t^3)\,dt = \frac{1}{3} + \frac{1}{2} + \frac{1}{4} = \frac{13}{12}.$$

**PROBLEM 10.30** If $f$ is a 0-form on $V_3$, i.e., a function of x, y, z, and C is a curve in $V_3$ represented by (10.57), show that

$$\int_C df = f^*(b) - f^*(a), \tag{10.60}$$

where $f^*(t) = f[x(t), y(t), z(t)]$.

**Solution:** By definition (10.58) of an integral and using (10.56),

$$\int_C df = \int_{[a,b]} (df)^* = \int_{[a,b]} d(f^*) = \int_a^b \frac{d}{dt}(f^*)\, dt = f^*(b) - f^*(a)$$

by the fundamental theorem of calculus.

**PROBLEM 10.31** Consider a curve $C$ on a plane represented by the transformation $x = t$, $y = t^2$ with $-1 \le t \le 1$. Then (a) if $\omega = y^2\, dx + 2xy\, dy$, compute $\int_C \omega$, and (b) find a function $f$ such that $df = \omega$ and check (10.60).

**Solution:** (a) Since $\omega^* = t^4\, dt + 2t^3\, d(t^2) = 5t^4\, dt$, then, using (10.59),

$$\int_C \omega = \int_{[-1,1]} \omega^* = \int_{-1}^{1} 5t^4\, dt = t^5 \Big|_{-1}^{1} = 2.$$

(b) For $\omega = y^2\, dx + 2xy\, dy$, let $f(x, y)$ be a function such that $df = \omega$. Then,

$$df = \frac{\partial f}{\partial x} dx + \frac{\partial f}{\partial y} dy = y^2\, dx + 2xy\, dy.$$

Thus,

$$\frac{\partial f}{\partial x} = y^2, \quad \frac{\partial f}{\partial y} = 2xy. \tag{10.61}$$

From the first equation of (10.61),

$$f(x, y) = xy^2 + g(y),$$

and hence,

$$\frac{\partial f}{\partial y} = 2xy + g'(y).$$

Comparing this to the second equation of (10.61), we have $g'(y) = 0$, that is, $g(y) = K$ = constant. Thus,

$$f(x, y) = xy^2 + K,$$
$$f^*(t) = f[x(t), y(t)] = t^5 + K.$$

By (10.60),

$$\int_C \omega = \int_C df = f^*(1) - f^*(-1) = (1 + K) - (-1 + K) = 2,$$

which agrees with the result of part (a).

A *smooth surface* $S$ in 3-dimensional space $V_3$, with coordinates $x$, $y$, $z$, is represented by the parametric equations

$$x = x(u, v), \quad y = y(u, v), \quad z = z(u, v) \tag{10.62}$$

with $a \le u \le b$, $c \le v \le d$. Thus, analogously, (10.62) can be represented by a differentiable transformation $T$ as

$$T: \; V_2 \longrightarrow V_3;$$

hence, a surface $S$ in $V_3$ is a mapping of a *closed rectangle* $D$: $a \le u \le b$, $c \le v \le d$ in 2-dimensional space $V_2$, with coordinates $u$, $v$, *into* $V_3$. (See Fig. 10.3.)

If $\omega$ is a 2-form on $V_3$, then the *integral* of $\omega$ over a surface $S$ is defined by

$$\iint_S \omega = \iint_D \omega^*. \tag{10.63}$$

Note that $\omega^*$ is the 2-form transformed from $\omega$ by $T$, and the right-hand side of (10.63) is an ordinary multiple integral.

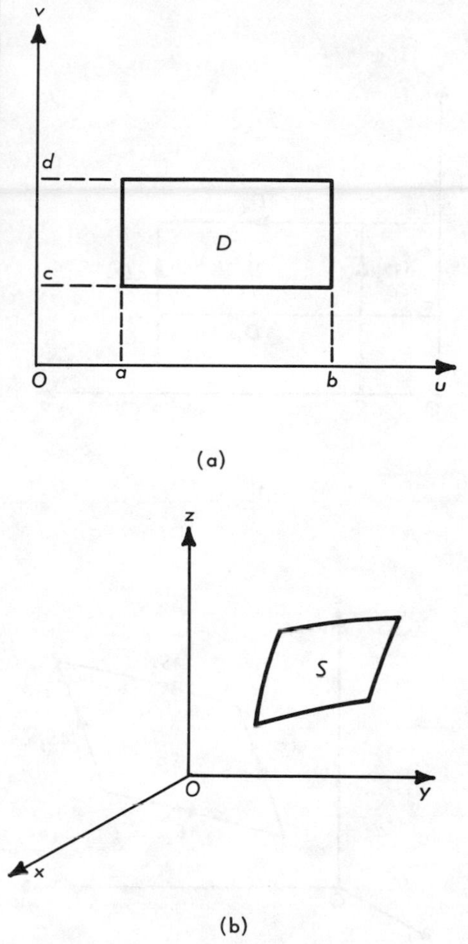


Fig. 10.3 Mapping of a closed rectangle in $V_2$ into a surface in $V_3$.

**PROBLEM 10.32** If $\omega = x\,dy \wedge dz + y\,dx \wedge dy$, and $S$ is the surface represented by the transformation $x = u + v$, $y = u - v$, $z = uv$, with $0 \le u \le 1$, $0 \le v \le 1$, compute $\iint_S \omega$.

**Solution:** Since the 2-form transformed from $\omega$ by $T$ is

$$\begin{aligned}\omega^* &= (u+v)\,d(u-v) \wedge d(uv) + (u-v)\,d(u+v) \wedge d(u-v)\\ &= (u+v)^2\,du \wedge dv - 2(u-v)\,du \wedge dv\\ &= (u^2 - 2u + v^2 + 2v + 2uv)\,du \wedge dv,\end{aligned}$$

then, by (10.63),

$$\begin{aligned}\iint_S \omega = \iint_D \omega^* &= \int_0^1 \int_0^1 (u^2 - 2u + v^2 + 2v + 2uv)\,du\,dv\\ &= \int_0^1 \left(v^2 + 3v - \frac{2}{3}\right) dv\\ &= \frac{7}{6}.\end{aligned}$$

**PROBLEM 10. 33** Compute $\iint_S \omega$, where $\omega = xy\,dy \wedge dz + x\,dz \wedge dx + 3zx\,dx \wedge dy$, and $S$ is the surface given by $z = x^2 + y^2$ with $0 \le x \le 1$, $0 \le y \le 1$.

**Solution:** Since $S$ can be described by the transformation

$$x = u, \quad y = v, \quad z = u^2 + v^2$$

with $0 \le u \le 1$, $0 \le v \le 1$,

$$\begin{aligned}\omega^* &= uv\,dv \wedge d(u^2 + v^2) + u\,d(u^2 + v^2) \wedge du + 3u(u^2 + v^2)\,du \wedge dv\\ &= uv\,dv \wedge (2u\,du + 2v\,dv) + u(2u\,du + 2v\,dv) \wedge du + (3u^3 + 3uv^2)\,du \wedge dv\\ &= (3u^3 + 3uv^2 - 2u^2v - 2uv)\,du \wedge dv,\end{aligned}$$

and by (10.63),

$$\begin{aligned}\iint_S \omega = \iint_D \omega^* &= \int_0^1 \int_0^1 (3u^3 + 3uv^2 - 2u^2v - 2uv)\,du\,dv\\ &= \int_0^1 \left(\frac{3}{4} + \frac{3}{2}v^2 - \frac{5}{3}v\right) dv\\ &= \frac{5}{12}.\end{aligned}$$

The *boundary* $\partial S$ of $S$ is formed by the *edge curves* of $S$ that are described by

$$\left.\begin{aligned} \partial S_1&: \quad x = x(u, c), \quad y = y(u, c), \quad z = z(u, c),\\ \partial S_2&: \quad x = x(b, v), \quad y = y(b, v), \quad z = z(b, v),\\ \partial S_3&: \quad x = x(u, d), \quad y = y(u, d), \quad z = z(u, d),\\ \partial S_4&: \quad x = x(a, v), \quad y = y(a, v), \quad z = z(a, v), \end{aligned}\right\} \tag{10.64}$$

with $a \leq u \leq b$, $c \leq v \leq d$. Then the boundary $\partial S$ of $S$ is expressed by

$$\partial S = \partial S_1 + \partial S_2 - \partial S_3 - \partial S_4. \tag{10.65}$$

The four edge curves (10.64) are the mappings of the four line segments that form the boundary of the rectangle $D$ in $V_2$ into $V_3$. (See Fig. 10.4.) The minus signs before $\partial S_3$ and $\partial S_4$ in (10.65) are due to the fact that a consistent trip around the rim of $D$, and thus of $S$, is assured by reversing the line segments $\partial D_3$ and $\partial D_4$. (See Fig. 10.5.)

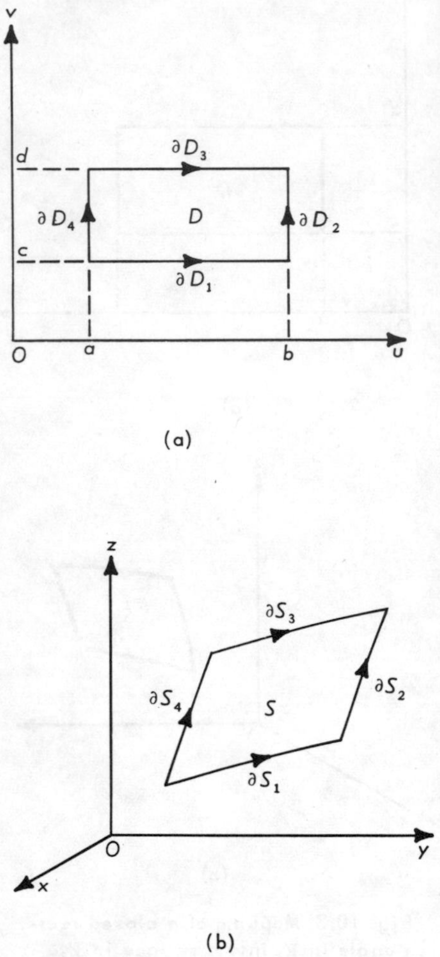


Fig. 10.4 Mapping of the boundary of a rectangle in $V_2$ into $V_3$.

If $\omega$ is a 1-form on $V_3$, then the *integral* of $\omega$ over the boundary $\partial S$ of $S$ is defined as

$$\begin{aligned} \int_{\partial S} \omega &= \int_{\partial S_1} \omega + \int_{\partial S_2} \omega + \int_{-\partial S_3} \omega + \int_{-\partial S_4} \omega \\ &= \int_{\partial S_1} \omega + \int_{\partial S_2} \omega - \int_{\partial S_3} \omega - \int_{\partial S_4} \omega \end{aligned} \tag{10.66}$$

since the direction in which the route of integration is traversed is taken care of by the relation

$$\int_{-\partial S_i} \omega = -\int_{\partial S_i} \omega. \tag{10.67}$$

*Stokes' theorem* states that if $\omega$ is a 1-form on $V_3$ and $S$ is the 2-dimensional surface $S$ on $V_3$, then

$$\iint_S d\omega = \int_{\partial S} \omega. \tag{10.68}$$

**PROBLEM 10.34** Verify Stokes' theorem (10.68) for 1-forms.

**Solution:** Express the 1-form $\omega$ on $V_3$ as

$$\omega = f_1\, dx + f_2\, dy + f_3\, dz, \tag{10.69}$$

where the $f_i$ $(i = 1, 2, 3)$ are differentiable functions of $x, y, z$. Then, the 1-form $\omega^*$, transformed from $\omega$ by $T$: $V_2 \longrightarrow V_3$ can be expressed as

$$\omega^* = f(u, v)\, du + g(u, v)\, dv, \tag{10.70}$$

where $f$ and $g$ are differentiable functions of $u$, $v$, i.e., of the coordinates of $V_2$. By the definition (10.20) of the exterior derivative of a 1-form,

$$d(\omega^*) = \left(\frac{\partial g}{\partial u} - \frac{\partial f}{\partial v}\right) du \wedge dv. \tag{10.71}$$

Now, by definition (10.63) of the integral and using (10.55) and (10.71),

$$\begin{aligned} \iint_S d\omega &= \iint_D (d\omega)^* = \iint_D d(\omega^*) = \iint_D \left(\frac{\partial g}{\partial u} - \frac{\partial f}{\partial v}\right) dudv \\ &= \iint_D \frac{\partial g}{\partial u}\, dudv - \iint_D \frac{\partial f}{\partial v}\, dudv. \end{aligned} \tag{10.72}$$

Treat these double integrals as iterated integrals. If the rectangle $D$ is given by $a \leq u \leq b,\ c \leq v \leq d$, then, integrating first with respect to $u$,

$$\iint_D \frac{\partial g}{\partial u}\, dudv = \int_c^d \int_a^b \frac{\partial g}{\partial u}\, dudv = \int_c^d I(v)\, dv,$$

where $I(v) = \int_a^b \frac{\partial g(u, v)}{\partial u}\, du.$

Since $v$ is a constant in the partial integral $I(v)$, the integrand is the ordinary derivative with respect to $u$. Thus, from the fundamental theorem of calculus,

$$I(v) = g(b, v) - g(a, v).$$

Hence,

$$\iint_D \frac{\partial g}{\partial u}\, dudv = \int_c^d g(b, v)\, dv - \int_c^d g(a, v)\, dv. \tag{10.73}$$

Now on the curve $\partial D_2$ in $\partial D$, since $du = 0$, (10.70) reduces to $\omega^* = g(b, v)\, dv$. (See Fig. 10.4.) Thus, by definition (10.58) of the integral,

$$\int_c^d g(b, v)\, dv = \int_{\partial D_2} \omega^* = \int_{\partial S_2} \omega. \tag{10.74}$$

By a similar argument,

$$\int_c^d g(a, v)\, dv = \int_{\partial D_4} \omega^* = \int_{\partial S_4} \omega. \tag{10.75}$$

Hence, substituting (10.74–5) into (10.73),

$$\iint_D \frac{\partial g}{\partial u}\, dudv = \int_{\partial S_2} \omega - \int_{\partial S_4} \omega. \tag{10.76}$$

Similarly, integrating first with respect to $v$,

$$\iint_D \frac{\partial f}{\partial v}\, dudv = \int_{\partial S_3} \omega - \int_{\omega S_1} \omega. \tag{10.77}$$

Thus, substituting (10.76–7) into (10.72) and using (10.66), we obtain the required result

$$\begin{aligned} \iint_S d\omega &= \int_{\partial S_2} \omega - \int_{\partial S_4} \omega - \int_{\partial S_3} \omega + \int_{\partial S_1} \omega \\ &= \int_{\partial S_1} \omega + \int_{\partial S_2} \omega - \int_{\partial S_3} \omega - \int_{\partial S_4} \omega \\ &= \int_{\partial S} \omega. \end{aligned}$$

In Prob. 10.30, if the two end points of curve $C$ are the boundary $\partial C$ of $C$, then Stokes' theorem for 0-form (10.60) is written as

$$\int_C d\omega = \int_{\partial C} \omega. \tag{10.78}$$

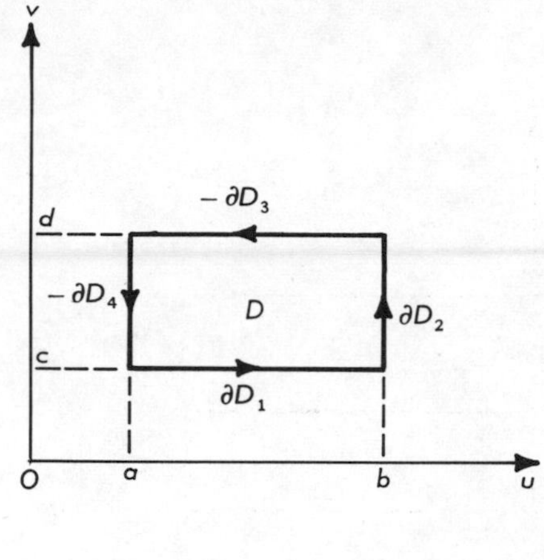


(a)

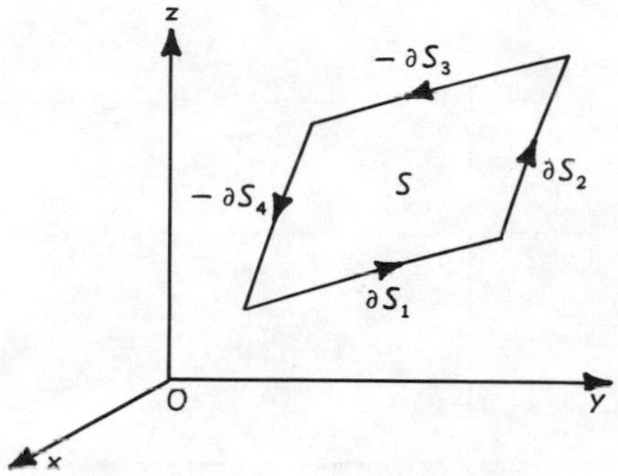


(b)

Fig. 10.5 Reversing the line segments in the mapping shown in Fig. 10.4.

The integral of a 0-form at a point $p$ is

$$\int_{\text{at } p} \omega = \omega(p). \tag{10.79}$$

Since it is beyond the scope of this book to define the integral of a $p$-form over a $p$-dimensional region on an $n$-dimensional space $V_n$, it suffices to state the *general Stokes theorem*:

Let $\omega$ be a differential form of degree $(p-1)$ defined on some bounded $p$-dimensional region $M$ in $V_n$ $(p \leq n)$ with a $(p-1)$-dimensional surface as its smooth boundary $\partial M$. Then,

$$\int_M d\omega = \int_{\partial M} \omega. \tag{10.80}$$

The general Stokes theorem shows the relation between the integral of a differential form $\omega$ and that of its exterior derivative $d\omega$.

The general Stokes theorem is related to Gauss', classical Stokes', and Green's theorems by the theorem:

Let $\mathbf{f} = [f_1, f_2, f_3]$ be a continuous differentiable vector function in a region $R$ of 3-dimensional space $V_3$, and let $\omega_1 = f_1\, dx + f_2\, dy + f_3\, dz$ be the corresponding 1-form. Then, comparing

$$\int_C \omega_1 = \int_C f_1\, dx + f_2\, dy + f_3\, dz = \int_{[a,b]} \omega_1^*$$

$$= \int_a^b [f_1^*(t)x'(t) + f_2^*(t)y'(t) + f_3^*(t)z'(t)]\, dt \quad [10.59]$$

and

$$\int_C \mathbf{f}\cdot d\mathbf{r} = \int_C (f_1\, dx + f_2\, dy + f_3\, dz), \quad [4.15]$$

we obtain

$$\int_C \omega_1 = \int_C \mathbf{f}\cdot d\mathbf{r}. \tag{10.81}$$

Thus, the integral of 1-form over a curve is referred to as a *line integral.*

If $\omega_2 = f_1\, dy \wedge dz + f_2\, dz \wedge dx + f_3\, dx \wedge dy$ is the 2-form corresponding to $\mathbf{f}$, whose surface integral can be expressed as $\iint_S \mathbf{f}\cdot d\mathbf{S}$ from (4.31), then

$$\iint_S \omega_2 = \iint_S \mathbf{f}\cdot d\mathbf{S}. \tag{10.82}$$

Thus the integral of 2-form over a surface is also referred to as a *surface integral.*

If $\omega_3 = f\, dx \wedge dy \wedge dz$ is a 3-form corresponding to the scalar function $f$, whose volume integral is $\iiint_R f\, dV$ from (4.43), then

$$\iiint_R \omega_3 = \iiint_R f\, dV. \tag{10.83}$$

Hence, the integral of a 3-form over a region $R$ corresponds to a *volume integral.*

**PROBLEM 10.35** A 2-form on $V_3$, with coordinates $x, y, z$, given by

$$\omega_2 = f_1 \, dy \wedge dz + f_2 \, dz \wedge dx + f_3 \, dx \wedge dy$$

corresponds to a differentiable vector function $\mathbf{f} = [f_1, f_2, f_3]$. Show that (10.80) corresponds to Gauss' theorem, or the divergence theorem, given by

$$\iiint_R \nabla \cdot \mathbf{f} \, dV = \oiint_S \mathbf{f} \cdot d\mathbf{S}. \qquad [4.58]$$

**Solution:** From the result of Prob. 10.13, the exterior derivative of a 2-form is

$$d\omega_2 = \left(\frac{\partial f_1}{\partial x} + \frac{\partial f_2}{\partial y} + \frac{\partial f_3}{\partial z}\right) dx \wedge dy \wedge dz,$$

which corresponds to $\nabla \cdot \mathbf{f}$. (See Fig. 10.1.) Thus if $M$ is the region $R$ in $V_3$, then its boundary $\partial M = \partial R$ is the closed surface $S$ which encloses $R$, and (10.80) reduces to

$$\iiint_R d\omega_2 = \iint_{\partial R} \omega_2. \qquad (10.84)$$

Thus, referring to (10.82) and (10.83), we see that (10.84) corresponds to the divergence theorem.

Writing (10.84) explicitly,

$$\iiint_R \left(\frac{\partial f_1}{\partial x} + \frac{\partial f_2}{\partial y} + \frac{\partial f_3}{\partial z}\right) dx \wedge dy \wedge dz = \iint_{\partial R} f_1 \, dy \wedge dz + f_2 \, dz \wedge dx + f_3 \, dx \wedge dy, \qquad (10.85)$$

which corresponds to the divergence theorem

$$\iiint_R \left(\frac{\partial P}{\partial x} + \frac{\partial Q}{\partial y} + \frac{\partial R}{\partial z}\right) dxdydz = \oiint_S (P \, dydz + Q \, dzdx + R \, dxdy). \qquad [4.66]$$

**PROBLEM 10.36** A 1-form $\omega_1$ of $V_3$ given by

$$\omega_1 = f_1 \, dx + f_2 \, dy + f_3 \, dz,$$

corresponds to a differentiable vector function $\mathbf{f} = [f_1, f_2, f_3]$. Show that (10.80) corresponds to the classical Stokes theorem given by

$$\iint_S \nabla \times \mathbf{f} \cdot d\mathbf{S} = \oint_C \mathbf{f} \cdot d\mathbf{r}. \qquad [4.104]$$

**Solution:** From the result of Prob. 10.12, the exterior derivative of a 1-form is

$$d\omega_1 = \left(\frac{\partial f_3}{\partial y} - \frac{\partial f_2}{\partial z}\right) dy \wedge dz + \left(\frac{\partial f_1}{\partial z} - \frac{\partial f_3}{\partial x}\right) dz \wedge dx + \left(\frac{\partial f_2}{\partial x} - \frac{\partial f_1}{\partial y}\right) dx \wedge dy,$$

which corresponds to $\nabla \times \mathbf{f}$. (See Fig. 10.1.) Thus, if $M$ is the 2-dimensional finite surface $S$ in $V_3$, then its boundary $\partial M = \partial S$ is the simple closed curve $C$ which bounds $S$, and (10.80) reduces to

$$\iint_S d\omega_1 = \iint_{\partial S} \omega_1. \qquad (10.86)$$

Thus, referring to (10.81) and (10.82), we see that (10.86) corresponds to Stokes' theorem given by (4.104). Again, writing (10.86) explicitly,

$$\iint_S \left(\frac{\partial f_3}{\partial y} - \frac{\partial f_2}{\partial z}\right) dy \wedge dz + \left(\frac{\partial f_1}{\partial z} - \frac{\partial f_3}{\partial x}\right) dz \wedge dx + \left(\frac{\partial f_2}{\partial x} - \frac{\partial f_1}{\partial y}\right) dx \wedge dy$$

$$= \iint_{\partial S} f_1\, dx + f_2\, dy + f_3\, dz, \qquad (10.87)$$

which again corresponds to Stokes' theorem given by

$$\oint_C P\, dx + Q\, dy + R\, dz = \iint_S \left(\frac{\partial R}{\partial y} - \frac{\partial Q}{\partial z}\right) dydz$$

$$+ \left(\frac{\partial P}{\partial z} - \frac{\partial R}{\partial x}\right) dzdx + \left(\frac{\partial Q}{\partial x} - \frac{\partial P}{\partial y}\right) dxdy \qquad [4.109]$$

**PROBLEM 10.37** Consider a 1-form $\omega$ on $V_2$, with coordinates $x$, $y$, given by

$$\omega = P(x, y)\, dx + Q(x, y)\, dy,$$

where $P$ and $Q$ are differentiable functions of $x$ and $y$. Show that (10.80) corresponds to Green's theorem in the plane given by

$$\oint_C P\, dx + Q\, dy = \iint_R \left(\frac{\partial Q}{\partial x} - \frac{\partial P}{\partial y}\right) dxdy. \qquad [4.110]$$

**Solution:** By definition (10.20), the exterior derivative of the given 1-form is

$$d\omega = \left(\frac{\partial P}{\partial x}\, dx + \frac{\partial P}{\partial y}\, dy\right) \wedge dx + \left(\frac{\partial Q}{\partial x}\, dx + \frac{\partial Q}{\partial y}\, dy\right) \wedge dy$$

$$= \left(\frac{\partial Q}{\partial x} - \frac{\partial P}{\partial x}\right) dx \wedge dy. \qquad (10.88)$$

Thus, if $M$ is the 2-dimensional finite region $S$ on $V_2$, i.e., the $xy$-plane, then its boundary $\partial M = \partial S$ is a simple closed curve $C$ which bounds $S$, and (10.80) reduces to

$$\int_{\partial S} \omega = \int_S d\omega, \qquad (10.89)$$

or, on writing (10.89) explicitly,

$$\int_{\partial S} P\, dx + Q\, dy = \int_S \left(\frac{\partial Q}{\partial x} - \frac{\partial P}{\partial y}\right) dx \wedge dy, \qquad (10.90)$$

which corresponds to Green's theorem in the plane given by (4.110).

## 10.8 Differential Forms of Maxwell's Field Equations

In electromagnetic field theory, the basic *Maxwell's equations* in vector form are

$$\nabla \times \mathbf{E} + \frac{\partial \mathbf{B}}{\partial t} = \mathbf{0}, \qquad [9.16]$$

$$\nabla \times \mathbf{H} - \frac{\partial \mathbf{D}}{\partial t} = \mathbf{J}, \qquad [9.17]$$

$$\nabla \cdot \mathbf{B} = 0, \qquad [9.18]$$

$$\nabla \cdot \mathbf{D} = \rho, \qquad [9.19]$$

where electric field intensity $\mathbf{E}$, magnetic field intensity $\mathbf{H}$, electric displacement $\mathbf{D}$, magnetic induction $\mathbf{B}$, electric current density $\mathbf{J}$, and charge density $\rho$ are all functions of the space variables $x$, $y$, $z$ and time $t$. (Cf., Sec. 9.3.)

Now introduce the differential forms

$$\omega_E = E_1\, dx + E_2\, dy + E_3\, dz,$$

$$\omega_H = H_1\, dx + H_2\, dy + H_3\, dz,$$

$$\omega_D = D_1\, dy \wedge dz + D_2\, dz \wedge dx + D_3\, dx \wedge dy,$$

$$\omega_B = B_1\, dy \wedge dz + B_2\, dz \wedge dx + B_3\, dx \wedge dy,$$

$$\omega_J = J_1\, dy \wedge dz + J_2\, dz \wedge dx + J_3\, dx \wedge dy,$$

$$\omega_\rho = \rho\, dx \wedge dy \wedge dz,$$

which correspond to vector functions $\mathbf{E} = [E_1, E_2, E_3]$, $\mathbf{H} = [H_1, H_2, H_3]$, $\mathbf{D} = [D_1, D_2, D_3]$, $\mathbf{B} = [B_1, B_2, B_3]$, $\mathbf{J} = [J_1, J_2, J_3]$, and a scalar function $\rho$, respectively.

**PROBLEM 10.38** Show that (9.16) and (9.18) can be expressed as

$$d\alpha = 0, \qquad (10.91)$$

and (9.17) and (9.19) can be expressed as

$$d\beta + \gamma = 0, \qquad (10.92)$$

where

$$\alpha = \omega_E \wedge dt + \omega_B, \qquad (10.93)$$

$$\beta = -\omega_H \wedge dt + \omega_D, \qquad (10.94)$$

$$\gamma = \omega_J \wedge dt - \omega_\rho. \qquad (10.95)$$

**Solution:** Substituting the values of $\omega_E$ and $\omega_B$ in (10.93),

$$\begin{aligned}\alpha &= \omega_E \wedge dt + \omega_B \\ &= E_1\, dx \wedge dt + E_2\, dy \wedge dt + E_3\, dz \wedge dt + B_1\, dy \wedge dz + B_2\, dz \wedge dx + B_3\, dx \wedge dy.\end{aligned}$$

Since $dx \wedge dx = dy \wedge dy = dz \wedge dz = dt \wedge dt = 0$ and $d(dt) = 0$ by (10. 39), then from (10.30) the exterior derivative of the first term above is

$$\begin{aligned}d(E_1\, dx \wedge dt) &= d(E_1\, dx) \wedge dt - E_1\, dx \wedge d(dt) \\ &= dE_1 \wedge dx \wedge dt \\ &= \left(\frac{\partial E_1}{\partial x} dx + \frac{\partial E_1}{\partial y} dy + \frac{\partial E_1}{\partial z} dz + \frac{\partial E_1}{\partial t} dt\right) \wedge dx \wedge dt \\ &= \frac{\partial E_1}{\partial y} dy \wedge dx \wedge dt + \frac{\partial E_1}{\partial z} dz \wedge dx \wedge dt.\end{aligned}$$

Similarly, the exterior derivatives of the other terms are

$$d(E_2\, dy \wedge dt) = \frac{\partial E_2}{\partial x} dx \wedge dy \wedge dt + \frac{\partial E_2}{\partial z} dz \wedge dy \wedge dt,$$

$$d(E_3\, dz \wedge dt) = \frac{\partial E_3}{\partial x} dx \wedge dz \wedge dt + \frac{\partial E_3}{\partial y} dy \wedge dz \wedge dt,$$

$$d(B_1\, dy \wedge dz) = \frac{\partial B_1}{\partial x} dx \wedge dy \wedge dz + \frac{\partial B_1}{\partial t} dt \wedge dy \wedge dz,$$

$$d(B_2\, dz \wedge dx) = \frac{\partial B_2}{\partial y}\, dy \wedge dz \wedge dx + \frac{\partial B_2}{\partial t}\, dt \wedge dz \wedge dx,$$

$$d(B_3\, dx \wedge dy) = \frac{\partial B_3}{\partial z}\, dz \wedge dx \wedge dy + \frac{\partial B_3}{\partial t}\, dt \wedge dx \wedge dy.$$

Adding all these terms,

$$\begin{aligned} d\alpha = &\left(\frac{\partial E_3}{\partial y} - \frac{\partial E_2}{\partial z} + \frac{\partial B_1}{\partial t}\right) dy \wedge dz \wedge dt + \left(\frac{\partial E_1}{\partial z} - \frac{\partial E_3}{\partial x} + \frac{\partial B_2}{\partial t}\right) dz \wedge dx \wedge dt \\ &+ \left(\frac{\partial E_2}{\partial x} - \frac{\partial E_1}{\partial y} + \frac{\partial B_3}{\partial t}\right) dx \wedge dy \wedge dt \\ &+ \left(\frac{\partial B_1}{\partial x} + \frac{\partial B_2}{\partial y} + \frac{\partial B_3}{\partial z}\right) dx \wedge dy \wedge dz, \end{aligned} \tag{10.96}$$

and $d\alpha = 0$ implies that all coefficients that are scalars are zero, and the first three coefficients are the vector components of $\nabla \times \mathbf{E} + (\partial \mathbf{B}/\partial t)$, and the last coefficient is $\nabla \cdot \mathbf{B}$. Thus we have established that

$$d\alpha = 0$$

represents (9.16) and (9.18).

Similarly, the exterior derivative of $\beta$ is

$$\begin{aligned} d\beta = &-\left(\frac{\partial H_3}{\partial y} - \frac{\partial H_2}{\partial z} - \frac{\partial D_1}{\partial t}\right) dy \wedge dz \wedge dt - \left(\frac{\partial H_1}{\partial z} - \frac{\partial H_3}{\partial x} - \frac{\partial D_2}{\partial t}\right) dz \wedge dx \wedge dt \\ &- \left(\frac{\partial H_2}{\partial x} - \frac{\partial H_1}{\partial y} - \frac{\partial D_3}{\partial t}\right) dx \wedge dy \wedge dt \\ &+ \left(\frac{\partial D_1}{\partial x} + \frac{\partial D_2}{\partial y} + \frac{\partial D_3}{\partial z}\right) dx \wedge dy \wedge dz, \end{aligned} \tag{10.97}$$

and, writing (10.95) explicitly,

$$\begin{aligned} \gamma = &J_1\, dy \wedge dz \wedge dt + J_2\, dz \wedge dx \wedge dt + J_3\, dx \wedge dy \wedge dt \\ &- \rho\, dx \wedge dy \wedge dz. \end{aligned} \tag{10.98}$$

Then adding (10.97) and (10.98),

$$\begin{aligned} d\beta + \gamma = &-\left(\frac{\partial H_3}{\partial y} - \frac{\partial H_2}{\partial z} - \frac{\partial D_1}{\partial t} - J_1\right) dy \wedge dz \wedge dt \\ &- \left(\frac{\partial H_1}{\partial z} - \frac{\partial H_3}{\partial x} - \frac{\partial D_2}{\partial t} - J_2\right) dz \wedge dx \wedge dt \\ &- \left(\frac{\partial H_2}{\partial x} - \frac{\partial H_1}{\partial y} - \frac{\partial D_3}{\partial t} - J_3\right) dx \wedge dy \wedge dt \\ &+ \left(\frac{\partial D_1}{\partial x} + \frac{\partial D_2}{\partial y} + \frac{\partial D_3}{\partial z} - \rho\right) dx \wedge dy \wedge dz \\ = &\ 0. \end{aligned} \tag{10.99}$$

Equation (10.99) implies that all coefficients that are scalars are zero, and the first three coefficients are the vector components of $\nabla \times \mathbf{H} - (\partial \mathbf{D}/\partial t) - \mathbf{J}$, and the last coefficient is $\nabla \cdot \mathbf{D} - \rho$. Thus we have also established that

$$d\beta + \gamma = 0$$

represents (9.17) and (9.18).

**PROBLEM 10.39** If $\gamma$ is given by (10.95), show that

$$d\gamma = 0, \tag{10.100}$$

and that this corresponds to the continuity equation

$$\nabla \cdot \mathbf{J} + \frac{\partial \rho}{\partial t} = 0. \qquad [9.3]$$

**Solution:** From (10.92),

$$\gamma = -d\beta. \tag{10.101}$$

Thus, taking the exterior derivative of (10.101) and using (10.38),

$$d\gamma = -d(d\beta) = 0.$$

Taking the exterior derivative of (10.98),

$$\begin{aligned} d\gamma &= dJ_1 \wedge dy \wedge dz \wedge dt + dJ_2 \wedge dz \wedge dx \wedge dt + dJ_3 \wedge dx \wedge dy \wedge dt \\ &\quad - d\rho \wedge dx \wedge dy \wedge dz \\ &= \frac{\partial J_1}{\partial x} dx \wedge dy \wedge dz \wedge dt + \frac{\partial J_2}{\partial y} dy \wedge dz \wedge dx \wedge dt + \frac{\partial J_3}{\partial z} dz \wedge dx \wedge dy \wedge dt \\ &\quad - \frac{\partial \rho}{\partial t} dt \wedge dx \wedge dy \wedge dz \\ &= \left( \frac{\partial J_1}{\partial x} + \frac{\partial J_2}{\partial y} + \frac{\partial J_3}{\partial z} + \frac{\partial \rho}{\partial t} \right) dx \wedge dy \wedge dz \wedge dt, \end{aligned} \tag{10.102}$$

and (10.100) clearly implies that

$$\frac{\partial J_1}{\partial x} + \frac{\partial J_2}{\partial y} + \frac{\partial J_3}{\partial t} + \frac{\partial \rho}{\partial t} = 0; \tag{10.103}$$

that is, $\nabla \cdot \mathbf{J} + \partial \rho / \partial t = 0$.

## 10.9 Supplementary Problems

**PROBLEM 10.40** If $\alpha = x\,dx - z\,dy + y^2\,dz$, $\beta = x^2\,dy \wedge dz + 2\,dz \wedge dx - y\,dx \wedge dy$, compute $\alpha \wedge \beta$.
*Answer*: $(x^3 - y^3 - 2z)\,dx \wedge dy \wedge dz$.

**PROBLEM 10.41** If $\alpha = dx \wedge dy + dy \wedge dz - dz \wedge dw$, $\beta = x\,dx \wedge dy + y\,dz \wedge dw$, compute $\alpha \wedge \beta$.
*Answer*: $(y - x)\,dx \wedge dy \wedge dz \wedge dw$.

**PROBLEM 10.42** Verify that

$$dx \wedge dy \wedge dz \wedge dw = \frac{\partial(x, y, z, w)}{\partial(r, s, t, u)} dr \wedge ds \wedge dt \wedge du,$$

when $x = x(r, s, t, u)$, $y = y(r, s, t, u)$, $z = z(r, s, t, u)$, and $w = w(r, s, t, u)$.

**PROBLEM 10.43** Evaluate $d\omega$ where

(a) $\omega = x^2 y\,dy \wedge dz - xz\,dx \wedge dy$,

(b) $\omega = 2xy\,dx + x^2\,dy$,

(c) $\omega = 2yz\,dy \wedge dz + xy\,dz \wedge dx - xz\,dx \wedge dy$.

*Answer*: (a) $(2xy - x)\,dx \wedge dy \wedge dz$, (b) 0, (c) 0.

**PROBLEM 10.44** Prove the *Leibnetzian formulas*

$$d(fg) = f\, dg + g\, df, \quad d(f\omega) = df \wedge \omega + f\, d\omega,$$

where $f$ and $g$ are 0-forms and $\omega$ is a 1-form.

**PROBLEM 10.45** Verify the invariance relation $(d\omega)^* = d(\omega^*)$, when $\omega = xy\, dx$ and $T$ is the transformation $x = u^2 + v$, $y = v$.

**PROBLEM 10.46** A differential form $\omega$ is called *closed* if $d\omega = 0$. It is called *exact* if $\omega = d\alpha$ for some form $\alpha$. Show that every exact form is closed.

**PROBLEM 10.47** Find a 1-form $\omega$ for which $d\omega = (x^2 + y^2)\, dx \wedge dy$.
*Answer*: $\omega = -x^2 y\, dx + xy^2\, dy$.

**PROBLEM 10.48** Show that a 1-form $\omega = 2xy\, dx + x^2\, dy + 2z\, dz$ is exact.
*Answer*: $\omega = d\alpha$, $\alpha = d(x^2 y + z^2)$.

**PROBLEM 10.49** The 1-form

$$\omega = \frac{-y}{x^2 + y^2}\, dx + \frac{x}{x^2 + y^2}\, dy$$

is defined on the $xy$-plane with the origin $(0, 0)$ removed. Show that (a) $\omega$ is closed, but not exact, and (b) on any closed curve $C$ that does not encircle $(0, 0)$,

$$\int_C \omega = 0.$$

**PROBLEM 10.50** Show that the volume of a region $R$ in $V_3$ is

$$V = \frac{1}{3} \iint_{\partial R} \omega,$$

where $\omega = x\, dy \wedge dz + y\, dz \wedge dx + z\, dx \wedge dy$.
[*Hint:* $d\omega = 3\, dx \wedge dy \wedge dx$.]

**PROBLEM 10.51** If $M$ is a region in 4-dimensional space with coordinates $x, y, z, w$, and $\partial M$ is its 3-dimensional boundary, show that

$$\int_M \left( \frac{\partial f_1}{\partial x} + \frac{\partial f_2}{\partial y} + \frac{\partial f_3}{\partial z} + \frac{\partial f_4}{\partial w} \right) dx \wedge dy \wedge dz \wedge dw$$

$$= \int_{\partial M} (f_1\, dy \wedge dz \wedge dw + f_2\, dz \wedge dw \wedge dx + f_3\, dw \wedge dx \wedge dy + f_4\, dx \wedge dy \wedge dz),$$

where the $f_i(x, y, z, w)$, $i = 1, \cdots, 4$, are differentiable functions of $x$, $y$, $z$, and $w$.

**PROBLEM 10.52** Let the differential form $\lambda$ be expressed as

$$\lambda = A_1\, dx + A_2\, dy + A_3\, dz - V\, dt,$$

where the vector potential $\mathbf{A} = [A_1, A_2, A_3]$ and scalar potential $V$ are functions of $x$, $y$, $z$, and $t$. If $\alpha$ is given by (10.93), show that $d\lambda = \alpha$ corresponds to the vector equations

$$\mathbf{B} = \nabla \times \mathbf{A},$$

$$\mathbf{E} = -\frac{\partial \mathbf{A}}{\partial t} - \nabla V.$$

# A

APPENDIX

# MATRIX NOTATION AND DETERMINANT

## A1. Matrix Notation

A *matrix* $A$ is an $m \times n$ array of numbers; i.e.,

$$A = \begin{bmatrix} a_{11} & a_{12} & \cdots & a_{1n} \\ a_{21} & a_{22} & \cdots & a_{2n} \\ \cdot & \cdot & \cdot & \cdot \\ \cdot & \cdot & \cdot & \cdot \\ \cdot & \cdot & \cdot & \cdot \\ a_{m1} & a_{m2} & \cdots & a_{mn} \end{bmatrix}.$$

A *general element* $a_{ij}$ of $A$ is the element in the $i$th *row* and $j$th *column*.

The *dimension* of a matrix with $m$ *rows* and $n$ columns is $m \times n$, read as "$m$ by $n$."

An $m \times n$ matrix $A$ is also written as $A = [a_{ij}]$, and the dimension can be indicated by writing $A = [a_{ij}]_{m\times n}$.

If $n = m$, the matrix is said to be a *square matrix*.

If $A = [a_{ij}]$ and $B = [b_{ij}]$ are two $m \times n$ matrices, then the matrices $A$ and $B$ are *equal* if their corresponding components are equal; that is, $A = B \longleftrightarrow a_{ij} = b_{ij}$.

If $A$ and $B$ are $m \times n$ matrices, then the *sum* of the matrices $A$ and $B$ is the matrix $C = [c_{ij}]$ whose elements are the sum of the elements of $A$ and $B$, that is, $C = A + B \longleftrightarrow c_{ij} = a_{ij} + b_{ij}$. Note that the sum matrix $C$ is also an $m \times n$ matrix.

If $A$ is an $m \times n$ matrix and $B$, an $n \times p$ matrix, then the *product* of the matrices $A$ and $B$ is the $m \times p$ matrix $C = [c_{ij}]$, where $c_{ij} = \sum_{k=1}^{n} a_{ik} b_{kj}$.

Note that the number of columns of $A$ must be *equal* to the number of rows of $B$. Thus, both of the matrix products $AB$ and $BA$ can only be defined if $A$ and $B$ are square matrices, and in general, $AB \neq BA$.

The *product* $\lambda A$ *of the scalar* $\lambda$ *and the matrix* $A$ is a matrix whose general element is $\lambda a_{ij}$; that is, $\lambda A = [\lambda a_{ij}]$.

## A2. Determinants

A real number known as the *determinant* of the matrix is associated with every square matrix that has real numbers as elements. The notation $|A|$ or *det* $A$ denotes the determinant of the matrix $A$; i.e.,

$$\text{determinant of the matrix } A = |A| = \det A.$$

For an $n \times n$ matrix $A = [a_{ij}]$, $|A|$ is the sum of all possible terms of the form

$$(-1)^q a_{1j_1} a_{2j_2} \ldots a_{nj_n},$$

where no two column indices are the same, and $q$ is the number of transpositions necessary to restore the column indices to their natural order. Thus if $A = \begin{bmatrix} a_{11} & a_{12} \\ a_{21} & a_{22} \end{bmatrix}$, then $|A| = a_{11}a_{22} + (-1)a_{12}a_{21} = a_{11}a_{22} - a_{12}a_{21}$; and if

$$A = \begin{bmatrix} a_{11} & a_{12} & a_{13} \\ a_{21} & a_{22} & a_{23} \\ a_{31} & a_{32} & a_{33} \end{bmatrix},$$

then

$$\begin{aligned} |A| &= a_{11}a_{22}a_{33} + (-1)a_{11}a_{23}a_{32} + (-1)a_{12}a_{21}a_{33} + (-1)^2 a_{12}a_{23}a_{31} + (-1)^2 a_{13}a_{21}a_{32} + (-1)a_{13}a_{22}a_{31} \\ &= a_{11}a_{22}a_{33} - a_{11}a_{23}a_{32} - a_{12}a_{21}a_{33} + a_{12}a_{23}a_{31} + a_{13}a_{21}a_{32} - a_{13}a_{22}a_{31}. \end{aligned}$$

If $A = [a_{ij}]$ is an $n \times n$ matrix, and $A_{ij}$ is the $(n-1) \times (n-1)$ matrix formed by deleting the $i$th row and $j$th column from $A$, the cofactors $\alpha_{ij}$ of $A$ are $\alpha_{ij} = (-1)^{i+j} |A_{ij}|$. Hence, the expansion by the $i$th row yields $|A| = \sum_{k=1}^{n} a_{ik}\alpha_{ik}$, and the expansion by the $j$th column yields $|A| = \sum_{k=1}^{n} a_{kj}\alpha_{kj}$. Thus, if the matrix is

$$A = \begin{bmatrix} a_{11} & a_{12} & a_{12} \\ a_{21} & a_{22} & a_{23} \\ a_{31} & a_{32} & a_{33} \end{bmatrix},$$

then its determinant by expanding by the 1st row is

$$\begin{aligned} |A| &= a_{11} \begin{vmatrix} a_{22} & a_{23} \\ a_{32} & a_{33} \end{vmatrix} - a_{12} \begin{vmatrix} a_{21} & a_{23} \\ a_{31} & a_{33} \end{vmatrix} + a_{13} \begin{vmatrix} a_{21} & a_{22} \\ a_{31} & a_{32} \end{vmatrix} \\ &= a_{11}(a_{22}a_{33} - a_{23}a_{32}) - a_{12}(a_{21}a_{33} - a_{23}a_{31}) + a_{13}(a_{21}a_{32} - a_{22}a_{31}) \\ &= a_{11}a_{22}a_{33} - a_{11}a_{23}a_{32} - a_{12}a_{21}a_{33} + a_{12}a_{23}a_{31} + a_{13}a_{21}a_{32} - a_{13}a_{22}a_{31}, \end{aligned}$$

and the determinant by expanding by the 1st column is

$$\begin{aligned} |A| &= a_{11} \begin{vmatrix} a_{22} & a_{23} \\ a_{32} & a_{33} \end{vmatrix} - a_{21} \begin{vmatrix} a_{12} & a_{13} \\ a_{32} & a_{33} \end{vmatrix} + a_{31} \begin{vmatrix} a_{12} & a_{13} \\ a_{22} & a_{23} \end{vmatrix} \\ &= a_{11}(a_{22}a_{33} - a_{23}a_{32}) - a_{21}(a_{12}a_{33} - a_{13}a_{32}) + a_{31}(a_{12}a_{23} - a_{13}a_{22}) \\ &= a_{11}a_{22}a_{33} - a_{11}a_{23}a_{32} - a_{21}a_{12}a_{33} + a_{21}a_{13}a_{32} + a_{31}a_{12}a_{23} - a_{31}a_{13}a_{22}. \end{aligned}$$

## A3. Properties of Determinants

*Property 1*: If two rows or columns of a square matrix $A$ are interchanged, the sign of $|A|$ is changed.

*Property 2*: If a row or a column of a square matrix $A$ is multiplied by a constant c, the value of the determinant is multiplied by c.

*Property 3*: If a multiple of a row or column is added to another row or column, the value of the determinant is unchanged.

*Property 4*: If a row or a column of a square matrix $A$ is a multiple of another row or column, $|A|$ is equal to zero.

# VECTOR DIFFERENTIAL OPERATIONS IN ORTHOGONAL COORDINATES

B APPENDIX

## B1. Rectangular Coordinates

$$\nabla\psi = \frac{\partial\psi}{\partial x}\mathbf{i} + \frac{\partial\psi}{\partial y}\mathbf{j} + \frac{\partial\psi}{\partial z}\mathbf{k}, \qquad \nabla\cdot\mathbf{f} = \frac{\partial f_1}{\partial x} + \frac{\partial f_2}{\partial y} + \frac{\partial f_3}{\partial z}, \qquad \nabla^2\psi = \frac{\partial^2\psi}{\partial x^2} + \frac{\partial^2\psi}{\partial y^2} + \frac{\partial^2\psi}{\partial z^2},$$

$$\nabla\times\mathbf{f} = \begin{vmatrix} \mathbf{i} & \mathbf{j} & \mathbf{k} \\ \dfrac{\partial}{\partial x} & \dfrac{\partial}{\partial y} & \dfrac{\partial}{\partial z} \\ f_1 & f_2 & f_3 \end{vmatrix} = \left(\frac{\partial f_3}{\partial y} - \frac{\partial f_2}{\partial z}\right)\mathbf{i} + \left(\frac{\partial f_1}{\partial z} - \frac{\partial f_3}{\partial x}\right)\mathbf{j} + \left(\frac{\partial f_2}{\partial x} - \frac{\partial f_1}{\partial y}\right)\mathbf{k}.$$

## B2. Cylindrical Coordinates

$$\nabla\psi = \frac{\partial\psi}{\partial\rho}\mathbf{e}_\rho + \frac{1}{\rho}\frac{\partial\psi}{\partial\phi}\mathbf{e}_\phi + \frac{\partial\psi}{\partial z}\mathbf{k}, \qquad \nabla\cdot\mathbf{f} = \frac{1}{\rho}\frac{\partial}{\partial\rho}(\rho f_\rho) + \frac{1}{\rho}\frac{\partial f_\phi}{\partial\phi} + \frac{\partial f_3}{\partial z}, \qquad \nabla^2\psi = \frac{1}{\rho}\frac{\partial}{\partial\rho}\left(\rho\frac{\partial\psi}{\partial\rho}\right) + \frac{1}{\rho^2}\frac{\partial^2\psi}{\partial\phi^2} + \frac{\partial^2\psi}{\partial z^2},$$

$$\nabla\times\mathbf{f} = \frac{1}{\rho}\begin{vmatrix} \mathbf{e}_\rho & \rho\,\mathbf{e}_\phi & \mathbf{k} \\ \dfrac{\partial}{\partial\rho} & \dfrac{\partial}{\partial\phi} & \dfrac{\partial}{\partial z} \\ f_\rho & f_\phi & f_3 \end{vmatrix} = \frac{1}{\rho}\left(\frac{\partial f_3}{\partial\phi} - \frac{\partial f_\phi}{\partial z}\right)\mathbf{e}_\rho + \left(\frac{\partial f_\rho}{\partial z} - \frac{\partial f_3}{\partial\rho}\right)\mathbf{e}_\phi + \frac{1}{\rho}\left(\frac{\partial f_\phi}{\partial\rho} - \frac{\partial f_\rho}{\partial\phi}\right)\mathbf{k}.$$

## B3. Spherical Coordinates

$$\nabla\psi = \frac{\partial\psi}{\partial r}\mathbf{e}_r + \frac{1}{r}\frac{\partial\psi}{\partial\theta}\mathbf{e}_\theta + \frac{1}{r\sin\theta}\frac{\partial\psi}{\partial\phi}\mathbf{e}_\phi,$$

$$\nabla\cdot\mathbf{f} = \frac{1}{r^2\sin\theta}\left[\sin\theta\frac{\partial}{\partial r}(r^2 f_r) + r\frac{\partial}{\partial\theta}(\sin\theta\, f_\theta) + r\frac{\partial f_\phi}{\partial\phi}\right] = \frac{1}{r^2}\frac{\partial}{\partial r}(r^2 f_r) + \frac{1}{r\sin\theta}\frac{\partial}{\partial\theta}(\sin\theta\, f_\theta) + \frac{1}{r\sin\theta}\frac{\partial f_\phi}{\partial\phi},$$

$$\nabla^2\psi = \frac{1}{r^2\sin\theta}\left[\sin\theta\frac{\partial}{\partial r}\left(r^2\frac{\partial\psi}{\partial r}\right) + \frac{\partial}{\partial\theta}\left(\sin\theta\frac{\partial\psi}{\partial\theta}\right) + \frac{1}{\sin\theta}\frac{\partial^2\psi}{\partial\phi^2}\right]$$
$$= \frac{1}{r^2}\frac{\partial}{\partial r}\left(r^2\frac{\partial\psi}{\partial r}\right) + \frac{1}{r^2\sin\theta}\frac{\partial}{\partial\theta}\left(\sin\theta\frac{\partial\psi}{\partial\theta}\right) + \frac{1}{r^2\sin^2\theta}\frac{\partial^2\psi}{\partial\phi^2}.$$

$$\nabla \times \mathbf{f} = \frac{1}{r^2 \sin\theta} \begin{vmatrix} \mathbf{e}_r & r\mathbf{e}_\theta & r\sin\theta\,\mathbf{e}_\phi \\ \dfrac{\partial}{\partial r} & \dfrac{\partial}{\partial \theta} & \dfrac{\partial}{\partial \phi} \\ f_r & rf_\theta & r\sin\theta\, f_\phi \end{vmatrix}$$

$$= \frac{1}{r\sin\theta}\left[\frac{\partial}{\partial\theta}(\sin\theta\, f_\phi) - \frac{\partial f_\theta}{\partial\phi}\right]\mathbf{e}_r + \frac{1}{r}\left[\frac{1}{\sin\theta}\frac{\partial f_r}{\partial\phi} - \frac{\partial}{\partial r}(rf_\phi)\right]\mathbf{e}_\theta + \frac{1}{r}\left[\frac{\partial}{\partial r}(rf_\theta) - \frac{\partial f_r}{\partial\theta}\right]\mathbf{e}_\phi$$

# APPENDIX C

# SUMMARY OF VECTOR RELATIONS

## C1. Equations of Vector Algebra

| Equation No. | Equation |
|---|---|
| (1.31) | $\mathbf{A}\cdot\mathbf{B} = \mathbf{B}\cdot\mathbf{A}$ |
| (1.32) | $\mathbf{A}\cdot(\mathbf{B}+\mathbf{C}) = \mathbf{A}\cdot\mathbf{B} + \mathbf{A}\cdot\mathbf{C}$ |
| (1.55) | $\mathbf{A}\times\mathbf{B} = -\mathbf{B}\times\mathbf{A}$ |
| (1.56) | $\mathbf{A}\times(\mathbf{B}+\mathbf{C}) = \mathbf{A}\times\mathbf{B} + \mathbf{A}\times\mathbf{C}$ |
| (1.58) | $\mathbf{A}\times\mathbf{A} = \mathbf{0}$ |
| (1.72) | $\mathbf{A}\cdot\mathbf{B}\times\mathbf{C} = \mathbf{A}\times\mathbf{B}\cdot\mathbf{C}$ |
| (1.76) | $\mathbf{A}\cdot\mathbf{B}\times\mathbf{C} = [\mathbf{ABC}]$ |
| (1.77) | $[\mathbf{ABC}] = [\mathbf{BCA}] = [\mathbf{CAB}] = -[\mathbf{ACB}] = -[\mathbf{BAC}] = -[\mathbf{CBA}]$ |
| (1.83) | $\mathbf{A}\times(\mathbf{B}\times\mathbf{C}) = (\mathbf{A}\cdot\mathbf{C})\mathbf{B} - (\mathbf{A}\cdot\mathbf{B})\mathbf{C}$ |
| (1.98) | $(\mathbf{A}\times\mathbf{B})\times\mathbf{C} = (\mathbf{A}\cdot\mathbf{C})\mathbf{B} - (\mathbf{B}\cdot\mathbf{C})\mathbf{A}$ |
| (3.112) | $\nabla(\phi+\psi) = \nabla\phi + \nabla\psi$ |
| (3.113) | $\nabla(\phi\psi) = \phi\nabla\psi + \psi\nabla\phi$ |
| (3.124) | $\nabla\phi = \nabla\phi(u) = \phi'(u)\nabla u$ |
| (3.128) | $\nabla\cdot(\mathbf{f}+\mathbf{g}) = \nabla\cdot\mathbf{f} + \nabla\cdot\mathbf{g}$ |
| (3.131) | $\text{div}\,(\text{grad}\,\phi) = \nabla\cdot(\nabla\phi) = \nabla^2\phi$ |
| (3.140) | $\nabla\times(\mathbf{f}+\mathbf{g}) = \nabla\times\mathbf{f} + \nabla\times\mathbf{g}$ |
| (3.142) | $\nabla\times(\nabla\phi) = \mathbf{0}$ |
| (3.143) | $\nabla\cdot(\nabla\times\mathbf{f}) = 0$ |
| (3.154) | $(\mathbf{f}\times\nabla)\cdot\mathbf{g} = \mathbf{f}\cdot(\nabla\times\mathbf{g})$ |
| (3.155) | $\nabla\cdot(\phi\mathbf{f}) = \phi\nabla\cdot\mathbf{f} + \mathbf{f}\cdot(\nabla\phi)$ |
| (3.156) | $\nabla\times(\phi\mathbf{f}) = \phi\nabla\times\mathbf{f} + (\nabla\phi)\times\mathbf{f} = \phi\nabla\times\mathbf{f} - \mathbf{f}\times\nabla\phi$ |
| (3.157) | $\nabla\cdot(\mathbf{f}\times\mathbf{g}) = \mathbf{g}\cdot(\nabla\times\mathbf{f}) - \mathbf{f}\cdot(\nabla\times\mathbf{g})$ |
| (3.158) | $\nabla\times(\mathbf{f}\times\mathbf{g}) = \mathbf{f}(\nabla\cdot\mathbf{g}) - \mathbf{g}(\nabla\cdot\mathbf{f}) + (\mathbf{g}\cdot\nabla)\mathbf{f} - (\mathbf{f}\cdot\nabla)\mathbf{g}$ |
| (3.159) | $\nabla(\mathbf{f}\cdot\mathbf{g}) = \mathbf{f}\times(\nabla\times\mathbf{g}) + \mathbf{g}\times(\nabla\times\mathbf{f}) + (\mathbf{f}\cdot\nabla)\mathbf{g} + (\mathbf{g}\cdot\nabla)\mathbf{f}$ |
| (3.163) | $\text{curl}\,(\text{curl}\,\mathbf{f}) = \nabla\times(\nabla\times\mathbf{f}) = \nabla(\nabla\cdot\mathbf{f}) - \nabla^2\mathbf{f}$ |
| (3.164) | $\nabla^2\mathbf{f} = \nabla(\nabla\cdot\mathbf{f}) - \nabla\times(\nabla\times\mathbf{f})$ |
| [Prob. 3.89(b)] | $\nabla\left(\dfrac{\phi}{\psi}\right) = \dfrac{\psi\nabla\phi - \phi\nabla\psi}{\psi^2}$ |

## C2. Equations of Vector Calculus

| Equation No. | Equation |
|---|---|
| (4.58) | $\iiint_R \nabla \cdot \mathbf{f}\, dV = \oiint_S \mathbf{f} \cdot d\mathbf{S}$ |
| (4.94) | $\iiint_R \nabla\phi\, dV = \oiint_S d\mathbf{S}\, \phi$ |
| (4.95) | $\iiint_R \nabla \times \mathbf{f}\, dV = \oiint_S d\mathbf{S} \times \mathbf{f}$ |
| (4.104) | $\iint_S \nabla \times \mathbf{f} \cdot d\mathbf{S} = \oint_C \mathbf{f} \cdot d\mathbf{r}$ |
| (4.115) | $\iint_S d\mathbf{S} \times \nabla\phi = \oint_C \phi\, d\mathbf{r}$ |
| (4.116) | $\iint_S (d\mathbf{S} \times \nabla) \times \mathbf{f} = \oint_C d\mathbf{r} \times \mathbf{f}$ |

# INDEX